HEGEL'S PHILOSOPHY OF NATURE

HEGEL'S PHILOSOPHY OF NATURE

Volume One
Introduction, Foreword and Mechanics

Volume Two
Physics

Volume Three
Organics

HEGEL'S
PHILOSOPHY
OF NATURE

EDITED AND TRANSLATED
WITH AN INTRODUCTION AND EXPLANATORY NOTES BY

M. J. PETRY
M.A., D.Phil.(Oxon.)

VOLUME II

LONDON · GEORGE ALLEN AND UNWIN LTD
NEW YORK · HUMANITIES PRESS, INC

FIRST PUBLISHED IN 1970

This translation © George Allen & Unwin Ltd., 1970

SBN 04 100022 6

PRINTED IN GREAT BRITAIN
in 12 on 13 point Bembo type
BY UNWIN BROTHERS LIMITED
WOKING AND LONDON

CONTENTS
SECTION TWO

PHYSICS § 272–273 9

Chapter One: Physics of Universal Individuality § 274 11
A The free physical bodies 11
  1 *The Sun, light and its reflection* (Light) § 275–278 12
  2 The bodies of opposition § 279 25
    a. *The Moon* 26
    b. *The Comet* 28
  3 *The planet as the body of individuality* (The body of individuality) § 280 30
B The elements § 281 33
  1 Air § 282 35
  2 The elements of opposition 38
    § 283 a. *Fire* 38
    § 284 b. *Water* 39
  3 *Earth* (The individual element) § 285 41
C *Meteorology* (The process of the elements) § 286 42
  § 287 1 *The tension of the process* 47
  § 288–289 2 *The dissolution of diremption* 50

Chapter Two: Physics of particular individuality § 290–292 55
A Specific gravity § 293–294 57
B Cohesion § 295 62
  § 296 1 *Adhesion* 63
  § 296 2 *Coherence* 64
    § 296 a. *Quantitative* 64
    § 296 b. *Qualitative* 64
  § 297–299 3 *Elasticity* 65
C Sound § 300–302 69
D Heat § 303–307 82

Chapter Three: Physics of total individuality § 308–309 94
A Shape § 310 96
  § 311 1 *Shapelessness* 98
  § 312–314 2 *Magnetism* 99
  § 315 3 *Crystallography* 112

B   *The particular properties of bodies* (The specification of the individual body) § 316   116

  1   Relationship to Light   121

    § 317   a.   *Transparency*   121

    § 318–319   b.   *Refraction of light*   125

    § 320   c.   *The theory of colours*   135

        i.   *Prismatic colour*   141

        ii.   *Entoptic, epoptic and paroptic colours*   155

        iii.   *Chemical colours*   156

  2   *The properties of opposition* (Difference in particularized corporeality) § 321   161

    § 321   a.   *Smell as specified airiness*   161

    § 322   b.   *Taste as specified water*   163

  3   *Electricity* (Totality in particular individuality; electricity) § 323–325   164

C   The chemical process   § 326   178

  § 327   1   *Synsomation*   182

  § 328–329   2   *The real process*   184

    (1   Combination)   191

    a.   Galvanism   § 330   191

    b.   *The* process of fire   § 331   205

    c.   *Salt formation* (Neutralization, the process of water) § 332   208

    d.   *Elective affinity* (The process in its totality)   § 333   210

  3   *The process of separation* (Separation)   § 334–336   213

NOTES   223

INDEX TO TEXT   442

INDEX TO NOTES   455

The words in roman are those of Hegel's headings which appeared in the first edition of this work. The words in italics did not appear as headings in the text, but such identification of these passages was made on the contents page of the first edition of the work

SECTION TWO

Physics

§ 272

Matter has individuality to the extent that it is determined within itself by having being-for-self developed within it. It is through this determination that matter breaks away from gravity and manifests itself as implicitly self-determining. This is its
5 **immanent form, by which it determines spatiality in the face of a gravity which formerly received this determination as something opposed to matter, and as a centre to which matter merely aspired.**

Addition. Bodies are now subject to the power of individuality, and this section will be concerned with the reduction of free bodies to the power of
10 the individual point of unity by which they are digested. Gravity is the essential being-in-self of matter, or mere inner identity, and as such passes over into the manifestation of essence, for essential externality constitutes its Notion. As such, it is the totality of the determinations of reflection; these are thrown into separation as shapeless elements however,
15 for although each appears as a particular and qualified material, it is not yet individualized. These materialized determinations of form are to be grasped in a double manner: in their immediacy, and in their positedness. In the solar system they appear in their immediacy, and then exist as essentially posited. Parents are an immediacy in that they are parents for
20 example, but they are also posited by having given life to their children. Similarly, light exists as the sun, and then also issues forth from external conditions. Primary light is in itself, and is generated in the Notion; it also has to be posited so that its determinate being may differentiate itself as a particular mode of existence.

§ 273

25 **Physics has as its content:**
   A. The universal individuality of immediate, free, physical qualities.

A* 9

B. The particular individuality of the relation of form, as a physical determination, to gravity, and of the determination of gravity by this form.

C. Total or free individuality.

Addition. This part of nature embraces finite corporeality, and is there-   5
fore the most difficult to grasp. The greatest difficulty is always encountered where there is difference, because there the Notion is no longer
present in its immediacy as it is the first part, and does not yet display the
concrete reality of its third part. In this second part, the Notion is ob-
scured, and only shows itself as the connecting bond of necessity, for   +
what appears is Notionless. In the first part, differences of form are con-
nectionless and mutually independent; in the second part individuality
is differentiated and in a state of opposition; it is only in the third part
that individuality is mistress over differences of form.

CHAPTER ONE

Physics of universal individuality

§ 274

Physical qualities in their primary immediacy are external to one another in an independent manner as the heavenly bodies, which are now physically determined. Secondly, they are related to the individual unity of their totality as the physical ele-
5 **ments. Thirdly, they are the process, which gives rise to what is individual in these elements—the meteorological process.**

A

The free physical bodies

Addition. The determinations of the Notion now take on materiality; the being-for-self of matter finds its point of unity, and as it is therefore the being-for-self of being-for-self, and the transition of the determina-
10 tions, the disappearance of these determinations into one another has
+ itself disappeared, and we enter logically into the sphere of essence. This is a return into self in its other; its determinations appear within each other, and intro-reflected in this way, now develop as forms. These forms are identity, variety, opposition, and ground. This is therefore an advance
15 upon the primary immediacy of matter, in which space and time, motion and matter, passed over into one another, until in free mechanics matter finally appropriated the determinations as its own, and so revealed itself as self-mediated and determined. Impact is no longer external to matter, which is now differentiated as internal and immanent impact. It differen-
20 tiates and determines itself by itself, and is intro-reflected. Its determinations are material, and express the nature of being material, and as it only consists of these determinations, it manifests itself within them. There are material qualities which belong to the substance of matter, and matter is whatever it is only through its qualities. In the first sphere the determi-
25 nations are still distinguished from the substance, they are not material determinations; substance as such is still shut up within itself and unmanifest; and it was this which resulted in its merely seeking for its unity.

1. Light
(The Sun, light and its reflection)

§ 275

Matter in its primary **qualified state** is *pure* **self-***identity***,**
unity of intro-reflection; as such it is the primary manifesta-
tion, and is itself still abstract. As *existent* **in nature, it is** *inde-* +
pendent self-relation opposed to the other determinations of
totality. This existing and universal *self* of matter is light, 5
which as individuality is the star, and as moment of totality, the
sun.

Addition. The apriori *Notional-determination* of light is now the *primary*
consideration. In the second instance we have to discover the mode and
manner in which this Notional-determination occurs in our sensuous 10
perception. As immediate, free, and independent motion returned into itself,
matter is the simple self-equality of integrality. As motion has returned into +
itself, the celestial sphere has perfected and concluded the independent and ideal
life within it. This completed being-in-self is the precise constitution of its integrality. As existent it is in itself; that is to say that this being-in-self of the totality +
is itself present. It contains the moment by which it is for another; that which is
for itself is the power of its centre, or its self-containedness. This simple power
is itself present however, and as it is the other of this determinate being, that
which is merely internal is to the same extent external. As immediate, pure
totality, matter therefore enters into the opposition between that which it is in 20
itself, and that which it is for another as determinate being; for its determinate
being does not yet contain its being-in-self. Apprehended as this incessant
rotation of self-relating motion, as the return to being-in-and-for-self, and as this
being-in-self which is there opposed to existence, matter is light. Light is the
self-contained totality of matter; as mere purity of power it is the self-conserv- 25
ing and intensive vitality which is the concentration of the celestial sphere. Its
rotation is precisely this immediate opposition of directions constituting self-
relating motion, in the flux and reflux of which all difference extinguishes itself. As existent identity it is pure line, and relates itself only to itself.
Light is this purely existent power, which fills space. Its being is absolute velo- 30
city, the presence of pure materiality, the being-in-self of real existence, or
actuality as a transparent possibility. That which fills space has two aspects +
however, and if this filling subsists in being-for-self, light does not fill

space, for the rigidity of that which offers resistance will then have lapsed. Light is present only in space therefore, and is certainly neither individualized nor exclusive. Space is merely abstract subsistence or implicit being, while as existent being-in-self, or determinate being which is in itself, and is
5 consequently pure, light is the power of being external to itself possessed by
+ universal actuality as the possibility of confluxing with everything; it is the affinity with all which yet abides in itself, and by means of which determinate being surrenders none of its independence.

When matter passes into being-for-self as light, and so begins to mani-
10 fest itself, weighted matter also manifests itself. Pressure, in which unity is sought through tendency towards another, is a merely hostile or discordant manifestation however; within it matter is certainly being-for-other, but it is this as exclusiveness, and as separation of the other from itself. As well as this mutual negation between the many, we now have
15 affirmative manifestation, for being-for-other is common to all. Light brings us into universal interrelation; it is by its being in light that everything may be easily penetrated by us, and grasped theoretically.

We have to grasp this manifestation in its *primary* determinateness, in which, within itself, it is completely universal, and as yet undetermined.
20 Its determinateness is indeterminateness, identity, intro-reflection, a complete physical ideality, contrasting with the reality of the weighted matter which we take to be differentiated and exclusive. This abstract manifestation, which is material identity with self, is not yet opposed to another; it is determinateness and *oscillation*, but only within itself. The being-for-self
25 of being-for-self as self-relating affirmative identity, is no longer an exclusiveness; the rigidity of the unit has melted, and as the indeterminate continuity of manifestation, has lost its opposition. This is the pure intro-reflection which, in the higher form of spirit, is the ego. The ego is infinite space, the infinite equality of self-consciousness with itself, the abstract
30 and empty certainty of myself, and of my pure self-identity. The ego is merely the identity of my own attitude as subject, to myself as object. Light corresponds to this identity of self-consciousness, and is the exact image of it. It is not the ego however, for *in itself* it is *not self-dimming and refractive*, but is merely abstract appearance. If the ego were able to main-
35 tain itself in a state of undisturbed equability, as the Indians would like it
+ to, it would pass away into the abstract transparency of light. Self-consciousness only has being as consciousness however; consciousness posits determinations within itself, and self-consciousness, in so far as it is its own object, is the pure reflection of the ego of consciousness into itself. The ego
40 resembles light in its pure self-manifestation, but it is at the same time the

13

infinite negativity of its return into self, out of itself as object. As the
infinite point of subjective individuality, it therefore excludes its other.
Light is not self-consciousness therefore, because it lacks the infinity of
return into self; it is mere self-manifestation, but only for another, not
for itself.   5

Light therefore lacks the concrete unity with itself which is possessed
by self-consciousness as the infinite point of being-for-itself; consequently
it is merely a manifestation of nature, and not of spirit. *Secondly*, this abstract manifestation is therefore at the same time spatial; it is absolute
expansion in *space*, but is not the resumption of this expansion into the 10
unifying point of infinite subjectivity. Light is infinite spatial diffusion,
or rather the infinite *generation of space*. As the determinations of nature fall
apart through their separation, this pure manifestation also exists for itself,
but as a false existence. Pure identity is not granted such a detached
existence in the infinite concreteness of spirit; for in self-consciousness   15
this thought is subsumed under the absolute subjectivity of the self.

Thirdly, light has to encounter its *limit*; yet the necessity of its striking
something other than itself is not the same as the absolute limitation of
being-for-self by which matter offers resistance. In that light is abstract
identity, difference is external to it as the absence of light. This consists of 20
the remaining reflective determinations of essence, expressed as physical
bodies. Light is the primary consummation of that in which everything
is made manifest. It is only the abstract understanding which regards this
physical universal as supreme. Self-determining and concrete rational
thought demands a self-differentiating universal which determines itself   25
within itself without losing its universality in this particularization. Light
is the beginning of material manifestation, and only constitutes its acme
in an abstract sense. It is because of this abstraction that light now finds a +
limit, or deficiency; and it is through this limit that it first manifests itself
Determinate content must come from elsewhere; in order that something   30
may be manifest, there must be something which is different from light.
Light as such is invisible, and in that nothing may be seen in it, pure light
resembles pure *darkness*; it is obscure and tenebrous. If we see in pure light,
then we are pure vision, but we do not as yet see anything. It is limit which
contains the primary moment of negation and therefore of determination,   35
and so gives rise to reality. As concreteness is the prime verity, not only
the one, but both abstractions go to make up existence. Light only manifests itself as such after it has differentiated itself as light by distinguishing
itself from shade.

After having developed the Notion of light, the question of its *reality* 40

naturally presents itself. When we say that we have to consider the existence of light, we are referring in fact to its being-for-other; but light
itself is the positing of being-for-other, so that in the existence of light we
have to take into account the being-for-other of this being-for-other.
5 How is visibility visible? How does this manifestation manifest itself? A
subject is necessary in manifestation; how does it exist? Light can only be
called material in so far as it exists for itself in the form of independent
individuality, and this individuation depends upon the corporeality of
light. Light constitutes the existence or physical import of the body of
10 abstract centrality, the real nature of which is a *luminous body*. This *self-
illuminating* body is the sun. At this juncture, this is an empirically presented
fact, and is all that we have to say of the sun at present. This body is the
primordial and uncreated light, it is immediate, and does not arise from
the conditions of finite existence. The stars are also self-illuminating bodies,
15 and their existence merely entails the physical abstraction of light. The
existence of abstract matter is precisely this abstract identity of light. The
stars are points of light, and do not shift out of this abstraction; this inability to assume concrete being is not impressive, it is a defect, and it is
consequently absurd to regard the stars as superior to plants for example.
20 The sun is not yet concrete being. Religiosity wants to deck out the sun
and moon with people, animals, and plants, but only a planet can rise to
+ these things. Introverted natural objects, and concrete shapes able to maintain themselves in the face of the universal do not yet exist on the sun.
There is nothing but luminous matter in the stars and the sun. The con-
25 nection between the sun as a moment of the solar system, and as self-
illumination, consists in its having the same determination in both cases.
In mechanics the sun is merely the self-relating corporeality, and this
determination is also the physical determination of the identity of abstract
manifestation. That is why the sun shines.
30   Further enquiry may be made into the *finite causes* of the existence which
shines in this way. If we ask how we receive the light of the sun, we are
assuming that it is something which is generated. In this determination we
see light associated with fire and warmth, as it is in our ordinary experience
of it as terrestrial light, where it occurs as a combustion. We might think
35 therefore, that the means by which the burning heat of the sun is maintained, were essential to any explanation of sunlight, and that these means
might be explained by analogy with the terrestrial igneous process, in
which fire has to consume matter in order to exist. It should be remembered however, that the conditions of the terrestrial process which occur
40 in individualized corporeality do not yet occur here in the relations of

free qualities. This primary light has to be distinguished from fire. Terrestrial light is for the most part connected with heat. Although sunlight is also warm, this heat does not belong to sunlight as such, but arises out of its contact with the earth. Sunlight, by itself, is cold, as we know from high mountains and balloon ascents. We have even empirical evidence of + flameless light, in the phosphorescence of rotten wood for example, as well as in electric light, where the fusion which electricity gives rise to is the result not of light, but of an explosion. There are also metals which + glow without burning when they are scratched or rubbed together with iron; minerals of this kind may even be more numerous than those which 10 do not give off light. Consequently, terrestrial light itself furnishes analogies from which one may infer that solar illumination is independent of the chemical process.

Light must also show itself to be a product of course. The physical conditions of solar light do not concern us here, because they are merely 15 empirical facts, and are not a determination of the Notion. Nevertheless, one could say that as the sun and the stars are rotating centres, their rotation constitutes a self-frictionalization. In its motion, the life of the sun is + merely this process of phosphorescence, in which light is given off; *consequently*, the mechanical explanation of it has to be sought in the axial 20 rotation of the sun, for this is its abstract relation to self. In so far as light has to be produced physically, we can say that all the bodies which belong to the solar system contribute to the production of their centre, and so posit their own luminary; neither of these two moments is without the other, for each is posited by the other. General *Alix*, a Frenchman who 25 lived for a long time in Cassel, published a paper in which he explained the way in which the luminous matter of the sun is generated, from the assumption that the solar body is perpetually giving off light through its illumination, and so continually losing. When he was questioned as to the origin of the hydrogen which is perpetually developing on the planets the general replied that as hydrogen is the lightest gas, it is not to be found 30 in the air, but that it furnishes the material which replenishes that which is lost by the sun. There is some truth in this idea, for the planets do project + their material development out of themselves, and so form the body of the sun, but the idea of ordinary physical and chemical mediation has to be 35 excluded here. The life of a star is perpetually being kindled and renewed by the elements which assemble themselves in the unity of its determinate being, by positing the ideal nature of multiplicity within their centre. In the terrestrial process, that which is individual is consumed in the simplicity of the flame; similarly, in the sun, multiplicity concentrates itself into the 40

simplicity of solar light. The sun is therefore the process of the whole
+ solar system, the culminating point in which it bursts forth.

§ 276

As the abstract *self* of matter, light is *absolute levity*, and
as matter, it is *infinite* self-externality. **It is this as pure**
5 **manifestation and** material ideality however, in the *self-externality* of which it is *simple* and *indivisible*.

Remark

To oriental intuition, it is the pure selfhood of consciousness which constitutes the substantial identity of spiritual
and natural, and this constitutes the self-identical thought
10 which in the abstract form of the *true* and the *good* is one
+ with light. There is an attitude of mind which is said to be
realistic, and which denies that ideality is *present* in nature;
it should be asked to concern itself among other things with
light, which is pure manifestation, and nothing but *mani-*
15 *festation.*
**The resultant self-identity now has matter within it as the
primary abstract self of centrality, and is the simplicity of existent
ideality. We have shown in the introduction, that in order to
prove that this thought-determination is light, an empirical pro-**
20 **cedure has to be adopted. Here as everywhere, that which is
immanently philosophical is the inherent necessity of Notional
determination, which then has to be illustrated by some
natural existence or other. Here I shall merely make a few
remarks on the empirical existence of pure manifestation as**
25 **light.**
Weighted matter is *divisible* into *masses*, since it is concrete, quantitative **being-for-self**; but in the quite *abstract*
ideality of light there is no such difference; a limit to the
infinite expansion of light does not destroy its absolute
30 continuity in itself. The conception of *aggregations* of discrete and simple *light-rays* and *particles*, out of which a
light which is limited in its diffusion is supposed to arise,
belong to the barbarous **categories** which have continued

to dominate physics, since *Newton* **made them current. The** +
most limited experience will show us that it is as impossible to
isolate light into rays and compress its beams into bundles, as it
is to pack it into sacks. The indivisibility of light in its infinite expansion, is physical extrinsicality maintaining its 5
self-identity; the understanding also has this abstract identity as its principle, and should therefore be the last to
pass it off as being *incomprehensible*.

Astronomers have taken to speaking of appearances in the
heavens which occurred 500 years or more before we per- 10
ceive them. In order to do this it is necessary on the one
hand to look upon the empirical appearances of the *propa-*
gation of light, which are valid in one sphere, as taken over
into another sphere in which they have no significance, **al-**
though such a determination of the materiality of light is not 15
incompatible with its simple indivisibility. On the other hand,
we can see there a past transformed into a present event,
as in the ideal process of memory. +

It is one of the tenets of optics that *each point* on a visible
surface radiates beams of light *in all directions*, so that a 20
material hemisphere of infinite dimensions is formed **from**
each point. It should be remembered moreover that each
person sees this surface from a different position. **If this**
were the case, the immediate result would be that each of this
infinity of hemispheres would resemble a hedgehog, and 25
penetrate all the others. A condensed and confused mass
would be produced between the eye and the object, and the
light which ought to render the object visible, would in
fact do the opposite. This whole way of conceiving of the +
situation is self-defeating however, and **resembles** the re- 30
presentation of a concrete body as a composition of various
matters, in the pores of one and all of which, all the others
exist, persist, and circulate. **What is more,** this conception +
of matter as being penetrated from all sides, contradicts
the hypothesis that the supposedly real nature of substances **is a** 35
discrete materiality, and tends rather to confirm that the
relationship between them is of a **completely** ideal nature.
It indicates moreover, that this relationship occurs here between
the object which is lighted and manifested, the principle which
lights and manifests, and that to which the object becomes mani- 40

fest. In itself, this relationship is a relationless intro-reflection, and consequently, all further forms of mediation used in explanation and exposition, such as corpuscles, waves, oscillations etc., as well as fine strands and bundles of rays, are to be removed from it.

5 *Addition.* It is in so far as the self-centredness of light animates and individualizes the things of nature so as to heighten and give coherence to their exclusiveness, that it makes its appearance in the individualization of matter, for its primarily abstract identity is merely the sublation and return into self of the particularity of the negative unity of individuality. Gravity,
10 acidity, and sound, are also manifestations of matter, but they do not have the purity of light, and they are not manifested without inherent and determinate modification. We can not hear sound as such, we merely hear a determinate sound, a certain pitch; it is always a determinate acid that we taste, never acidity as such. Only light exists as this pure manifestation,
15 this abstract and unindividualized universality. Light is incorporeal, it is in fact immaterial matter; although this appears to be a contradiction, it
+ is an appearance which cannot depend upon us. Physicists used to say that light might be weighed. Large lenses were used in order to concentrate it into focus, which was then directed onto the scalepan of a pair of ex-
20 tremely sensitive balances. The balances were usually unmoved, and when they were, it was discovered that this was brought about solely by the
+ heat that was concentrated within the focus. Matter is weighted in so far as it still seeks its unity as place, but light is matter which has found itself. Light contains the moment of unity with self, and displays an absence
25 of elision or finitude, consequently it was one of the first objects to be venerated, and has been regarded as the element in which mankind has become conscious of the absolute. It is the contrast between thought and being, subject and object, which exhibits the highest opposition however, and this was not to be found in light. The posited opposition between
30 man and nature belongs only to the fullest form of self-consciousness. The religion of light is more sublime than that of the Indians or Greeks, but it is also the religion in which man has not yet risen to an awareness of
+ opposition, to self-knowing spirituality. It is interesting to consider light. One always tends to think that with
35 natural objects, the individual is this *present* reality. Light is a contradiction of this however, since it is the expression within nature of the simplicity
+ of thought itself. In nature it is the understanding which occurs; the forms of the understanding exist within nature. If one wants to imagine light, one has to discard all determinations relating to composition etc. Physicists

who postulate particles of light, are in no way superior to the man
who built a windowless house, and wanted to carry the light into it in
sacks. A bundle of rays is nothing but a convenient expression, for these   +
rays are the whole of light, which is merely limited externally, and which
is no more divided into bundles of rays than is the ego or pure self-   5
consciousness. The same principle applies if I talk about my own time, or
the time of Caesar. This particular time has also been the time of all other
things, but I speak of it here with regard to Caesar, and confine it to him,
without his having had a ray or bundle of exclusive and inherently real
time about him. The Newtonian theory, according to which light diffuses   10
itself in lines, or the wave-theory, according to which it diffuses itself in
waves, like *Euler's* ether and the vibration of sound, are material representations which are quite useless in the cognition of light. The shade in
light is supposed to be a series of curves passing through the motion of
light which may be calculated mathematically. This abstract determination   15
has merely been hauled in here, but it is now generally supposed to be a
triumphant advance upon *Newton*. This is not a physical determination   +
however, and neither of these two theories will do here, because any thing
empirical is necessarily invalid. Corpuscles of light or ether are as non-
existent as nerves composed of series of globules which set one another   20
in motion by receiving and imparting an impulse.   +

The propagation of light falls within time, because as activity and
change, light cannot dispense with this moment. Light is immediate expansion, but through its materiality, its luminous corporeality, it relates
itself to another body, and a division, or at least a kind of disjunction is   25
therefore present within its continuity. The sublation of this division constitutes motion, and it is in the relationship between terms of this kind
that time also occurs. The distances which light is supposed to traverse fall
within time, for illumination, whether through penetration of a medium
or the transmission of reflection, is an affection of matter requiring time.   30
In the sphere of our planetary system therefore, i.e. in a more or less
transparent medium, the propagation of light involves a time-determina-
tion, because the rays are refracted by the atmosphere. The continuation
of this in distant regions without an atmosphere, and in the apparently
empty space around the stars, is a different matter however. One might   35
say that these spaces have a content only as inter-stellar distance, which
means in effect that they are empty, and are merely negations of union.
Laws governing the propagation of light which had been deduced principally from the observation of Jupiter's satellites, have been applied by
Herschel to stellar spaces; but Herschel himself admits that these distances   40

+ are merely hypothetical. From the periodic appearance and disappearance
of certain stars and nebulae, *Herschel* concluded that because of the time
which light takes to reach us, there is a difference of 500 years between
the time when we see them, and the time when these changes actually take
5 place, and that there is something completely spectral about being thus
affected by something which has long since passed away. One must accept
the condition of time without becoming involved in these further con-
+ sequences.

§ 277

Light, as universal **physical** identity, **relates itself to the matter**
10 **qualified by the other moments of the Notion. It does this in the**
first instance as something different from this matter (§ 275),
and therefore as something which is distinct from and external
to it. **The matter is therefore determined as the negation of light,**
or as a *darkness,* **and in so far as it also subsists for itself, and is**
15 **different from light, light only enters into relation with its surface,**
which as the initiation of opacity, is therefore made manifest. If
this surface is smooth **and devoid of any further particularization**
however, it also, inseparably, manifests itself, and becomes ap-
parent to another **surface. As each therefore appears to the**
20 **other, and only the other appears to each, the extro-positing of**
this manifestation is the abstract infinity of intro-reflection,
through which there is as yet nothing which appears to itself
as self-subsistent. In order that something may ultimately
appear and become visible, further particularization of some
25 **physical kind or another, such as roughness or colour etc., must**
therefore be present.

Addition. Matter, in contrast to this pure self, is the equivalent lack of
self, or darkness. Its relation to light is that of sheer opposition.
Consequently the one is positive and the other negative. For dark-
30 ness to be positive, corporeal individualization is required. The body
is individualized, and regarded as such, it is merely the negative aspect of
its abstract identity with itself. Darkness vanishes before light; the dark
body is the only corporeality to oppose it, and it now becomes visible.
In order that I may see, there must not only be light, but also a body;
35 *something* to be seen. Consequently light is only visible as a lighted body,
although when the dark matter which becomes visible through light is

taken in its affirmation, it is shape as an abstract aspect of the body. There is an external relation between light and darkness, and the existence of light first occurs on the boundary between them, in the being-for-other of which something is illuminated. The limitation of light in space should be considered only as a point of arrest in the direction pursued by the 5 light, for it would cease to be if its connection with the central body were severed. The limit is therefore posited by the dark body which is lit up. The darkness of weighted matter is specified matter in that it is externally related to light; yet the primary specification here is the spatial difference of surfaces; matter may be rough, flat, jagged, in such and such a position 10 etc. Visible things are distinguished as spatial shapes; this only gives rise to light and shade however, and as yet there is no question of colour. In this primary abstract manifestation, corporeality, which is otherwise particularized into manifold shape, is reduced to surface; it exhibits no particularization here, for it is merely the positing of manifestation as such, 15 and is consequently a merely spatial determination.

§ 278

The manifestation of objects to each other, as limited by their opacity, is the self-externality of s p a t i a l relation, which, as it has no further determinations, is therefore d i r e c t or rectilinear. Since surfaces are so related to each other, and can occupy various 20 positions, the manifestation of one visible object to another in a smooth surface is increased by a third and fourth surface etc. The image of the object, the location of which is taken to be the mirror, is reflected by another surface, i.e. the eye or another mirror etc. In these particularized spatial determinations, e q u a l i t y can 25 be the only law of manifestation, and it entails the equality of the angle of incidence with the angle of reflection, as well as the unity of the plane of this angle. Nothing whatever is present whereby the identity of this relation might be changed.

Remark

In this paragraph, the determinations which may already seem 30 to belong to more determinate physics, contain the transition from the universal limitation of light by dark matter, to its more determinate limitation by the particular spatial determinations of this matter. This determination is usually lumped together with the

representation of light as ordinary matter. Yet it contains nothing but the fact that as inseparable self-externality, the abstract ideality of this pure manifestation is able to receive determinate limits as the result of its own spatiality. This limitability,
5 which is the result of particularized spatiality, is a necessary determination, which is devoid of furthur content, and excludes all material categories of transmission, and of the physical reflection of light etc.

The phenomena which have given rise to the clumsy concept
10 of what has been called fixed polarization or the polarity of light,
+ are associated with the determinations presented in this paragraph. In simple mirroring from a single plane, the so-called angle of incidence is equal to the angle of reflection; consequently, when a second mirror is introduced to communicate the illumination
15 reflected from the first, the position of the first plane as related to the second has its influence upon the position, brightness, or darkening of the object as it appears in the second reflection, through the direction of the first reflection, and the position of the second plane. For the natural undisturbed clarity of the twice
20 reflected brightness of light, the normal position is therefore necessary, so that the planes of all the respective angles of incidence and reflection may coincide. Conversely, the darkening and disappearance of a twice reflected brightness follow with equal necessity if the two planes stand in what one has to call a
25 negative or perpendicular relation to one another (cf. Goethe 'The Science of Nature' vol. I sect. I bottom of p. 28 ff, and sect. 3
+ Entopt. Colours VIII. XIX. p. 144 et seq.). Malus has concluded from the modification in the brightness of the mirroring which this position brings about, that molecules of light, even in their
30 various aspects, are in implicit possession of different physical properties. From this it has also been concluded that the so-called
+ rays of light are four-sided. It is upon this basis, together with the further implications of entoptical colour phenomena, that a vast maze of extremely complicated theory has been built. It
35 constitutes a prime example of the strange conclusions physics can draw from experience. Malus's polarization theory originated in the first phenomenon, from which the only valid conclusion to be drawn is that the bright condition of the light in the second reflection can only occur if the angle of reflection occurs
+ on the same plane as the angle of the first.

23

Addition. As light encounters matter and makes it visible, it enters generally into the preciser determinateness of the various directions and quantitative differences of degrees of brightness. This *reflection* of light is a more difficult determination than one might think. To say that objects are visible is to say that light is reflected in all directions. In their visibility, objects are for 5 another, to which they are therefore related. Consequently, this visible aspect of them is in another, which means that light is not irrelative, but involves another with itself, and therefore that the objects are in another. Here we have the precise nature of the reflection of light. The sun shines, and light is therefore for another. Within its dimensions, this other, which 10 might for example be a surface, becomes a surface of sunlight. It therefore shines, although in the first instance it can give off no light of its own, its shining being merely derived. Yet as the surface behaves at each point like the sun, it is being-for-other, both externally and therefore in the other. This is the main determination of reflection. 15

We can only see something in a surface therefore, in so far as spatial shapes such as roughness occur on it. If it is smooth, no visible difference will be present. That which is visible here is not something which belongs to the surface itself, for the surface is not differentiated. It is merely something else which becomes visible, it is not a determination of the surface, 20 i.e. the surface mirrors something. Uniform smoothness has no spatial difference, and as we see nothing determinate on an object if roughness is lacking, we therefore see nothing in the smoothness but a general gleam, which is a general abstract shining, an indeterminate illumination. It is consequently this smoothness which manifests the unturbid image of the 25 other. On a smooth surface one therefore sees another determinate object, for this object is only visible in so far as it is for another than itself. If the surface combines smoothness with opacity, (transparency also mirrors however, cf. § 320 Add.), and this other object is placed before it, the object will be visible within it, for to be visible is to be in another. If we 30 place another mirror in front of the first, and a light in the middle, the light will be visible in both mirrors at once, but in each only with the determination of the other. An image of itself will likewise be visible in each, because each mirror is visible to the other. If the mirrors are placed at an angle to one another, the progression here is infinite, for one is then 35 able to see the objects as many times as the breadth of the mirrors allows. If one tries to explain this by mechanical representations, one merely plunges into the wildest confusion. If we call the two mirrors A and B, and ask what is visible in A, the answer is B. But B is that in which A is visible. Therefore A is visible in A in that it is visible in B. What is visible 40

in B then? A itself, and A as visible in B. What then is visible in A? B, and
that which is visible in B, i.e. A itself, and A visible in B etc. We therefore
have a perpetual repetition of the same relation, although in each repetition the terms have a particular existence. A great deal of light can also
+ be concentrated upon a single point by means of mirrors.

    Light is active identity, and posits the identification of everything. As
this identity is still entirely abstract however, there is as yet no real identity
of things. Things are for another, and posit themselves as identical with
another in another. This positing of identification is therefore external to
10 things, which are indifferent to being illumined. It is therefore necessary
that they should be posited for themselves in concrete identity; light
should become their own, and so complete and realize itself. Light is still
entirely abstract selfhood, and is therefore the not-self, the free self-identity
which is devoid of all opposition within itself. The other to which light
15 relates itself in its free existence as solar body, is external to light. Consequently, light resembles the understanding, for its material is external to it.
Until now we have merely called this negative term darkness, but it also
has an immanent determination of its own. In its abstract determination,
this physical opposition still has its own independent existence, and it is
+ this that we now have to consider.

2. The bodies of opposition

§ 279

Dark matter is primarily the negation **of light, and constitutes
the opposition to its abstractly identical ideality; it is** *opposition*
in its own self. It has material reality, and within itself falls
apart into a *duality* of (1) corporeal *variety*, **which is** the
25 material being-for-self of *rigidity*, and (2) the *opposition* as
such. **By itself,** this opposition is not controlled by individuality, but is merely sunk within itself, and so constitutes
dissolution and *neutrality*. This duality marks the difference
between the *lunar* and *cometary* bodies.

Remark

30 As *relative centres of corporeality* within the gravitational
system, both these bodies also have **a peculiarity** which is
based on the same concept as their physical **peculiarity,** and

which may be stated here **with more exactness, i.e.** neither
turns upon its axis. As the *body of rigidity* is a formal being- +
for-self, its independence **is caught up in** the opposition, and
consequently it does not constitute individuality. It is
therefore *satellitic,* and *subservient* to another body, in 5
which it has its *axis.* The *body* of *dissolution* is the antithesis
to that of rigidity, for it behaves *aberrantly,* and displays
the same contingency in its eccentric revolution as it does
in its physical existence. Comets present themselves as a +
superficial concretion, which may disperse again with equal 10
contingency.

The *moon* has no atmosphere, and therefore lacks the
meteorological process. It exhibits only high conical moun- +
tains, in which craters correspond to valleys, and afford
evidence of the internal combustion of this rigidity. Its +
form is crystalline, and *Heim,* one of the limited number +
of profound geognosts, has indicated that the Earth **also** +
had this form in its original and purely rigid state. The
comet appears as a formal process, an unstable and vaporous
mass; not one has given indication of a *nucleus* or anything 20
rigid within it. The ancients regarded comets as mere
momentary meteoric **formations** like fire-balls and shooting
stars. Nowadays astronomers are not so reticent and stand-
offish as they used to be with regard to this view. So far,
only **a few cases** of their return **have been confirmed;** the ap- 25
pearances of others have been calculated and expected, but
have failed to materialize. **The idea that the solar system is in
itself a true system on account of its essentially coherent totality,**
necessarily rules out the formal interpretation of the comets, in which their appearances are regarded as being in 30
accidental opposition to the entirety of this system when
they cross and impinge upon it. **It is therefore possible to**
conceive of the other bodies of the system as *protecting*
themselves against comets, i.e. **as having to maintain and
preserve themselves** as the necessary moments of an organism. 35
There are better grounds of reassurance to be found in this
conception, **than those that have so far been advanced against**
the potential menace of the comets, **for by and large these
reassurances have merely been based upon the fact that in the
vastness of the heavens, the comets have so much space through** 40

26

which to move upon their ways, that there is only a minimal chance of their encountering the Earth. The plausibility of this argument is not increased by its being transformed into a theory
+ **of probability.**

5 *Addition.* As this is a free opposition, these two logical sides to it exist here as external to each other. Consequently the two terms do not meet accidentally in the solar system; if one has thoroughly grasped the nature of the Notion, it will not seem strange that even such things have to display themselves as having entered into the sphere of the Idea, by which
10 alone they are legitimatized. They constitute the moments of the dissolving Earth which have been rendered independent. The Moon resembles the hard core of the Earth, the comet is a durable meteor, a part of its
+ atmosphere which has become independent (see below § 287). As it is an animated whole, the Earth can and must release its crystalline and
15 moribund essence. It therefore discharges this moment, which constitutes its inner determination, so that the Moon remains the regent of the Earth's individual process, just as the Sun remains regent of its universal pro-
+ cess. On the other hand, it is part of the Notion of dissolution that this moment has freed itself, flown off into independence and severed its connection with the
+ Earth.

Rigid being-for-self is concentrated into itself, opaque, and by itself indifferent; the independence of this being-for-self is rigid in so far as it is still immobile. The principle of rigidity, of brittleness, is puncticity, each point of which is individual. This is the mechanical appearance of simple
25 rigidity, the physical determination of which is combustibility. Real being-for-self is self-relating negativity, the process of fire, which consumes itself by consuming another. Rigidity is only implicitly combustible however, it is the possibility, and not yet the efficacy of fire. Consequently the process of fire, which is the active inter-relation of difference, is not
30 to be found here, where we still have the free inter-relation of qualities. Clouds and animated changes of atmosphere may be seen on Mercury
+ and Venus, but the Moon has neither clouds, seas, nor rivers, for if there were water surfaces and silver threads upon it, they would be very easy to pick out. Ephemeral points of light are often seen on the Moon, and
35 are thought to be volcanic eruptions. Air is undoubtedly one of the conditions of these phenomena, although the lunar atmosphere has no hu-
+ midity. *Heim*, the brother of the doctor, has attempted to show that in the era which preceded the geological revolutions of which we have evidence, the form of the Earth must have resembled that of the Moon.

27

The Moon is crystalline, but it lacks water, and it might be said that by attempting to quench the thirst of its rigidity by integrating itself with our sea, it causes the ebb and flow of the tides. The waters rise, having a mind to escape to the moon, and the Moon is about to clasp them unto itself. *Laplace* ('Exposition du système du monde' vol. II pp. 136–138), 5 has discovered by observations and theory, that lunar tides are three times as strong as solar tides, and that the flow is at its strongest when the two coincide. Consequently the position of the moon in the syzygies and quadratures is qualitatively the most significant factor. +

Rigidity which is bound up within itself, is as impotent as the abstract 10 neutrality and susceptibility to determination found in the corresponding fluidity. Since the opposition exists only as opposition, it has no fixity, and merely collapses internally. As the extremes enter actively into the determination of opposition, a middle is necessary in order to bring them together and support them. If rigidity and neutrality were united in this 15 third term, we should have a real totality. The comet is a translucent, transparent, aqueous body, which certainly does not belong to our atmo- + sphere. If it had a nucleus it would be recognizable by its shadow, but comets are thoroughly permeated with brightness. The stars may be seen through a comet's tail, and even through the comet itself. One astronomer 20 thought that he had seen a nucleus, but it turned out to be a fault in his telescope. As its ellipse has an exaggerated elongation, the comet makes + an almost parabolic orbit about the Sun; it then disperses again, and reproduces itself in another form. The most certain and regular return is that of *Halley's* comet, which appeared last in 1758, and is to be expected 25 again in 1835. An astronomer has shown by calculation that many of these appearances may be reduced to an orbit which could belong to a single comet. Halley's comet has been seen two or three times, but according to calculation it ought to have appeared five times. Comets inter- + sect the planetary orbits in all directions. The independence with which 30 they are credited should enable them to touch the planets. If people are frightened by this they can draw no consolation from the vastness of the heavens and the consequent improbability of this happening, for each point is as susceptible to being touched as any other. It is necessary to + conceive of the comets as being parts of our solar system however. It 35 should be apparent therefore that they do not arrive as unfamiliar guests, but have been engendered here, and that their orbits are determined by the system. The other bodies consequently preserve their independence of the comets, because they are equally necessary moments of this system.

The comets have their centre in the Sun. The Moon, because of its 40 rigidity, has a greater affinity with the planets, for it represents the nucleus of the Earth for itself, and also contains the principle of abstract individuality. In an abstract manner therefore, comet and Moon reproduce the Sun and planet. The planets are the middle term of the system; the Sun is one extreme, and the dependent bodies of the opposition, which is still disintegrated, are the other (U-S-P). This is the immediate and purely formal syllogism; but it is not the only one. The other, more determinate relation, is that in which the dependent bodies are the mediating terms the Sun the one extreme, and the Earth the other (S-U-P), for the Earth, relates itself to the Sun through its dependence. As the middle term, the dependent body must have the two moments of extremity within it however, and as it is their unity, it must be divided within itself. Each moment must belong to one extreme; as the lunar moment belongs to the planets, the cometary moment must belong to the Sun, because the comet, having no internal fixity must relate itself to the formal centre. The courtiers who are personally attendant upon the sovereign have little independence because of the closeness of their relation to him, while the ministers and their subordinates act with more regularity and consequently with more uniformity, as functionaries. The third syllogism is that in which the Sun itself is the middle term (P-U-S).

This physical relationship between the heavenly bodies, together with their mechanical relation, constitutes cosmic nature, which is the foundation, the completely universal life, in which the whole of animate nature participates (see above § 270 Add.). One ought not to speak of the Moon's influence upon the Earth as if this were an external action however. Universal animation is much more passive with regard to individuality, and the dominion of the sidereal powers becomes less effective as the strength of individuality increases. It is through participation in this universal life about us that we sleep and wake, and that our morning and evening moods are not the same. The periodicity of the Moon's phases may be traced in living things, particularly in sick animals. Yet a healthy animal, and to an greater extent, a spiritual being, will sever itself from this universal life, and oppose it. The position of the Moon is supposed to have an influence upon the demented, and upon lunatics however. The effect of the weather may also be felt in scars when the wounds have left a certain weakness behind. Although much has recently been made of cosmic conditions and relationships, the evidence brought forward has consisted, for the most part, of empty turns of phrase, generalities, or completely isolated instances. The influences of the comets can scarcely be denied. I once made Mr. *Bode* sigh by saying that we know from experience that comets are followed by good vintage years, as was the case in 1811 and 1819, and that this double experience was just as good, if not better, than that regarding the return of the comets. What makes comet-wine so good is that the water-process abandons the Earth, and so brings about an alteration in the state of the planet.   5

3. The body of individuality
(The planet as the body of individuality)

§ 280

The opposition which has returned into itself is the *Earth*, or the *planet* in general. This is the body of *individual* totality, in which rigidity is *opened up* into the separateness of real differences, and this dissolution is held together by the *self-like point of unity*.   10

Remark

The axial rotation **of the planets,** combined with their moving around the central body, **is** the expression of animation, and is the most concrete form of motion. Similarly, the luminous nature of the central body is *abstract* identity, the truth of which, like the truth of thought, is the concrete Idea of individuality.   15

Astronomy has not yet discovered the actual law governing the planetary series, i.e. the primary determinateness of the *distances* between these bodies. The attempts made in +
natural philosophy to demonstrate the rationality of the 20
series from its physical constitution, **and by analogies with a series of metals, have been equally fruitless, and can hardly be regarded as providing a satisfactory basis for research.** It is however irrational to regard contingency as the basic factor here, **as** *Laplace* **does when he** treats *Kepler's* attempts at +
grasping the order of the solar system according to the laws of musical harmony, as the mere *aberration* of **a bemused** *imagination*, and so fails to appreciate the deep faith which Kepler had in the inherent *rationality of this system*;
a faith which was the sole foundation of the brilliant 30
discoveries made by this **extraordinary man**. *Newton's* +

application of numerical tonal relations to *colours*, which is
utterly inept, and **which, with regard to the data, is completely**
+ erroneous, has on the other hand won fame and approval.

Addition. The planet is the veritable prius, the subjectivity in which these
5 differences are merely moments of an ideal nature, and in which life first
has determinate being. The Sun is subservient to the planets, just as the
Sun, Moon, comets, and stars in general, are merely aspects of the Earth.
The Sun therefore has neither engendered nor thrown off the planets;
the whole solar system is an entirety, for the Sun and the planets are en-
10 gendered reciprocally. Just as the ego, although it is not yet spirit, finds
its truth within spirit, so light finds its truth in the concrete being of the
planet. Taken alone and by itself, the ego in its asserted supremacy is an
empty negation, and not spirit. The ego is certainly an absolute moment
of spirit, but not to the extent that it isolates itself.
15   There is little more to be said here about the body of individuality,
and that which follows is nothing more than the explication of this individuality. We are concerned here with the abstract determination of it.
It is the property of the Earth or of organic being to digest the completely
universal astral powers which appear to have independence as heavenly
20 bodies, and to bring them under the sway of individuality, so that these
gigantic members reduce themselves to moments. Quality, in its totality,
is individuality, as the infinite form which is one with itself. If there is any
talk of pride of place, it must be this our Earth which we regard as su-
+ preme. If one reflects quantitatively, one can certainly let the Earth sink
25 away beneath one as, 'a drop in the ocean of infinitude'; size, however is a
very external determination. We now come to stand upon the Earth
+ therefore, which is not only our physical, but also our spiritual home.
    There are a number of Earths and planets which together form an
organic unity, and many correspondences and resemblances can be
30 adduced in connection with them, although they do not yet accord
+ completely with the Idea. *Schelling* and *Steffens* have drawn a parallel
between the planetary series and that of metals. This is an ingenious and
pregnant comparison, but it is not a new idea, for the representation of
Venus by copper, Mercury by quicksilver, the Earth by iron, Jupiter by
35 tin, and Saturn by lead, is a commonplace, just as it is to call the Sun
golden and the Moon silver. There is something completely natural about
this, for metals are the most compact and independent bodies to be found
on Earth. The planets do not belong to the same field as the metals and
the chemical process however. Cross-references of this kind are external

31

comparisons, and decide nothing. They merely sparkle before the imagi- +
nation without furthering the scope of knowledge. Commonsense and
instinct enabled *Linnaeus* to classify plants; others have done the same with
animals. Metals are arranged according to their specific gravity, but in
space the planets arrange themselves, and if one searches amongst them for 5
a law resembling that found in a mathematical series, one merely finds
that the same law is repeated in each term. The whole conception of a
series is unphilosophical however, and contrary to the Notion. The formations of nature occur in masses, and are not ranged in such a scalari-
form manner; the universal diremption comes first, and then follows 10
the further subdivision within each genus. The 24 classifications of
the plants drawn up by Linnaeus are not a natural system, and the great
divisions were seen more clearly by the Frenchman *Jussieu*, when he
divided plants into monocotyledons and dicotyledons. *Aristotle* did much +
the same with regard to animals. It is because they do not constitute a +
static series that the planets also demand such an interpretation. In his
'Harmonia Mundi' *Kepler* treated the distances between the planets as
tonal relationships, a thought which had already been developed by the
followers of *Pythagoras*. +

It is a matter of history that *Paracelsus* said that all terrestrial bodies are +
composed of the four elements of mercury, sulphur, salt, and virgin earth,
and that these correspond to the four cardinal virtues. Mercury is metalline,
and as metal is abstract matter; it is self-identical in its fluid corporeality,
and corresponds to light. Sulphur is rigidity, the possibility of combustion; fire is not alien to it, but constitutes its self-consuming actuality. Salt 25
corresponds to water, which is the cometary principle, and its dissolution
constitutes indifferent reality, or the subsidence of fire into independence.
Finally, virgin earth is the simple innoxiousness of this movement, the
subject which constitutes the extinction of these moments; this was the
accepted expression for the abstract earthiness of pure silica. If this 30
is interpreted as a chemical theory, it will soon be discovered of course
that there are many bodies in which there is no mercury or sulphur.
The essential point of such assertions is however that there are four
moments to real corporeality, not that these materials are really present.
Such theories should not be taken literally, for if they are, *Jacob Boehme* 35
and others may well be thought of as nonsensical and lacking in experience. +

B

The elements

§ 281

The determinations of the elemental totality, which are, by themselves, an immediacy of freely independent bodies, are contained in the body of individuality as subordinate moments. As such, they constitute its universal *physical*
5 *elements*.

Remark

In recent times, chemical simplicity has been arbitrarily accepted as the definition of an element. This definition has nothing to do with the Notion of a physical element, which is a real matter, and is not yet volatilized into chemical abstraction.

10 *Addition.* So far we have looked at nature in general, and seen the cosmic forces as independent and objective corporealities which nevertheless remain fixed in their connections. We now pass over to a consideration of these bodies as moments of individuality. It is precisely individuality which brings their existence into a fuller truth. Light, as positing the
15 identical, is not confined solely to the illumination of dark matter, but subsequently advances into real activity. The particularized matters are not merely mutually apparent, so that each remains what it is, but they change themselves into one another. This positing of themselves as identical and of an ideal nature is also the activity of light. Light kindles,
20 stimulates, and generally governs the elemental process. This process belongs to the individual Earth, which is at first however, still the abstract universal individuality, and which has to solidify to a much greater extent in order to become true undividuality. Here the subjective principle of individuality, which is an infinite self-relation, is still exterior to the
25 universal individuality which is not yet reflected into itself, i.e. to the stimulating and animating principle of light. Here we have anticipated the occurrence of this relation, but before we consider the elemental process, we shall have to consider the nature of its individualized differences as they are by themselves. It was only by us that the body of individuality was
30 determined as having the moments of the solar system within it; in its further determination as such, it is autonomous. In the planet, the bodies

of the solar system are no longer independent, but are predicates of a subject. There are now four of these elements, and their order is as follows. The air corresponds to light, for it is passive light which has sunk to the level of a moment. The elements of opposition are fire and water. Rigidity, which is the lunar principle, is no longer indifferent being-for- 5 self, but as an element entering into relation with something other than itself, i.e. individuality, it is the full process of active and restless being-for-self, and is therefore liberated negativity, or fire. The third element, water, corresponds to the cometary principle. The fourth is earth once again. The history of philosophy makes it clear that the main importance of 10 *Empedocles* consists in his having been the first definitely to have grasped and distinguished these basic forms in their physical universality. +

The elements are universal natural existences, which are no longer independent, and yet are still not individualized. In chemistry, an element is to be understood as a general constituent of bodies, all of which are sup- 15 posed to consist of a definite number of these elements. The assumption here is that all bodies are composite, so that thought has as its object the + reduction of the infinite variety of qualified and individualized corporealities to a few incomposite and therefore general qualities. On the basis of this criterion, the concept of the four elements, which has been a common- 20 place since the time of Empedocles, has been rejected as a puerile phantasy, the elements being regarded as composite ! No educated person, and certainly no physicist or chemist is now permitted, under any circumstances, to mention the four elements. The search for the sort of simple and universal existence present-day chemists have in mind is a matter only for 25 chemistry. The chemical point of view will be treated later on. Chemistry assumes the individuality of bodies, and then attempts to break down this individuality and the point of unity in which the differences are contained, and to free these differentiae from the force which constrains them. The combination of acid and base gives rise to a salt, which is their unity, the 30 third term. As crystallization, this third term also has shape however, so that it is not just the simple abstract unity of chemical elements, but individual unity of form. If the body is merely the neutrality of its differences, we shall be able to point out its aspects when we break it down. These aspects are not universal elements and original principles however, they 35 are merely qualitatively, i.e. specifically determined constituents. The individuality of a body is much more than the mere neutrality of these aspects however; it is infinite form which is the main thing, particularly in living existence. When we have exhibited the constitutents of a vegetable or animal, they are no longer its constituents, for the vegetable or animal 40

34

will have been annihilated. Consequently, in its attempt to attain simplicity, chemistry destroys individuality. If that which is individual is neutral, as a salt is, chemistry will be able to exhibit its distinct aspects, for chemical analysis will only destroy the merely formal unity of its differ-
5 ences. If an organism is broken down however, it is not only the unity which is destroyed, but also the organism one is attempting to understand. In dealing with the physical elements, we are not in the least concerned with elements in the chemical sense. The chemical standpoint is certainly not the only one, it is merely one particular sphere, with no right
10 whatever to impose itself upon other forms, as if it were their essence. It is merely the becoming of individuality that we have before us here, and at first, only the universal individual, the Earth. The elements are the diverse matters, which constitute the moments of this becoming of the universal individual. In short: we must not confuse the standpoint of chemistry with
15 that of the still wholly universal individuality. The chemical elements exhibit no order whatever, and are quite heterogeneous as regards one another. The physical elements on the contrary are universal matters, particularized solely in conformity with the moments of the Notion. There are consequently only four of them. The ancients certainly asserted that
20 everything is composed of these four elements, but they only had the
+ abstract thought of this truth before them.

We now have to examine these physical elements more closely. In themselves they are not yet individualized, they are shapeless, and they therefore fall apart into chemical abstractions. Air breaks down into oxy-
25 gen and nitrogen, water into oxygen and hydrogen. Fire does not break down, for it is the process itself, the only material residue of which is luminous matter. At the other extreme of subjectivity, living matters such
+ as plant-saps, and even animal fluids, may be analysed into these abstract chemical substances, and the specific residue is the smaller part. It is the
30 inorganic physical individuality of the intermediary moment which is the
+ most difficult to deal with however. This is because matter here is specified through its individuality, which at the same time is still immediate and lacking in life and sentience; as quality therefore, it is immediately identical with the universal.

+   1. Air

§ 282

35 The element of undifferentiated simplicity is no longer
the positive identity with self and self-manifestation of

light as such; it is mere *negative universality* **reduced to the** selfless moment of *an other*, **and consequently it also has weight. As negative universality,** this identity is the unnoticed but insidious and consuming power **to which individual and orga-** +
nic nature are subject. It is in fact *air*, **a fluidity which is** *transpa-* 5
rent **and passive with regard to light, but which sublimates all individuality within itself, and which by its mechanical** elasticity, pervades everything.

Addition. (*a*) The inner self of the individual body is the bond of its individuality or the reciprocal relation of its moments. This selflike nature, 10
considered by itself as free and devoid of all *posited* individualization, is air.
Nevertheless, this element contains the *implicit* determination of being-for-self, or puncticity. Air is the universal as posited in relation to subjectivity, to infinite self-relating negativity, to being-for-self, and is therefore the universal as a subordinate moment in the determination of 15
relativity. Air is indeterminate and absolutely determinable; it is not yet determined within itself, but is merely determinable through its other; this other is light, because light is the free universal. Air is thus related to light; to light it is absolute transparency, it is passive light; in general, it is the universal posited as passivity. In the same way, the good, as the uni- 20
versal, is also passive, for it is first actualized through subjectivity, and does not activate itself. Light is also implicitly passive, but is not *posited* as such. +
As it is merely implicit individuality; air is not dark but transparent;
opacity first occurs in terrestrialness.

(*b*) In its second determination, air is related to individuality as simple 25
activity and effective identity, while light was merely abstract identity.
The lighted object posits itself in another in a merely ideal manner:
but air is this identity which is now among its equals, and relates itself to physical materials, which exist for one another and touch one another in accordance with their physical determinateness. The univer- 30
sality of air is consequently the effort which it makes to posit the real identity of the other to which it relates itself. The other which air posits as being identical with itself is however individualization and particularization in general. Yet air itself is mere universality, and consequently it does not come forth in its activity as an individual body having the power to 35
decompose this individualization. Air is therefore purely corrosive, and is hostile to the individual, which it posits as a universal element. Nevertheless, the destruction is not apparent; it is motionless, and does not manifest itself as violence. It slinks in everywhere, without any connection

with air: like reason, it insinuates itself into the individual and dissolves it. Consequently, it is the air which gives rise to odours, for odour is merely this invisible and ceaseless process between individual being and air. Everything evaporates and disperses into its parts, and the residue is
+ odourless. Organic being also comes into conflict with the air through respiration, the elements in general being in a state of conflict with it. A wound, for example, only becomes dangerous through exposure to the air. Only organic life has the determination of perpetually restoring itself in the process of its destruction. Inorganic being, which cannot endure this
10 conflict, must decay, and although that which is of greater consistency conserves itself, it is ceaselessly attacked by the air. Animal forms which are no longer alive, may be preserved from decay if they are removed from contact with the air. This destruction can be mediated however, as when humidity brings the process to a certain product. This is only
15 mediation however, for it is still the air *as such* which destroys. As the universal, the air is pure, but it is not an inert purity, for that which evaporates into the air does not preserve itself there, but is reduced to simple universality. In mechanical physics it is supposed that when such a body has been dissolved, fine particles of it continue to float about in the
20 air, and can no longer be smelt simply because they have been so finely dispersed. Physicists are in fact reluctant to allow these bodies to disintegrate, but we ought not to feel so much compassion for matter, for it is
+ only in the understanding's system of identity that it has permanence. Air purifies itself and converts everything into air; it is not a mish-mash of
+ matters, and neither odorousness nor chemical investigation suggests that it is. The understanding employs the expedient of tenuity of course, and has an overriding prejudice against the word 'transmute', but empirical physics has no right to assert the existence of that which is not given by perception. If it wishes to proceed purely empirically, it has to admit that
30 this body passes away.

(*c*) Air offers resistance, as does matter in general, but it does so merely quantitatively as mass, and not by means of punctation or individuality as do other bodies. Biot in his 'Traité de Physique' vol. I. p. 188 says there-
+ fore that, 'Tous les gaz permanents, exposés à des températures égales,
35 sous la même pression, se dilatent exactament de la même quantité'. Since air only offers resistance as mass, it is indifferent to the space it occupies. It is not rigid, but lacks cohesion, and has no exterior shape. To a certain degree it is *compressible*, for it is not absolutely spaceless i.e. it is an extrinsicality which is however not atomistic, and in which the
40 principle of individuation might seem to have assumed existence. This is

why different kinds of gas occupy the same space, and it is this that constitutes the appearance of penetrability which is part of the universality of
air, and by virtue of which it is not individualized within itself. If a glass
container is filled with atmospheric air, and another is filled with steam,
and the contents of the second container are poured into the first, the first 5
will take as much of the steam as it would if it contained no air at all. Air
may be so compressed by mechanical force, and so posited as such an
intensity, that its spatial extrinsicality is completely sublated. This is one of
the finest of discoveries, and is of course used in lighters, in which tinder
is placed at the bottom of a cylinder which is filled with a piston, so that 10
when the piston is forced in, the compressed air emits a spark which lights
the tinder. If the tube is transparent, the spark may be seen. The whole +
nature of air becomes apparent here in the universal self-identity of its
destructiveness. This invisible odourizing element is here reduced to a
point, and active being-for-self, which was formerly implicit, is therefore 15
posited as the being-for-self of being-for-self. This is the absolute origin of
fire, the active universality which consumes and takes on form where
indifferent subsistence ceases. It is no longer universal, but is a restless self-
relatedness. The great value of this experiment is that it demonstrates the
connection between air and the fire within it. Air is a slumbering fire, and 20
in order to bring fire forth from it, one merely has to modify its existence.

2. The elements of opposition

§ 283

(a) **Primarily,** the elements of opposition are being-for-self,
not however the *indifferent* being-for-self of rigidity, but a
moment posited within individuality **as the being-for-self of
its restlessness, i.e.** *fire*. **In itself air is fire, and it shows this when it** 25
**is compressed. It is posited in fire as negative universality or
self-relating negativity.** Fire is materialized *time*, **or selfhood
in which light is identical with heat.** In its simple restlessness
and destruction, into which, as in friction for example, the
self-consumption of a body breaks forth, and in the con- 30
verse but identical activity, **by which it penetrates into a body**
and destroys it from without, **fire is the consumption of another**
which simultaneously consumes itself, **and as such passes over
into neutrality.**

38

Addition. Air is already the negativity of particularity, although this is not apparent because it is still posited in the shape of undifferentiated sameness; but in its isolated individuality, differentiated from other modes of existence, and posited within a determinate place, it is fire. Fire exists only as this relationship to a particular, which it not only exhausts, rendering it tasteless and odourless by transforming its matter into an insipid indeterminateness, but whose particularity as matter it destroys. Heat is merely the appearance of this destruction in the individual body, and is therefore identical with fire. Fire is existent being-for-self, which is negativity as such. It is not however the negativity of another, but negation of the negative which results in universality and sameness. Primary universality is lifeless affirmation; fire is the true affirmation. Not-being is posited within it as being, and vice versa, so that fire is time. Fire is simply conditioned as one of the moments, and like air, exists only in relation to particularized matter. It is activity which is only in opposition, it is not the activity of spirit. In order to consume, it must have something to consume, and if it has no material, it disappears. The life process is also the process of fire, for it also consists of the consumption of particularities, although it is ceaselessly reproducing its material.

That which is consumed by fire is sometimes concrete, and sometimes in opposition. To consume concrete being is to bring it into opposition, to animate or ignite it. The oxidation in the causticity of an acid works in this way. This is how concrete being is brought to the extreme point of consuming itself, and so into a state of tension with another. The other aspect of this process is that the determinate, differentiated, and individualized particularity which is present in all concrete being, is reduced to the unity and indeterminateness of neutrality. This is why every chemical process will produce water and give rise to opposition. Fire is air posited with a difference, it is negated unity, and an opposition which is however also reduced to neutrality. The natural element into which fire subsides, and by which it is extinguished, is water. The manifest unity of the triumph of ideal identity to which particularized being is brought, is abstract, the selfhood of light. Since terrestrialness remains over as the foundation of the process, and it is here that all the elements make their appearance.

§ 284

(*b*) The other element of the opposition is neutral. It is opposition which has coincided with itself in a thorough-going equilibrium; consequently, although it lacks the

39

being-for-self of individuality, and is therefore devoid of rigidity and internal determination, it dissolves all mechanical determinations posited within it. Its shape is limited only from without, **and it is there that it seeks it through adhesion.** In itself its process is quiescent, for it is simply the possibility of dissolubility. **In its ordinary state, it constitutes an internal indeterminateness, but in an extraordinary condition it can assume the form of gaseousness or rigidity.** This element is *water*.

Addition. (α) Water is the element of selfless opposition, it is passive being-for-other, while fire is active being-for-other. Water has existence as being-for-other therefore. In itself, and throughout its being, it exhibits neither cohesion, odour, taste, nor shape; its determination consists in its not yet being anything in particular. It is abstract neutrality, not individualized neutrality like salt; since very early times it has therefore been called, 'the mother of everything particular'. Like the air it is *fluid*, but this is not an elastic fluidity which expands on all sides. It is more terrestrial than air, and tends towards a centre of gravity. It comes close to attaining individuality, because in itself it is concrete neutrality, although it is not yet posited as such. Air, on the other hand, is not even implicitly concrete. Water is therefore the real possibility of difference, although this does not yet exist within it. As it has no centre of gravity within itself, it is merely subject to the direction of gravity, and since it lacks cohesion, each point is pressed in the vertical, linear direction. As no part of it is able to offer resistance to this, water settles into *horizontality*. Consequently, mechanical pressure from without leaves no permanent mark upon it; the point brought under pressure is unable to maintain itself as such, but communicates itself to the others, which annul the pressure. Water is still transparent, but because it is more terrestrial, it is no longer so transparent as air. As it is neutral, it is the *dissolvent* of salts and acids. Whatever is dissolved in water, loses its shape; its mechanical relationship is sublated, and only its chemical relationship remains. Water is indifferent to varieties of shape, and a possibility with regard to its elastic fluidity as *steam*, its liquidity in drops, and its rigidity as ice. The whole of this is merely a state, and a formal transition however. In that they are merely produced externally by a change of temperature, these states depend upon a condition independent of water itself. This is the *first* consequence of the *passivity* of water.

(β) A *second* consequence is that water is not compressible, or only very slightly so, for there is no absolute determination in nature. It offers

resistance only as a mass, not as an internal individualization, that is to say, in its ordinary state as a liquidity liable to form drops. Compressibility might be regarded as the consequence of passivity; it is precisely on account of its passivity however, that water is not compressible, and does
5 not alter its spatial magnitude. Since air is active intensity, though only as the universal power of being-for-self, it is indifferent with regard to its extrinsicality or determinate space, and can therefore be compressed. A spatial change in water would therefore imply an intensity which it does not possess; if its spatial magnitude is changed, this happens in con-
10 junction with a change in its condition. In its elastic fluidity, and as ice, water takes up more room precisely because its chemical quality has been
+ changed. Physicists are not justified in attributing the increased space
+ occupied by ice to the bubbles of air which occur within it.

(γ) A *third* consequence of this passivity is the ease with which water
15 separates, as well as its tendency to *adhere* and so make things *wet*. It clings to everything, and enters into closer relationships with the bodies it touches, than with itself. It separates itself from its whole, and is not only able to receive any shape from without, but is in essence prone to distribute itself throughout such external firmness and connection, precisely
20 because it lacks anything of this kind within itself. Its relation to oily and
+ fatty substances is of course an exception to this.

Summarizing the character of the three elements under consideration, it must be said that air constitutes the universal ideality of everything alien to it; that it is the universal in relation to its other, and that it effaces all
25 opposing particularity. Fire is the same universality, but it appears as such, and therefore has the form of being-for-self, it is existent ideality therefore, or the nature of air which has passed into existence; by appearing, it reduces its other to an appearance. The third element is passive neutrality. These are the necessary thought-determinations of these elements.

3. The individual element
(Earth)

§ 285

30 Primarily, the element of *developed* difference, and its *individual* determination, is *terrestrialness* as such. In its distinctness from the other moments, this element is as yet indeterminate; **as the totality which holds together the variety of these moments in individual unity however, it is the power which**
+ **kindles and sustains their process.**

C.

The process of the elements
(Meteorology)

§ 286

The individual identity which binds the different elements, as well as the variety which they exhibit both
amongst themselves and with regard to their unity, is a
dialectic which constitutes the physical life of the Earth,
the *meteorological process*. It is in this process alone that the 5
elements, as dependent moments, have their subsistence,
their existence being *generated* **and posited within it, after having
been developed out of implicitness as moments of the Notion.**

Remark

Just as the determinations of ordinary mechanics and of
dependent bodies are applied to absolute mechanics and the 10
free bodies of centrality, so the *finite* physics of *single*
individual bodies is taken to be the same as the free and
independent physics of the terrestrial process. It is taken to
be a great scientific accomplishment that the determinations
which appear in the processes of isolated bodies may also 15
be recognized and demonstrated in the universal process of
the Earth. **It is only in the field of these isolated bodies that the
determinations immanent within the free existence of the Notion
are reduced to a relationship in which they are mutually external,
and exist as mutually independent circumstances. The activity also** 20
**appears as an externally regulated contingency, so that its pro-
ducts, too, remain the external formations of corporealities as
persisting in their independence.** This likeness, **or rather analogy,**
may be demonstrated **by making an abstraction** from particular differences and determinations. **It is this abstraction which** 25
elicits superficial generalities such as attraction, forces, and laws,
which fail to account for both particularity and determinate conditions. **Concrete modes of these activities appear in
isolated corporeality, and when these are applied to a sphere in
which diverse corporeal existences are no more than moments,** 30

the external circumstances peculiar to the former sphere tend to be partly overlooked, and partly distorted by the analogy. In general, these applications of categories draw upon a field of finite relations, which they make us of in a sphere in which relations are
5 infinite, and therefore conform to the Notion.

Consideration of this field suffers from a basic defect, which has its origin in the fixed conception of a substantial and unalterable *variety* of elements. This conception is taken over by the understanding from the processes of *isolated* sub-
10 stances and used without discrimination. **Where** more complex transitions also appear in these finite processes, where for example, water is fixed in a crystal, or light and heat vanish etc. **reflection has recourse to nebulous and meaningless expressions concerning** *dissolution, ligation, latence,* and
15 suchlike **(see below** § 305 Rem. **and Addition**). This way of thinking may be seen in the wholesale transformation of phenomenal relationships into partly *imponderable 'stuffs'* and *'matters'*, a transformation which pitches each physical **existence** into the *chaos* already mentioned (§ 276 Rem.), in
20 which pores are postulated, through which matters are supposed to enter and leave one another, so that not only the Notion, but even commonsense is put to rout. **It is mainly simple experience which is pushed aside, for assertions of this kind still assume an empirical existence, even when they**
25 **can no longer lay claim to empirical evidence.**

Addition. The main difficulty one encounters in grasping the meteorological process comes from confusing physical elements with individual bodies. The first are abstract determinatenesses, for they are still lacking in subjectivity, and what is true of them, is therefore not yet true of sub-
30 jectivized matter. The natural sciences fall into the greatest confusion when these differences are overlooked. The attempt is made to put everything on the same level. Everything can of course be treated from a chemical point of view, but everything can also be treated from a mechanical point of view, or as electricity. When bodies are treated at one stage, this does
35 not exhaust the nature of other bodies however, as for example when vegetable or animal bodies are treated chemically. This division, by which each body is treated according to its particular sphere, is essential. The appearance of air and water in their free elemental connection with the Earth at large, is quite different from what it is when they are submitted

to the conditions of a completely different sphere. In a parallel situation, one might wish to observe the human spirit, and to this end one might bring customs officers or sailors under observation; one would then encounter the spirit in its submission to finite conditions and precepts which would not exhaust the nature of it. Water is expected to reveal its 5 nature in the retort, and to display no further characteristics in its free connections. The attempt is usually made to demonstrate the universal appearances of physical objects, such as water, air, and heat. 'What are they? What do they do?' are the questions that are asked. It is not thought determinations, but the modes of material existence that are expected to 10 constitute this 'what'. Existent material forms have two sides, for they are air, water and heat, conjoined into another object. Phenomenal appearance is the result of both these aspects. The other object with which air and water etc. combine, is always a particular, so that the effect also depends upon the nature of this particularity. This is why the fact 15 may not be ascertained in universal appearance, but only in relation to particular objects. If one enquires as to the effect of heat, the answer is that it should cause expansion; but it also causes contraction. It is impossible to + mention any universal appearance to which no exceptions might be found; some bodies give rise to one result, and others to another. The 20 other appearances of air and fire etc. are therefore of no significance in the determination of the present sphere. The appearances of finite individual relationships are taken as a basic universal, and then used to explain the free meteorological process; this is a μετάβασις εἰς ἄλλο γένος. + Lightning, for instance, is supposed to be no more than the flash of an 25 electrical discharge produced by friction in the clouds. Yet there is no glass, sealing-wax, resin, rubber, or rotation etc. in the sky. Electricity is + the scapegoat which has to be released everywhere; it is well known however that electricity is completely dispersed by moisture, and that lightning occurs in air impregnated with humidity. Assertions of this kind 30 transfer finite conditions into the free life of nature, particularly when living matter is under consideration, and a sensible person will not be taken in by such explanations. +

The physical process is determined by the transmutation of the elements into one another. This transmutation is quite unknown to finite 35 physics, in which the understanding always holds fast to the persistence of abstract identity, whereby the elements, being composite, are merely dispersed and separated, not really transmuted. Water, air, fire, and earth, are in conflict within this elementary process. Water is the existent material of the process, and as it is neutral, mutable, and determinable, it plays the 40

principle role. Air, as the unobstrusive destructive principle positing that which is of an ideal nature, is the activity which sublates determinate being. Fire is the appearance of being-for-self, the ideality which attains the moment of appearance in which destruction becomes evident. The
5 simplicity of the relationship is therefore that water is transformed into air and vanishes; conversely, air becomes water, and breaks out of being-for-self into the inert neutrality of its opposite, which for its part tenses itself to become being-for-self. The ancients, one might mention *Heraclitus* and
+ *Aristotle*, regarded the process of the elements in this way. There is no diffi-
10 culty in acquainting ourselves with this process, for it is evident in experience and observation. The *formation of rain* is the main point. Physics itself admits that rain has not been satisfactorily explained. The difficulty originates solely in the physics of reflection however, which despite all observation, holds fast to its double assumption that (*a*) 'That which takes place
15 within free connections, must also be possible within conditioned and external circumstances.' (*b*) 'That which takes place within conditioned connections, also takes place within free connections; consequently that which maintains its self-identity in the former case, is also a merely implicit identity.' We maintain on the contrary, that once water has evaporated,
20 the form of the vapour vanishes completely.

If one now applies mechanical determinations and the determinations of finite phenomena to this, the *first* thought that arises is that the water must be preserved, and that it is only the condition of its form which changes. This accounts for *Gren's* statement (Physics, § 945) that, 'Evapo-
25 ration can take place in the complete absence of air. *Saussure* has shown that at equal temperatures, and at its maximum elasticity, air laden with water vapour has a lower specific weight than dry air. This would not be the case if water were dissolved in air in the same way as a salt is dissolved in water. Water can only be held in air as a specifically lighter elastic
+ vapour therefore.' The particles of water are also said to be filled with air when in a vaporous state, and therefore to be merely finely distributed, to be simply driven apart quantitatively. This vapour occurs at a certain temperature, and condenses into water again if this temperature is not maintained. According to this theory, rain is merely a reconglomeration
35 of that which has been present all along, but which has been imperceptible because of its minuteness. Rain and mist are supposed to be explained by nebulous ideas of this kind. This theory has been most fully refuted by *Lichtenberg*, who took the diadem from a prize-essay on rain which had
+ been crowned by the Berlin Academy, and made it laughable. Lichten-
40 berg followed *Deluc*, who made a valid observation upon this point,

45

although he slipped into fantasy by connecting it with the creation of the world, and pointed out in fact, that on the highest Swiss mountains, the hygrometer indicates that in the time immediately preceding the formation of mist and clouds which are about to transform themselves into rain, it is possible for the air to be completely dry. Rain comes, so to speak, out + of dry air, a fact for which physics can offer no explanation. This happens in the summer as well as in the winter, and it is during the summer, precisely when evaporation is at its height, and humidity ought therefore to be at a maximum, that the air is driest. This theory makes it quite impossible to say where the water stays. One might suppose that the water vapours 10 would rise because of their elasticity, but it is even colder at these higher altitudes, so that once they had risen, they would very soon be reduced to water again. Air, therefore is not merely dried as an oven is, by the external removal of humidity; on the contrary, its dehydration is to be compared with the disappearance of what is called crystallization-water into 15 the crystal, for humidity reappears in the same way as it disappears.

The *second* is the chemical approach, in which water is regarded as breaking down into its basic elements of hydrogen and oxygen. It is true that in such a gaseous form it can have no effect upon the hygrometer, because hydrogen attracts heat, which gives rise to gas. But on the other 20 hand, the old question naturally arises as to whether or not water in general is *composed* of oxygen and hydrogen. A flash of electricity certainly turns them both into water, but water is not composed of these two gases. One would be more justified in saying that these gases are merely two different forms in which water is posited. If water were merely 25 a compositum of this sort, all kinds of water might be divided into these parts. *Ritter*, a physicist who died in Munich, made a galvanic experiment by which he demonstrated irrefutably that water cannot be considered as being composed of parts. He took a U-shaped glass tube, filled it with water, and dropped some quicksilver into it in order to separate the water 30 contained within the two branches. Having maintained communication between the branches by means of a metal wire passed through the mercury, he brought the water into contact with a galvanic pile. The water contained in one branch changed into hydrogen, and that in the other into oxygen, so that only one of these gases occurred in each branch of the 35 tube. If the two branches had not been separated by the mercury, it might have been possible to say of this phenomenon that the hydrogen had drifted one way and the oxygen the other. This way of arguing around a conclusion—though no one sees the alleged transference of the two gases—is not possible here. If evaporation also decomposes water, one might well +

ask what becomes of these gases. The air could be augmented by oxygen, but the quantities of oxygen and nitrogen within it are almost always the same. *Humboldt* has taken air from the mountains, and the so-called bad air of a dancing-hall, which is supposed to contain a greater quantity of
5 nitrogen, and after submitting them both to chemical analysis, he found
+ no difference in the proportion of oxygen they contained. It is in the summer in particular, when evaporation is at its height, that the air ought to contain more oxygen, but this is not the case. Nor is hydrogen to be found anywhere at this time; the clouds are not formed at a very
10 high altitude, but there is no evidence of hydrogen either above or below them. Streams may be dry for months, and there may no longer be a trace of moisture in the ground, but one will still find nothing of this element in the air. These methods of presentation run counter to observation therefore, and are merely a cultivation of ideas which have been
15 transplanted from another field with more wishes than wisdom. When General *Alix* wanted to account for the source of the material which the Sun is perpetually consuming, he said that it was replenished by hydrogen. This is also an empty representation of course, but nevertheless it shows some insight, in that Alix thought he should show where this hydrogen is
+ conserved.

   The representation of heat and crystal-water etc. as reduced to latency is a similar conception. It is said for example that heat is still present, even when there is no evidence of it, and it may no longer be seen or felt etc. That which is not subject to observation does not exist in this field how-
25 ever, for existence is just that being-for-other which causes itself to be noticed; and this is precisely the sphere of existence. Reduction to latency is therefore an utterly empty form, for that which is transformed is taken to be a non-existence which nevertheless exists. It is in this way that thought which is based upon the understanding falls into the most glaring incon-
30 sistency in its efforts to maintain the identity of things, and is led into faulty conceptions which are as false in their thought as they are untrue to experience. Philosophy does not ignore conceptions of this kind, but is fully aware of their indigence. It is the same in spirit: a man with a weak
+ character is weak; virtue is not latent within him, for he lacks it entirely.

§ 287

35 The process of the Earth is kindled perpetually by its *universal self*, which is the activity of *light*, or its original solar relationship. **It is then further particularized into climates**

47

and seasons according to the position of the Earth in relation to the Sun. *One moment* of this process is the *diremption* of **individual** identity, or the tension established in the rigidity and self-less neutrality of the moments of independent opposition. Through this tension, the Earth tends to resolve itself on the one hand into the crystalline form of a Moon, and on the other into the fluid body of a Comet, while *the moments* of **individuality** seek to realize their connection with their *independent* origins.

Addition. As the universal principle of ideality, light is here no longer the mere antithesis to darkness, and so no longer the ideal nature of the positing of being-for-other; it is the ideal nature of the positing of real being, the positing of real ideality. This real and active relationship of solar light to the Earth gives rise to the difference between night and day etc. The Earth would not have a process if it lacked this connection with the Sun. The more precise manner in which this effect appears, is to be considered under two aspects, for it is both a simple variation of condition, and a qualitative alteration in the actual process.

The difference between heat and cold, winter and summer, belongs to the first of these aspects, in which changes of temperature depend upon the position of the Earth in relation to the Sun. The variation in condition is not merely quantitative however, but also appears as an internal determinateness. Since the Earth's axis always maintains the same angle with the plane of its orbit, the change from summer to winter is really no more than a quantitative difference, for the Sun may be seen to rise higher and higher every day, and after it has obtained its highest point, to sink again to its lowest. If the extremes of heat and cold depended only upon this quantitative difference and on solar radiation, they ought to occur at the solstices, during the months of June and December. The change in condition is attached to specific nodes however. The equinoxes etc. form qualitative points, and the thermal increase or decrease which they initiate is not merely quantitative. Consequently, the lowest temperatures occur between January 15 and February 15, and the highest in July or August. In the former case, one might conclude that extreme cold takes some time to reach us from the poles, but Captain *Parry* informs us that even there the situation is the same. After the autumnal equinox we have cold spells and storms in early November; in December the cold becomes less severe again, until the lowest temperatures are reached in the middle of January. The pattern at the vernal equinox is the same, and cold spells and storms follow fine weather at the end of February, for March and April behave in much the same way as November. A drop in temperature in July, immediately after the summer solstice, is also a common occurrence.

5 Qualitative change is now the essential factor, and consists of the tension within the Earth itself, and between the Earth and the atmosphere. Its process is the alternation between the lunar and cometary moments. Cloud-formation is not a mere ascent and vaporization therefore; the essence of it is this striving of the Earth toward one extreme. Cloud-for-
+ mation is an incidental by-product of the reduction of air to neutrality; but clouds can form for weeks without the occurrence of thunderstorms and rain. The true disappearance of water is not merely a privative determination, but is a conflict within water itself, a drive and impetus towards the consuming element of fire, which as being-for-self, is the
15 sharpness with which the Earth tears itself asunder at this extremity. Heat and cold are here merely accessory conditions, which do not belong to the determination of the process itself, and therefore have an accidental effect, as for example in the formation of hail.

The specific gravity of air is increased by this tension, for the increase in
20 air-pressure, which causes the quicksilver in the barometer to rise, merely shows that the intensity or density of the air has increased; for the quantity of air has not been augmented. One might think that it was the water absorbed by the air which causes the barometer to rise, but it is precisely when the air is filled with vapours or rain that its specific gravity is
25 diminished. *Goethe* says ('The Science of Nature' vol. 2, section i p. 68), 'The formation of water ceases when the barometer is high. The atmosphere can either carry moisture, or decompose it into its elements. When the barometer reading is lower, what often appears to be a limitless for-
+ mation of water can take place. By exercising its power and increasing
30 its attractive force, the Earth overcomes the atmosphere, and completely appropriates its content. Whatever happens to arise in the atmosphere must fall as *dew* and *hoar-frost*, while the sky remains comparatively clear. What is more, the level of the barometer does not cease to respond to the winds. The quicksilver is high when the wind blows from the
35 north and east, and lower when it blows from the west and south. In the first case humidity drifts to the mountains, in the second, from the
+ mountains to the lowlands.'

§ 288

The *other moment* **of the process consists of the being-for-self** towards which the **sides** of the antithesis tend, sublating itself as negativity driven to its limit. It thus constitutes + the *self-igniting destruction* of the distinct subsistence sought **by the two sides.** It is through this that the Earth has estab- lished **the essential inter-connectedness of these sides,** and as- 5 sumed **its real nature as fertile individuality.**

Remark

Earthquakes, and volcanoes and their eruptions, may be regarded as belonging to the process of fire in which rigidity passes over into the negativity of a being-for-self, in the process of becoming free. Such phenomena also occur on the Moon. Clouds, on the 10 **other hand, may be regarded as rudimentary cometary bodies.** The *thunderstorm* is the completest manifestation of this process **however, for it is as** rudiments, or moments and em- bryonic expressions of itself, **that it contains the** other mete- orological phenomena **of which it is composed.** *Deluc* drew 15 conclusions from his observations, and in Germany the penetration of *Lichtenberg* has enabled him to point out + inconsistencies in the *theories of dissolution*, but despite this, physics **has so far been** unable to reach satisfactory conclusions 20 with regard to the formation of rain, lightning, and thun- der. It has had as little success in explaining other meteoro- logical phenomena. This is especially true of *aerolites*, in which the process even progresses as far as a rudimentary terrestrial nucleus. **So far, very little has been done in physics to** 25 **provide a satisfactory explanation of these commonplace pheno- mena.**

Addition. The sublation of tension is, as rain, the Earth's reduction to neutrality, its relapse into unresisting indifference. The tensioned shape- lessness of the cometary element also passes over into becoming in being- 30 for-self however. Similarly, pushed to this extreme point of opposition, the + opposites simultaneously collapse into one another. However, their unity breaks forth as insubstantial fire, which has as its moments pure fluidities

+ instead of material forms. This is aerial fire, a flash which suffers immediate extinction and is not fed. Thus both sides sublate themselves within themselves; their being-for-self is simply the destruction of their determinate being. The existence of the self-destruction is realized in the flash, and it is this
5 spontaneous ignition of the air which constitutes the climax at which the tension collapses.

This moment of self-destruction may also be found in the tension of the Earth itself. The Earth *tenses itself within itself* in the same way as organic bodies do; it converts itself into the animation of fire, as well as into the
10 neutrality of water, into volcanoes, and *springs*. Consequently the principles of vulcanism and neptunism which are employed in geology, are
+ both essential, and belong to the process of terrestrial formation. The fire submerged within it melts the crystalline composition of the Earth, and the crystal becomes volcanic as spontaneous combustion takes place. Volcanoes
15 are not susceptible to mechanical explanation therefore, but are to be considered as subterranean storms, accompanied by earthquakes. Conversely, the thunderstorm is a volcano in the clouds. There is no doubt that external circumstances are also necessary to an outbreak, but when recourse is had to releases of captive gases etc. in the explanation of
20 earthquakes, use is being made of mere fabrications, or of conceptions
+ borrowed from the sphere of ordinary chemistry. It is quite evident that an earthquake of this kind belongs to the living totality of the Earth. This can be seen from the fact that animals and the birds in the air sense its approach some days before, just as we notice a sultriness before a thunder-
+ storm. The whole organism of the Earth goes to produce these phenomena, just as mountain-chains determine the formation of clouds. There are many circumstances therefore, which point to the fact that none of these phenomena is isolated, but that each event is an integral part of the whole. The level of the barometer is therefore determined by the great
30 increase or decrease in the specific gravity of the air during these atmospheric changes. *Goethe* has compared barometrical readings taken at the same latitudes on different meridians in Europe, America, and Asia, and has discovered that changes take place simultaneously right around the Earth (see below Addition to § 293). This is a most remarkable discovery,
35 but because of the limitations of the data, the co-ordination of it is difficult to pursue. The physicists have not yet got round to making simultaneous observations, and both in this field and in the field of colours, they have failed to follow up the work done by the poet.

The mechanical point of view also fails to explain the formation of
40 springs. They are a special process in which of course terrain plays a

determinate part. Hot springs are said to be the result of the continuous combustion which follows once carboniferous seams have caught fire, but hot springs are, like other springs, living eruptions. Their reservoirs are said to be situated high in the mountains. Rain and snow have an influence upon them of course, and in an extended drought springs can 5 dry up. Springs must be likened to clouds which turn to rain without lightning, while volcanoes have their atmospheric counterpart in lightning. The crystal of the Earth is perpetually reducing itself to this abstract neutrality of water, just as it transforms itself into the animation of fire.   +

The entire condition of the atmosphere, including the *trade-winds* is 10 likewise, a vast living whole. *Goethe* considers the paths of storms to be more topical or local however ('The Science of Nature' vol. II p. 75). In   + Chile, each day exhibits the meteorological process in its completeness. At about three in the afternoon a storm develops, and as is usual at the equator, the winds and the barometer readings are constant. In the tropics 15 therefore, the trade winds blow constantly from the east. When their area is first approached from Europe, these winds blow from the north east, but as one comes closer to the line, they veer further round towards the east. On the line, a dead calm has generally to be reckoned with. South of it the winds gradually assume a southerly to south-easterly direction. 20 Beyond the tropics one loses the trade-winds and comes into the region of variable winds again, as in our European seaways. In India, barometer   + readings are almost always the same; with us they are irregular. *Parry*   + observed no thunderstorms in the polar regions; but almost every night he saw the *northern lights* in all directions, and often in opposite quarters at 25 once. All these phenomena are isolated, formal moments of the complete process, and appear within the whole as contingencies. The aurora borealis is merely a dry luminescence which lacks the further materiality of the thunderstorm.   +

Goethe is the first to have spoken intelligibly about clouds, and he 30 distinguishes three principle forms. Delicately curled or fleecy clouds (cirrus), are either in a state of self-dissolution, or in the initial stage of formation. The rounder forms which may be seen on summer evenings are those of cumulus; finally, there is the broader form (stratus) which is the immediate source of rain.   +

Shooting stars and aerolites also constitute isolated forms of the total process therefore. The air proceeds into water through the rudimentary cometary nature of the clouds, and it is in accordance with the same principle that this atmospheric independence can advance to other materials such as lunar matter, petrified formations, and metals. The primary con- 40

tent of clouds is mere humidity, but they also contain fully individualized
matter, and these results transcend all conditions attaching to the processes
between particular bodies. *Livy* says, 'lapidibus pluit', but until thirty
years ago, when stones fell upon the heads of people at *Aigle* in France, no
5 one believed him. Since then the phenomenon has been observed more
+ frequently. The stones have been examined, compared with older objects also thought to have been of meteoric origin, and found to have the
same composition. There is no point in enquiring into the origin of the
nickel and iron contained in the aerolite. According to one theory, the
10 Moon has dropped something; someone else mentions the dust from the
highways, the hoofs of the horses etc. Aerolites are accompanied by an
explosion in the clouds. The transition is accomplished by a *fireball*, which
expires and blows up with a bang, and is followed by a hail of stones.
There is no variation in the composition of the stones, and the same amal-
15 gam may also be found in the earth. Pure iron does not occur as a fossil,
but deposits of iron having a content like the stones from Aigle are very
common, and occur in Brazil, Siberia, and also in Baffin's Bay. They also
contain a sort of stone, and have a nickel content. The atmospheric origin
+ of these stones may also be traced in their exterior construction.
20   The water and fire which transform themselves into this metal are em-
+ bryonic moons, which are the movement-into-self of individuality.
Aerolites exhibit the Earth's tendency towards the assumption of lunar
characteristics, just as the transient forms of *meteors* exhibit its cometary characteristics. The dissolution of the real moments is the essence of both tendencies.
25 The meteorological process is the manifestation of this tendency towards
individualization, in which free qualities are led back into the concrete
point of unity in spite of their inclination to extrinsicality. At first, these
qualities were still determined in their immediacy as light, rigidity,
fluidity, and terrestrialness, so that gravity had first one, and then another
+ quality. In these basic parts, weighted matter is the subject, and the
qualities are the predicates; hitherto this has been our subjective act of
judgement, but this form has now become existent, the Earth itself being
posited for the first time as individuality. Previously, individuality was an
empty word, for it was immediate, and not yet self-producing. This
35 return, which is the whole of this self-supporting subject, is the process
which constitutes the fertility of the Earth. This universal individual is completely
indigenous to its moments, and as the determinate being of these moments is
complete, it no longer has anything either inward or outward which is alien to
it. In themselves its abstract moments are the physical elements, which are
+ themselves processes.

§ 289

In the first instance, gravity is the *Notion* of matter, and deploys its moments **as** independent **but elemental** realities, so that the Earth is the *abstract* ground of individuality. In its process, the Earth posits itself as the *negative unity* of juxtaposed and abstract elements, and therefore as *real* 5 **individuality**.

Addition. The Earth exhibits its real nature in this selfhood, and so distinguishes itself from gravity. Whereas previously we had only the general determinations of weighted matter, we now have qualities which differentiate themselves from it. Weighted matter now relates itself to 10 determinateness therefore; previously it did not do so. This selfhood of light, which was formerly opposed by weighted corporeality, is now the selfhood of matter itself. This infinite ideality is now the nature of matter itself, and a relationship is therefore posited between this ideality and the subdued being-in-self of gravity. The physical elements are therefore no 15 longer mere moments of a single subject; the principle of individuality is pervasive, and is therefore the same at all points of this physicality. Instead of one general individuality, we therefore have a multiplication of individualities which also partake of the form of the whole, for each has the form of the whole within it. It is these into which the Earth individualizes 20 itself, and which have to be considered in the second part of the physics.

CHAPTER TWO

Physics of particular individuality

§ 290

Former elemental determinatenesses are now subject to the individual unity, which is therefore the immanent form by which matter is independently determined in opposition to its gravity. In its search for a point of unity, gravity makes no infringement
5 **upon the extrinsicality of matter, i.e. space, or rather a specific quantity of space, is the measure of the particularizations of the differences of weighted matter, or masses. In themselves, the determinations of physical elements do not yet constitute a concrete being-for-self, and consequently they are not yet op-**
10 **posed to the being-for-self to which weighted matter aspires. Now however, through its posited individuality, matter is in its very extrinsicality a centralization, and is opposed to this extrinsicality and to its tendency towards individuality. It differentiates itself from the ideal centralization of gravity, and constitutes an im-**
15 **manent determining of material spatiality, which is distinct from that of gravity and the direction of gravity. This part of physics is the mechanics of individualization, because in it, matter is determined by immanence of form, and in accordance with the nature of space. Primarily this gives rise to a relation-**
20 **ship between the two, i.e. between spatial determinateness as such, and the matter which belongs to it.**

Addition. As the unity of gravity is not the same as the other material parts, the individual point of unity pervades the differences as selfhood, and constitutes their soul. Consequently, they are no longer external to
25 their centre, but the centre is the light which they have within themselves. The selfhood of light is therefore the selfhood of matter itself. The standpoint of individuality which we have here, is that quality has returned into itself. We have two kinds of unity, which stand at first in a relative

relation to one another. We have not yet reached their absolute identity, for selfhood itself is still conditioned. It is here that extrinsicality, as opposed to and determined by being-for-self, makes its first appearance. Being-in-self therefore posits another centre and another unity, and so brings about a liberation from gravity. 5

§ 291

This individualizing determination of form is at first implicit or immediate, and therefore not yet posited as totality. Consequently the particular moments of form are mutually indifferent and external to one another as they attain existence, and their form-relation is a relationship of distinct terms. This is a cor- 10 **poreality of finite determinations, conditioned from without, and disintegrating into many particular bodies. Consequently difference appears partly in the comparison between various bodies, and partly in the relation between them, which although it remains mechanical, is of a more real nature. Independent** 15 **manifestation of form, which needs neither comparison nor solicitation, first appears in shape.**

Remark

As is the case everywhere in the sphere of finitude and conditionality, this sphere of conditioned individuality is the most difficult to separate from the further context of the concrete ob- 20 **ject, which has to be firmly distinguished for what it is. This difficulty is increased by the finitude of the content of the object standing in contrast and contradiction to the speculative unity of the Notion, which can be the only determining principle.**

Addition. For us, this is the initial production of individuality, which is 25 therefore itself only primary individuality, and is consequently conditioned and as yet unrealized. It is merely universal selfhood, which arises out of the absence of individuality, and is therefore abstract individuality, which in the mere differentiation from its other, is still inwardly unfulfilled. Its otherness is not yet appropriated by it, and is therefore a 30 passivity, and it is of course precisely because individuality is not yet a totality, that it is distinct from the gravity which it determined. In order that selfhood may be free, it is necessary that it should posit its own difference, but this difference is as yet only a presupposition. It has not yet

deployed its determinations within itself, whereas total individuality has deployed the determinations of the heavenly bodies within itself. Here we have only the derivation of shape. As the determining principle, individuality merely posits single determinations in the first instance, and it
5 is only with the positing of the totality and the singularity of these determinations, that individuality which has developed its entire determinateness is posited. The goal is reached therefore when selfhood becomes the whole, and we shall find this selfhood fulfilled in sound. As it is immaterial, sound passes away, and so presents another form of abstraction.
10 Nevertheless, it is shape in its unity with matter. Here we have to consider the most finite and external aspects of physics; aspects of this kind do not have the same interest for us as does the Notion, or the totality which is the realization of the Notion.

§ 292

The determinateness imposed on gravity is (*a*) simple and ab-
15 **stract, and is therefore present in it as the purely quantitative**
relationship of specific gravity; (*b*) cohesion, i.e. a specific
mode of the relation of material parts. (*c*) This relation of ma-
terial parts, as an independent, existent ideality is (*i*) sound, or
the merely ideal nature of sublation, and (*ii*) heat, or the real
20 **nature of sublated cohesion.**

A

Specific gravity

§ 293

The *simple* abstract specification of matter is *its specific gravity* or *density*. In this, the *weight* of the mass is related to the *volume*, and it is by means of this that material self-**hood** tears itself away from **the universal gravity** of its abstract
25 relationship to the central body, ceases to be the uniform content of space, and opposes abstract extrinsicality with a specific being-in-self.

Remark

Differences in the density of matter are explained by pos-
+ tulating *pores*. Densification **is accounted for by the** invention

of empty interstices therefore, and these are spoken of as if they were actually present, although they have not been demonstrated by physics, despite its claim that it bases itself upon experience and observation. The fact that a bar of iron which is balancing on its fulcrum will lose its equilibrium when it is mag- 5 netized, so that the weight of one of its poles will show itself to be greater than that of the other, is an example of the existence of the specification of gravity. One part is so infected here, that it becomes heavier without changing its volume. Consequently the specific gravity of the matter increases, without any aug- 10 mentation of its mass. Physics attempts to explain density in its own way, by assuming certain propositions, i.e. (1) That given an equal number of material parts of equal size, there will be no difference in weight. From this it follows (2) that it is the measure of the number of parts which deter- 15 mines the weight. It also determines the space, so that (3) two entities of equal weight also fill the same amount of space. Consequently, (4) when two entities of equal weight have different volumes the amount of space they *occupy* as materials is the same, and their difference is assumed to be 20 the result of their pores. The first three propositions make it necessary to postulate the pores in the fourth. These propositions are not based upon experience however, they are based merely upon the understanding and its proposition of identity. They are therefore formal apriori inventions, as the pores are. *Kant* has 25 already opposed *intensity* to the quantitative determination of *amount*, and posited a constant number of parts with a higher *propensity* for *filling space*, instead of more parts in an equal volume. In this way he has initiated a so-called *dynamic physics*. The determination of *intensive* quantum + would be just as valid as that of *extensive* quantum, although the popular conception of density mentioned above has confined itself to the latter category. In this instance however, the determination of *intensive* magnitude has the advantage of implying measure, and above all of indicating a *being-in-* 35 *self* which in its Notional determination is *immanent determinateness of form*, and which only appears, by means of comparison, as a general quantum. Dynamic physics gets no further than regarding these differences as extensive or intensive, and so fails to express any reality (§ 103 Rem.).   40

Addition. In the determinatenesses we have dealt with, gravity and space were still not separated, so that the difference between bodies was merely one of mass, which is merely a difference of one body from another. In this case, difference is measured by the amount of space filled, the greater
5 number of parts corresponding to the larger space filled. A different measure now occurs in being-in-self, where different weights occupy equal spaces, or the same weights occupy unequal spaces. This immanent relationship constitutes the selfhood of a material thing, and is in fact specific gravity. This is being-in-and-for-self, which relates itself only to
10 itself, and is completely indifferent to mass. As density is the ratio of weight to volume, one side may be posited as the unity just as well as the other. We treat the volume of a cubic inch of water as being equal to that of a cubic inch of gold, but their weights are quite different, for gold is nineteen times heavier than water. One could also say that a pound of water
15 occupies nineteen times more space than a pound of gold. That which is purely quantitative gives way here to qualitativeness, for matter now has its own determination within itself. Specific weight is a fundamental determination therefore, and pervades bodies completely. Each part of corporeal matter contains this specific determinateness, whereas in the sphere
20 of gravity, this centrality merely belonged to a single point.

Specific gravity belongs to the Earth generally, to the universal individual, as much as it does to particular bodies. In the process of the elements, the Earth was merely an abstract individual; specific gravity is the first indication of individuality. As process, the Earth is the ideality of
25 particular existences. Its individuality also shows itself as simple determinateness however, which appears in specific gravity, and which in the form of the barometic level, is an index of the meteorological process. *Goethe* has occupied himself a good deal with meteorology. The barometer in particular has claimed his attention, and he takes delight in pre-
30 senting his views upon it. His work is important, particularly his compilation of a comparative table of barometrical readings covering the whole of December 1822, and taken in Weimar, Jena, London, Boston, Vienna and Töpel (situated at a high altitude near Töplitz), which he has presented
+ as a series of graphs. The conclusion he wants to draw from this is not
35 only in that in all areas the variations in the level of the barometer exhibit the same relationship, but that these variations follow the same course at the various heights above sea-level. It is well known that the barometer will give a lower reading on a mountain than it will at sea-level, and that given a constant temperature, for the checking of which one has to have
40 a thermometer handy, one is able to ascertain the height of mountains

from these differences. Consequently, if the heights of the mountains are taken into consideration, barometrical variations at high altitudes are found to be analogous to variations at sea-level. 'When,' says Goethe ('The Science of Nature' vol. II p. 74), 'in a line from Boston to London, and from there via Carlsruhe to Vienna etc. the rise and fall of the baro- 5 meter constantly follows an analogous sequence, this cannot possibly depend on an external cause, but must be attributed to an inner one.' And on p. 63, 'When the rise and fall of the barometer are considered (the numerical ratios alone are evidence of the close correlation), one is struck by the perfectly proportionate rise and fall of the column of quicksilver 10 from the highest point to the lowest. If for the time being, we accept the influence of the Sun as being productive merely of heat, we find that we are left with only the Earth. It is therefore not outside, but within the terrestrial globe, that we look for the causes governing barometric variation; they are neither cosmic nor atmospheric, but telluric. There are 15 variations in the attractive power of the Earth, and consequently it draws to a greater or lesser extent upon the vapour which envelops it. This vapour has no weight, and exerts no pressure, but when it is more powerfully attracted, it appears to press and weigh down more heavily.' According to Goethe, the atmosphere has no weight, but there is no difference 20 between being attracted and having weight.* 'The attractive power develops in the whole mass of the Earth, evidently from the centre to the surface which is known to us, and then from the sea to the highest peaks, diminishing in the regions beyond these peaks. At the same time, it reveals itself in a purposefully limited pulsation.' The main point is, that Goethe 25 rightly attributes the variations to the specific gravity of the Earth as such. +
We have already noted (§ 287 Addition), that the formation of water ceases when the barometer rises, and takes place when it falls. The Earth shows its determining power, as well as its individuality, in its specific gravity. As the barometer rises, tension increases, and as there is then a 30

*If we want to reduce Goethe's conception to Hegelian thought, we shall merely have to replace a variable power of attraction, which apparently must in fact always be the same, by a variable elasticity, or rather more precisely, by contraction and expansion, tension and emollescence (§ 287 Add.). If we then wish to speak of a variation in the power of attraction as gravity, it will be specific gravity, and not gravity as such. By absorbing all the water vapours into itself, the air becomes more elastic, and generally denser and heavier, and so exerts more pressure upon the quicksilver, and causes the barometrical column to rise. The formation of water is an emollescence of the atmosphere however, and by exerting less pressure, allows the barometer to fall. It is this variation in the pressure of the atmosphere upon the quicksilver which Goethe calls a variation in the attractive power of the Earth, and looked at in this way, even the empirical physicists can have no objection to Goethe's thesis.

Note by Michelet.

greater concentration of the Earth into itself, matter has some of its abstract gravity drawn out of it. Specific gravity has in fact to be grasped
as being drawn out of universal gravity by individuality.

A pound of gold used to be thought of as having the same number of
5 parts as a pound of water, the only difference being that they were packed
together nineteen times as tightly, so that water had nineteen times more
pores, empty space, or air etc. than gold. Such empty representations are
+ the stock-in-trade of reflection, which is incapable of grasping an immanent determinateness, and which, as it wants to maintain the numerical
10 equality of the parts, is obliged to fill in the rest of the space. Ordinary
physics has also reduced specific gravity to the antithesis of repulsion and
attraction: bodies are said to be denser where matter is subject to more
attraction, and less dense where repulsion predominates. These factors
have no meaning in this context however. The antithesis of attraction and
15 repulsion as two independent forces existing for themselves, belongs only
to the reflective understanding. If attraction and repulsion were not in
simple equilibrium, one would be involved in contradictions in which the
falsity of this reflection becomes apparent, as we have seen above in connection with the motions of the heavenly bodies (§ 270 Remark and
20 Addition).

§ 294

At first, density is merely a *simple* determinateness **of
weighted matter, but as matter remains the essential extrinsicality,
the determination of the form is still a specific mode of the spatial
interrelation of its elemental multiplicity. It is in fact c o h e s i o n.**

25 *Addition.* Like specific weight, cohesion is a determinateness which distinguishes itself from gravity. It is more comprehensive than specific
weight however, for it not only constitutes another general centrality,
but a centre related to a plurality of parts. Cohesion is not merely a comparison of bodies according to specific weight; their determinateness is
30 now posited so that the relation between them is of a real nature, the bodies
touch each other.

B

Cohesion

§ 295

In cohesion, immanent form posits the spatiality of the separate existence of material parts in another way from that which is determined by the direction of gravity. This is therefore a specific mode of the consistence of the material parts, and is first posited in these parts as generally different, for it has not yet returned into 5 **itself as self-enclosed totality or shape. Consequently, it appears only in the face of uniformly and coherently varied masses, and therefore displays itself in its mechanical response to other masses, as a distinctive mode of resistance.**

Addition. We have seen that pressure and impact constitute a purely 10 mechanical relatedness. In the present kind of pressure and impact however, bodies no longer act merely as masses, as they do in a mechanical relationship, but in this independence of quantity, they display a particular mode of self-preservation, and of the positing of their unity. The proximate mode to this consistence of material parts was gravity, through which 15 bodies have a centre. The mode now being considered is immanent, and is manifested by the bodies through the mutual accordance of their particular weight.

Cohesion is a word to which many of the current philosophies of nature have given a very indeterminate meaning. There has been 20 a lot of chat about cohesion, without there being any progress beyond opinion and a vague groping around an indeterminate Notion. Total cohesion is magnetism, and occurs first in shape. Abstract cohesion is not yet the syllogism of magnetism, which distinguishes extremes, and yet posits their point of unity, so that both extremes and unity maintain 25 their distinctness. Consequently magnetism does not yet belong here. Nevertheless, although magnetism and cohesion belong to completely different stages, Schelling has lumped them together. In itself, magnetism +　is a totality, even if it is still an abstract totality, for although it is linear, its extremes and its unity are already developing themselves in differen- 30 tiation. This is not yet the case with cohesion, which belongs to the becoming of total individuality, while magnetism belongs to total individuality. Cohesion is therefore still in conflict with gravity; it is still a moment of the determination opposed to gravity; it is not yet the totality of this determination.

§ 296

In cohesion, the unity of form of manifold extrinsicality is in itself manifold. (a) Its primary determinateness is completely in-
5 determinate consistence, in so far as that which in itself is co-hesionless coheres. It is therefore adhesion to another. (b) The coherence of matter with itself is (i) purely quantitative. It is ordinary cohesion, which is the strength of consistence in resisting weight. It is also (ii) qualitative, in that it is able to yield to the
10 pressure and impact of external force, and precisely by this means, to show independence of form. The internal mechanizing geometry of this, which operates in accordance with the specific mode of spatial forms, produces the property of maintaining a specific dimension within the consistencies, i.e. punctuality, which
15 constitutes brittleness; linearity, which constitutes rigidity in general, and more particularly, tenacity; and superficiality, which constitutes ductility or malleability.

Addition. As passive cohesion, adhesion is not being-in-self, but affinity with more than self or with another, just as light is when it shines or shows
20 itself in something else. This is why water in its neutrality, is adhesive and makes things wet, i.e. more specifically, because of the absolute displace-ability of its parts. Hard bodies which definitely have inner cohesion also adhere in so far as their surfaces are not rough but perfectly smooth, so that all their parts can make complete contact with one another. These
25 surfaces are then devoid of all difference, not only in themselves, but also in their relation to the other, which is equally smooth, so that they can both posit themselves as identical. Polished glass plates for example, adhere very strongly, particularly if water is poured between them and com-pletely fills in every kind of unevenness on their surfaces. A considerable
30 weight will then be required in order to pull them apart again. *Gren* says therefore ('Physics', § 149–150), 'The strength of adhesion depends in
+ general upon the number of points of contact.' Adhesion has various modifications. Water in a glass clings to the sides for example, and stands higher at the sides than it does in the middle. In a capillary tube, water
35 rises entirely of its own accord etc.

In that which concerns the cohesion of matter within itself as specific

being-in-self however, coherence, as mechanical cohesion, is therefore merely the interior consistence of a homogeneous mass as opposed to the positing of a body within this mass. In other words, it is a ratio of the intensity of the coherence to the weight of the body. Consequently, if a mass is pulled or pressed by a weight, it counteracts this with a certain 5 quantity of its being-in-self. The amount of weight determines whether the mass retains or relinquishes its coherence. Consequently, glass and wood etc. can bear a certain number of pounds without breaking, and it is not necessary that the pull should be exerted in the direction of gravity. The grading of bodies according to their coherence bears no relation to 10 their grading according to specific gravity. Gold and lead for example, are specifically heavier than iron and copper, but they are not so firm.*
Similarly, the resistance which a body offers to impact, is not the same as when it merely has to offer resistance in the single direction towards which the impact drives. The breaking of impact forms an angle with this di- 15 rection and is therefore a surface force; it is this that gives rise to the infinite force of impact. +

True qualitative cohesion consists of homogeneous masses with an immanent and characteristic form or limitation, and becomes explicit here as the abstract dimensions of space. That is to say, that the characteristic 20 shaping can be nothing other than a mode of specific spatiality which the body displays in itself, for coherence is the identity of the body in its extrinsicality. Qualitative coherence is therefore a specific mode of juxtaposition, i.e. a determination of space. Individual matter itself contains this unity as a consistence opposed to the general unity which it seeks in 25 gravity. Matter now maintains the characteristic directions of various sides

---

Schelling says in his 'Journal for Speculative Physics' (vol. II, pt. 2, § 72), 'The augmentation + and diminution of cohesion stand in a determinate inverse relation to the augmentation and diminution of specific weight. The ideal principle' (form, light), 'conflicts with the force of gravity, and as this has its greatest preponderance at the centre, it is also there that it manages most easily to combine rigidity with the greatest specific weight, so that it brings A and B' (subjectivity and objectivity), 'under its control, within a smaller degree of difference. Specific gravity is overcome as this degree increases, but it can also increase so far, that cohesion sets in. At a certain point cohesion diminishes, and specific gravity predominates again, until both finally disappear together. According to *Steffens,* we see specific gravity diminish in the metallic series from platinum and gold etc. to iron, while active cohesion increases, and reaches its maximum in iron. We then see it give way again to a considerable specific gravity, in lead for example, and finally diminish, together with specific gravity, in the metals which are still lower down the metallic scale.' This is taken out of the blue. Specific gravity certainly contributes to cohesion, but if, by taking a determinate progression in the relationship between cohesion and specific gravity as his point of departure, Schelling is attempting to base the difference of bodies in general upon difference in cohesion, one has to insist that although nature certainly tenders the rudiments of such a progression, it also gives the other principles free rein, posits these properties in a state of reciprocal indifference, and certainly declines to limit itself to such a simple and purely quantitative relationship.

within itself, and these differ from the vertical direction of gravity. This cohesion is an individuality, but it is at the same time still a conditioned individuality, because it is only through the influence of other bodies that it makes its appearance. It is not yet free individuality of shape which is
5 the total individuality of the forms which it posits. Total shape is there in its mechanical determination of sides and angles of course, but matter merely has primary character as the inner shape of this totality, i.e. it is simply a shape, and is not yet there in its developed determinateness. This also becomes apparent through its only displaying its character by
10 means of another. Coherence is therefore merely a mode of resistance to another, the precise reason for this being that its determinations are merely isolated forms of individuality which do not yet stand forth as totality. A brittle body may not be hammered or stretched; it will not yield in a linear direction, but preserves itself as a point and is not continuous. It is
15 in fact internally fashioned hardness. Glass shatters on account of its brittleness, as do most combustible materials. Brittleness is one of the properties which distinguishes steel from iron; steel and cast iron both have a granular fracture. When it is cooled quickly glass is extremely brittle, but not when it is cooled slowly; powder is obtained by breaking the
20 former kind. Metals on the contrary have more continuity, but they also vary in degrees of brittleness. A tough body shows itself to be fibrous, and instead of breaking, continues to hold together. Iron may be drawn into wire, although there are exceptions to this. Forged iron is more malleable than cast iron, and can be given a linear form. Here we have the ductility
25 of bodies, the final characteristic of which is that ductile bodies may be beaten into sheets. There are metals which may be beaten into mere surfaces, while others crack. Iron, copper, gold, and silver may be worked into sheets, they are softness which gives way, and which is neither brittle nor tough. There are irons suitable only for surfaces, or only for lines,
30 while others such as cast iron maintain themselves only as point. The plane becomes surface, or the point in it becomes the whole; so similarly, no general malleability is in its turn the ductility of the whole. It is an unshaped interior which affirms its general consistence as the consistence of the mass. It should be noted that these moments are merely single dimensions, each of
35 which constitutes a moment of the real shaped body. No one of these
+ moments constitutes shape however.

§ 297

(c) **When one corporeality gives way to the violence of another, and at the same time asserts its distinctiveness, it is giving way to** another corporeal individual. In its coherence, the body in itself is also a juxtaposing materiality however, and as the whole is submitted to violence, the parts of this materiality do violence to, and give way to one another. As they are equally independent however, they sublate the negation to which they have been ₅ submitted, and re-instate themselves. This giving way, with its own exterior self-preservation, is therefore directly bound up with this inner activity of giving way and preserving itself in the face of itself, i.e. with elasticity.

Addition. Elasticity is cohesion displaying itself in motion. It is the whole ₁₀ of cohesion. We already encountered it in the first section, where we dealt with matter in general, in which numbers of bodies press and touch one another in mutual resistance, negating their spatiality, and at the same time re-instating it. That was abstract elasticity, and was directed outwards. This elasticity is internal to the self-individualizing body. ₁₅

§ 298

As matter, material parts were merely in search of ideality, and it is here that this ideality reaches existence as the point of unity which is for itself, and in which, in their actual attraction, these parts would merely be negated. In so far as the parts are merely heavy, this point of unity is in the first instance external ₂₀ to them, and is therefore merely implicit. It therefore implies that these parts suffer a negation, within which this ideality is now posited. It is still a conditioned ideality however, for it is only one side of the relationship, the other side of which is the subsistence of the juxtaposed parts, the negation of which consequently ₂₅ passes over into their re-establishment. Consequently, elasticity is merely a change of specific gravity which returns to its former state.

Remark

Wherever the question of material parts arises, one should not think of them as atoms or molecules, i.e. as separated and self- ₃₀ subsistent, but as merely quantitatively or contingently distinguished, so that their continuity is essentially inseparable from their distinctness. Elasticity is precisely the existence of the dialectic of these moments. That which is material has its indif-

ferent and specific subsistence as its place. The ideality of this subsistence is therefore continuity posited as unity of a real nature, i.e. a unity in which two material parts which formerly subsisted external to one another, and which are therefore to be
5 thought of as occupying different places, now occupy one and the same place. This is the contradiction, and it has material existence here. It is the same contradiction which lies at the basis of Zeno's dialectic of motion, the only difference being that in motion the contradiction concerns abstract places, while here
10 material places and parts are involved. In motion, space posits itself temporally, and time spatially (§ 260). Zeno's antinomy is insoluble, and motion falls into it if places are isolated as spatial points, and moments of time as points of time. The solution of the antinomy, i.e. motion, can only be grasped through the in-
15 herent continuity of space and time, and the simultaneity of the autonomous body's both being and not-being in the same place, so that it is simultaneously in another; just as the same point of time at once is and is not, i.e. is simultaneously another point
+ of time. In elasticity therefore, the material part, atom or mole-
20 cule, is posited as in the affirmative and subsistent occupation of its space, and at the same time, as being equally non-subsistent as a unified quantum of size which is both extensive and merely intensive.
+ Contrary to the unity of material parts which is posited in
25 elasticity, another so called explanation of it is provided by postulating the porosity which has so often been mentioned. Although it will certainly be admitted in abstracto that matter is perishable and not absolute, difficulties occur in the application of this principle if matter is in fact grasped as negative, and
30 negation is posited as implicit within it. Pores certainly constitute negation, for whatever one says, one has to come back to this determination. They are looked upon as a negative which merely supplements matter however, as the negative which is where matter is not, not the negative of matter itself. Consequently,
35 matter is in fact regarded as merely affirmative, and as absolutely independent and eternal. This error has its origin in the general error of the understanding, which regards metaphysics as a mere figment of thought, which fringes actuality, and is therefore external to it. Consequently a faith in both the
40 non-absoluteness and in the absoluteness of matter, is professed

67

**at one and the same time. If it is accepted, the first tenet does
not apply within the bounds of science; it is essentially the second
which is prevalent in science.**

Addition. When one body posits itself in another, and they therefore
have a certain common density, it follows firstly, that the specific gravity 5
of the one in which the other posits itself is altered. The second moment is
the resistance which is produced, the negating, the abstract self-preservation. The third moment is the reaction of the body, by which it repulses
the first from itself. These are the three moments known as *softness, hardness*, and elasticity. The body no longer gives way in a merely mechanical 10
manner, but does so inwardly, through altering its density. Softness of
this kind is *compressibility*. Consequently matter is not immutable and im-
penetrable. When the weight of the body remains the same while its
volume diminishes, its density increases. Density can also be decreased
however, by heat for example. An increase in density also takes place in 15
the tempering of steel, although as contractility this is the opposite of
elasticity. Elasticity is retreat into self for the subsequently immediate
re-establishment of self. When the coherent body is struck, pushed, or
pressed, the spatiality of its materiality is negated together with its place.
Consequently, there is a negation of material extrinsicality, as well as the 20
negation of this negation, in which materiality is reinstated. This is no
longer the general elasticity already considered, in which matter merely
reinstates itself as mass, it is far more of an inner reaction. It is this immanent form of matter which here affirms itself in accordance with its
qualitative nature. Each particle of coherent matter consequently behaves 25
as centre. This single form is common to the whole, it penetrates matter
like a fluid, and is unattached to extrinsicality. If an impression is made
upon matter, so that the body receives a negation from without which
effects its interior determinateness, an interior reaction is posited within
the body by means of its specific form, and the impression made is there- 30
fore cancelled. In form, every particle has its particular place, and is the
preserver of this particular relationship. In general elasticity, the body
affirms itself merely as mass, but it is here that motion persists within itself,
not as reaction outwards, but as reaction inwards, until the form has reinstated itself. This is the oscillation and vibration of the body, which is 35
now internally continuous, despite the abstract reinstatement of general
elasticity having been accomplished. It is true that the motion began externally, but collision has touched the inner form of the body. This
fluidity of the body within itself is total cohesion.

§ 299

The ideality which is posited here is an alteration which consists of a double negation. The negating of the extrinsic subsistence of the material parts is itself negated as the reinstating of their juxtaposition and their cohesion. As the exchange of mutually cancelling determinations, this single ideality is the inner vibration of the body within itself, i.e. sound.

Addition. The determinate being of this oscillation within itself seems to differ from the determination we had in elasticity. The being-for-other of this determinate being is sound, which is therefore the third determination.

C

Sound

§ 300

Through density, and through the principle of its cohesion, a body possesses a specific simplicity of determinateness, which in its initially interior form, by emerging from its submergence in material extrinsicality, becomes free in the negation of the self-contained subsistence of this state of juxtaposition. This is the transition of material spatiality into material temporality. In vibration, this form is therefore the ideality of materiality; it is consequently simple form existing for itself, and makes its appearance as this mechanical animation. Vibration of this kind is the momentary negation of parts, and the equally momentary negation of this negation; these two connected moments function inseparably, so that in this form the body oscillates between its subsistence, and the negation of its specific gravity and cohesion.

Remark

The clarity or lack of clarity in tone itself, and that which distinguishes it from the mere ring obtained by striking a solid body, and noise etc. depends upon the homogeneity of the vibrating body. It also depends upon the specific cohesion of the body, and upon the determination of its further spatial dimensions, i.e. whether it is a material line or surface, and then again, whether it is a bounded line or surface, or a solid body. Water has no cohesion and no tone, its movement is merely the external 5 friction of freely displaceable parts, and gives rise only to a murmuring sound. Glass rings on account of the continuity existing in its inner inflexibility, while metal, on account of its flexible continuity, rings resonantly etc.

The transmissibility of sound, what might be called its 10 soundless propagation, as distinct from the repetition and oscillation of vibration, reveals an ideality which freely penetrates all kinds of inflexibility etc., as well as various specific bodies. Solid bodies are more open to it than is the air; it penetrates for many miles into the Earth, and according to calculation, travels ten 15 times faster through metals than it does through air; it takes account only of the abstract materiality of these bodies, and while it brings their parts into negation and causes them to vibrate, it remains indifferent to the specific determinations of their density, cohesion, and further formations. In itself this idealization is 20 merely the transmission of sound.

The qualitative nature of sound in general, and of tone or self-articulating sound, depends upon the density, cohesion, and further specified modes of cohesion of the sounding body, for the ideality or subjectivity which constitutes vibration is a negation 25 of these specific qualities, which it has as its content and determinateness. This is why vibration is specified, together with sound itself, and why instruments have their characteristic tone and timbre.
+

Addition. As it is associated with weighted matter, sound belongs to the 30 mechanical sphere. Form, as wresting itself from weightedness, and yet as still attached to it, is therefore conditioned. It is the free physical expression of ideal nature, although it is still linked to the mechanical sphere. It is freedom from weighted matter, but is at the same time *of* this matter. Bodies resound only when they are struck, they do not sound of their own 35 accord as organic bodies do. The external impact of motion is self-propagating because inner cohesion displays its self-preservation in opposition to it, as it does to the simple relations of mass according to which cohesion ought to be treated. We are in no way unfamiliar with these

70

appearances of corporeality, which are at the same time very varied however, and it is therefore difficult to present them in the necessity of their Notional connection. As we find them trivial, we disregard them, but they also have to display themselves as necessary moments, having their
5 position within the Notion. When a body sounds, we feel that we are entering a higher sphere, for tone affects our innermost feelings. As tone is itself inwardness and subjectivity, it speaks to the inner soul. Sound by itself is the self of individuality; it is not of an abstractly ideal nature like light however, but is as it were mechanical light, manifesting itself only
10 as the time taken by motion in cohesion. Individuality includes matter and form. Sound is this total form, which makes itself known in time; it is the whole of individuality, which is nothing more than that this soul is now posited in its unity with materiality. It dominates this unity as a quiescent subsistence. That which displays itself here is not based on
15 matter, for it does not have its objectivity in a material being. It is only the understanding which, for purposes of explanation, assumes an objective being, and speaks of material sound in the same way as it speaks
+ of material heat. The natural man marvels at sound, because a being-in-
+ self reveals itself within it, and he presumes that it is something soul-like
20 rather than material. We have here a phenomenon similar to that met with in motion, where mere velocity or, in the case of the lever, distance, shows itself to be a mode which can replace quantitative materiality. A phenomenon such as this, in which a being-in-self assumes physical existence, holds no surprises for us, for it is precisely thought-determinations
25 showing themselves to be active principles, which constitute the basis of the philosophy of nature.

The preciser nature of sound need only be sketched, for this determination of thought has to be treated empirically. There are plenty of words, such as sound, tone, noise, and creak, hiss, rustle etc., for language
30 has a completely superfluous richness for its determination of material phenomena. Once a sound is given, there is no difficulty in making a
+ sign which directly corresponds to it. Pure fluidity is not resonant. The impression certainly communicates itself to the whole, but the transmission originates in complete formlessness and lack of inner determina-
35 tion, and is in itself form. Compact continuity, and the homogeneity of matter within itself, are necessary for the production of a clear tone, so that metals (particularly precious metals) and glass give a clear ring. These properties are developed by smelting. On the other hand, if there is a crack in a bell for example, we hear not only its vibration, but also
40 the other properties of material resistance, rigidity, and lack of uniformity,

so that the sound is not clear, but a mere noise. Stone slabs, despite their being so brittle, also have a tone. Air and water do not ring of their own accord however, although they are also able to transmit sound.

It is difficult to grasp the origin of sound. Specific being-in-self, divorced from gravity, emerges as sound. It is the plaint of ideal nature in the midst of violence, but as it preserves itself against this other, it is also its triumph over it. Sound is produced in two ways: (a) by friction, (b) by vibration proper, or the elasticity of being-in-self. Vibration is also present in friction, for while it lasts, a multiplicity is posited in unity, the different juxtaposed material parts being brought momentarily into contact. The position, and therefore the materiality of each part is sublated, although this coincides with each reinstating itself. It is precisely this elasticity which gives evidence of itself in sound. When the body is rubbed however, the grating itself is heard, and this tone corresponds more to what we call sound. If the vibration of a body is posited by a body which is external to it, it is the vibration of both bodies which reaches us; each disturbs the other, and obliterates all purity of tone. In this case, the tremor is forced by each on the other, rather than being independent. This is what we call a noise, and it may be heard in the clattering or mechanical grinding of bad instruments, in the scrape of the bow upon the violin for example, or in the quivering of the muscles in a bad voice. The other tone is of a higher nature, and is the vibration of the body within itself, its inner negation and self-restoration. Sound itself is resonance, the unhindered inner vibration of the body freely determined by the nature of its coherence. There is also a third form, in which the external stimulation and the sound emitted by the body are alike, i.e. human song. It is in the voice that this subjectivity or independence of form first occurs, and this purely tremulous motion consequently possesses something which is in conformity with spirit. The violin too does not reverberate; it sounds only when its strings are touched.

If we have sound in general in mind, and ask why it relates itself to *hearing*, we have to reply that this is because hearing is a sense which belongs to the mechanical sphere; it is in fact the sense which relates itself to the flight from materiality, and the transition to that which is immaterial, spiritual, and of an ideal nature. On the other hand, everything associated with specific gravity and cohesion, relates itself to the sense of feeling. The *sense of touch* is therefore the other sense of the mechanical sphere, that is to say, in so far as this sphere contains the determinations of materiality itself.

The particular note produced by a substance depends upon the nature

72

of its coherence; and these specific differences also have a connection with the pitch of this note. Strictly speaking, particular determinateness of tone can only be obtained by comparing the various tones of the body itself however. With regard to the first point, it should be remembered that
5 silver and bronze have their specific and determinate ring, as do metals in general. Rods consisting of various substances, but of equal thickness
+ and length, give different notes. *Chladni* has noticed that whalebone gives A, tin B, silver D an octave higher, Cologne pipes E, copper G,
+ glass C in an even higher octave, deal C sharp etc. I remember *Ritter*
10 having done a lot of research into the sound given off by the various parts of the head which have a hollow ring. By tapping upon the various bones of the same, he discovered a variety of notes, which he arranged into a
+ definite scale. There are also whole heads which sound hollow, but this kind of resonance was not enumerated on the scale. It might be worth
15 asking whether or not one can really hear a difference in the case of those heads which are said to be hollow.

According to the researches of *Biot*, not only the air, but every other body transmits sound. If, for example, one taps an earthenware or metal pipe belonging to a water-system, the sound may be heard several miles
+ away at the other end of the pipe. Two sounds will then be distinguishable, for that conducted by the material of the pipe will be heard much sooner than that conducted by the column of air. Neither mountains, water, nor forests, will check the sound. The transmission of sound by the earth is remarkable; by putting one's ear to the ground for example,
+ it is possible to hear a cannonade taking place ten to twenty miles away. What is more, sound travels through the ground ten times faster than it does through the air. This transmission is also remarkable in a more general way, for it shows the complete untenability of the physicists' postulate of a
+ phonic substance which moves rapidly through the pores of bodies.

§ 301

30 **In vibration, oscillation as an external change of place has to be distinguished; this, as a change of spatial relationship to other bodies, constitutes motion in the ordinary, proper sense. Although this oscillation is different however, it is at the same time identical with the inner motion determined previously, which is**
35 **subjectivity becoming free, the manifestation of sound as such.**

As the result of its abstract universality, the existence of this ideality displays merely quantitative differences. Consequently

in the realm of sounds and notes, the further differences of harmony and disharmony rest upon **numerical relationships**, and their more or less complex and remote agreement.

Remark

The vibration of strings, columns of air, bars etc., is an alternating transition from the straight line into the arc, and also into 5 converse arcs. This is merely an apparent external change of place in relation to other bodies, and is directly bound up with the inner, alternating change of specific gravity and cohesion. The side of the material line lying against the centre of the arc of oscillation is shortened, while the outer side is lengthened. Consequently, 10 the specific gravity and cohesion of the latter side are diminished, while those of the former side are simultaneously increased.   +

As regards the power of the quantitative determination in the ideal nature of this realm, we should remember the phenomena produced when a vibrating line or plane is submitted to mechan- 15 ical interruptions. The quantitative determination introduced in this way imparts itself to the oscillation of the whole line or plane beyond the mechanical point of interruption, and gives rise to nodes of vibration within it. In **Chladni's** experiments these phenomena are made visible. It is here that one has to consider the +
harmonizing notes which neighbouring strings will give rise to in one another if they are brought into specific quantitative relationships to the sounding string. **Tartini** was the first to draw attention to some of the most important phenomena in this field. He noticed that when notes which in respect of their oscillations stand 25 in certain specific numerical relationships to one another, are sounded together, they give rise to further notes, which are different, and which are produced only by these relationships.   +

Addition. Vibrations are the tremulations of matter within itself. Matter is not annihilated within this negativity, but maintains itself as sonority. 30 A sonorous body must be a material physical surface or line; it must also be limited, so that the vibrations travel along the whole line, are checked, and return. A stone merely sounds when it is struck; there is no sonorous tremulation, because although the shock certainly propagates itself, it does not return to itself. 35
Notes are therefore the modifications of sound elicited by the recursive

regularity of vibrations; this constitutes the more important variety of sounds which shows itself in *music*. *Unison* occurs when two strings make the same number of vibrations in the same time. On the contrary, the different notes of a string or wind instrument, depend upon the difference
5 in thickness, length, and tension, of the strings or columns of air from which the sound is elicited. Consequently, if two of three determinations of thickness, length, and tension are equal, the note will depend upon the difference of the third factor and since vibration in tension is easiest to observe in strings, this is generally the basis used for calculating various
10 vibrations. Variation in tension is effected by carrying the string over a bridge, and attaching a weight to it. If only the length is varied, then the
+ shorter a string is, the more vibrations it will perform in a given time. In the case of wind instruments, the shorter the pipe in which a column of air is made to vibrate, the higher will be the note; in order to shorten
15 the column of air one merely has to slide in a piston. By dividing the string of a monochord, one finds that the number of vibrations occurring in a given time is inversely proportional to the parts of the determinate length of the string; a third of the string vibrates three times more rapidly than the whole string. The minute vibrations of *high* notes may no longer
20 be counted because of their great rapidity, but by taking into account the length of the string, their numbers may be determined by analogy
+ with great exactness.

As notes are a mode of our sensation, we find them either agreeable or disagreeable; this objective mode of *euphony* is a determinateness which
25 enters into this sphere of mechanism. What is most interesting here is the coincidence between that which the ear takes to be a harmony, and certain numerical ratios. *Pythagoras* was the first to discover this correlation, and it induced him to express the relationships of thought itself in the form of
+ numbers. That which is harmonious rests upon the facility of consonances,
+ and like architectural symmetry, is a unity perceived amid difference. Do the harmony and *melody* which can call forth our feelings and passions by their enchantment, depend upon abstract numbers? It seems remarkable, and even astonishing, but this is the only determination present, and within it we may see a glorification of numerical ratios. The simpler
35 numerical ratios, which constitute the ideal nature of the basis of that which is harmonious in notes, are more readily grasped; and these are primarily those based on the number two. Half the string produces the octave above the note of the whole string, i.e. the *key-note*. If the lengths of two strings are in the ratio of 2 : 3, so that the shorter is two-thirds the
40 length of the other, and therefore vibrates three times in the time taken

75

by the other to vibrate twice, the shorter string will give the *fifth* of the longer. If $\frac{3}{4}$ of a string vibrates, it yields the *fourth*, which makes four vibrations while the key-note makes three; $\frac{4}{5}$ gives the major *third*, with five vibrations against four; $\frac{5}{6}$ the minor third, with six vibrations against five etc. If one makes $\frac{1}{3}$ of the whole string vibrate, one has the 5 fifth an octave higher. If one makes $\frac{1}{4}$ vibrate, one has the octave above that. A fifth of the string yields a third of the third octave above, or the double octave of the major third; $\frac{2}{5}$ yields the third of the next octave: $\frac{3}{5}$ the *sixth*. A sixth gives the higher fifth of the third octave etc. The key-note vibrates once while its octave vibrates twice therefore; the third 10 vibrates $1\frac{1}{4}$ times, and the fifth $1\frac{1}{2}$, and is the *dominant*. The ratio of the fourth is already more difficult: the string vibrates $1\frac{1}{3}$ times, which is more complicated than $1\frac{1}{2}$ and $1\frac{1}{4}$, and is also the reason for the fourth being a more vivid note. In an *octave*, the numerical ratio of the vibrations is as +
follows therefore: if C vibrates once, D vibrates, $\frac{9}{8}$, E $\frac{5}{4}$, F $\frac{4}{3}$, G $\frac{3}{2}$, A $\frac{5}{3}$, B $\frac{15}{8}$, 15
C 2; which is equivalent to $\frac{24}{24}$, $\frac{27}{24}$, $\frac{30}{24}$, $\frac{32}{24}$, $\frac{36}{24}$, $\frac{40}{24}$, $\frac{45}{24}$, $\frac{48}{24}$. If one thinks of a string as being divided into five parts, and causes the only fifth which has been divided off to vibrate, nodes are formed in the rest of the string, as it divides itself into the other parts. If small pieces of paper are placed on the points of division, they remain there, while they fall off if they are 20 placed elsewhere. At these points the string does not vibrate therefore; these are in fact the vibration nodes, and they entrain further consequences. +
A column of air also forms nodes of this kind, in a flute for example, when the vibrations are interrupted by holes. Now the ear picks out divisions based upon the simple numbers 2, 3, 4, 5, and finds that they 25 give rise to agreeable sensations. These numbers can express specific relationships analogous to the determinations of the Notion, despite the fact that the other numbers, are intrinsically multiple compositions and therefore become indeterminate. Two is the production of one out of itself; three is the unity of one and two, and this is why Pythagoras used them 30 as symbols for Notional determinations. If the string is divided into two, +
it is too much of a monotone to produce difference or harmony. If it is divided into 2 and 3 however, it will produce harmony as the fifth: it is the same with the third, which is divided into 4 and 5, and the fourth, which is divided into 3 and 4. 35

The *harmonic triad* consists of the key-note, the third, and the fifth. This gives a definite system of notes, but is still not the *scale*. The ancients tended to keep to this form, but now something further is required. If, for +
example, we start with an empirical note C, then G is the fifth. As the choice of C as the key-note was arbitrary however, every note may be 40

taken as the basis of a system. In each note's system, notes therefore occur which also occur in the systems of others, although the third of one system may be the fourth or fifth of another. This gives rise to the relationship in which one and the same note, which fulfills different functions in
5 different scales, and which therefore runs through them all, is isolated and considered separately, and given a general position and a neutral designation such as G etc. This need to consider a note abstractly also appears as another formal need, consisting of the ear's propensity to progress by a series of notes which ascends and descends by equal *intervals*.
10 When this is combined with the harmonic triad, it gives rise to the scale. How, as a matter of history, it became customary, as it is now, to regard the succession of notes C, D, E, F, as fundamental, is unknown to me.
+ Perhaps the organ has contributed. The relationship of third and fifth is of no significance here, where the arithmetical determination of unifor-
15 mity, which is *by itself* limitless, is the only determining factor. The *harmonic limit* to this ascent is given by the ratio 1 : 2, or the key-note and its octave. It is from between these limits therefore, that one must also pick out the absolutely determinate notes. The parts of the string from which these notes are to be produced must be greater than half of it, for if they
20 were less than this, the notes would be higher than the octave. Now in order to bring forth the said uniformity, one has to interpolate notes into harmonic triad which are related to one another much as the fourth is to the fifth. In this way the *whole tones* arise, forming a complete interval like that in the progression from the fourth to the fifth. The interval be-
25 tween the key-note and the third is filled by the *second*, which is produced when $\frac{8}{9}$ of the string vibrate. This interval between key-note and second (from C to D), is the same as that between the fourth and the fifth (from F to G), and between the sixth and the *seventh* (from A to B). The second (D) is therefore also related to the third (E), and this is also approximately
30 a whole tone, although it only expresses roughly the same ratio as that existing between C and D, the two ratios not being in exact agreement. The fifth bears the same ratio to the sixth (G to A), as D to E. The ratio of the seventh (from $\frac{8}{15}$ of the string) to the octave above (B to C), is as the ratio of the third to the fourth (E to F) however. In this advance from
35 E to F, and from B to C, there is an inequality which is even greater than that in the other intervals into which the so-called *semitones* are inserted for the sake of equality, i.e. the black notes of the pianoforte. It is precisely in the intervals between E and F, and B and C that this progression is interrupted. One has a uniform succession therefore, although it is never
40 completely uniform. The other intervals are also called whole tones, but

as we have seen, they are not perfectly equal, and are further distinguished as greater and lesser, or major and minor tones. The intervals from C to D, F to G, and A to B, are major, while the intervals from D to E, and G to A, although they are certainly equal to each other, differ from the former in not being quite a whole tone. In musical theory, this small difference between the intervals is called the *comma*. The basic determinations of fifth, fourth, third etc. must remain the foundation however, and the formal uniformity of progression has to give way to them. An ear which is attuned to purely mechanical arithmetical progression, in which there are no ratios (1,2,3,4), and which can merely pass from 1 to 2, must give way as it were, to an ear which is attuned to the absolute ratios in the division of tonality. The difference is, after all, very slight, and the ear submits to the predominance of the inner harmonic ratios.

It is in this way that the first opposition to occur here is formed by the harmonic foundation and the uniform progression of its moments. As the two principles are not in exact agreement, it is to be feared that their difference will become more apparent through a further development of the tonal system, i.e. when a note in one particular scale is made the key-note of another scale (and in itself it makes no difference which note this is, for they can all be used in this way), for which the same notes have to be used, probably through several octaves. When G is the key-note for example, D is the fifth; but in the key of B, D is the third; and in the key A, it is the fourth etc. As it is the same note which is successively the third, the fourth and the fifth, it may not be played with complete correctness on instruments in which the notes are fixed. The difference here becomes increasingly apparent in further developments. Notes which are right in one key do not fit into another, which would not be the case if the intervals were equal. The keys thereby acquire an inner diversity, which depends upon the nature of the ratios of the notes which constitute their scale. It is known for example, that when the fifth in the scale of C (G) is made the key-note, and its fifth (D) is taken as the key-note to produce a further fifth etc., the eleventh and twelfth fifths are no longer true on a piano, and fail to fit into the system in which these notes were tuned in accordance with C. Relative to C these are therefore false fifths. It is to this that changes in further tones and semitones etc. are related, and it is because of it that there are even earlier emergences of impurities, differences, and discordances. This confusion may be cleared up to a certain extent by spreading the inequalities in a uniform and equitable manner. Completely harmonic harps have been constructed for example, in which each system, C, D, etc., has its own semitones. Recourse has been

had (*a*) to a slight diminution of each fifth from the very beginning, in order to spread the difference uniformly. As sensitive ears could detect the defect here however, one had to (*b*) limit the range of the instrument to six octaves, although even within these limits there are aberrations enough in
5 instruments with fixed and neutral notes. In general (*c*) the keys in which dissonances of this kind occur are either used sparingly by performers, or else the particular combinations containing notes which are strikingly false
+ are avoided.

It only remains to make mention of the way in which harmony appears
10 *objectively*, i.e. its essential efficacy. There are appearances here which seem at first to be paradoxical, for no basis can be found for them in the mere audibility of notes, and they are only to be grasped through numerical ratios. Firstly, if one causes a string to vibrate, it will, by vibrating, divide itself of its own accord into these ratios. This is an immanent and charac-
15 teristic ratio of nature, an activity of form within itself. One can hear not only the key-note (1), but also the fifth of the higher octave (3), and the third of the octave above that (5), and a practised ear is also able to pick out the octave of the key-note (2), and its double octave (4). The notes which are represented by the whole numbers 1,2,3,4,5, may therefore be
20 heard. As there are of course two fixed points on strings of this kind, a node of vibration forms in the middle, and then relates itself to the ends once more, giving rise to the phenomenon of different but harmonious
+ sounds.

Secondly, notes can be elicited from a string not by touching it, but by
25 touching other strings. It is said to be understandable that a string, when touched should produce its own note, but it is more difficult to see why, when various notes are played, it often happens that only one note is audible; or why, when two notes are played, a third is audible. This also depends upon the nature of the relation between these numerical deter-
30 minations. (*a*) One phenomenon is that when one selects notes which have a certain relationship to each other, and touches all their strings at once, only the key-note is heard. For example, the organ has a register in which five pipes may be brought into play by the touching of one key. Each pipe certainly has its particular note, and yet the result of these five notes is
35 merely a single note. This takes place when these five pipes or notes are as follows: (1) the key-note C; (2) the octave of C; (3) the fifth (G) of the next octave; (4) the third C; (5) the third (E) of the third octave. Only the key-note is then audible, because the vibrations coincide. The various notes have of course to be selected at a certain pitch, which is neither too
40 high nor too low. The reason for this coincidence is as follows. When the

79

lower C vibrates once, its octave vibrates twice. The G of this octave vibrates three times while the key-note vibrates once, for the proximate fifth vibrates $1\frac{1}{2}$ times, and this G therefore vibrates three times to the once of the key-note. The third C vibrates four times, and its third vibrates five times, to the once of the key-note, for the third vibrates $\frac{5}{4}$ as 5 quickly as the key-note, while the third of the third octave vibrates four times as quickly again, and therefore makes five vibrations. These vibrations are therefore so composed that those of the other notes coincide with that of the key-note. The strings of these notes are in the numerical ratio of 1,2,3,4,5, and all their vibrations finish simultaneously, for after five 10 vibrations of the highest note, the lower notes have completed precisely four, three, two, or one vibration respectively. It is because of this coincidence that only the single C is audible.

(b) The other case, noticed by *Tartini* is similar, and equally remarkable. + If one plucks two different strings of a guitar, a third note is heard, as well 15 as the other two, and this is not just a mixture of the first two, or a merely abstract neutrality. If C and G are played together at a certain pitch for example, the C of the octave below will also be heard. The reason for this is as follows. When the key-note vibrates once, the fifth vibrates $1\frac{1}{2}$ times, or three times while the key-note vibrates twice. When the key- 20 note vibrates once, the second vibration of the fifth has already begun while this first vibration is still taking place. But the second vibration of C, which begins during the second vibration of G, ends at the same time as the third vibration of G; consequently the recommencement of the vibrations of the two strings takes place simultaneously. 'There are periods,' 25 says *Biot* ('Traité de Physique' vol. II p. 47), in which vibrations reach the ear simultaneously, and others in which they do so separately.' It is the + same when one person takes three steps in the time taken by another to take two, so that after the first has taken three steps, and the second has taken two, they are both stepping off together. It is in this way that a 30 periodic coincidence occurs after every two vibrations of C. This coincidence is twice as slow or half as quick as the vibration of C. When the vibrative determination of one note is half the speed of another however, the lower octave occurs, which vibrates once while that above it vibrates twice. This can best be demonstrated on a well-tuned organ. The lower + octave may also be heard on a monochord for example, although this note is beyond the range of the instrument itself. Abbot *Vogler* has based a special system of organ-building upon this principle; numerous pipes, each of which has its own note, produce a further clear note when played together, and no separate pipe or key is required for this effect. +

If harmony is considered only from the standpoint of hearing, and no attention is paid to numerical relationships, it is quite impossible to explain how notes which are heard at the same time, are heard as a single note, although they are in themselves different. In the consideration of
5 harmony one should not confine oneself solely to hearing therefore, one must recognize and understand its objective determinateness. This leads on into physical and then into musical theory. In so far as the note is this ideality in the sphere of the mechanical however, what has been said here belongs here. It has to be recognized as a mechanical determinateness
10 therefore, and it is that which constitutes this mechanical determinateness which has to be apprehended.

§ 302

Sound is the alternation between the specific juxtaposition of material parts and their negatedness. It is the mere abstract ideality of this specificness, or perhaps one might say, merely the
15 **ideal nature of its ideality. In its own immediacy however, this alternation is consequently the negation of materially specific subsistence; and this negation is therefore the real ideality of specific gravity and cohesion, i.e. heat.**

Remark

Sonorous bodies will grow hot when they are struck or rubbed
20 **together, and it is in this phenomenon that heat originates with sound in conformity with the Notion.**

Addition. The being-in-self which reveals itself in sound, is itself materialized. It dominates matter, and acquires a sensuous existence by submitting it to violence. As notes, being-in-self is merely conditioned
25 individuality, it is not yet real totality, and its self-preservation is therefore
+ only one aspect of its being. The other aspect is however that this materiality, which is pervaded by being-in-self, is also destructible. Consequently, this internal disturbance of the body within itself contains not only the ideal nature of a sublation of matter, but also the real sublation of it by
30 heat. Instead of the body displaying itself in a specific manner as self-conserving, it tends to pass over into negating itself. The reciprocity of its internal cohesion is at the same time the posited negation of this cohesion, an incipient sublation of its rigidity; and this is precisely the nature of heat.

There is therefore a direct relation between sound and heat. Heat is the consummation of sound, and distinguishes itself materially as the negativity of this material being; sound itself is able to break or melt things, and a shriek will even shatter a glass. Sensuous intuition certainly separates sound from heat, so that it may be surprising to see them brought together 5 in this way; yet a bell will become hot by being rung for example, and this is a heat which is developed within it by its own interior vibration, it is not external to it. The instruments get warm as well as the musician. +

D

Heat

§ 303

Heat is matter's restoration of itself to formlessness, it is the fluidity of matter and the triumph of its abstract homogeneity 10 over specific determinatenesses. As a negation of a negation, its abstract and merely implicit continuity is posited here as activity, or existent dissolution. Heat therefore appears formally, i.e. in relation to spatial determination in general, as expansion; it does this in that it sublates the specifying of the indifferent 15 occupation of space constituted by boundedness. +

Addition. When real connection yields to force and dissolves, the disruption and shattering are merely the dissolution of passive quantitative cohesion, although the cohesion here has also displayed its own type of determinateness (§ 296). The other form of dissolution however, which is 20 heat, is related only to specific qualitative cohesion. The most important factor in sound is the repulsion of external force through the subsistence of form, and of the parts contained by form. In heat however, attraction comes to the fore, so that at the same time as the specific and internally coherent body repulses force, it also yields inwardly to it. If the cohesion 25 and rigidity of the body are overcome, the ideal nature of the subsistence of the parts will be posited, and they will therefore be altered. By becoming fluid in this way, the body gives birth to the heat in which sound perishes, for fluidity resembles mere rigidity, brittleness, and pulverization, in that it is no longer resonant. Heat merely disperses bodies into a 30 permanent connection, it does not shatter them into masses. It is the intimate internal dissolution of the repulsion by which the body maintains the

juxtaposition of its parts. Consequently, the unity engendered within bodies by heat is more intimate than unity of form, but it is without determination. This dissolution is the triumph of form itself; the external force which constitutes the inert matter which maintains itself within
5 repulsion, annuls itself. This dissolution is *mediated* by cohesion, for without cohesion force is only able to shatter; a stone for example, is merely breakable. Mere rigidity presents the transmission of heat with an obstacle, for transmission requires the inner fluidity of connection and expansibility which constitute the inner elasticity whereby the particles posit
10 themselves within each other. It requires in fact the opposite of rigidity or inflexibility, and at the same time, the destruction of the connection in which the parts subsist. In fusion, form preserves itself as soul, but nevertheless, fire also posits the destruction of form.

It is therefore as the repulsion of external force, and the yielding to it
15 as an inner state, that sound and heat are opposed, and this is precisely why sound also passes over into heat. This opposition is still in evidence in higher natures such as organisms, where the subject possesses and preserves its ideality, and where it is drawn *outwards* by heat into real existence. It is in plants and flowers that the variety, as well as the pure abstract for-
20 mation and brilliance of individual colour may be seen most clearly. The self of the plant or flower is drawn forth by external light, and poured into existence as sheen. The colours of animals are generally duller however. Birds display the most gorgeous colours, and there are tropical birds whose self hood is drawn forth, plantwise, by the light and heat of the climate,
+ into the vegetative covering of their plumage. Northern birds are drabber, but better songsters however, witness the nightingale and the lark, which are not to be found in the tropics.* With tropical birds it is therefore the heat which, rather than preserving the integrity of this being-inself, this issuing forth of their inner ideality as song, melts it and pours it
30 forth as the metallic sheen of colour; i.e. sound is mastered by heat. It is

+ *Spix and Martius ('Travels', vol. II, p. 190–191), 'It was in these forests (of Brazil, beyond Santa Cruz) that we first noticed the song of a greyish brown bird, probably a thrush, which haunts the bushes and the damp floor of the forest, and which in its singing frequently repeats the scale from B^1 to A^2 with such regularity, that not a single note is missed. It usually sings each note four or five times, and then passes imperceptibly on to the following quarter tone. It is customary to deny that the *songsters of the American forests* have any harmonic faculty, and to concede them a superiority only in respect of their gorgeous colouring. Although it is generally true that the gentle inhabitants of the torrid zone are more distinguished by the beauty of their colours than by the power and richness of their song, and seem to have nothing to match the clear and melodious flutings of our nightingale, yet this small bird illustrates the fact, as others might, that they do at least possess the rudiments of melody.—It is indeed conceivable, that once the almost inarticulate grunts of degenerate men have ceased to sound through the forests of Brazil, many of the feathered songsters there will pour forth finer melodies.'

true that bird-song is a higher determination than sound, but nevertheless, the opposition also comes into evidence here through the song, and the heat of the climate.

§ 304

This real negation of the body's own nature is therefore its state of not belonging affirmatively to itself in its determinate being, so 5 that its existence is rather a community with other bodies, and the communication of itself to them, i.e. external heat. The passivity of corporeality in regard to heat rests upon the implicit continuity of material being, which is present in specific gravity and cohesion. It is because of the primary ideality of this contin- 10 uity, that in the positing of this community, the modification of specific gravity and cohesion is unable to form any actual barrier to transmission.

Remark

Incoherent substances such as wool, and those such as glass or stones, which are either brittle or implicitly incoherent, are 15 worse conductors of heat than metals, which are characterized by the compact uninterruptedness of their internal continuity. Simi-larly, it is because of their lack of cohesion, and more generally because of their incorporeal materiality, that air and water are such bad conductors of heat. It is mainly the transmissibility of the heat 20 which appears to leave a body after being initially present in it, and which therefore appears to be independent, and to have come to the body from without; together with the further mechanical de-terminations connected with this which may be introduced into the diffusion of heat, such as reflection by a concave mirror; and 25 thirdly, the quantitative determinations which occur in connec-tion with it, which has given rise to heat being envisaged as a material substance having an independent existence (cf. §286 Rem.). However, there is at least a certain reluctance to call heat a body, or even a corporality, which would already imply 30 that in its appearance, a particular existence is at once capable of various categories. Consequently, the apparently limited particularity of heat, and the fact that it can be distinguished from the bodies in which it occurs, do not justify the application to it of

the category of matter, for as this category is essentially a totality
in itself, it would at least imply weight. The said appearance of
particularity is mainly due to the external way in which heat appears in relation to the bodies involved in its transmission.
5 The conception of heat as a particular and independent existence
could have been completely discarded long ago, on account of
Rumford's experiments with the heating of bodies by friction.
By his experiments with the boring of cannon for example, Rumford demonstrated irrefutably, that in its origin and nature, heat is
+ simply a modal condition of matter. By itself, the abstract
conception of matter implies the determination of continuity,
which makes transmission possible, and which as activity, constitutes the actuality of this transmission. This implicit continuity
becomes activity as the negation of form, i.e. of specific gravity
15 and cohesion, and subsequently of shape.

Addition. In the world of appearance, sound and heat are themselves
appearances. Transmissibility and having been transmitted constitute the
predominant moment in the nature of a condition, which is an essentially
communal determination, dependent upon environment. Heat there-
20 fore is transmissible because it is determined as an appearance, and not
merely as such, but within the field in which the reality of matter is presupposed. It is a being which is at the same time show, or a show which is
still being. The being is the coherent body, the show is its dissolution, the
negation of coherence. Heat is not matter therefore, it is the negation of this
25 reality. It is no longer the abstract negation of sound however, nor is it yet
the completed negation of fire. As materialized negation or negative
materialization, it is a presence, and has the shape of universality, com-
+ munity. It is the general determinate being of passivity, for it is still real
subsistence as much as it is negation. As this merely apparent negation,
30 heat is not for itself, but is dependent upon another.

Heat therefore is essentially diffusible, and so posits an equality between
bodies. This diffusion is therefore externally determinable by surfaces, and
heat may therefore be concentrated by means of burning-glasses and concave
mirrors. I believe Professor *Pictet* of Geneva has experimented in the same
+ way with cold. Now since bodies are themselves capable of being posited
as apparent, they cannot ward off heat, for the potential negation of their
coherence is implicit within their nature. Implicitly therefore, they are
that which reduces determinate being in heat, and it is precisely this
implicitness which constitutes their passivity. It is precisely that which is

passive, which is merely implicit; a person who is merely implicitly rational, is a passive person for example. The condition communicated is therefore a determinateness which is posited through another in accordance with this implicit aspect of the body. It is a general phenomenal manifestation of its mere implicitness, although as activity it must also be 5 actual. This mode of appearance is therefore twofold; it is an active initiating manifestion, and it is passive. One body may have inner sources of heat therefore, while another may receive it from without, as something not generated within it. The transition from the original production of heat in the alteration of cohesion, to the external relationship of something 10 already present being added to something else, as in the transmission of heat, reveals the absence of selfhood in these determinations. On the other hand, gravity or weight cannot be transmitted.

As the general nature of heat consists in the idealization of specific and real juxtaposition, and we regard it as being based upon this negation, 15 we can no longer postulate a calorific matter when considering this aspect of it. The postulation of such a matter, like the postulation of material sound, is based upon the principle that that which makes a + sensuous impression, must also have a sensuous subsistence. Now although the Notion of matter has been extended to the point at which its 20 basic determination of gravity has been abandoned on account of its having been asked whether this calorific matter is weighable or not, the + objective subsistence of a matter which is indestructible and self-contained in its independence, which comes and goes, and which can increase and diminish in any given place, continues to be presupposed. The meta- 25 physics of the understanding gets no further than this conception of external accretion, and makes it the original relationship, especially of heat. Caloric is supposed to add itself, be accumulated, and lie latent where it does not appear, and yet heat is subsequently present. There are experiments designed to display the materiality of heat, and trifling inferences 30 have often been drawn from the most tenuous of their circumstances, but + the researches of *Count Rumford*, in which he attempted to calculate the heat of cannon barrels, told heavily against them. The general opinion was that the intense heat which occurs in the metal fragments, is drawn from the proximate bodies by the strength of the friction. Rumford 35 maintained that it is generated in the metal itself, for he found that when he enclosed the whole in wood, which as a bad conductor of heat did not let the heat through, the fragments of metal which fell out were just as glowing hot as they were when there was no such covering. The under- + standing creates substrata for itself which we do not recognize through the 40

Notion. Sound and heat do not exist on their own account as does weighted matter, and the postulated materiality of heat and sound is a mere fiction, introduced into physics by the metaphysics of the understanding. Sound and heat are conditioned by material existence, and constitute their
5 negativity; they are no more than moments, but as determinations of what is material they are quantitative, and may therefore be determined by *degrees*, according to their intensity.

§ 305

In itself, the transmission of heat to various bodies contains only the abstract continuation of this determination through indeter-
10 **minate materiality. In transmission therefore, heat has no internal qualitative dimensions, only the abstract antithesis of positive and negative, quantum and degree, which it displays as an abstract equilibrium, a standard temperature, in the bodies among which the varying degrees of temperature are distributed. As heat is an**
15 **alteration of specific gravity and cohesion however, it is at the same time bound up with these determinations, and like temperature communicated from without, is conditioned with regard to the determinateness of its existence by the particular specific gravity and cohesion of the body to which it is communicated.**
20 **This is specific thermal capacity.**

Remark

Specific thermal capacity, combined with the category of matter and stuff has given rise to the conception of a material heat which is latent, imperceptible, and unexcited. As it may not be perceived, such a determination lacks the warrant of observation and experience, and as inferred, it rests upon
25 **the supposition of the material independence of heat (cf. § 286 Rem.). In its way, this postulate makes the independence of heat as a matter empirically irrefutable, precisely because the postulate itself is not empirical. If one points out the disappearance**
30 **of heat, or its appearance where it was not formerly present, the first is explained as a mere concealment or a fixation in a state of imperceptibility, and the second as an emergence from mere imperceptibility. It is in this way that the metaphysic of independence**

87

is set up against the experience mentioned, and the experience is indeed presupposed a priori.

The import of the determination of heat which is given here, is
that it is empirically confirmed that the determination which is
by itself necessary through its conformity with the Notion, i.e. the 5
alteration of specific gravity and cohesion, displays itself pheno-
menally as heat. The close connection between them makes
itself abundantly apparent in the various productions and the
equally various disappearances of heat in fermentation and other
chemical processes, in crystallizations, and in the dissolution of the 10
same, in the inner and outer mechanical disturbances which have
already been considered, such as the ringing of bells, beating of
metals, frictions etc. The friction of pressure and rapid movement,
such as occurs when savages rub together pieces of wood for exam- +
ple, or in the ordinary striking of a light, momentarily draws the 15
material extrinsicality of the body together into one point, so that
a negation of the spatial subsistence of ǀits material parts bursts
forth in heat and flame, or in the throwing off of a spark. The other
difficulty lies in grasping the connection between heat and specific
gravity and cohesion as the existent ideality of material being: 20
in grasping heat moreover as an existent negative, which itself
contains the determinateness of that which is negated, which has
the further determinateness of a quantum, and which, as the ideality
of a subsistence, is its self-externality and self-positedness within
another, which is in fact transmission. The task here is the same as 25
that throughout the whole of the philosophy of nature; it is
merely to replace the categories of the understanding by the
thought-relationships of the speculative Notion, and to grasp and
determine the phenomenon in accordance with the latter.

Addition. Each body has a specific heat, just as it has a particular kind of 30
sound, depending upon its specific cohesion. When qualitatively different bodies are brought to the same temperature, i.e. have the same
quantity of heat applied to them, they are heated differently. Each body
appropriates the temperature of the air differently. When the air is cold
for example, iron will become much colder than stone, and when the air 35
is warm, water is always cooler. It is reckoned that in order to raise water
and mercury to the same temperature, thirteen times more heat is required for the former. The melting-point elicited by transmitted heat is
equally variable; for example, much less heat is required in order to

liquefy mercury than is required for any of the other metals. The body displays its specificity as soon as heat is imparted to it, and this raises the question of the form of the being-in-self which appears here. The forms of being-in-self are 'cohesion, punctiformity, lineality, and superficity, together with the simple determinateness of specific gravity. It can only be the simple mode of being-in-self which displays itself in specific heat. Heat is the sublation of the specific extrinsicality of cohesion; in its subsistence however, the body is at the same time still preserved within its specific being-in-self. Now being-in-self, together with self-sublating cohesion, is still only the universal and abstract being of specific gravity. Consequently, it is specific gravity which displays itself here as affirmative being-in-self.

It is in this way that thermal capacity is related to specific gravity, which is the being-in-self of bodies opposed to mere gravity. This is an inverse relationship, for bodies with a higher specific gravity heat up much easier, i.e. become hotter at the same temperature, than do those of lower specific gravity. It is said therefore, that calorific matter becomes latent in the latter bodies, and free in the former. Similarly, it is maintained that calorific material has been latent, when it is quite clear that the heat did not come from without, but has generated itself internally (see § 304 Addition). Heat is also supposed to become latent when cold is brought forth by the evaporation of naphtha. It is said that at zero, frozen water loses the heat which is applied to make it fluid; as its temperature is not raised by this heat, the calorific material is said to have become latent within it. The same is said to occur in the elastic steam into which water transforms itself; for water does not get hotter than 80°R, and at a higher temperature merely evaporates. On the contrary, vapours and elastic fluids at a particular temperature, generate greater heat while precipitating than they do while they remain in their expanded state, i.e. expansion does duty for temperature as intensity (cf. § 103 Add.) Recourse is had to the expedient of latency, whenever the phenomena make it abundantly clear that the heat has occurred through an internal change in cohesion. An example of this may be found in water which is some degrees below zero and which rises to zero as it freezes. Calorific material is supposed to be perpetually coming and going; but as heat cannot be allowed to disappear if it is held to be substantial and independent, it is said to be still present, but simply latent. How can something be present however, if it does not exist? This 'something' is merely an empty figment of thought, and it is precisely the aptitude heat has for being transmitted which tends to prove the dependence of it as a determination.

89

It might be thought that a high specific gravity must also produce more heat, but it is the bodies of higher specific gravity which are still simple in their determinateness, which have an occluded, unindividualized being-in-self, and which have not yet progressed to further immanent determinations. On the contrary, the opposition which individuality offers to 5 heat is of a higher kind. Consequently, organic being is much less apt to receive external heat. Generally speaking, the importance and interest of specific gravity and thermal capacity disappear in higher organic natures such as plants and animals, and on the whole therefore, differences between types of wood are of no significance in this respect. Specific 10 gravity and thermal capacity are of prime importance with regard to metals however. Specific gravity is not yet cohesion, even less is it individuality; it is on the contrary merely an abstract general being-in-self, which is not immanently specified, and is therefore most easily penetrated by heat. It is a being-in-self, which is most easily and readily receptive with 15 regard to the negation of specific relatedness. That which is coherent and more individualized however, endows its determinations with a much greater permanence, so that they do not receive heat so readily.

By starting from the specific determinedness of material being-in-self, we have considered the cohesive aspect of the *generation* of heat. This is 20 (*a*) the characteristic origin of heat, which can become apparent through vibration, and also for example, as the spontaneous combustion of fermentations, which take place of their own accord. One of the Empress Catherine's frigates caught fire of its own accord in this way; even roasted coffee ferments, and the heat rises until flames occur; this is 25 probably what happened too in the ship. Flax, hemp, and tarred rope finally set fire to themselves. The fermentation of wine or vinegar also + generates heat. The same occurs in chemical processes, for the dissolution of crystals always involves an alteration in the state of cohesion. It is known however that heat has a double origin in this mechanical field of 30 gravitational relationship. (*b*) The second source of heat is friction as such. Friction merely disturbs the parts of the surface, it is not a thoroughgoing vibration. It is friction of this kind which is the common and usual source of heat. But this also must not be regarded as purely mechanical however, as it is in the 'Göttingen Literary Advertiser' (1817 sect. 161), 'It is known 35 that a body will lose a part of its specific heat when it is submitted to heavy pressure, or rather, that when submitted to heavy pressure, a body cannot contain the same amount of specific heat as it can when the pressure is not so great. This accounts for the development of heat by the striking and rubbing of bodies, by the rapid compression of air, and similar means.' +

This liberation of form is still conditioned however, and as yet, is neither the truly independent totality of the self, nor the immanent self-preserving activity of unity. That is why heat can be produced in an external and mechanical way by friction. As it rises into flame, heat is the free triumph
5 of pure ideality over this material extrinsicality. That which is struck *from* steel and flint is only a spark, for the more resistance there is in the interior hardness of the body, the stronger is the disturbance in those parts of it *exposed* to friction. Wood is *consumed* however, for it is a material which
+ can further heat.

§ 306

10 **As temperature in general, heat is primarily the dissolution of specified materiality, a dissolution which is still abstract, and conditioned by the existence and determinateness of heat. In its self-
fulfilment, and the actuality of its realization however, this consumption of bodily peculiarity attains to the existence of pure
15 physical ideality. This is the liberating negation of material being,
and it comes forth as light, or rather as flame ; as bound to matter,
and as negation of it. Fire is posited here as it was when it first
developed out of the immediacy of matter (§ 283): conditioned
from without, it propagates itself out of the moments of the
20 Notion existing within the sphere of conditioned existence. What
is more, it destroys itself in this finitude, together with the conditions which it consumes.**

Addition. Light as such is cold, and the light which gives so much heat in summer, does so in conjunction with the Earth's atmosphere. It is quite
25 cold on a high mountain, even at the height of summer, and it is there that the eternal snow lies, although these regions are nearer the Sun. It is only through its contact with other bodies that light produces heat, for light is selfhood, and that which is touched by light also acquires selfhood, i.e. displays an incipient dissolution, or heat.

§ 307

30 **Real matter is imbued with form, and in the totality of its
development, passes over into the pure ideality of its determinations, into abstractly self-identical selfhood, which externalizes
itself as flame in this sphere of external individuality, and so**

91

disappears. The conditionality of this sphere consists of form as a specification of weighted matter, and of individuality as having been initially implicit only as totality. The real dissolution of immediacy is accompanied by the reciprocal indifference of specified material beings, and it is this moment which is posited in 5 **heat. Consequently, form is now a totality which is immanent within material being which offers it no resistance. As infinite self-relating form, selfhood as such has therefore entered into existence; it maintains itself in the externality which is subject to** + **it, and as the freely determining totality of this material being,** 10 **constitutes free individuality.**

Addition. The *transition* now has to be made to real individuality or shape, the moments of which have been seen in that which preceded. The assembling of form within itself, the soul which escapes as sound, together with the fluidity of matter, are the two moments constituting the 15 real Notion of individuality. In its submission to infinite form, gravity is the totality of free individuality, in which material being is completely permeated and determined by form. The shape which is developed within itself into determining a multiplicity of material beings, is absolute centrality, which unlike gravity, no longer has multiplicity merely 20 external to it. As nisus, individuality is so constituted, that initially, it posits its moments as individualized figurations. Whereas the figurations of space, the point, line and surface, were merely the negations of space however, they are now described by form within a matter which it alone determines. They are no longer described in their simple spatiality, but as 25 differences within material connection, and as the real spatial figurations of matter completing themselves in the totality of the surface. In order that sound may form within materiature as force, and not escape from it as soul, there has to be a posited negation of the firm subsistence of matter. + The existence of this negation is posited in the dissolution of matter by 30 heat. The penetrability of matter, which was at first posited through the Notion, is posited here in its resulting existence. A beginning was made with being-in-self as specific gravity, in which matter was taken as so constituted within its immediacy, that form might build itself into it. It was on account of this implicitness, that matter was susceptible to pene- 35 tration and dissolution; its existence in cohesion also had to be shown however. This cohesion is itself sublated in the dissolution of its extrinsicality, and that which remains is specific gravity. As primary subjectivity, this was simple abstract determinedness, which is the note when

determined as totality within itself, and which is heat in its fluidity. The prime immediacy must display itself as sublated and as posited, and one must therefore always return to the beginning. It is through matter that cohesion constitutes the conditioned being of form. As opposed to this
5 conditioned being, cohesion itself is the intermediary which brings forth heat within the negation. It therefore negates itself by negating the mere implicitness of being which is the simple conditioned way in which form exists. It is easy to make mention of these moments, but it is difficult to regard them individually if one wants to develop within existence that
10 which corresponds to the determinations of thought, for each of these determinations also has its corresponding existence. This difficulty is particularly noticeable in chapters such as this, where the whole is merely a nisus, so that the determinations come forth only as separate properties. In accordance with the Notion, the abstract moments of individuality
15 such as specific weight and cohesion etc., have to precede free individuality, so that this may proceed out of them as their result. In total individuality, where form accedes to its sovereignty, all moments are now realized, and form dwells within it as determinate unity. Shape requires soul, and the unity of form with itself, together with the determinations
20 of the Notion as its being-for-other. Form is free in its positing of these differences, and is at the same time their unconditioned unity. The freedom of specific gravity is only abstract, for it is also related indifferently to another, and falls into external comparison. True form is related by itself to another, and not through a third term. As the materiature is
25 melted by heat, it is receptive of form, and as finite form, the conditioned being of sound is therefore sublated. This form finds no further opposition, as it would in a further relation. Heat is the shape liberating itself from shape, it is a self-substantiating light which contains the moment of passive shape as sublated within it.

CHAPTER THREE

Physics of total individuality

§ 308

In that it is weighted, matter first constitutes the totality of the Notion in an implicit manner, and so lacks intrinsic form. Initially the Notion is posited within it in its particular determinations, and exhibits a finite individuality falling apart into particularities. As the totality of the Notion is now posited, the centre of 5 **gravity is no longer a subjectivity sought by matter, but is immanent within it as the ideality of these form-determinations, which are initially immediate and conditioned, but which from now on are developed as moments, out of the core of the Notion. Material individuality, being thus identical with itself in its de-** 10 **velopment, constitutes an infinite being-for-self, although it is at the same time conditioned, for it is only the primary immediacy of subjective totality. Consequently, although it is infinite in this being-for-self, it contains relationship to another, and it is only in process that the externality and conditionedness** 15 **involved in this, are posited as self-sublating. It is thus that this individuality becomes the existent totality of material being-for-self, which implicitly is then life, and which in the Notion, passes over into life.**

Addition. The two distinct moments of a real physical body are form as 20 an abstract whole, and whatever material it determines. In themselves, these are identical, and are therefore capable of passing into one another in accordance with the Notion, for form is pure self-relating physical identity, and has no determinate being, and fluid matter also exists as this non-resistant universal identity. Within itself, matter resembles form 25 through its lack of difference, so that it is itself form. In its universality, matter is determined as being determined within itself, and this determining is the precise function of form, in which matter is implicit. We started with individuality in general, and this individuality was then posited in the finitely restricted determinateness of its differentiation from gravity. Thirdly, individuality returns into itself out of differentiation, and this third moment also has three shapes or determinations.

§ 309

+ **Total individuality is:**
5 (*a*) **the Notion of immediate shape as such, and the abstract principle of this appearing in free existence, i.e. magnetism.**
+ (*b*) **It determines itself into difference, into the particular forms of corporeal totality; heightened to its extreme, this individual particularization is electricity.**
10 (*c*) **The reality of this particularization constitutes the chemically differentiated body and its relatedness; it constitutes the individuality which, while realizing itself as a totality, has bodies as its moments, i.e. the chemical process.**

Addition. In shape, infinite form is the determining principle of the
15 material parts, which are now no longer merely related indifferently in space. This is the Notion of shape, but as shape is not quiescent subsistence but is self-differentiating, it does not remain with it, but unfolds its essence into real properties. These properties are not held within the unity in an ideal manner, but are also endowed with a particular exis-
20 tence. These differences are determined as having qualitative individuality, and constitute the elements. They are specified by belonging to the sphere of individuality however, and are therefore united with individual corporeality, or rather transformed into it. In this way, the defect still attaching to form has implicitly overcome itself within the Notion.
25 Necessity now demands a further positing of this implicitness however, influencing the way in which shape engenders itself, so that the transition also has to be made within existence. It is as the result of this transition that shape is engendered. A return is made to the primality therefore, although this now appears as being engendered. Consequently, this return is at
30 the same time a progressive transition, and the chemical process therefore contains in its Notion the transition into the organic sphere. At first, we found process in the sphere of mechanics, as motion; then in the process of the elements, and now in the process of individualized matter.

A

Shape

§ 310

As total individuality, body in its immediacy is quiescent totality. It is therefore a form of the spatial assemblage of material being, and initially therefore, it constitutes a further form of mechanism. Shape is thus the material mechanism of individuality, which is now unconditioned and free in its determining. It 5 **is the body which is determined by the activity of immanent and developed form, not only in the specific mode of its interior consistence, but also in its external limitation in space. It is in this way that form itself is made manifest, and shows itself as something more than a characteristic of the resistance offered to** 10 **an alien force.** +

Addition. Formerly, being-in-self only displayed itself through an external impetus and the corresponding reaction. Here on the contrary, form manifests itself neither through external force, nor as the destruction of materiality. The body has a concealed and tacit geometer 15 within it, which as form is all-pervading, and which, without impulse, organizes it both externally and internally. This interior and exterior limitation is necessary to individuality, as is the surface of the body, which is limited by its form. The body is sealed off from others, and displays its specific determinateness in its quiescent subsistence, independently of 20 external influence. The crystal is certainly not mechanically compounded; nevertheless, mechanism is resumed here as an individual factor, for this is precisely the sphere of the quiescent subsistence of extrinsicality, despite the relation of the parts being determined by immanence of form. That which is shaped in this way is withdrawn from gravity and can grow 25 upwards for example. It is possible to observe the thoroughgoing reticulation of natural crystals. We do not yet find soul here as we find it in life however, because the individual here is not yet distinct from itself. It + is this distinctness which constitutes the difference between inorganic and organic being. Individuality is not yet subjectivity; if it were, the infinite 30 form which is differentiated within itself and holds together its differentiation, would also be for itself. This first occurs in sentient being; here however, individuality is still immersed within matter; it is not yet free, it merely is.

The *determinateness* attained in inorganic shape, as distinguished from organic being, now has to be considered more closely. In the shape which 5 we have here, the spatial determinations of form are primarily those of the *understanding*, i.e. straight lines, plane surfaces, and definite angles. The reason for this has to be given here. The form which deploys itself in crystallization is a mute vitality, which is active in a truly remarkable way within that which is purely mechanical. Within stones or metal, 10 which appear to be externally determinable, it displays itself in characteristic shapes as an organic and organizing tendency. These shapes grow forth freely and independently, and those who are not used to the sight of these regular and delicate formations, will take them to be the work of human art and labour, rather than the products of nature. The activity 15 which gives rise to the regularity of art is motivated by an external purpose however, and in the case in question we should not think of the external purposiveness of an alien material being moulded to a person's purpose. In the crystal, form is not external to matter, for the matter itself is the end, and operates in and for itself. There is therefore an invisible + germ in water, a constructive force. This shape is regular in the strictest sense, but as it is not yet a process in itself, it is merely a regularity within the whole, the various parts of which constitute this single form. It is not yet organic shape outstripping the determinations of the understanding, for it lacks subjectivity, and its form is therefore still inorganic. In or- 25 ganic being however, shape is so constituted, that the whole shape appears in each part, not so that each particular part is only understandable with reference to the whole. In living being therefore, each peripheral point is the whole, so that each part of a person's body is sentient. This explains why organic shape is not based on straight lines and plane sur- 30 faces, which only belong to the abstract direction of the whole, and are not in themselves totalities. As each part of a curve can only be grasped through the whole law of the curve, a living shape will display curves, while this is never the case with shapes which may be grasped by the understanding. The roundness of organic being is not that of the circle 35 or the sphere however; for these are once again curves which may be grasped by the understanding, as the relation of all peripheral points to the centre is itself that of abstract identity. The curved line which is apparent in organic being must be differentiated within itself, but its differentials are in turn subject to equality. Consequently, living existence exhibits the 40 *elliptical line*, into which the equality of both parts enters once again, and what is more, does this in the direction of the major and minor axes. More precisely, it is the oval line which dominates here, and which only exhibits this equality in a single direction. It was on the basis of this, that *Möller* made the valuable observation that all organic forms such as those of feathers, wings, the head, and lines of the face, as well as all the shapes 5 of leaves, insects, birds, fishes, etc., are modifications of either the elliptical or the undulant line, which he therefore also calls the *line of beauty*. + Curved lines do not yet occur in inorganic being however, which displays geometrically regular figures with equal and correspondent angles, everything being necessitated by the progression of identity. This secret 10 tracing of lines, and determining and limiting of surfaces by parallel angles, is the figuration now to be considered.

This shape has to be regarded in its individual *determinations*, of which there are three to be distinguished. *Firstly* there are the abstract moments of shape, which are in fact shapeless; *secondly*, there is restricted shape in its 15 state of process and of becoming, in the activity of shaping in which shape is not yet completed, i.e. magnetism; *thirdly*, there is real shape, the crystal.

§ 311

1. **Shape in its immediacy is posited as internally formless; at the one extreme it constitutes punctiformity and brittleness, at the other, self-globulizing fluidity. It is therefore shape as** 20 **inner shapelessness.**

Addition. The determinations of form controlled by this interior geometry are firstly the point, then the line and the surface, and finally the overall volume. A brittle body is pulverizable and singular, properties we have already encountered as constituting a simple mode of cohesion. It 25 is granular, as is particularly evident in grains of platinum. It stands op- + posed to globularity, the general self-rounding fluidity which effaces every dimension within itself, and which, while it is certainly the complete realization of all three dimensions, is a totality in which determinateness is not developed. The globular shape is universal, and has a formal regu- 30 larity. It is freely poised, so that as universal individuality, it is also the shape of the free bodies of the heavens. Fluid matter globulizes itself, for as it is inwardly indeterminate, atmospheric pressure is the same on all sides of it; consequently, the determination of its shape is also the same on every side, and no differentiation is posited in it as yet. The shape is a 35 real principle however, and is not merely an abstract determination, i.e. it is a real totality of form.

§ 312

2. As the **implicit totality of formative individuality,** a brittle body opens itself to the difference of the Notion. The point first passes over into the line, **where form** posits itself in the opposition of the extremities. **These extremities have no sub-**
5 **sistence of their own as moments, but are merely maintained by their relation,** which appears as their middle term and the point of indifference in their opposition. This syllogism constitutes the developed determinateness of the *principle* of *figuration*, which in this still abstract rigour constitutes
+ *magnetism.*

Remark

Magnetism is one of the determinations which inevitably became prominent when the **Notion** began to be aware of itself in determinate nature, and grasped the Idea of a *philosophy of nature.* This came about because the magnet
15 exhibits the nature of the Notion, both in a simple straightforward way, and in its developed form as syllogism (§ 181). Its poles **are the sensibly existent ends of a real line such as a rod, or a dimensionally more fully extended body.** Their reality as poles is of an ideal nature however; it is not
20 sensibly mechanistic, **for the poles are simply indivisible.** The point of indifference, which constitutes their substantial existence, is their unity as determinations of the Notion, **and consequently it is from this unity alone that they derive their significance and their existence. Polarity is the relation between**
25 **mere moments of this kind. Apart from the** determination **posited here, magnetism has** no **further particular** property. The phenomenon of an individual magnetic needle swinging sometimes *north* and sometimes *south*, is an aspect of the general *magnetism of the Earth.*
30 There is an unwarranted ambiguity about the statement that all bodies are magnetic however. It is true that all shape of a real nature which is not merely brittle **involves this principle of determination.** It is not true however, that all bodies are also capable of displaying the *existence* of this
35 principle in its bare *abstractions* as magnetism. To attempt

to demonstrate a Notional form within nature in this way, so that it carries the *universal existence* of its abstractness into determinateness, it not a philosophic endeavour, for nature is the Idea in the element of extrinsicality, and like the understanding, it holds fast to the *dispersed* moments 5 of the Notion and so expresses their reality. In higher + things however, it unites the different forms of the Notion into the highest concretion of unity. (**see Rem.** § **seq.**). +

Addition. (*a*) The union of globularity and brittleness gives rise to the first generally real shape. Posited within brittleness as centrality, infinite 10 form posits its differences, and while giving them a subsistence, still holds them in unity. It is true that space is still the element in which they exist; it is this simplicity of character which constitutes the Notion however, this is the tension which in its diremption remains this pervasive universal, and which, when separated from the general being-in-self 15 of gravity, is itself the substance or existence of its differences. Mere inner shape does not yet exist in itself, it exists by splitting mass; the determination which is posited here however derives from shape itself. This individualizing principle is the end which translates itself into reality, but it is still distinct as end, and as yet unfulfilled. Consequently, it only 20 expresses itself as the process of the two principles of brittleness and fluidity; it is in this process that form impregnates the determinability of indeterminate fluidity. This is the *principle of magnetism*, the *tendency towards figuration* which has not yet come to rest, or the shaping form as a yet unrealized tendency. Primarily, magnetism is only the subjective 25 being of matter therefore, the formal existence of differences in the unity of the subject, the activity of cohesion, by which it brings different material points under the form of unity. The sides of magnetism are still simply bound to subjective unity therefore; their opposition is still not present as an independence. In points of brittleness as such, the difference 30 is still completely unposited. As we now have total individuality however which is supposed to be present spatially, and which has to posit itself in differences in that it is concrete, the point now distinguishes itself from a point while relating itself to it. This relation is linear, and is not yet the plane, or the totality of three dimensions, for the shaping tendency 35 does not yet exist as a totality, while in reality, the two dimensions immediately become the three dimensions of the surface. We therefore have the complete abstraction of spatiality as linearity, and this is the first general determination. But the straight line is the natural line so to speak, the line as such; in the curved line we already have a second **determination** and this would at once involve the positing of the plane.

(*b*) How is magnetism *manifest*? The motions which are present in it are only to be grasped in the ideality of their nature, for magnetism cannot be
5 interpreted sensuously. Sensuous comprehension merely binds together multiplicity in an external manner; it is true that this external unification also takes place in the two poles and the point of indifference which unites them, but these merely constitute the *magnet*, which is not yet magnetism. In order to ascertain what is contained in this *Notion*, we must
10 first remove completely the sensuous image of a loadstone, or of iron which has been rubbed with it. The phenomena of magnetism also have to be compared with its Notion however, in order to find out whether or not they correspond to it. Here the differentials are not posited in an external manner as being identical, but posit themselves as being so. In
15 so far as it is true that the motion of the magnet is still external, and that negativity still has no real and independent sides however: in so far, that is to say, as the moments of totality are not yet liberated so as to be differentiatedly independent in their relation to one another, the centre of gravity is not yet dispersed. Consequently, the development of these
20 moments is still posited as an externality or merely by means of the *im-*
+ *plicit being of the Notion*. Poles occur because the separable point opens itself to the differences of the Notion. In the physical line, which has difference of form within it, these poles are the two live ends, each of which is posited so that it is only in its relation to its other. Each only has
25 a significance through the being of the other. They are external to one another however, and each is the negative of the other; their unity also exists in the space between them, and it is here that their opposition is sublated. This polarity is often applied indiscriminately, where it is completely out of place, for nowadays everything is full of polarity. This
30 physical opposition is nothing sensuous and determinate; one cannot cut down the north pole for example. If one divides a magnet in two, each piece in itself will be a whole magnet: the north pole immediately arises
+ again in the broken part. Each pole posits the other and excludes it from itself; the terms of the syllogism can only exist in the connection, they
35 cannot exist for themselves. Here therefore, we are wholly in the field of the supersensual. If anyone is of the opinion that thought is not present in nature, he can be shown it here in magnetism. Magnetism on its own account is therefore a very striking phenomenon, but it becomes even more remarkable when one attempts to comprehend it. That is why it was taken
40 to be a main principle and given pride of place in the philosophy of

nature. The reflection certainly speaks of magnetic matter, which in itself +
however is not present in the phenomenon: that which operates here is
not anything material, it is pure immaterial form.

If we have a magnetized iron bar with a north and south pole which we
are able to distinguish, and move small non-magnetic iron bars towards it, 5
a motion will eventually become apparent if these small bars are able to
move freely and are not submitted to mechanical restraint. The small bar
may be balanced on a needle for example. In this case, one of the ends of
this small bar will join up with the north pole of the magnet, while the
other end will be repelled by it; consequently, the small bar itself will 10
become a magnet by acquiring a magnetic determinateness. This determinateness is not confined to the extremities however, for iron filings will
hang from a magnet up to its midpoint. A neutral point will then be
reached however, at which *attraction* and *repulsion* of this kind no longer
occur. It is in this way that one may distinguish between *passive* and *active* 15
magnetism. The absence of any effect upon unmagnetic iron may also be
defined as passive magnetism. A free centre resembling that which we
encountered earlier when considering the Earth, is now posited by this
neutral point. If one removes the small bar from its first position, and
places it at the other pole of the magnet, that end which was formerly 20
repelled by the first pole will then be attracted by it, and vice versa. There
is still no determination present here to show that the ends of the magnet
in themselves are opposed, for this in an empty spatial difference, which has
no more intrinsic significance than that between the two ends of a line.
If we then compare these two magnets with the Earth however, we find 25
that at one end they point in a direction which is roughly north, while at
the other they point south. It now becomes apparent that the two north
poles of the two magnets repel each other, as do the two south poles,
while the north pole of the one and the south pole of the other attract
each other. The direction north derives from the path of the sun, and is 30
not peculiar to the magnet. Since a single magnet with one of its ends
pointing north has the other pointing south, the Chinese are quite as
justified in saying that the magnet points south as we are when we maintain that it points north, for it is one and the same determination. This is +
also merely a relation of two magnets to one another, for it is the mag- 35
netism of the Earth which determines the bar magnet. We should realize
however, that that which we call the north pole of a magnet (a nomenclature which has given rise to much confusion because of the contra-
dictory ways in which it is now used) is in fact the south pole according
to the nature of the matter, for it is the south pole of the magnet which 40

moves towards the north pole of the Earth. This phenomenon constitutes the *entire theory* of magnetism. The physicists say that it is not yet known what magnetism is, and that it might be a current etc. All this belongs to the metaphysics which are not recognized by the Notion. There is nothing mysterious about magnetism. If we take pieces of loadstone, not a line, the magnetic impulse still falls invariably into the ideal nature of the line which forms the axis. In such a fragment, which might have the form of a cube or of a sphere etc. various axes might occur. This accounts for the Earth's having various magnetic axes, none of which coincides directly with that of its rotation. In the Earth, magnetism becomes free, for the Earth does not attain to the character of a true crystal, and as that which gives birth to individuality, fails to get beyond the abstract yearning of its urge towards shape. As the Earth is now a living magnet whose axis is not fixed to a definite point, the direction of the magnetic needle is approximately that of the true meridian, although it does not coincide with it exactly. It is this difference which gives rise to the *declination* of the magnetic needle to the east and west, a declination which varies at different times and in different places, and is in fact an oscillation of a more universal nature. With regard to the general significance of the relation of the magnetic needle to such an axis, the physicists now dispense with such an iron rod, or what amounts to the same thing, a specific existence in the direction of the axes. They have discovered that the data may be sufficiently accounted for by assuming that at the centre of the Earth there is a magnet of infinite intensity and no extension, i.e. a magnet which is not a line in which one point is stronger than another, as is the case with magnetic iron, at the pole of which iron filings are much more strongly drawn than they are at the centre, and in which there is a regular decrease in this attraction from the poles to the centre. In the Earth however, magnetism constitutes this complete generality, this ubiquitous whole. Two *secondary points* arise here.

(c) *The kind of bodies* in which magnetism is manifest are a matter of complete indifference to philosophy. It occurs principally in *iron*, but it also occurs in nickel and in cobalt. *Richter* thought he had obtained pure cobalt and nickel, and claimed that even these had magnetic properties. Others maintain that there is still some iron present in them, and that this is the sole reason for their being magnetic. It is no concern of the Notion that iron, because of its cohesion and inner crystallization, should be the element which causes this tendency towards figuration as such to display itself within it. There are other metals which also become magnetic at particular temperatures. Consequently, the appearance of magnetism within a body is related to its cohesion. It is generally only metals which may

be magnetized however. This is because a metal is not absolutely brittle, and has within it the compact continuity of simple specific gravity, which is precisely the abstract shape that we are now considering. Consequently, metals are conductors of heat and magnetism. Magnetism as such does not appear in salts and earths, because they are neutralities in which differen- 5
tiation is paralysed. This leads us on to enquire into those properties which make iron of all metals the most conducive to the appearance of magne- tism. The cohesion of iron is able to preserve the tendency towards shaping as an implicit tension, without realizing any result, precisely because in this metal there is a certain equilibrium between brittleness and continuity. 10
It can be brought from a state of extreme brittleness to that of extreme malleability, and unlike the compact continuity of the precious metals, it is therefore able to unite these extremes. Magnetism is precisely the brittle- ness which is *open* to continuity however, and which has the peculiarity of having not yet passed over into compact continuity. Consequently, iron 15
is *subject* to the activity of acids to a *much greater extent* than are those metals which have the highest specific gravities, and which, like gold, lack any apparent difference on account of the compactness of their unity. On the other hand, it easily maintains its reguline shape, while those metals of lower specific gravity crumble readily and semi-metals can scarcely main- +
tain their metallic shape, when attacked by acids. In iron, this existence of a north and south pole which are external to and distinct from the point of indifference, is yet another instance of the naïvety of nature, which sets forth its abstract moments in individual things in a way which is equally abstract. It is in this way that magnetism appears in iron ore; although it is mag- 25
netic iron-stone which appears to be the specific body in which magnetism reveals itself. There are magnets which act on the compass needle and yet +
will not magnetize other iron. *Humboldt* discovered one in a serpentine rock near Bayreuth. In the mine, each potentially magnetic body, and +
even magnetic pyrites, is not yet magnetic, and only becomes so once it 30
has been extracted. The stimulation of the light in the atmosphere is therefore necessary to the positing of differentiation and tension. +

(*d*) This leads us to enquire into the *circumstances* and *conditions* under which magnetism appears. If iron is heated until it is molten, it loses its magnetism; this also happens when it is fully oxidized as it is in the case +
of calcined iron, for the cohesion of the metal's reguline state has then been completely destroyed. Forging, hammering etc., also introduces modifications. Forged iron readily becomes magnetic, and loses the pro- perty with an equal facility. Steel on the other hand, in which iron assumes an earthy and granular fracture, is much harder to magnetize, but keeps 40

+ the property longer. This may well explain the greater brittleness of steel. The fugitive nature of the magnetism is apparent in its production, for it comes and goes, and is by no means stable. The mere stroking of iron will render it magnetic, and what is more, at both poles; but it must be
5 stroked in the direction of the meridian. The same effect may be obtained by striking or knocking it with the bare hand, or by shaking it in the air. The vibration of cohesion creates a tension; and this constitutes the shaping impulse. After some time, even iron rods which have merely been stood on end in the open air, become magnetic. In fact all kinds of iron objects,
10 iron ovens, iron crosses on churches, weathervanes etc., readily acquire a magnetic property, and only very weak magnets are enough to demon-
+ strate their magnetism. In fact the greatest difficulty has been found simply in producing non-magnetic iron, and keeping it in this state. This can only be done by making it red hot. When an iron bar is rubbed therefore, a
15 point occurs at which one of its poles is non-magnetic, and on the other side the other pole is similarly ineffective at a certain point. These are
+ *Brugmann's two points of indifference,* and they differ from the general point of indifference, which itself falls a little off centre. Is *latent* magnetism also going to be foisted upon these points? *Van Swinden* called the point at
+ which the action of each pole is greatest the *point of culmination.*

If a small unmagnetized iron rod is balanced on a needle, its ends form-ing a horizontal maintained by the equilibrium, one end will dip as soon as the rod is magnetized (§ 293 Rem.). In the northern hemisphere it is the northern end which dips, and in the southern hemisphere, the southern
25 end. The motion is more pronounced at higher latitudes because of greater proximity to the geographical locality of the poles. When the magnetic needle finally forms a right-angle with the line of the magnetic meridian at the pole, it assumes a vertical position, that is to say that it becomes a straight line representing a pure specification and distance from the Earth.
30 This is *inclination,* which thus varies according to time and place. On his expedition to the north pole, *Parry* experienced this to such an extent,
+ that he was no longer able to make use of the magnetic needle. In inclination, magnetism displays itself as gravity, and in a way which is even more remarkable than the attraction of iron. Considered as
+ mass and lever, the magnet has a centre of gravity, so that although masses which fall on both sides of it are in a state of free equilibrium, they are also specified and therefore unequal in weight. Specific gravity is here posited in the simplest manner; it is not changed, it is merely determined differently. The Earth's axis also has an inclination to the ecliptic; but this belongs strictly to
+ the determination of the heavenly bodies.

It is in the pendulum however, that the genuine distinctness of the specific and universal moments of gravity occurs all over the Earth. In this case, the force of definite masses varies from place to place; the same masses may be seen + to behave differently, their specific gravity being greater at the poles than it is at the equator. Under these circumstances, bodies can only be compared in so far 5 as they exhibit the force of their mass as a free and constant dynamic power, which remains equal to itself. The magnitude of the mass enters into the pendulum as a motive force; consequently, the motive force of the volume in the pendulum with a greater specific gravity must increase the nearer this pendulum is to the poles. Centripetal and centrifugal force are supposed to act as separate + forces on account of the rotation of the Earth, but it makes no difference whether we say that a body has more centrifugal force and so escapes more forcefully from the direction of falling, or that it falls more strongly. It is a matter of indifference whether it is called falling or projection. Now although the force of gravity does not vary when height and mass remain the same, in 15 the pendulum, this force itself is specified, and so acts as if the body fell from a greater or lesser height. Consequently, the difference in the extent of the pendulum's swing at different latitudes is also a specification of gravity itself + (see § 270 Rem. I 267,31 Add. I 274,1).

§ 313

In so far as this self-relating form exists at first in this abstract 20 **determination of the identity of subsistent differentiations, so that it has not yet been paralysed into becoming a product within the totality of shape, it is, as activity in the sphere of shape, the immanent activity of free mechanism, and as such determines relationships of place.** 25

Remark

A word should be said here about the identity of magnetism, electricity, and chemism, which is now generally accepted, and + **which in physics, has even become fundamental. The opposition of the form within individual material being also goes on to determine itself with greater reality in electricity, and with** 30 **even more completeness in chemism. The same universal totality of form lies, as their substance, at the basis of all these particular forms. As processes moreover, electricity and chemism are the activities of an opposition which is of a more real nature, and which**

physically is more determined than that of magnetism; what is more, these processes have as their principal content alterations in the relationships of material spatiality. This side of this concrete activity is at the same time a mechanizing determination;
5 implicitly, it is magnetic activity. The empirical conditions necessary for making magnetism as such appear within these more concrete processes, have been discovered in recent times. It is therefore to be regarded as an important advance in empirical science, that the identity of these phenomena should have been
+ generally recognized. This identity has been given various names, such as electro-chemism, magneto-electro-chemism etc., yet it is equally important that the particular forms in which the universal exists, and the particular phenomena of these forms, should also be distinguished from each other. The name
15 'magnetism' should therefore be reserved for the express form and for its manifestation; a manifestation which is in the sphere of shape as such, and which therefore relates itself only to the determinations of space. Similarly, the word 'electricity' should be applied only to those phenomenal determinations ex-
20 pressly defined by it. Magnetism, electricity, and chemism, were formerly regarded as wholly separate and independent forces having no connection with each other. It is philosophy which has grasped the idea of their identity while expressly maintaining that they are different. The latest way of regarding the matter
25 in physics seems to have swung to the other extreme and to treat the phenomena as identical, so that it is now necessary to establish the fact and manner of their distinctness. The difficulty lies in the need to reconcile their identity with their distinctness, and is to be resolved only by the nature of the Notion, not by identity,
30 which merely confuses the names of these phenomena under the
+ heading of magneto-electro-chemism.

Addition. The *second point* concerning the linearity of magnetism (cf. prev. § Add. *(a)* II. 100, 9) is the question of the *determinate modes of this activity*. Since there is as yet no specific determinate being in matter, but
35 only spatial relationships, change is nothing more than *motion*, for motion is precisely this change of spatial being within time. It is precisely because it is still immersed within matter without having attained to actualization however, that this activity must have a material *substratum* to support it; for in the substratum, the form is present only as the direction of a single

straight line. In living existence however, matter is determined by animation itself. Here too, it is true to say that the determinateness is *immanent*, and merely determines gravity in an immediate manner, without any further physical determination. The activity penetrates into matter without being communicated to it by any external mechanical impulse however, and as the *form* which is immanent to matter, it is a materialized and materializing activity. As this motion is not indeterminate, but has in fact very definite determinations, it is either *convergence* or *divergence*. Magnetism differs from gravity however, in that it submits corporeality to a completely different direction from that of the gravitational vertical; a typical determination of its effect is to be found in its preventing iron filings from falling where they would under the influence of gravity alone, and of remaining there. This motion is different from that of the heavenly bodies in that it is not rotatory, not a curve, and is not therefore *devoid* of attraction and repulsion. Within a curve, such as that of the heavenly bodies, convergence and divergence are *one*, and attraction and repulsion are therefore also indistinguishable. Here however, these two motions have *distinct* existences as convergence and divergence, for we are dealing with finite individualized matter, in which the moments held within the Notion are seeking freedom; their unity, which also emerges in contrast to their difference, only constitutes their implicit identity. The universal of the two moments is *quiescence*, and this quiescence constitutes their indifference, for the point of quiescence is necessary to their separation, and therefore to specific motion. In motion itself however, the opposition is that of activity in a straight line, for the only determinateness present is that of simple divergence and convergence along the same line. The two determinations always remain simultaneous, they neither alternate nor divide on two sides, for here we have spatiality which is not temporal. Consequently the body which is determined by attraction must be precisely the same body simultaneously determined by repulsion. The body approaches a certain point, and in so doing has something communicated to it; it is itself determined, and being determined in this way, has to move simultaneously from the other side.

The connection between electricity and magnetism has been studied mainly as it displays itself in the voltaic pile. Thought grasped this connection long before it was discovered experimentally; and in general it is just this searching out and exhibiting the identity of the Notion as the identity of phenomena which constitutes the work of the physicist. Philosophy does not grasp this identity in a superficial and abstract manner however, it does not present magnetism, electricity, and chemism, as one and the same thing. Philosophy has maintained for some time now, that magnetism is the principle form, and that electricity and the chemical process are merely other forms of this principle. Magnetism was formerly isolated and relegated into the background; its importance to navigation was recognized, but there was a general ignorance of its importance in the system of nature. Its connection with chemism and electricity has been touched upon. Chemism is the totality into which bodies enter in accordance with their specific particularity. Magnetism however is merely spatial. Yet in certain circumstances, magnetic poles, too, differ electrically and chemically. Conversely, magnetism is easily generated by the galvanic process, for the closed circuit responds very sensitively to magnetism. The differentiation is posited in electro-galvanic activity and in the chemical process, and is a process of physical opposites. It is therefore quite natural that these concrete opposites should also be manifest at the lower level of magnetism. The electrical process too is quite clearly a motion, but it is also a conflict of physical opposites. What is more, the two poles are free in electricity, while in magnetism they are not. In electricity therefore, there is an opposition between particular bodies, so that the existence of the polarity within it is quite different from that of the merely linear polarity of the magnet. Yet if metallic bodies in which there are no prior physical determinations present are set in motion by the electrical process they will display this process within themselves in their own manner. This manner is the simple activity of motion, which is in fact magnetism. In each phenomenon, we have therefore to pick out the electric and the magnetic moment etc. It has been said that all electrical activity is magnetism, and that magnetism is the force which is fundamental to the differentials, as well as to the persistence of differentiation, and the simple relatedness of it. This is of course the case in the electrical and chemical processes, although in a more concrete manner than it is in magnetism. The chemical process is the shaping process of matter individualized in a real manner. The shaping tendency itself is therefore a moment of chemism. It is mainly in the galvanic circuit that this moment becomes free; there is tension throughout the circuit, but it does not pass over into the product as it does in chemical being. This tension is concentrated at the extremities; and so it is here that an influence upon the magnet is apparent.

In this connection it is also interesting to note that when the activity of the galvanic process sets a magnetically determinate body in motion, it allows it to *deviate*. This gives rise to the antithesis in which the magnet deviates either to the east or to the west, according to the deviation of the

south and north pole. With this in mind, my colleague Professor *P. Erman*
has devised an ingenious apparatus in which a galvanic circuit is freely
suspended. A strip of cardboard or of whalebone is so cut that a small
copper or silver container may be fitted into one of its ends, or perhaps
also into the middle. This container is filled with acid, into which a zinc
strip or wire is inserted. This strip is then led round to the other end of
the whalebone, and from thence back to the other side of the container.
This gives rise to galvanic activity. If the whole apparatus is then rendered
mobile by being suspended by a thread, it will exhibit differentiation when
the poles of a magnet are brought to bear upon it. Erman called this suspended mobile galvanic battery a 'rotation circuit'. Its $+E$ wire is aligned
north-south. To quote him, 'If one approaches the north end of the apparatus from the east, with the north pole of a magnet, *this end will be
repulsed*. If the same north pole is brought up from the west however,
attraction will take place. The total result is the same in both cases, for
whether it is attracted or repulsed, a rotation circuit at rest in a south-
north position always turns to the west, i.e. from left to right, once it is
brought under the influence of the north pole of a magnet placed beyond
its arc. The south pole of a magnet produces the opposite effect.' *East-
west* chemical polarity, and *north-south* magnetic *polarity* run counter here;
in the Earth, the second of these achieves a wider significance. The transience of magnetic determinateness also comes into evidence here. If the
magnet is held over the galvanic circuit, the determination is quite
different from that which results when it is held on the same level; the
apparatus turns completely round.

§ 314

**The activity of form is none other than that of the Notion in
general; it is the positing of differentiated identity and of
identical differentiation. Here therefore, in the sphere of
material spatiality, that which is identical in space is posited as
differentiated through its divergence from itself in repulsion,
and that which is differentiated in space is posited as identical
by being brought into convergence and contact through attraction. As this activity constitutes magnetism merely on account
of its still existing abstractly within a material being, it only
animates a linearity (§ 256). In this linearity, the two determinations of form can emerge separately only within the difference
of the two ends. Consequently, the active magnetic difference**

of the form consists merely in one of the ends or poles positing its identity with the same third term, i.e. with that which the other pole repels from itself.

Remark

The law of magnetism is expressed by saying that like poles
5 repulse each other and unlike poles attract, like poles being hostile to each other while unlike poles are friendly. The only determination implied by this likeness is however that poles are like if they are both equally attracted or repulsed by a third term. However, the precise determination of this term too is simply
10 that it repulses or attracts, either these like poles, or some other term. All these determinations are purely relative, and are devoid of distinct, sensible, neutral existence. It has already been observed (Rem. § 312). that terms such as north and south contain no such original primary or immediate determination. Con-
15 sequently, the attraction of unlike and the repulsion of like poles, are certainly not the secondary nor yet the particular phenomenon of a presupposed magnetic principle which already has its own determinateness. They express nothing but the nature of magnetism itself, and are therefore expressions of the pure nature
20 of the Notion, when it is posited within this sphere as activity.

Addition. A third question therefore presents itself here. What is approached and what is diverged from? Although magnetism is this diremption, the fact is not yet evident. When something is put into relation with something else which is still in a state of indifference, this second term is
25 affected in one way by one extremity of the first, and in another way by the other extremity. The infection consists of the second term's being made the opposite of the first, in order that as other (and as posited as other by the first term), it may be posited as being identical with this first term. Consequently, it is the activity of the form which first determines
30 the second term as an opposition; the form therefore comports itself with regard to the other as an existing process. The activity relates itself to another, which it posits as its opposite. This other was initially only another through our subjective comparison; it is now form determined as other, and then posited as identical. Conversely, the other side exhibits
35 the opposite side of the determination. It has to be assumed that linear activity has also been imparted to the second term, and that one side of it

has been infected as opposition; consequently, its other extremity is at once identical with the first extremity of the first term. If this second extremity of the second material line is now brought into contact with the first extremity of the first, it is identical with this extremity, and is therefore repulsed. Sensuous conception, as well as that of the under- 5 standing, is unable to comprehend magnetism. To the understanding, identity is nothing but identity, and differentiation nothing but differentiation, which implies that the side on which two things are identical is the side on which they are not different. One finds in magnetism however that it is precisely to the extent that identity is identical that it is posited as 10 being differentiated, and to the extent that differentiation is differentiated that it is posited as being identical. The difference consists in the terms being themselves and their opposites. The identity in both poles posits its differentiation, and the differentiation in both poles posits its identity. This is the transparently active Notion, which is as yet unrealized how- 15 ever.

This is the activity of *total* form as the posited identity of opposites. It is the concrete activity contrasting with the abstract activity of gravity, in which these opposites are already implicitly identical. On the contrary, the activity of magnetism consists in first infecting the other in order to 20 give it weight. Although it can attract, gravity is not active as magnetism is, for that which it attracts is already implicitly identical. Here however, the other is first made capable of attracting and being attracted, so that only here does form become active. When something is drawn, something is simply *done*, and that which is drawn is involved to the same 25 extent as that which draws. +

Magnetism now constitutes the *middle term* between the two extremities of subjectivity which contains itself in a point, and fluidity which is a mere liberating of the form, which becomes a material product in the crystal, and which is already displayed in the *ice-spicula* for example. Magnetism + persists as this being-in-self and accomplished self-realization. It is the impotence of nature which separates off the motive activity in magnetism; it is left to the power of thought to relate such a part to the whole.

§ 315

3. **The activity which has passed over into its product is shape, and is determined as crystal. The differentiated magnetic poles** 35 **are reduced to neutrality in this totality, and the abstract linearity of the place-determining activity is realized as the plane and as**

the surface of the whole body. More precisely, rigid punctiformity is on the one hand extended into developed form, while on the other hand, a limit is set to the formal extension of the sphere. It is the one form which operates (a) in limiting the sphere and so crystallizing the body outwardly; and (b) in shaping punctiformity and so thoroughly crystallizing the inner continuity of the body through the passage of the folia, i.e. its nuclear shape.

Addition. This third moment is, in the first instance, shape as the unity of magnetism and sphericity; the still immaterial determining becomes material, and with this the restless activity of magnetism reaches complete quiescence. Attraction and repulsion no longer occur here, for everything is now set in its place. Initially, the tension of the magnet passes over into the crystal of the Earth, which is the universal independence, in which the line passes over into the spatial completeness of the sphere. As real magnetism however, the individual crystal is this totality, in which the drive has ceased, and the oppositions are neutralized into the form of indifference. Magnetism then expresses its differentiation as the determination of surface. Consequently we no longer have inner shape, the being of which would require another, but a shape which is there by itself. All figuration contains magnetism, for it is a complete limitation in space posited by the immanent drive of its *overseer*, which is form. This is an inarticulate activity of nature, which deploys its dimensions timelessly; it is the intimate vital principle of nature which expounds without action, and of whose figures one can only say that they are there. The principle is omnipresent in the fluid sphericity, and finds no opposition there. It is the unobtrusive formative principle which links together all the indifferent parts of the whole. Magnetism as such is not present in the crystal, although it is in the crystal that it finds its fulfilment. The inseparable sides of magnetism, which have a subsistent determinate being and are at the same time discharged here into indifferent fluidity, are the shaping which dies out in this indifference. When one is dealing with the philosophy of nature, one is therefore justified in saying that magnetism is a completely universal determination; but it is wrong to follow this up by attempting to show that magnetism as such is present in shape. As an abstract drive, the determination of magnetism is still linear. In its completeness however, magnetism is the principle which determines spatial limitation in every dimension. Shape is an immobile matter extending into all dimensions; it is the neutrality of infinite form and of materiality. It is here therefore that form displays its control over the whole mechanical mass. The body certainly still has weight with regard to the Earth; this primary substantial relationship is still preserved, and even man, who is absolute lightness as spirit, does not cease to have weight. Consequently, the outer connection of parts is now determined from within by a principle of form which is independent of   5 gravity. This is the first instance of the purposiveness of nature itself. This + purposiveness is a relation between various indifferent moments constituting a necessity, the moments of which have a stable determinate being, or the being-in-self which is present.—This purposiveness is an act of intelligence on the part of nature itself, and consequently does not resemble the 10 understanding in merely imposing a form on matter from without. The preceding forms are not yet purposive, they are merely determinate being, which as such has no relation to another. The magnet is not yet purposive, for its two poles merely have a simple necessity for each other, and are not yet indifferent. Here however there is a unity of indifferents, or of moments each 15 of which has a free existence in relation to the other. The lines of the crystal constitute this indifference, one may be separated from the other without ceasing to exist, but it is only through their relation to one another that they have a significance, and it is purposiveness which gives them this unity and significance. 20

As the crystal is this quiescent end, motion constitutes something other than its end; the end is not yet a temporal matter. The separate con- cretions still lie there in a state of indifference, and the acuminations of the + crystal may be split off and separated from each other. Now this is not the case with magnetism; consequently, it is wrong if we also call the 25 acuminations of a crystal poles because they, too, are opposites determined by a subjective form, for the differences in a crystal have reached a state of quiescent subsistence. As shape is the equilibrium of + differentials, it also has to display these differentiations within itself; to the extent that it does this, the crystal contains the moment which represents 30 its external relation, and displays its character in the break-up of its mass. Shape itself must also submit to differentiation, and be the unity of these differentials, so that the crystal has an *interior* as well as an *exterior* shape as the two wholes of its form. This double geometry or shaping is as it were Notion and reality, soul and body. The crystal is built up + of layers, but its *fracture* cuts across all layers. The inner determination + of form is no longer merely the determination of cohesion, but all the parts belong to this form; matter is thoroughly crystallized. The crystal is likewise bounded externally, and regularly enclosed in an internally differentiated unity. Its planes are completely smooth 40

and mirrorlike, and have edges and angles forming shapes ranging from simple regular equilateral prisms etc. to those which are outwardly irregular, though a law is traceable even in these. There are of course fine-grained earthy crystals, the shape of which is predominantly super-
5 ficial; as punctiformity, the precise nature of earth is the shape of shape-lessness. When pure crystals such as Iceland spar are struck so that they are free to fracture in accordance with their inner form however, they reveal in the smallest of their particles their previously quite indiscernible shape. Huge rock-crystals three feet long and a foot thick, and still preserving
10 their hexagonal shape, have been found in the St. Gotthard pass, and on
+ the island of Madagascar. It is the permeation of this nuclear shape which is their most remarkable feature. Iceland spar is rhomboid; if it is fractured, its parts are found to be perfectly regular, and if the fractures take place in accordance with its inner texture, all the planes are mirrorlike. No
15 matter how often it is fractured, it will always display the same features; the ideal nature of its form is soul-like and omnipresent in its permeation of the whole. This inner shape is now a totality. In cohesion it was a single determination such as the point, line or surface, which dominated. Now however, shapes are formed in all three dimensions. *Werner* called this the
+ passage of the folia, but it is now known as fractural texture or nuclear shape. The nucleus of the crystal is itself a crystal, and its inner shape is a dimensional whole. The nuclear shape may vary; there are gradations in foliar shape from flat or convex folia to a completely determinate nuclear shape. In its outer crystallization, the diamond is octahedral, and although its clarity is
25 of a very high order, it is also internally crystallized. It disintegrates into lam-ellae, so that if one attempts to polish it, it is difficult to leave acute acu-minations. There is a way of striking it so that it fractures in accordance
+ with the nature of the passage of its folia however, and its planes are then perfectly mirrorlike throughout. *Hauy* has mainly concentrated upon
+ *describing* the forms of crystals, and others after him have added to his work.

Finding the connection between the inner and outer form (forme primi-tive et secondaire), and deriving the latter from the former, constitutes an interesting and delicate part of *crystallography*. All observations have
35 to be referred to a general principle of transformation. The outer crystal-lization does not always accord with the inner; not all rhomboid Iceland spars have the same outward determination as they have internally for example and yet both their figurations are the expression of a single unity. *Hauy*, as is known, has traced the geometry of this relation between inner and
+ outer shape in fossils, but he was unable to demonstrate its inner necessity, and

also failed to show that the shape had any connection with specific gravity. He
assumes the nucleus, and postulates what he calls 'integrant molecules' which
arrange themselves on its planes by a kind of aggregation. The outer shapes are +
then presumed to arise out of this aggregation by the decrement of the layers of
the base, while the law of this aggregation is still determined by the primitive 5
shape. Crystallography also has to determine the relationship between crys- +
talline shapes and chemical substances, for one shape is more characteristic
of a chemical substance than another. In the main, salts are both outwardly +
and inwardly crystalline. Metals on the other hand, as they are not
neutral bodies, but are merely abstractly undifferentiated, tend to be con- 10
fined to formal shape; their nuclear shape is more hypothetical, and has
only been perceived in bismuth. Metal is still substantially uniform, but +
a weak acid works upon its surface, and an incipient crystallization is
certainly apparent in the resultant 'waterings' of tin or iron for example. +
The figurations are not regular however, and only the rudiment of a 15
nuclear shape is discernible.

B

The specification of the individual body
(*The particular properties of bodies*)

§ 316

The figuration **which, as the individualization of mechanism
determines space,** passes over into **physical specification**.
The individual body **is in itself the physical totality; this
totality is to be posited in the body as difference, but as differ-** 20
**ence determined and contained within individuality. As the
subject of these determinations, the body contains** them as
properties or *predicates*; **it does this so that they are at the same
time related to their untrammelled and universal** elements **however, and form** processes **with them. The chemical process first** 25
**constitutes the specific positing of these determinations; within
this subject they are still implicit and have not yet been led back
into individuality, so that they merely constitute relationships
with these elements, not the real totality of process. These determinations differ from one another on account of their elements,** 30
**the logical determinateness of which has been indicated in their
sphere** (§ 282 **et seq.**).

Remark

According to an ancient and general opinion, each body consists of four elements. In more recent times, *Paracelsus* has regarded them as being composed of mercury or fluid-
+ ity, sulphur or oil, and salt, which Jacob Boehme called
+ the great triad. It has *of course* been very easy to refute these opinions and others of their kind, when these names have been taken to mean the individual empirical substances to which they refer in everyday usage. It should not be overlooked however, that in their essence they contain and
10 express the determinations of the Notion. One ought
+ rather to admire the strength of the yet unliberated thought which, when dealing with such sensuous and particular existences, grasped and held fast to nothing but the universal significance of its own determination. Consequently,
15 it is also quite irrelevant to refute these doctrines in an experimental manner (see above Add. to § 280, II. 32, 30). *What is more*, as this manner of conceiving and determining draws its strength from the energy of reason, which does not allow itself to be completely forgotten, and is not led
20 astray by the sensuous play and confusion of appearance, it is immensely superior **to mere** investigation, and to the undigested enumeration of the *properties* of bodies. The merit and glory of this investigation is thought to be its
+ ceaseless provision of *new facts*, instead of the bringing of
25 **such a plurality of particulars** back to the universal through the recognition of the Notion within them.

Addition. In crystal, infinite form has only established itself within weighted matter in a spatial manner, and still lacks the specification of difference. Now however, the determinations of form themselves have to
30 appear as differentiated matter, and so constitute the reconstruction and recomposition of the physical elements through individuality. The individual body or the element of earth is the unity of air, light, fire and water; and it is the way in which these elements exist in earth which constitutes the specification of individuality. Light corresponds to air, and the
35 light which is individualized by the darkness of the body is the specific obscuration of a colour. In so far as the combustible and igneous principle is a moment of the individual body, it constitutes its smell. It is the

continuous but insensible course of its consumption, it is not what is called its oxidization or combustion in a chemical sense however, it is the individualization of the air in the simplicity of its specific process. As individualized neutrality, water is salt and acid etc., and constitutes the body's taste. Its neutrality is already an indication of the solubility of the body, 5 or of its real relationship with something else, which constitutes the chemical process. Colour, odour, and taste are properties of individual bodies; they do not exist independently for themselves, but are inherent within a substratum. In the first instance, they are only held within an immediate individuality, and they are therefore mutually indifferent; 10 the properties are therefore material, as is the case with pigments for example. Individuality is still weak, and is unable to retain its hold upon the properties; the unifying power of life is not yet present here as it is in organic being. As particular existences these properties also have the general significance of preserving their connection with that from which they 15 originate: colour is related to light, by which it is bleached; odour is a process involving air; and taste, likewise, keeps up a relation with its abstract element, which is water.

The mere names of the properties which are about to be discussed bring sensation to mind; this is particularly true in the case of smell and 20 taste, for the physical properties belonging to the body are not merely objective, but also designate the subjectivity of their existence for the subjective senses. Consequently, as these elementary determinatenesses come forth within the sphere of individuality, their relationship with the senses also has to be noticed. This immediately gives rise to two questions. 25 Firstly, why is it that the *relationship between the body and the subjective sense* occurs at this particular juncture? Secondly, to which objective properties do our five senses correspond? Colour, odour and taste have just been mentioned, but they only constitute the three which corresponds to the senses of sight, smell, and taste. Hearing and touch do not occur here, so 30 that one might well ask where these other two senses have their corresponding objective properties.

(a) The following observation may be made with regard to the relationship here. We have an individual and self-contained shape, which because of the self-sufficiency it enjoys as a totality, is no longer a differential im- 35 plied by another, and which therefore has no practical relationship with another. The determinations of cohesion are not indifferent to another, but are merely related to another; shape on the other hand is indifferent to this relation. It is true that shape may also be treated mechanically, but since it is self-relating, its relation to another is merely contingent, and 40 never necessary. Such a relationship between it and another might be called a theoretical relationship, but it is only *sentient*, and at a higher level, thinking *natures*, which have such a relationship *to something*. The precise condition necessary for such a theoretical relationship, is that the sentient being should maintain its freedom with regard to the object by being related to another, and at the same time to itself. This also means that the object is left inviolate. Two individual bodies such as crystals certainly leave one another alone, but only because they are not related to one another. In order to be related, they have to be chemically determined by means of water; otherwise they are only related by a third term, i.e. the ego which compares them. Consequently, this theoretical relationship is based solely upon the absence of any mutual relation. A true theoretical relationship is only present where an actual relation between two sides occurs in conjunction with the freedom of its constituent term, and it is precisely this relationship which exists between sensation and its object. Consequently, the completed totality now under consideration is given freedom by its other, and is related to it only in this way. That is to say that in the sphere which we are about to consider, physical totality exists for sensation, and as it also deploys itself in its determinate modes, it also exists for the distinct modes of sensation, or the senses. That is why the relationship between figuration and the senses is considered here, although it is not yet necessary to touch upon it (see below § 358), for it does not belong to the physical sphere.

(*b*) Here we have found that colour, odour, and taste are the determinations of shape experienced through the three senses of sight, smell, and taste. The sensuous being of the other two senses of touch and hearing has already been considered (see above Add. to § 300, II. 72, 31). The mechanical individuality of shape as such corresponds to feeling in general, and it is here that heat also belongs. We relate ourselves to heat in a more theoretical manner than we do to shape in general however. We feel shape only in so far as it offers resistance to us; we have to press and touch it, which is already a practical relationship, for the one side does not leave the other alone. In the case of heat however, there is still no resistance. As we have seen, hearing corresponds to the mechanically conditioned individuality of sound. Consequently, the sense of hearing coincides with this specialization, in which infinite form is related to material being. This soul-like element is only related externally to material being however; it is the form which is merely escaping from mechanical materiality, so that it is not yet permanent, but is disappearing in its immediacy. Hearing is the sense of the ideal nature of the appearance of mechanical totality;

it has its opposite in touch, the object of which is the terrestrial principle of gravity, the shape which is not yet specified within itself. We have already had the two extremes, the ideality of the sense of hearing and the reality of touch, in total shape. Differences of shape confine themselves to the other three senses. The specific physical properties of individual shape + are not themselves shape, but the manifestations of it which maintain their essence through their being for other. It is with this that the pure in- difference of the theoretical relationship begins to efface itself. The other to which these qualities relate themselves is their universal nature or element; it is not yet an individual corporeality. At the same time, it is 10 here that a relation of process and differentiation is formed, although it can only be an abstract relation. Nevertheless, as the physical body is not merely one particular difference, and does not break down simply into these determinatenesses, but is the totality of these differentials, its breaking down is merely a differentiation which is implicit within it as its proper- 15 ties, and in which it remains as a single whole. In this way we have differentiated body in general, which as a totality relates itself to other similar differentials. The differentiation of these total shapes is an out- wardly mechanical relationship, since they have to remain what they are, and their self-preservation is not yet dissolved. This expression of persis- 20 tent differentials is electricity, which is at the same time a superficial pro- cess of this body opposed to the elements. Consequently, on one side we have specific differentials, and on the other the totality of differentiation in general.

We now have to present the precise *division* of that which follows. 25 *Firstly*, there is the relationship of the individual body to light; *secondly*, there are differentiated relationships as such, i.e. smell and taste; *thirdly* there is the general differentiation between two total bodies, i.e. electricity. Here we shall only consider the physical determinatenesses of the indi- vidual body as they are related to their respective universal elements, in 30 regard to which they are, through their individualization, total bodies. Consequently, individuality as such is preserved rather than dissolved in this relation, and as a result of this, we shall only be considering properties here. It is in the chemical process that an actual dissolution of shape first occurs, so that which constitutes properties at this juncture, occurs there 35 as a specific matter. As pigment for example, materialized colour no longer belongs to the individual body as a total shape, but is separated from it through chemical dissolution, and posited for itself. It is certainly also permissible to call a property such as this, which exists outside its association with the self of individuality, an individual totality. A metal 40

would provide an example of one, although it is not a neutral body, but is merely undifferentiated. In the chemical process we shall also notice that bodies of this kind are merely formal and abstract totalities. These specifications occur initially in the Notion on our account, for like shape,
5 they are implicit, and have an immediate being. They are subsequently posited through the *actual* chemical process however, and it is there that the true conditions of their existence lie, as do those of shape.

1. Relationship to light

§ 317

**The primary determination of shaped corporeality is its self-identical selfhood, the abstract self-manifestation of itself as
10 simple indeterminate individuality, i.e. light. Shape as such is not luminous however, for this property is a relationship to light (prev. §). (*a*) Body as pure crystal, in the perfect homogeneity of its neutrally existing inner individualization, is transparent and is a medium for light.**

Remark

15 **The transparency of the air is related to its lack of inner cohesion, as is the transparency of the concrete body to the homogeneity of its coherent and crystallized shape. In that it is unspecified, the individual body is certainly as transparent and translucent as
+ it is opaque etc.; transparency is its immediate and primary
20 determination as crystal however, the physical homogeneity of which is not yet specified and deepened within itself into any further determination.**

Addition. At this juncture, shape is still the quiescent individuality which occurs in mechanical and chemical neutrality, though unlike complete
25 shape it does not possess the latter at all points. Shape, as the pure form, by which matter is completely determined and pervaded, is merely self-identical in matter, and dominates it throughout. This is the *first* determination of shape in thought. In materialized being, this self-identity is physical; light represents this abstract physical self-identity, so that the
30 primary specification of shape is its relationship with light. It is because of this identity that it has light within itself. This relationship, through

which shape posits itself for another, is strictly theoretical, not practical; it is rather of a completely ideal nature. This identity, which is no longer merely posited as effort as it is in gravity, but which has acquired its liberty in light, and is now posited in terrestrial individuality, is the dawning of the lighted aspect in shape itself. As shape is not yet absolutely free + however, but is a determinate individuality, this terrestrial individualization of its universality is still not the interior relation of individuality to its own universality. It is only sentient being which possesses the universal principle of its determinateness with itself as a universality. It is only organic being which appears before its other with its universality con- 10 tained within it. Here on the other hand, the universal of this individuality is still another, an element which is external to the individual body. The Earth moreover is only related to the sun as a universal individual, and this is still a completely abstract relation, while the relation between the individual body and light is at least real. In the first instance, the individual 15 body is certainly dark, for this is the general determination of abstract matter which is for itself, but this abstract darkness is overcome by the individualization of matter through the pervasion of form. Colours are the particular modifications of this relationship to light, so that they will also have to be treated here. On the one hand they belong to the real 20 individual body, but on the other hand they also merely waver outside the individuality of bodies. As yet, no objective material existence can + be attributed to these shadowy entities; they are appearances which are simply dependent upon the relationship between light and a darkness which is still incorporeal. They are in fact a spectrum. Colours are thus in 25 part completely subjective, and are conjured up by the eye; they are the action of a brightness or darkness, and a modification of their relationship in the eye, although they certainly also require an external brightness. *Schulz* ascribes a particular brightness to the phosphorus in our eyes, so that it is often difficult to say whether the brightness and darkness and the 30 relationship between them lie in us or not. +

We now have to consider this relationship between individualized matter and light, *firstly*, as identity which lacks opposition, and which is not yet posited as different from any other determination. This is general, formal transparency. *Secondly*, we have to consider this identity as specified 35 with respect to another, in the comparison of two transparent media. This is refraction, in which the medium is not purely transparent, but is specifically determined. *Thirdly* we have to consider colour as a property. This is metal, which is a mechanical but not chemical neutrality.

It should be noticed *first* of all with regard to transparency, that opacity 40

and darkness belong to the abstract individuality of the element of earth. On account of their elementary universality and neutrality, air, water, and flame are transparent and not dark. Pure shape is transparent for the same reason, i.e. because it has overcome darkness, or the abstract, brittle,
5 unrevealed being-for-self of individual matter, as the non-manifestation of itself. By so doing, it has established its transparency simply by bringing itself back to the neutrality and uniformity, which constitute a relation to light. Material individuality is an inward darkening, since it seals itself off from the ideal nature of manifestation to another. The individual form
10 which has pervaded its matter as a totality, has thereby posited its manifestation however, and so advances to this ideality of determinate being. Self-manifestation is the explication of form, the positing of one determinate being for another, so that this relation is at the same time held within an individual unity. Consequently the Moon, which is the body of
15 rigidity, is opaque, while the comet is transparent. Since this transparency is the formal factor, the crystal has it in common with the intrinsically shapeless elements of air and water. However, the transparency of the crystal differs from that of these elements on account of its origin. These elements are transparent because they have not yet attained to internal
20 individuality, the element of earth, obscuration. Shaped bodies are certainly not light, for they are individual matter, but in so far as the punctiform self of individuality is unhindered in its internal formativeness, it has nothing further within this dark material being which is alien to it. Consequently, this being-in-self, which has passed over in its purity into the
25 developed totality of form, is here introduced into the homogeneous sameness of matter. Free and unrestricted form, embracing the whole as well as the individual parts, is transparency. All the individual parts are made completely the same as this whole, so that there is no difference between them, and they exhibit no isolation within mechanical penetration.
30 It is therefore the abstract identity of the crystal, its completely undifferentiated mechanical unity, and the neutrality of its chemical unity, which constitute its transparency. Although this identity does not shine itself, it is so closely related to light, that it comes very close to shining. It is the crystal to which light has given birth; light is the soul of this
35 being-in-self, for mass is completely dissolved in its ray. The archetypal crystal is the diamond of the Earth, in which every eye rejoices, and
+ recognizes as the firstborn son of light and gravity. Light is the abstract and completely free identity. Air is the elementary identity. The subjected identity is passive with regard to light, and so constitutes
40 the transparency of the crystal. Metal on the other hand is opaque,

since the individual identity within it is concentrated into being-for-self through a high specific gravity (see Addition to § 320, towards the end). Transparency requires that the crystal should have no earthy fracture, for it would then belong to the sphere of brittleness. A transparent body may also be rendered opaque without submitting it to chemical modifications. This may be done by a merely mechanical change; it is a phenomenon which is common enough, and requires only that the body should be divided into individual parts. Powdered glass for example, and water whipped into foam, are opaque. Their mechanical undifferentiation and homogeneity are removed and interrupted, and brought into the form of individualized being-for-self, while they were formerly a mechanical continuum. Ice is already less transparent than water, and once it is crushed, it becomes completely opaque. *Whiteness* arises out of transparency, when the continuity of the parts is converted into a plurality, as for example in snow. For us, it is as whiteness that light has its primary determinate being, and so stimulates our eyes. To quote *Goethe* ('On the Theory of Colours' vol. I, p. 189) 'One might say that the *contingent* (i.e. mechanical) opaque condition of a perfectly transparent body is white. In their pure condition, ordinary (undecomposed) earths are white, but they become transparent through natural crystallization.' That is why lime and silica are opaque, for although they have a metallic base, it has passed over into opposition and differentiation, and so become neutral. Consequently, there are chemically neutral substances which are opaque, and are therefore not completely neutral, i.e. they contain a residual principle which has not entered into relationship with another. Transparency occurs however, when silica is crystallized into rock-crystal without the help of acid, alumina into mica, magnesia into talc, and of course when carbonic acid is poured on lime. This phenomenon of a body passing easily from opacity to transparency is not rare. A certain stone, hydrophane, is opaque, but becomes transparent when saturated with water; the water neutralizes it, and so effaces its disconnectedness. When borax is dipped in olive oil, it also becomes completely transparent through the positing of the continuity of its parts. Since what is chemically neutral has a tendency to become transparent, there are also metallic crystals which, in so far as they are not pure metals but metallic salts (vitriols), become translucent by virtue of their neutrality. There are also coloured bodies such as precious stones which are transparent; they are not completely transparent however, simply because the metallic principle to which they owe their colour is neutralized, but not completely subdued.

§ 318

(b) The primary and simplest determinateness possessed by the physical medium is its specific gravity, the peculiar nature of which is specifically manifest in comparison. The same is therefore also true with regard to the peculiar nature of the transparency of the physical medium, which is only manifest in comparison with the different density of another medium. In order to facilitate the exposition and illustration of this point, let it be assumed that the two media are water and air. In this case, if for example the first medium is further from the eye, its action upon the second will simply be that of density, determining place in a qualitative manner. Consequently, the volume of water containing the image is seen in the transparent air, as if the same volume of air in which the volume of water is posited had the greater specific gravity of the water i.e. as if this volume of air were contracted into a correspondingly smaller space. It is this that is called refraction.

Remark

To speak of the refraction of light is to use a sensuous expression, which has its validity. It is valid for example when one is referring to a rod's appearing to be broken when it is held in water, and the expression also lends itself naturally to the geometrical demonstration of this phenomenon. The physical existence of the so-called refraction of light and lightrays is something quite different however, and is a phenomenon which is not so easy to understand as it might appear to be at first. Apart from the invalidity of the usual presentation of this phenomenon, it is quite evident that the perplexity into which it is bound to fall is the result of the distorting assumption that there are luminous rays which radiate into a hemisphere from a point. As this theory is supposed to explain the phenomenon, attention must be drawn to the essential and observable fact that the flat bottom of a vessel which is filled with water appears to be flat, and therefore to be completely and uniformly raised. This fact stands in complete contradiction to the theory, but as is usually the case in circumstances like this, the only result is that it is ignored or glossed over in the textbooks. It is important to note that in a single medium, we merely have simple transparency as such, and that it

125

is only the relationship of two media of different specific gravities, which gives rise to a particularization of visibility. This is a determination which at the same time merely determines place, i.e. is posited by completely abstract density. An active relationship between two media is not the result of their indifferent 5 juxtaposition however. It occurs only when one of these media is posited within the other as something which is simply visible, as visual space. This second medium is taken over so to speak, by the immaterial density of that which is posited within it; consequently it displays the visual space of the image within 10 itself in accordance with its own limitation, and so limits this space. It is here that the purely mechanical property of density, which is only determinative of space, and which is of an ideal nature and has no physical reality, comes expressly to the fore. It appears to be effective outside the material being to which it 15 belongs, because its effect is derived solely by the space occupied by the visible object. The relationship cannot be grasped if this ideality is not recognized.

Addition. As we have now considered the transparency of crystal, which is invisible in so far as it is transparent, our *second* consideration must be 20 the visibility in this transparent body, but at the same time the visibility of the opaque body. We have already considered (§ 278) the visible body positing itself within an indeterminate transparent one, the linearity of one body positing itself in an ideal manner within another, i.e. the reflection of light. Further specifications occur within the formal identity of the 25 crystal however. The transparent crystal which has achieved the ideality of its darkened being-for-self, allows other dark bodies to appear through it, so that it is the medium, the intermediary, by which one body appears in another. Two phenomena occur here, the *refraction* of light, and the *double image* displayed by a number of crystals. 30

The visibility in question here is that in which something is seen through several transparent bodies, and so through various media; for we have here the transparency of the individual specifically determined body, which therefore occurs only in relation to another transparent medium. As specifically determined, the medium has its own specific gravity, as 35 well as other physical qualitites. This determinateness only finds expression when the medium comes into relation with another transparent medium, and the appearance is mediated by them both. In one medium the mediation is uniform, and appearance is merely determined by the expansion

of light; it is also possible to see in water for example, only not so distinctly. Consequently, if there is only one medium, there is only one density, and also only one determination of place. If there are two media however, there are also two determinations of place. It is here that the
5 most remarkable phenomenon of refraction is produced. It is an everyday sight, and appears to be simple and even trivial. Refraction is merely a word however. Through each medium taken separately, the eye sees the object in a straight line, and in the same relationship with other objects; it is only the relationship between the two media which gives rise to the
10 difference. If the eye sees an object through another medium, so that the sight traverses two media, the object appears to be in a different place from that in which it would display itself without the specific constitution of this second medium. Consequently it has another place in the context of light, from that which would be ascribed to it by touch in the context of
15 material being. This accounts for our being able to see the image of the sun even after it has dipped below the horizon. An object in a vessel will appear to be displaced and raised if the vase is filled with water. Those who shoot fish know that because the place in which they see their prey is raised, they must aim below it.

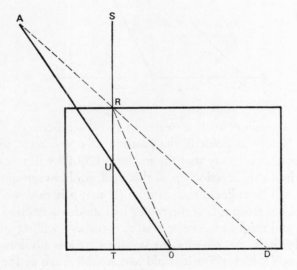

20 In this diagram, the angle (ARS) made by the line (AD) from the eye (A) to the object as it is seen (D), and the perpendicular through the point of incidence (ST), is greater than the angle (AUS) made with the

perpendicular, by the line (*Ao*) from the eye to the point (*o*) at which the object is actually situated. It is usually said that light is refracted when it is diverted from its path (*OR*) by passing from one medium into another, so that the object is seen in the changed direction (*ARD*). When this statement is more closely considered, it is found to be meaningless, for a single medium does not refract, and it is only in the relation between the two media that the principle giving rise to this mode of visibility is to be looked for. When the light emerges from one medium, it has not acquired any particular quality which has altered it so that it may be redirected by the other medium. This following diagram will make this clear.

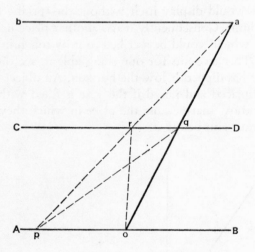

If there is a medium such as water in the space between *AB* and the position of the eye at point *a*, the position of *o* will seem to be in the direction *aqo*; that is to say that the medium *CDAB* will not change the direction *qo* into the direction *qp*. If this medium between *ab* and *CD* is removed, it will be ridiculous to assume (i) that *o* is now no longer derived from *q*, but from *r*, as if the ray *oq* had suddenly realized that it had air above it, and might emerge at *r*, so that the eye will see *o* through *r*. Consequently, it is also senseless to say (ii) that *o* is no longer derived from *q*, through which point it could just as well reach *a*; for *o* emerges everywhere, at *q* just as well as at *r* etc.

This is a perplexing phenomenon, because it is a spiritualization of sensuous being. The difficulty which it presents has often occupied my thoughts, and I shall now explain the way in which I have resolved it.

The truth of the matter is that *CDAB* is not merely transparent, for its peculiar nature is also apparent. In other words, the ideal nature of the relationship mediates the visibility between *AB* and *a*. When we deal with visibility, we find ourselves in the field of ideality, for in visibility in
5 general there are two terms, one of which posits itself ideally within the other. Since that which is posited is of an ideal nature and is not yet identified with the corporeal phenomenon, the principle determining the sight is merely determinateness of an ideal nature, which is implicit and therefore incorporeal, and is in fact specific gravity. Only spatial relationship
10 is affected, not colour and other propertie s. In other words, the immaterial determinateness of the medium *CDAB* is seen hear as independent of the activity of its corporeal existence as such. The difference between matters as such does not affect the eye, and even if the lighted space, or the medium in which the eye is situated is at the same time ma-
15 terial, this materiality will only affect its determining of the spatial element.

In order to grasp the matter more precisely, we shall keep to the relationship between water and air, despite their being merely elementary transparencies which are not posited by the form which has overcome gravity. We shall posit them as the two neighbouring media, remem-
20 bering that although in their abstract determinateness they occur prior to specific gravity, we still have to take all their qualities into consideration if they are to be determined as physically concrete, although in the development of their own peculiar nature, these qualities may be disregarded. With water and air as the media between the object and the
25 eye, we see the body in a different position from that which it occupies. It is the reason for this which constitutes the subject of our enquiry. The ideal nature of the entire medium *CDAB*, together with its object *o*, is posited in the medium *CDa* in accordance with its qualitative nature. What do I see of its qualitative nature however? What is there of it that
30 enters into the other medium? The answer is that it is its immaterial qualitative nature, as water for example, which enters into the other medium. It is only its incorporeal qualitativeness, not its chemical nature as water, which enters into and determines visibility however. With regard to visibility this qualitative nature is now posited as being effective in
35 the air, i.e. the water with its content is seen *as if it were air*. The essential point is, that the qualitative nature of the water is visibly present in the air. The visual space formed by the water is transported into another visual space, which is formed by the air in which the eye is located. What particular determinateness does it preserve in this new visual space?
40 Through what particular determinateness does it become effective, and

E   129

so give notice of its visibility? It is not through shape, for it is as a result of their transparency that water and air are shapeless with regard to one another. Nor is it through cohesion. It is therefore through specific gravity. Oiliness and combustibility also make a difference, but we shall keep to specific gravity, and not attempt to apply everything to every- 5 thing. It is only the specific determinateness of the one medium which shows in the other. The difficulty is that the quality of specific gravity determines place, while here it is liberated from its materiality, and *only* determines the place of visibility. But what is specific gravity, if it is not a form which determines space? Here therefore, the specific gravity of 10 water can have no other effect than to posit the specific gravity of water within the visual space occupied by air. The visual space from which the eye starts is that of air, and it is this that constitutes its principle and its unity. Yet it now has a second visible space before it which is occupied by water, and in the place of which it posits the space of the air, reducing 15 the former to the latter. As it is merely this difference which is of significance here, the eye reduces the visual space occupied by the water; for the space occupied by the water becomes visible in another space, i.e. the space occupied by the air. A certain amount of water is therefore made into air, while it retains the specific gravity of water. This means that a 20 portion of the visible air-space, equal to that of the water is now specified by the specific gravity of the water, and given a smaller volume while maintaining the same content. While the water-space is now transposed into air-space, so that the eye perceives the medium of air instead of that of water, the quantum of air remains the same extensive quantum as 25 before of course. However, the volume of water only appears to be as large as it would if an equal amount, i.e. volume of air had the specific gravity of water. Consequently, it is also possible to say that this specific amount of air is changed qualitatively and contracted into the space which it would occupy if it were converted into water. Air is specifically 30 lighter, so that when a certain space is filled with air, it contains a lesser volume than when it is filled with water. Consequently the space is raised and also reduced in size on all sides. This is the way in which this pheno- +
menon is to be grasped; the explanation of it may appear to be artificial, but that is how it is. It is said that the ray propagates itself, and that light +
traverses the medium. Here however, the whole medium, which is the transparent and lighted water-space, is posited within another medium in accordance with its specific quality, and not merely as a radiation. It is not permissible to think of a material propagation of light therefore, for the visibility of the water is ideally present within the air. This presence is 40

a specific gravity, and it is solely by means of this specific determinateness that water maintains itself and operates within that into which it has been transformed, by transforming its transformation into itself. It is as if a human soul should be transplanted into the body of a beast, and by pre-
5 serving itself, should transform it into a human body. Similarly, it is as if the soul of a mouse were to become elephantine within the body of an elephant, and at the same time diminish and bedwarf this body into its own dimensions. The best illustration of it may be found in the world of sensuous activity, in which this relationship is of an ideal nature, while
10 common thought brings about this belittlement. When a small mind has the deeds of a hero forced upon its attention, its narrow mindedness will accept this greatness according to its own proportions, and reduce the object to its own level, so that it will only see the greatness in the light of its own pettiness. When I think about the activity of a hero, this activity
+ is within me, but only in an ideal manner. *Similarly, the air assimilates the visual space occupied by the water, and reduces it to its own dimensions.* It is the *assimilation* which is the most difficult to grasp, precisely because it is of an ideal nature, and yet is also an active and determinate being of a real nature. It is precisely through its transparency that the medium consti-
20 tutes this immateriality, this light-like quality, which can be immaterially present elsewhere, and yet remain as it is. It is thus that the material body is clarified into light in transparency.

The empirical phenomenon is that the objects in a vase of water for example, are raised. The angle of refraction was discovered by a Dutchman
+ *Snellius*, and it was *Descartes* who took the matter up. A line is drawn from the eye to the object, and although light manifests itself rectilinearly, the object is not seen at the end of this line, but appears to be raised. The place in which it is seen is determinate, and another line may be drawn between it and the eye. The extent of the difference between these two places may
30 be exactly determined geometrically by dropping a perpendicular from the point of incidence to the point on the surface of the water at which the first line emerges, and then calculating the angle which the line of vision makes with this perpendicular. If the medium in which the eye is located has a lower specific gravity than that in which the object is
35 situated, the object will appear to be further removed from the perpendicular than when it is only seen through the first medium. This means that this second medium increases the angle, and this change is determined by mathematical physicists from the sine of the angle, as the index of refraction. If no such angle occurs, but the eye is located on the surface of the
40 medium, and right on the perpendicular, it is certainly a direct consequence

of the determination of the sine, that the object is not displaced, but is seen in its true position. This is expressed by saying that the ray which falls perpendicularly upon the refractive surface is not refracted. +
The fact that the object is still raised is not accounted for in this determination, for in this case, although it is seen in the same direction, it still 5
appears to be closer. The mathematical physicists and the textbooks on physics in general, only give the law of the extent of refraction as related to the sine, they do not mention the raising itself, which also takes place, even when the angle of incidence is nil. It follows from this that the +
determinations of the sine of the angle are insufficient, for they do not 10
apply to the phenomenon of the object's appearing closer. From this law alone it would follow, that the point from which a perpendicular line may be drawn to the eye, would be the point perceived at its real distance, and that the other points on this line would only be seen as a gradational approach to it. If this were the case, it would also seem as if the bottom 15
were domed towards the middle like part of a sphere, with its edges raised, and a uniformly levelling concave shape. This is not the case however, for the bottom appears to be perfectly flat, although closer. So much for the physicists' explanation. The circumstances do not allow one to take the angles of incidence and refraction and their sine, as one's point of 20
departure. Yet this is what the physicists do, although one is unable to regard this determination as the sole cause of the change. According to this theory, the perpendicular is not affected when the angle and sine are nil, but in this case there is in fact just as much elevation as elsewhere. Consequently, any explanation has to begin with the raising, and the determina- 25
tion of the angle of refraction among various angles of incidence will then follow.

The refractive power depends upon the various specific gravities of the media. It is generally the case that those media with a higher specific gravity also give rise to greater refraction. This phenomenon is not solely 30
dependent upon specific gravity however, there are also other determinations which have an effect upon it, and the principles of oiliness or combustibility will also be determinative. *Gren* cites examples (§ 700) of substances, the refractive powers of which are independent of density. For example, light is perceptibly refracted by alum and vitriol, although their 35
specific weights are not noticeably different. If one takes borax and satur- +
ates it with olive oil, both of which are combustible, the refraction does not conform to the specific weights of the two bodies. Water and oil of turpentine etc. produce the same effect. *Biot* comments upon this ('Traité de Physique', vol. III p. 296), and says that although earthy substances tend 40

to comport themselves in accordance with their densities, this is by no means true of combustible and gaseous substances. On the following page he writes, 'On voit que des substances de densités très-diverses peuvent avoir des forces réfringentes égales, et qu'une substance moins
5 dense qu'une autre peut cependant posséder un pouvoir refringent plus fort. Cette force dépend surtout de la *nature chimique* de chaque particule. La force la plus énergique réfringente est dans les huiles et resines, et l'des-
+ tillée ne leur est pas inférieure.' The principle of combustion, which manifests itself here in a characteristic way, is therefore something specific. Con-
10 sequently, oil, the diamond, and hydrogen have a higher refractive index. Here however, we have to be content with keeping to and establishing a general point of view. Few phenomena are as complicated as this one. The particular nature of this complication lies in the advanced spirituality of that which is posited here under material determinations. In this pheno-
15 menon, that which is earthly is breached by divinity, although in this marriage between the body and the pure inviolable virginity of light, each
+ side simultaneously maintains its right.

§ 319

The different densities which determine visibility, and which exist in various media such as air, water and glass etc. are in the
20 first instance only externally compared and posited in unity; in the nature of crystals however, this comparison is internal. On the one hand, crystals have a general transparency, but on the other hand, they possess in their inner individualization or
+ nuclear shape, a form which deviates from the formal equality
25 to which this general transparency belongs. This shape is also shape as nuclear shape, but it is likewise a subjective form of an ideal nature, which like specific gravity, acts in determining place. Consequently, it also determines spatially manifest visibility in a specific manner and is therefore distinct from primary transparency.
30 It is in fact double refraction.

Remark

The category of force might well be used here, for the rhom-
35 boidal form, which is the commonest form in crystals with an internal deviation from this formal equality of shape, thoroughly
+ individualizes the interior of the crystal. However, this only takes

place when the crystal is not accidentally splintered into lamellae, does not come into existence as shape, and when there is not the slightest break or flaw in its homogeneity and transparency; when it is in fact only active as immaterial determinateness.

With regard to the transition from a relationship which is pri- 5
marily posited externally, to the form of this relationship which is active as an interior determinateness or force, I can cite nothing more apposite than Goethe's words on the relation between the external arrangement of two mutually reflecting mirrors, with a cube of glass placed between them, and the phenomenon of the 10
entoptic colours which is produced within this glass. In his 'On +
the Science of Nature' vol. I part 3, Sect. xxii, p. 148, while con-sidering, 'natural transparent, crystallized bodies,' he says, 'Nature has constructed the same mirroring apparatus in the inner-most parts of these bodies, as we have constructed by external 15
physico-mechanical means.' (cf. ibid. p. 147); it has woven an +
interior damask web. As we have already noticed, this collation of +
exterior and interior phenomena is not a matter of the refraction mentioned in the previous paragraph, but of an external double mirroring, and of the corresponding phenomenon in the crystal's 20
interior. A similar distinction has to be made therefore in con-nection with what Goethe says on p. 147 of the same work, 'In a rhombohedron of Iceland spar, it could be seen quite clearly, that the immediate cause of this phenomenon is to be found in the variegated passage of the folia, and the interplay of mirrorings 25
resulting from this'. This passage is concerned with what one +
might call rhomboidal force or activity, not with the action of existent lamella (cf. 'On the Science of Nature' vol. I part i p. 25). +

Addition. Of the two images produced by Iceland spar, one is in its ordinary position, for it is merely the product of ordinary refraction. The 30
second is called the extraordinary image; its appearance is raised by the shape of the rhomboid, which is a deformed cube, the integrant molecules of which have neither the form of a cube nor that of a double pyramid. There are two different place-positionings and two different images therefore, but they occur within a single shape, for while the shape is 35
passive in its reception of light, and so simply transmits the image, it also asserts its materiality to the extent that the internal contexture of the body forms a surface. *Goethe* has concerned himself extensively with this phenomenon, which he attributes to the existence on crystals of fine

fissures or lamellae. It is not the fissures, but merely the interior shape which gives rise to the displacement however, for colours appear as soon + as there is an actual splintering present (see § seq.). There are other bodies through which not only a double line, but even a double pair of lines 5 may be seen. Many more bodies exhibiting double refraction have recently been discovered. The phenomenon seen by the sea-shore, in which the double image of an object appears, and which is called a mirage by the French, but is generally known as the *fata morgana*, finds its place here + (Biot 'Traité de Physique' vol. III p. 321). This is a phenomenon of 10 refraction, not of reflection, and resembles the case of Iceland spar in that the object is seen through layers of air which are heated differently and therefore have different densities.

§ 320

(c) **This immaterial being-for-self of form is a force which progresses into interior existence, and supersedes the neutral** 15 **nature of crystallization. It thus gives rise to the determination of immanent punctiformity and brittleness and the resultant cohesion, to the still more perfect but formal transparency which is displayed by brittle glass for example. This moment of brittleness differs from the self-identical manifestation of** 20 **light and illumination. It is therefore the internal beginning or principle of darkening, of an as yet unexistent darkness, which is however active. It is well known that although brittle glass is perfectly transparent, it is the condition for the entoptic colours.**

Darkening does not remain a mere principle, but in contrast to 25 **the simple indeterminate neutrality of shape, and apart from externally and quantitatively affected darkenings and reductions in transparency, it progresses to the abstract one-sided extreme of compactness, which is the passive cohesion of metallic being. There is therefore a darkness which also exists for itself, and an actual** + **brightness which is for itself. These, at the same time, are posited through the intermediation of transparency, in the concrete and individualized unity of the manifestation of colour.**

Remark

Abstract darkness is immediately opposed to light as such (§ 277 and Add.) The principle of darkness attains the primary

reality of its nature as physically individualized corporeality however. The process of darkening which has been described is the
individualization of the principle of brightness, or in this case,
of the transparent body of passive manifestation in the sphere of
shape fulfilled in the being-in-self of individualized matter. The 5
transparent body is homogeneous and neutral in its existence; it
is the principle of darkness which is individualized in itself into
being-for-self, but which exists only as a force opposed to brightness, rather than a punctiformity, and which is therefore also able
to exist in a state of perfect homogeneity. The metallic prin- 10
ciple is known to be the material principle of all colouring, or the
universal colouring matter, if one wants to express it in this
way. It is only the high specific gravity of metals which has to be +
considered here, and it is into the extreme intensity of this preponderant particularization that specific matter withdraws, in 15
opposition to the disclosed and inner neutrality of transparent
shape. In the chemical sphere, the metallic principle is to the same
extent a one-sided and indifferent base.

In the exposition of the process of darkening, it was necessary to +
mention the empirical ways in which it appears, and not merely its 20
abstract moments. It is quite clear that both aspects present difficulties, but physics aggravates its difficulties still further by lump-
ing together determinations or properties which belong to completely distinct spheres. Although it is essential to search through +
various conditions and circumstances in order to discover the 25
simple specific determinateness of universal phenomena such as
heat and colour etc., on the other hand it is equally essential not
to disregard the differences bound up with the manifestation of
these phenomena. Empirical physics cannot establish colour and
heat etc. in accordance with the Notion, but only in accordance 30
with their modes of production. There are however vast
differences between these modes. The preoccupation with a
search for nothing but general laws leads to essential differences
being ignored, and to the most heterogeneous things being chaoti-
cally forced together in the light of an abstract view-point, as for 35
example when chemistry categorizes gases, sulphur, and metals
etc. as simple bodies. The very desire to discover general laws and
determinations must have been prejudiced by its failure to consider
modes of action as particularized by the various media and
spheres in which they occur. The conditions giving rise to the 40

phenomenon of colour are jumbled together in just such a chaotic manner, and experiments relating to the most specialized sets of circumstances are, as a matter of course, cited in preference to the simple and general conditions in which the nature of colour, the
+ archetypal phenomenon, reveals itself to an unprejudiced intelligence. This confusion, which reigns under the guise of a precise and well-grounded experimentation, but which is in fact crude and superficial, can only be countered by paying attention to a phenomenon's different modes of production. One must
10 therefore know what these modes are, and respect their distinctness.

First of all, one must see the value of the fundamental determination that the hindering of illumination is bound up with specific gravity and cohesion. With regard to light as such, or to the abstract identity of pure manifestation, the determinations
15 here are the characteristics and specifications of corporeality. Beyond these determinations, corporeality retreats further into itself, into darkness. It is these determinations which are the immediate constitution of the progression from conditioned to free individuality (§ 307), and which appear here in the relation of the for-
20 mer to the latter. It is interesting to note that in entoptic colours, the principle of darkening, which in this case is brittleness, is an immaterial punctiformity, which is only active as force. It exists in an external manner and gives rise to opacity when a transparent crystal is reduced to powder, or when froth forms on a
25 transparent liquid etc. (§ 317 Add.)—Pressure on a lens, which gives rise to epoptic colours, is an externally mechanical alteration of nothing but specific gravity, in which there is no division into lamellae and suchlike existing hindrances to illumination. When metals are heated so that a change of specific gravity takes
30 place, 'their surfaces exhibit a succession of fleeting colours, which can even be fixed there at will'. (Goethe 'Theory of Colours' pt. i
+ p. 191.) An entirely different principle occurs in the chemical determination of colour by acid however; in this case a lightening of darkness, a more immanent self-manifestation, a fiery activity
+ is involved. In considering colours as such, we should in the first instance exclude any hindering, darkening or brightening brought about by chemical action, for the chemical substance, like the eye in the case of the subjective physiological phenomena of colour, is a concrete entity containing many further determinations, and
40 those connected with colour cannot therefore be identified and

isolated with any degree of certainty. The identification of any-thing in the concrete object relating to colour in the abstract, will in fact presuppose a knowledge of abstract colour.

We have been considering inner darkening in so far as it belongs to the nature of the body; it is interesting to demonstrate its relation to colour since the dimness it produces is not posited as existing by itself in an external manner, and cannot therefore be exhibited as such. External dimming is not a simple weakening of light like that brought about by distance: an obscuring medium existing externally is less transparent however, it is simply a general translucency. The element of air has no concrete principle such as that which is present even in the neutrality of unindivi-dualized water, but a quite transparent substance such as water or pure glass exhibits rudimentary dimness on account of a thickening of the medium, especially if there is an increase in the existence of layers, i.e. in the boundaries dividing it. The prism is the best known means for producing external obscuration: its dimming action is the result of a twofold circumstance, which depends firstly upon its exterior boundary as such, upon its edges in fact, and secondly upon its prismatic shape, or the inequality in the diameters of its profile, which may be drawn from the whole expanse of one of its facets to the opposite edge. The prism is a dimming agency which does not function uniformly, but in accordance with the various lengths of its diameter between the various parts through which the light passes; the incomprehensible features found in many theories of colour may be traced, among other things, to the failure to take this property into consideration.

Darkening in general is however only one factor, the other is brightness, and colour requires a more precise determination of the relation between them. Light illumines, the day drives away darkness; as the simple blending of brightness with present dark-ness, this duskiness generally gives rise to grey. In colouring how-ever these two determinations are combined in such a way, that although they are held asunder, they are to the same extent posited in unity. Although they are separate, each also shows in the other. This is a combination which has to be called an individualization; it is a relationship which resembles that considered in what is called refraction, in which one determination is active within another, and yet has a determinate being of its own. This is the way of the Notion in general, which as a concrete principle contains moments in their difference, and at the same time unites them within their ideality. It is this determination which makes it difficult to grasp Goethe's exposition, in which it is expressed in the sensuous manner appropriate to it. Goethe maintains that in a prism, brightness is imposed upon darkness or vice versa, so that although it is dimmed, brightness still pervades darkness as independent brightness; and that in the case of the prism, if the common displacement is taken into account, it remains in its position, while it is simultaneously displaced. Where brightness or darkness, or rather the brightening or darkening agent (both terms are relative), has a distinct existence within dim media, the dim medium maintains its characteristic appearance, and there is no change in the intensity of its brightness or darkness when it is placed in front of a dark or bright background, and so has a brightening effect upon it. The one is posited simultaneously and negatively within the other, and both are therefore posited as being identical. It is in this way that the difference between colour and mere grey is to be grasped. Taking grey shadow as an example however, it is probably true to say that it is a rarer phenomenon than one might think. In the case of the colour square, the same difference occurs in green and red; green is the mixture of the opposed colours blue and yellow, while red constitutes their individuality.

According to *Newton's* well-known theory, white or colourless light *consists* of *five* or *seven* colours, the theory itself not being too clear on this point. It is *impossible* to denounce this *barbarous* manner of presentation *too energetically*. Even in its representation of light, it makes use of the concept *of composition*, which is one of the worst forms of reflection. What is more, *brightness* is supposed to consist of seven *darknesses*, which is about as sensible as saying that clear water consists of seven kinds of earth.

The *ineptitude* and *incorrectness* of Newton's observations and experiments complement their *inanity*, and **Goethe has even shown** that they are not entirely above board, **but one of** Newton's most glaring and elementary errors is the false assertion that when a monochromatic part of the spectrum produced by a prism passes through a second prism, it will also reappear in its merely monochromatic form (Newton Opt. Book I pt. i prop. 5 in fine).

The conclusions, deductions and proofs which Newton based upon this impure empirical data are no better. He not only made use of the prism, but was aware of the fact that if it is to produce colour, this will necessarily involve a boundary dividing light from shade (Opt. Lib. II pt. ii p. 230 ed. lat. Lond. 1719). Yet despite this, he was capable of overlooking darkness as an active dimming factor. He only mentions this condition in connection with a very special case, and long after he has completed his theory. The only purpose served by his mentioning it, is therefore that it enables the partisans of the theory to say that it was not unknown to him, for it cannot be said that it has been accepted with light as being fundamental to any consideration of colours. On the contrary, the fact that colour cannot appear without darkness being present is omitted from the text-books. The text-books also overlook the simple fact that if a completely white or single-coloured wall is viewed through a prism, no colour will be apparent if the wall is white, and otherwise, only the colour of the wall. Colours will appear however as soon as a nail is driven into a wall, or some kind of unevenness is introduced. They will only appear at this particular spot however. To the disadvantages in the presentation of this theory one has to add that it has led to the ignoring of so many experiments which contradict it.

This leads on into details of the thoughtless inconsistency with which so many of the immediate implications of the theory, such as the impossibility of an achromatic telescope, have been abandoned, while the theory itself has been accepted.

Finally, attention should be drawn to the blindness of the *prejudice* which asserts that this theory is based upon something *mathematical*. As if these partly false and one-sided *measurings* deserved the name of mathematics. As if the quantitative determinations introduced into the conclusions drawn from it provided any sort of justification of the theory itself, or for the nature of the subject matter.

Goethe's erudite elucidation of this darkness in light is as lucid as it is *profound*, and there is no doubt that the main reason for its not having been more actively adopted, is that this would involve the confession of far too much thoughtlessness and stupidity. Instead of Newton's absurd conceptions having been toned down however, they have

recently been worked up into a further metaphysical gali-
+ matias (cf. above § 278 Rem. II.23,9) in the discoveries of
+ *Malus* relating the *polarization* of light, in nothing less
+ than the *four-sidedness* of sunbeams, the *rotatory movement* of
5 red light-corpuscles from *right to left* and of blue **corpuscles**
+ from *left to right*, **and most brilliantly in the revival of the**
Newtonian fits, the 'accès de facile transmission' and
+ **'accès de facile reflexion' (Biot, vol. IV p. 88 et seq.). Some**
of these conceptions arose from the application of the formulae of
10 **differential calculus to the phenomena of colour; that is to say that**
while aspects of this calculus were effectively and rationally em-
ployed in mechanics, they have also been perverted by being ap-
+ **plied to the determinations of a completely different field.**

Addition. Firstly, what is called double refraction also occurs in the
15 prism, and it is here that the further determinateness occurs, in which
transparency passes over into darkening, and so gives rise to colours. The
brittleness of glass is apparent as a dimming of brightness, even when the
glass is perfectly transparent. The same effect may be seen in milky glass
and in an opal; in these cases however, obscurations are produced which
20 give no indication of outward existence. Light does not dim itself, for it is
rather that which is undimmed, and consequently the idea of colour is
primarily involved with what is individual and subjective, with what
divides itself into its differences while binding them within itself. The preciser definition of this belongs to empirical physics, yet as this is concerned
25 not only with observation, but also with the reduction of observations to
general laws, it is relevant to the philosophic consideration of colour.
There are *two* prevailing *ideas* about colours; the one with which *we* con-
cur recognizes the simplicity of light, the other maintains that light is
composite, which is the crudest of metaphysical propositions, and stands
30 in direct contradiction to every Notion. It is pernicious, because it is
symptomatic of the whole way in which things are treated. It is with light
that we put aside the contemplation of separateness and plurality, and
have to raise ourselves to the abstraction of existent identity. It is therefore necessary to think in an ideal manner when thinking about light,
35 although the coarsening influence of the Newtonian doctrine has tended
to make this impossible. Under no circumstances is composition the
concern of philosophy therefore. Philosophy has to do with the Notion,
and with the unity of differences, and this is immanent, not external or
superficial. In order to bolster up the Newtonian theory, an attempt has

been made to dispense with composition by saying that the light produces these colours by self-determination, just as electricity or magnetism polarizes itself into differences. But Newton himself admits (II. 140, 5) that colours only occur on the boundary between brightness and darkness. An external determination or condition is always present when light determines itself as colour, and like the infinite resistance postulated in Fichtean idealism, it is moreover specific. If light dimmed itself, it would be the inwardly differentiated Ideal. It is however only an abstract moment; it is gravitational centrality, the selfhood of gravity which has reached abstract freedom. It is the standpoint from which light is to be considered which has to be settled *philosophically*. The sphere of physical determination is therefore still external to light. *White* is the corporeal fixation of brightness, and is as yet achromatic; *black* is the materialization and specification of darkness; colour occurs between these two extremes. It is the combination of light and darkness, and particularly the specification of this combination, which first gives rise to colour. Outside this relationship both light and darkness are as nothing. Night holds all powers within it as self-dissolving ferment and deracinating strife, it is the all-embracing and absolute possibility, the chaos in which matter has no being, and whose annihilation therefore contains all things. Light is purity of form, and it is in its unity with night, which is the mother and nourisher of all, that it has its initial being. All powers stand in awe of night, and shift and tremble quietly before it; the brightness of day is the self-externality of night, which has no inwardness, and which is shed and dissipated as a spiritless and powerless actuality. As has become evident however, the truth lies in the unity of both and is not the light which shines in the darkness, but that which is penetrated by darkness as by its essence, and is thereby substantiated and materialized. It does not shine into darkness, and it neither illumines it nor is it blended by it; it is rather the inwardly disrupted Notion, which as the unity of light and darkness displays itself in the differences of its moments. This is the gay realm of colours, the living movement of which brings forth a *variety of hues* and constitutes, in its further development, the realized actuality of colour. Everyone knows that colour is darker than light; according to the Newtonian doctrine however, light is not light but is intrinsically dark, and only occurs when one mixes together these various colours, which are supposed to constitute its original elements. To quarrel with Newton appears to be presumptuous; the empirical approach is the only way to deal with the matter however, and this has been Goethe's procedure, while Newton blurred the issue by his ossified reflective concepts. It is only because the physicists have been blinded by this ossification, and have

therefore been unable to assess experiments, that the Newtonian system has been able to survive into the present. I need not expand upon this subject, for there is every likelihood that in the near future a special series of lectures will be given at the University on this extremely interesting mat-
5 ter of colours. The monstrous error of Newton, and the thoughtless and blind acquiescence of the physicists, will be clearly demonstrated by
+ experiments.

Both *transparency* and the prism as such have to be regarded as conditioned *by a dimming medium*, and it is at this point that the initial con-
10 sideration of colours is to be taken up. In this free and simple state, colour has need of another principle to give it actuality, i.e. a definite and uneven figure, the sides of which form different angles. It is this which gives rise to the varying intensities of brightness and dimming. It is the further lighting and dimming which results from the interplay of these intensities, which
15 give rise to the *free colours*. In order to obtain these various degrees of darkening, we usually use transparent glasses, although these are by no means necessary in order to produce colour, and the colour which they give rise to is of a more complex composition. One can cause various darkenings and illuminations, such as daylight and candlelight to fall
20 directly on one another, and when the dark shade of one light is lightened by the light of another, this immediately gives rise to coloured shadows. Consequently, one has the two shadows as well as two illuminations of these shadows. The interplay of multifarious and irregular dimmings gives rise to a colourless grey, such as we usually see in ordinary shadows,
25 which constitute an indeterminate lighting. If only a few, perhaps two distinct differences in illumination fall upon one another however, this immediately gives rise to colour, which is a qualitative difference, while shadows only display quantitative differences. Sunlight is too preponderant to allow any other brightness to counter it, and it is by means of sun-
30 light that a whole area has a single and general source of light. If there is an interplay of various lightings within a room, even if it is only the blue sky which supplements the sun, this gives rise immediately to coloured shadows. Consequently, when one begins to concentrate one's attention upon the various colourings of the shadows, one is unable to find grey
35 shadows; coloured shadows are everywhere, but they are often so weak, that their colours do not individualize themselves. The most beautiful shadows are produced by candlelight and moonlight. If a stick is held in these two brightnesses, both shadows will be illuminated by both lights, i.e. the shadow of moonlight will be illuminated by candlelight and vice
40 versa. This gives rise to a blue and reddish yellow, while two candles alone

give rise to a colour which is clearly yellow. This contrast also appears with candlelight at daybreak and twilight, when the sunlight is not bright enough to drive out the coloured shadows by the multiplicity of its reflections.

Newton thought he had discovered a striking proof of his theory by painting all the colours on a *revolving disc* and then spinning it rapidly. The result of this experiment is that none of the colours is seen clearly; one sees only a whitish shimmer, and this is supposed to prove that white light consists of seven colours. What one sees however is a sort of dirty grey, for because of the speed, one is no longer able to distinguish between the colours. It is the same when one faints, and one's giddiness prevents one from retaining a definite image of the surrounding objects. Will anyone maintain that one sees an actual circle when a stone is swung round on the end of a string? This is the fundamental experiment of the Newtonians, and it is a direct contradiction of what it is supposed to prove, for if these colours were the irreducible origin of white light, the principle of dimming which they contain would be completely incapable of reducing itself to brightness. The principle of dimming is not an original element of light, and the nightwatchman's song, in which light is said to drive away darkness, gives a truer account of the matter. Conversely however, where the principle of dimming prevails, the weaker element of lighting disappears. Consequently, when one places glasses of various definite colours on top of one another and looks through them, one sees white if the glasses are lightly coloured, and black if they are darkly coloured. This should make the Newtonians say that darkness also consists of colours, and another Englishman has in fact maintained that black is composed of all the colours. This obliterates the particularity of colour.

The *procedure of the Newtonian reflection* is found throughout the whole of his physics, and is simply as follows:

(a) By starting with the phenomena produced by a glass prism in a completely dark room, Newton displays his pedantry at the very outset, for the foramen ovale and so on are completely superfluous. To use his own expression, he then allows 'rays of light' to fall upon the prism. Various colours may then be seen through the prism, and the light-image as such in which the colours are arranged in a particular order may be seen in another place; violet is at the top for example, and red at the bottom. Here we have the phenomenon in its simplicity. Newton then says that as one part of the image has diverged more than the other, and other colours are visible in the place in which the divergence is greater, one colour must have diverged more than another. This is then expressed

by saying that the intrinsic difference in the nature of colours consists in
the *diversity* of their *refrangibility*. Each colour is therefore present in light
as an original, distinct, and finished constituent. Consequently, the prism
for example, merely elicits the appearance of a variety which was already
present, it does not give rise to a procedure which brings this variety into
being. It might be compared with the scales on the wings of a butterfly
for example, which become visible with the aid of a microscope, although
they are invisible to the naked eye. This is the way in which he reasons.
This supple, delicate, infinitely determinable, absolutely self-identical
principle of light, which gives way to every impression, and in its complete indifference simply receives every external modification, is supposed to consist of fixed elements. One might argue in an analogous
manner in another field. When various keys are played on a piano, they
give rise to various notes because, in fact, various strings are struck.
Similarly, each note of an organ has a pipe, which produces a particular
note when it is blown. If a horn or a flute is blown however, various
notes will be audible, although there are no special keys or pipes to be
seen. There is, it is true, a type of Russian horn music in which each note is
produced by a particular horn, so that each performer only produces one
note with his instrument. If, after hearing the Russian horn-music, one
then hears the same melody played on an ordinary French horn, one
might emulate Newton by arguing in the following way, 'In this single
horn there are several hidden horns, which can be neither seen nor felt.
Here the performer corresponds to the prism however, and causes these
horns to be heard. Since he produces different notes, he must blow into a
different horn each time, for each note is in itself a firm and finished whole,
which has its own subsistence and its own horn.' We also know of course,
that in the case of the horn, its different notes are produced by various
movements of the lips, and by inserting the hand in the instrument's
mouth etc. This is supposed to be of no effect however, and to be a purely
formal activity which merely causes the various notes which were already
there to be heard; it is not supposed to bring forth the variety of the notes
themselves. We also know that the prism is a sort of condition, by means
of which the different colours appear, in that different darkenings of light
are imposed upon one another through the different densities presented by
its shape. Even when one demonstrates that colours also originate under
these conditions however, the Newtonians continue to insist that with
regard to light, these various activities do not give rise to varieties in the
product, but that the products are already there in their entirety before
they are produced. This attitude towards light is identical with the attitude

towards the French horn which insists that there are different notes within it regardless of whether or not I open or close my lips in a certain way, and thrust my hand in such and such a manner into the instrument's mouth; and that these activities are not modifications of the sound, but merely a repeated blowing into one horn after the other. It is Goethe's merit to have over- 5 thrown the prism theory. Newton concludes that, 'what is elicited by the prism is originally there'; but it is a barbarous conclusion. There are various ways in which the atmosphere has a dimming effect; for example, the sun is redder when it rises, because the air then contains more vapours. The dimming effect of water and glass is even greater. As Newton does 10 not take into account the way in which the instrument darkens light, he regards the darkening which appears behind the prism as constituting the original constituents into which the prism is supposed to decompose light. To say that the prism has a dispersive power is irresponsible however, for it presupposes the theory which the experiment is supposed to prove. It is 15 as if, wanting to prove that water in its original state is not clear, I began by tying a filthy rag to a stick and stirring the water with it until it was dirty.

(b) Newton also maintains that the seven colours violet, indigo, blue, green, yellow, orange and red, are simple and indecomposable; but it will + be impossible to persuade anyone that violet for example is a simple 20 colour, for it is a mixture of blue and a kind of red. Every child knows that green may be produced by mixing yellow and blue, and that if one adds a little less red to blue than is necessary for violet, the result is lilac; simi- larly, that orange is produced by mixing yellow and red. To the New- tonians however, green, violet, and orange are primary colours, and there 25 is an absolute difference between indigo-blue and light blue (celadon, which has a touch of green in it), although there is no qualitative difference between them whatever. No artist is stooge enough to be a Newtonian; artists have red, yellow, and blue, and make the other colours out of them. + Even the mechanical mixing of yellow and blue as two dry powders gives 30 rise to green. The Newtonians have to admit that there are many colours which are produced by mixing, and in order to justify their theory of the simple nature of colours, they say that the colours produced by the pris- matic spectrum (one might say spectre), are originally different from the + other natural colours of the material pigmentations. This is not a valid 35 distinction however; colour is colour, and is either homogeneous or heterogeneous, regardless of how it is produced or whether it is physical or chemical. In fact, mixed colours are produced in the prism just as they are elsewhere. We have here a specific appearance in its production as appearance, which is therefore mainly a mixture of appearances, and has no 40

further connection with chromatic being. If one holds the prism close to the wall, it is only the edges of the colour-image which show blue and red, the middle remains white. It is said that white light occurs in the middle
+ because there is an interplay of many colours there. What nonsense! The
5 extent to which people will pursue an absurdity is quite incredible; and drivelling on in this way becomes a mere habit. When the prism is moved further away from the wall, the bands become wider, until the white finally vanishes completely and green is produced where they impinge upon one another. The object of this Newtonian experiment is to prove
10 that colours are simply homogeneal (see above Rem. II. 139, 24), but the isolated colour which is seen through a prism when a hole is made in a wall and light falls on to the opposite wall certainly does not exhibit the various colours so perfectly. What is more, it is only natural that the colours which are formed at the edges should not be so bright, since their
15 base is of another colour. The situation is the same when I look at things about me through a coloured glass. One should in no wise allow oneself to be imposed upon by the authority of Newton therefore, nor even by the framework of mathematical proof which, mainly in recent times, has been erected around his doctrine. It is thought that by saying that Newton
20 was a great mathematician, one thereby justifies his theory of colours. It is however magnitude alone, and not physical being, which is susceptible of mathematical proof. Mathematics has nothing to do with colour, although it does enter into optics, and if Newton has measured colours, one can scarcely call this a mathematical procedure. The bands vary in breadth,
25 and he noted the ratio in which they stand to one another. He informs us that as his eyes were not sharp enough for the job, he employed a *good*
+ *and trusted friend* to do it for him. Newton then compared these proportions with the numerical relationship between musical notes (see above § 280
+ Rem.), but this is also unmathematical. What is more, even when one is
30 presented with a large image, it is impossible for the sharpest eyes to assess where the different colours begin. A single look at the spectrum makes it quite clear that it displays no definite boundaries (confinia) which might be determined as lines. The complete absurdity of the matter becomes apparent when we remember that the widths of the edges vary
35 enormously according to the distances. At the maximum distance for example, green has the greatest width, since yellow and blue as such become increasingly narrower as their bands expand and so impinge upon one another to a greater extent.

(c) A third conception of Newton's which Biot has made much of
40 is that different colours have different tendencies; this is deduced from the

fact that when a lens is pressed against a glass, a ring composed of a number of superimposed iridescent circles becomes apparent. At one point, for example, a yellow ring becomes apparent, and all the other colours are absent; the yellow is then said to have the impulse to appear, while the other colours are said to have fallen into a paroxysm of self-effacement, 5 and to have refused to show themselves. Transparent bodies are supposed to let certain rays through, and to stop others. Consequently, it is in the nature of colour to have the impulse to appear and to pass through. This is a completely empty conception, in which mere appearance is taken up into the rigid form of reflection. +

We have to thank *Goethe* for *the conception of colour which conforms to the Notion*. Goethe was drawn into a consideration of colours and light very early, mainly as the result of his interest in painting. The simple purity of his feeling for nature, which is the prime faculty of the poet, was bound to resist the barbarity of reflection one encounters in Newton. He has 15 examined the interpretations and experiments relating to light and colour which have been made from Plato onwards. He has grasped the phenome- + non in its simplicity; the true instinct of reason consists in grasping that aspect of the phenomenon in which it displays its greatest simplicity. In its further determinateness, the *archetypal phenomenon* is involved in a whole 20 multitude of conditions, and if one starts with these conditions, it is difficult to understand the essence of it.

(*a*) The main feature of Goethe's theory is that light is for itself, and that darkness is another principle, which is external to it. *White* is visible light, *black* is visible darkness, and *grey* is their *primary* and purely quantitative 25 relationship, which is therefore either a diminution or augmentation of brightness or darkness. In the *second* and more determinate relationship however, in which light and dark maintain this fixed specific quality in face of each other, the deciding factor is which of the two is basic, and which constitutes the dimming medium. There is either a bright base 30 present with a more shaded principle imposed upon it, or vice versa. It is this that gives rise to colour. This unity of differences conforms to the Notion, and it was Goethe's superior sense which enabled him to say that *this is so*. It is only thinking consciousness which can reckon with the fact that rationality implies an identity within the persistence of variety. For 35 example, only animal sensation is present if selfhood fails to keep aloof from the object, and flows together with it. However, if I say that I feel something warm etc., consciousness posits an object, and despite this division, hold both terms together in a single unity. Thus the relationship 3 : 4 is something quite different when I merely put these numbers 40

148

together as 7 (3 + 4), or 12 (3 × 4), or 4 — 3 = 1, for in the first instance three counts as three, and four as four. With colours the mutual relation between the principle of brightness and darkness must be the same; the medium and substratum must remain separate, so that the medium is in
5 fact a medium, and does not emit light. (i) Although I can imagine a basic shadow with sunlight shining upon it, it is not a medium. Instead of colour, disturbing media can also merely produce grey however, as for example when I look at a black object through transparent muslin, or through black muslin at a white object, for special conditions are necessary in order
10 to make colour in general definitely perceptible. Differences of sight and setting are also determining factors when colour appears in this way. A feeble show of colour will seem to be merely grey if there is near it another more specific degree of darkness or brightness, or another more pronounced colour. Eyes also differ widely in their ability to perceive
15 colours; it is possible however to sharpen one's observation; for example,
+ the brim of a hat seen through muslin appears to me to be bluish. Mere dimming has therefore to be distinguished from (ii) brightness and darkness *reciprocally showing through each other*. The sky is night, it is black. As air our atmosphere is transparent, and if it were completely pure we should
20 only see the black sky. It is filled with vapours however, and is therefore a disturbing medium, so that it appears to us to be coloured—*blue*. In the mountains the air is purer however, and the sky seems to be blacker. Conversely, if we have a bright base such as the sun, and look at it through a dark glass such as glass porcelain, it appears to us to be coloured *yellow* or
25 *red*. There is a certain *wood*, the decoction of which is yellow if held in front of something bright, and blue if held in front of something dark. This is the simplest of relationships, and is basic to any colour. It is by means of it that each diaphanous medium is active, although it may as yet lack any definite colour. There is a kind of opal for example, which is yellow or
30 red when it is held up against the sky, and blue when viewed against a
+ dark background. Looking out of my window on January 5, 1824, I saw smoke rising from a chimney; the sky was overcast, and the background was therefore white. While the smoke was rising against this background, it was yellowish; when it began to settle, and had dark roofs and dark
35 leafless trees behind it, it was bluish; and when it had settled still further,
+ and had the white walls of the houses behind it, it was yellow again. There are also beer bottles which exhibit the same phenomenon. Goethe had a Bohemian tumbler, and covered half the inside edge of it with black, and
+ half with white paper; the glass was then blue and yellow. It is this that
+ Goethe calls the archetypal phenomenon.

(b) This kind of dimming may also be brought about by means of the prism. If one has a piece of white paper with black figures on it, or a piece of black paper with white figures on it, and looks at it through a prism, one sees coloured edges. This is because the prism is both transparent and opaque, so that it presents the object in both the place in which it is, and in another place. Consequently, although no simple dimming occurs, the edges become boundaries, and are superimposed upon one another. In the passage quoted above (§ 320 Remark II. 140, 5), Newton expresses his surprise (Opt. p. 230) at the fact that certain fine lamellae or bubbles of glass (p.217) which are perfectly transparent, and show no trace of shadows, appear to be coloured when viewed through a prism (annulos coloratos exhibeant), 'cum e contrario, prismatis refractione, corpora omnia *ea solummodo sui parte* apparere soleant coloribus distincta, ubi vel *umbris terminentur*, vel partes habeant *inaequaliter luminosas*'. How could he see these glass bubbles in the prism independent of that which surrounded them? The prism always displaces the sharp division between the image and its setting; or rather, it posits its limit as *limit* (see § 92 Add.). +
This is the situation, although it has not yet been adequately explained. +
We see a double image in Iceland spar, because while its transparency allows the natural image to appear, its rhomboid form displaces it, and the case must be the same with other glasses. In the prism therefore, I postulate two images immediately condensed into one; the ordinary image, which remains in its place in the prism, acts from this place and is projected into the transparent medium as a mere appearance; and the displaced or extraordinary image, which is the dimming medium of the first one. Consequently, the prism posits within light the diremption of its Notion, + a diremption which has its reality through darkness (II. 142. 29). The general way in which the prism produces its effect is however (*a*) by displacing the ,entire image, an action determined by the nature of the medium. (*b*) Prismatic shape is also a determining factor however. It certainly accounts for the *size of the image,* ˈfor it is precisely in prismatic shape that there is a further displacement *within itself* of the image fixed by refraction. It is this *within itself* which is the main point here; for example, if the angle points downwards, and the prism is therefore thicker at the top than it is at the bottom, the light will fall differently on each point of it. Consequently, primatic shape produces an additional specific displacement. Although this explanation may also be somewhat inadequate, the crux of the matter certainly lies in the image's being simultaneously and inwardly projected into another place. This internality is modified still further by the chemical composition of the glass. Flint glass and other

substances exhibit their own peculiar crystallization for example, and therefore have their own way of directing an image.

(c) Even at the distance of a few feet, our eyes only enable us to see the edges and borders of objects rather indistinctly. It is very easy for me to see the colour of the wide edges of a window frame, which on the whole seem to be in a grey half-shadow, without blinking; here too is a double image. Double images of this kind also occur objectively through what is called the inflection of light. The perception of a hair will be doubled or even trebled if light is let into a dark room through a tiny aperture. Of Newton's experiments, only that with the two knife blades is of interest; the others which he cites, including the one just mentioned, are of no significance. The most remarkable fact about the experiment with the two knife blades, is that the borders become broader as the knife is moved away from the opening in the window (Newton opt. bk.iii, p.328). It is apparent from this that the phenomenon is closely related to that of the prism, for here too light appears as a limit to its other. Its deviation is not brought about by the external force of the prism however, for its reality consists precisely in its relating itself to darkness, in inflecting itself toward it, and in forming a positive boundary with it, i.e. a boundary on which one passes over into the other without there being any clear-cut line. The inflection of light is present wherever light and darkness meet, and it gives rise to the penumbra. The light deviates from its direction, and light and shade blur their sharp boundaries and pass into one another. This might be compared to the formation of an atmosphere, in so far as odour enters into this formation, as when one speaks of an acid, metallic, or electric atmosphere etc.; it is the emergence of that which is of an ideal nature and which appears to be bound to the shape as thing. The boundary also becomes positive therefore, not merely a general mixture, but a penumbra, which is bounded on the lighted side by light, but which is also separated from darkness by the light on the dark side. Consequently the penumbra is blackest on the light side, and shades off towards the light which separates it from the darkness. As there is a multiple repetition of this shading, it gives rise to the juxtaposition of the shadow lines. In this inflection, light is the freedom of its own refrangibility, although it still requires a particular figure in which these syntheses and this neutrality may be presented as qualitatively determined.

(d) The relationship between *colours in their totality* still has to be indicated. Colour is now *determinate*, although its determinateness is now no longer general but actual, for it has the difference of the Notion within it, and is therefore no longer an indeterminate determinateness. Gravity is universal and immediate being-in-self in otherness, and as such contains the inessentiality of immediate difference, a certain mass; the largeness and smallness are quite devoid of qualitative difference. Heat on the contrary, as inwardly negative, acquires qualitative difference through the various temperatures of heat and cold, although in the first instance these merely differ quantitatively. As genuine negativity, as actuality, colour contains immediate difference as it is posited + and determined through the Notion. We know from sense-perception that *yellow, blue,* and *red* are the primary colours, and that they are accompanied by *green,* which is a mixed colour. As is shown by experience, the relationship here is as follows. The first colour is yellow, which, as Mr. *Schulz* expresses it, is a duller medium 10 *pervasively brightened* or *illumined* by a bright base. That is why the sun appears to us to be yellow, with only a superficial darkening. The other extreme is blue, which, to use Mr. Schulz's form of expression once again, is a brighter medium *pervaded by the shadow* of its darker base. This ac- + counts for the sky's being blue where the atmosphere is vaporous, and a 15 deep dark blue which is almost black-blue when it is seen from a balloon or from high mountains such as the Swiss Alps, in which cases one is above the dimming medium of the atmosphere. By blinking, one makes + the eye's crystalline lens into a prism, by half covering it. One side of a flame will then seem to be yellow, and the other blue. In that they have 20 lenses, telescopes are also prismatic, and consequently exhibit colours. Perfect achromaticism can only be obtained by superimposing one prism upon another. Blue and yellow are the simplest colours, and red and green, + which no longer belong to this completely simple and general opposition, fall between these extremes. Red is the one mediatory colour, into which 25 both blue and yellow may be intensified. Yellow is readily drawn into red by intensified darkening. In the spectrum, red is already present in violet, and at the other end, it occurs with yellow in orange. Red occurs when yellow is pervaded once again by shade, or blue is pervaded once again by light; red is therefore yellow drawn further into shade, or blue 30 drawn further into brightness. Red is the mediation of yellow and blue, it has to be regarded as the active, subjective and individual determin-ation of both colours; it therefore stands in contrast to green, which constitutes the passive mediation of these two. Red is the royal colour, it is light which has overcome and completely penetrated darkness; it 35 strikes the eye, it is active and powerful, and is the intensity into which both extremes are concentrated. Green is the simple mixture, the common neutrality of yellow and blue; this may be seen quite clearly in the prism when there is a superpositioning of yellow and blue. Green is the neutral colour, and is therefore the colour of plants, from the greenness of 40

which their further qualitative moments are engendered. Yellow, as the first colour, is the simple dimming of light, it is a warm colour, and is the immediate determinate being of colour. The second colour is mediatory, and the antithesis itself is doubly represented within
5 it as red and green, which correspond to fire and water, and which have already been considered (§ 283 and § 284). Blue is the third stage, which is a cold colour; it is the dark foundation which may be seen through brightness, a base which does not attain to concrete totality. The blue of the sky is, so to speak, the ground out of which the
10 Earth proceeds. There is a *symbolism* attached to these colours. Yellow is the gay and noble colour, which delights us by its vivacity and purity. Red expresses seriousness and dignity, as well as kindness and charm. Blue ex-
+ presses tender and profound feelings. It is easy for red to break into green and vice versa, for they constitute the opposition, and are closely related.
15 An intensified green has a reddish tinge. The extract of a plant such as sage looks quite green. If this liquid is a dark green, and is then poured into a glass vessel shaped like a champagne glass and held up to the light, the lower part of it will appear to be green, and the upper part a most beautiful purple. Where the glass is narrow the colour will be green,
20 which will pass through yellow into red. If this liquid is poured into a large broad bottle, it is red; while it is being poured out, it looks green. It is therefore its intensity which makes it red; or rather, when green is intensified, it appears to be red. The light of a flame is blue at the base where it is thinnest, and red at the top where its intensity is greatest and
25 the flame is hottest; the dark part is at the base therefore, the middle of the flame yellow.

(*e*) That which is objectively necessary is also connected within subjective vision. When one colour becomes apparent, the eye demands another. Yellow demands violet, orange blue, purple green, and vice versa. Con-
+ sequently, Goethe called these *complementary colours*. The yellow or bluish shadows of morning and evening twilight, in their interplay with moonlight and candlelight (see above II.143,33) might be cited here. According to an experiment of Goethe's, if one holds a red glass behind a light, one then has red lighting. If one then places another candle there, the shadow
35 on which the red light falls is red, while the other shadow appears to be green, which is the complementary colour to red. This is the physiological
+ phenomenon. Newton should have tried to tell us where the green comes from. If one looks at light and then closes one's eyes, one sees a circle of the opposite colour to that which one has been looking at. The following
40 experiment may be made with this subjective image. For a certain time

I gazed at the image of the sun in the focus of a lens. The image which I continued to see when I had closed my eyes had a blue middle, while the rest of its concentric surface was a beautiful sea-green. The middle was the same size as the pupil, while that which surrounded it was larger than the iris, and somewhat elliptical. When I opened my eyes the image did   5
not disappear; seen against a dark background the middle was still a beautiful sky blue, and that which surrounded it was green; seen against a bright background the middle was yellow however, and that which surrounded it was red. If one places a stick of red sealing-wax on a sheet of paper and stares at it for some time, a green tint becomes apparent   10
when one looks away. The purple colour of a rough sea is a complementary colour; the lighted parts of the waves appear in their own colour which is green, while the shaded parts appear in the opposing colour, which is purple. In meadows where there is nothing but greenness to be seen, the tree-trunks and pathways often seem to have a reddish tinge   15
when the sky is moderately bright. Mr. Schulz, the government official, has made some extremely important and interesting experiments with these physiological colours, which he has communicated to Goethe and to a few friends here, and which he will soon make known to the public.   +
One has to keep to the archetypal phenomenon indicated by Goethe.   20
Insignificant appearances brought about by complicated circumstances are supposed to call it in question. Even Newton's experiments are confused, irrelevant, pettily executed, hashed and messy. His theory of colours is regurgitated in hundreds of compendiums. Nevertheless, the view of the matter championed by Goethe has never lacked adherents, as he has   25
shown by the literature he has catalogued. Goethe has been opposed be-   +
cause he is a poet and not a professor. The professionals only allow validity to the peculiar idiom of certain theories etc., they completely overlook what others say, and treat it as if it had not been said. People of this kind often want to form a closed circle, to be in exclusive possession of science.   30
and to extirpate other forms of judgement; jurists are an example of this. The law is for everyone however, and so is colour. A closed circle such as this develops certain intellectual habits which have a straitening effect. If one is not automatized by these habits one is supposed to be uninitiated, for only the club members are supposed to understand the matter. This is   35
not a false supposition, for as one does not employ the metaphysical category of the *understanding* according to which they consider the matter ought to be regarded, one certainly does not understand what they understand. Philosophers are usually cold shouldered, although it is in fact their task to criticize these categories.   +

Secondly, there are other phenomena which present us with a further kind of darkening. Darkening is the shapelessness of punctiformity, brittleness and pulverization, but only in principle, not as the actual sublation of cohesion by dispersal. Consequently, a further darkening occurs
5 in glass which is rapidly cooled after rapid heating, for this glass is extremely brittle; and for this reason it is also very fragile.

(a) It is at this juncture that the *entoptic* colours occur. In his mor-
+ phology, Goethe has treated this stage in an extremely ingenious manner. The phenomenon only occurs in a cube or square plate of this brittle
10 glass. If one places an ordinary non-brittle glass cube on a black base, and faces the bright part of the sky (which in the morning is the west, for the darkest part is that which is closest to the sun), the image of this brightness will become apparent as it falls upon the small plate and becomes visible to the eye as reflection (cf. above § 278 Add. II. 24, 26). In summer, when the
15 sun stands high in the sky at midday, the whole horizon is bright, and then this phenomenon will appear anywhere. The brightness will then occur in all types of glass, but if brittle glass is used, dark patches will occur in the four corners of the small plate, so that the brightness forms a white cross. If one then places oneself at a right angle to one's former direction
20 and looks across the small plate to the south instead of the west, one sees four bright spots instead of four dark ones, and a black instead of a white cross. Here we have the archetypal phenomenon. If one augments the obscuration by means of reflection, rings of colour occur at the four points. Consequently one has here the production of obscuration within the
25 brightness of this transparency. On the one hand, the darkness is brought forth by the edge of the plate, on the other, by the refractive nature of the medium. In this relationship therefore, darkness and brightness are further determined, differentiated, and imposed upon one another, and so yield the various colours in an order which is reversed in the other position.
30 Thus, if the four points are white and the cross black, the first colour dimming gives rise to is yellow, which passes into green and blue. Conversely, if the cross is white and the corners dark, an increase in darkening gives rise to blue first, as the brightness is then driven into the dark foundation. Consequently, here in the transparent medium we have a further
35 darkening, which is driven on to colour, and depends upon the qualitative nature of the brittle body.

(b) *Epoptic* colours are related to this phenomenon, and are mechanically produced by pressing a lens against a plate of glass (see II.137, 25; 147, 38). The point of contact is at first black, but as pressure is increased, it expands
40 and differentiates itself into various circles of colour, green, red and yellow.

The same happens with ice, when one presses it with a stone. Here it is merely the mechanical pressure which produces the colours, and this pressure is nothing but a change of cohesion in the nearest parts. It therefore resembles heat, which is also a mere change of cohesion. In sound, vibration is an expansion of the mechanical impression, a vibration which sublates itself. Here in glass one has a similar phenomenon, a perenniating form of undulation, an unequal resistance to pressure, a persistent inequality of cohesion, which gives rise to different darkenings in different places. While it was brittleness which gave rise to entoptic colours, here it is the interruption of cohesion.

(c) If this interruption of cohesion goes still further, we have the *paroptic* colours. Lamellae and tiny fissures occur in this glass, especially in lime spar, so that the colour often passes over into an iridescence like that on a pigeon's neck. A darkening occurs here which is caused by the diaphanous body's having reached the actual division of its contexture.

These determinations belong to the transition from brightness to darkness. In this totality of light and darkness, light no longer conforms to its Notion; by abandoning the pure quality which constitutes its essence, it has clearly become something else. In other words, physical being comes forth as a unity pervaded by light, and as the substance and possibility of gravity and process. The constant physical colours, which may be exhibited as pigments, are in the *third* instance this fixed darkening of bodies, which no longer appears as an external determination, and as a mere play of light over the body. On the contrary, the essence of the darkness of matter in these substances is itself merely a darkening of matter within itself, for light has pervaded the body in an immanent manner, and is specifically determined within it. What is the difference between this corporeal colour, and merely bright or darkened translucent colour? Since the physical body has an intrinsic colour, gold for example is yellow, the question arises of the way in which light enters into this corporeality. How does light coagulate when it falls upon matter from without, and so becomes a pigment bound to a dark corporeality? We have taken brightness as the point of departure for our progress so far, and so we must also take it as our point of departure with regard to pigment. The primary characteristic of the crystal was its abstractly ideal equality, the transparency traversed by the light which entered it from without. All bodies are only bright in so far as they are lighted, and primarily this only occurs on their surfaces; they are visible because an external light falls upon them. Crystal preserves brightness within itself however, because it has the theoretical or ideal nature of the possibility of being in another, and of

156

positing itself within it. As this visibility appears not as the real nature of brightness, but as this theoretical nature in general, and shape punctualizes itself into the inner indifference of the being-in-self of specific gravity, so that it progresses to the unified being-for-self of real brittleness, colour is
5 this progress of visibility into darkness, it is the sublation of free internal crystallization. Colour is therefore physical being which has come to the surface as pure appearance, and which therefore no longer has an interior or exterior as heat does in shape. Everything that it is implicitly is also there. Consequently, the determinate physical body has a colour.
10 This obscuration of shape is the sublation of its uniform neutrality; i.e. of the form which preserves itself as such even in neutrality, by persisting as the pervasive unity of its moments, whose specific distinctness it negates. Colour is the sublation of this indifference and indentity, to which form has brought itself. The obscuration of the form is therefore the positing of an
15 individual form-determination as a sublation of the totality of differences. As mechanical totality, body is form which is thoroughly developed within itself. The reduction of this form to abstract indifference is the chromatic obscuration of the individualized body. This posited determinateness is the liberation of singularity, in which shape now posits its
20 parts in a mechanical manner as punctiformity. But this liberation is an indifference which is inherent within the general continuity of shape. The ideality and absolute self-identity of light becomes the form of material individuality which returns to precisely this identity. This is however an identity which, as a reduction of real form to indifference, consti-
25 tutes a specific darkening. It is inner crystallization, which darkens itself by sublating differences of form, and so returning to the pure compact indifference of a high specific gravity. This compactness of dark matter is a being-in-self which, as an inwardly amorphous and merely intensive internal identity, is the *metallicism* which constitutes the principle of all
30 colouring. It is the luminous side of the body represented as substance, and the high specific gravity is precisely the unrevealed being-in-self, the simplicity which has not yet disintegrated. Specific gravity has a significance in metal, but is practically without significance in other bodies.

One of the two moments posited here as a distinct determinateness is
35 therefore pure and abstract identity, which is at the same time the real identity of bodies, and also the materialized identity of the light which is so posited within the body itself as its peculiar colour. It is in this way that this universal element becomes a particular moment, separated from the whole; and the other moment is the antithesis. Transparent being is also
40 undifferentiated, although as it has this characteristic on account of its

form, this lack of differentiation is opposed to the dead and dark undifferentiation we have here. As in the case of spirit, it is the predominance of form which gives it its internal brightness, while the simple compactness of the body with itself, which constitutes the undifferentiation of darkness, is due rather to the dominance of material being. We have already encountered the separation of matter and form in our consideration of epoptic and paroptic colours, where it is the point at which darkness begins, and colours appear. This is also formlessness as separation into single points, but to an even greater extent, it is an externally posited mode of darkening. In itself, amorphous being is not a plurality but an unshaped undifferentiation. Consequently, metallic being does not exhibit much diversity. Metal is not in itself a multiple body, and is neither combustible nor neutral.

It is empirically verifiable that every metal in its reguline state has its particular colour. Schelling says that gold is coagulate light. Iron on the other hand has a tendency towards blackness for it is magnetic. Everything that is coloured may be presented as a metal if its colour is separated as a pigment. This is a matter for empirical investigation. When they are blended, even the colours of plants, such as indigo, have a metallic sheen and a general metallic appearance. The redness of blood may be traced to iron etc. The colour of a metal may be modified however by being brought into a chemical relationship, or even by the action of heat. It is by means of the latter, that the infinitely transient nature of colour becomes apparent. When silver is melted, there is a point at which the metal reaches its brightest lustre; this is its highest degree of fusion, which the metallurgists call the lightening of silver. It is only a momentary phenomenon, and may not be prolonged. Prior to this lightening it runs through all the colours of the rainbow, which shimmer over it in waves in the order red, yellow, green and blue. In a passage which follows that cited above (Rem. II. 137, 30) Goethe says, 'If polished steel is heated, it turns yellow at a certain temperature. If it is quickly removed from the furnace, it retains this colour. As soon as its heat is increased, the yellow darkens, and when the temperature is increased still further, it changes suddenly into purple. It is difficult to retain this colour, for it passes quickly into a light blue. It is possible to retain this fine colour by rapidly removing the steel from the heat and covering it with ashes. This is how blue coloured steel products are manufactured. If one continues to hold the steel over the fire however, it soon becomes bright blue, and remains so. If a pen-knife is held in a flame, a coloured strip will occur across the blade. The part of the strip which went furthest into the flame is bright blue, and shades off

into a bluish-red. Purple occurs in the middle, and is followed by a yellowish-red and then yellow. The explanation of this is to be found in what has been said above. The part of the blade nearest the handle is heated less than the point which is held in the flame. Consequently, all
5 the colours which would otherwise occur successively, must here occur simultaneously, and it is here therefore that one has the best chance
+ of fixing them.' Here also it is merely a change of density which determines chromatic difference therefore, for colour is brought forth by the darkness of the body being posited in various determinations.
10 Consequently, metallicism is the established stability of this physical self-likeness. The colour which is contained by metal is still an intimate aspect of the light which retains its qualitative purity, and has not yet decomposed. It is in fact *lustre*. Metal is opaque, transparency is the lack of light in something to which actual light is alien.

15 The chemical significance of metal is therefore that it is oxidizable; it is an extreme of form, opposed to the neutrality of the same in its reduction to formal undifferentiated identity. A weak acid will easily turn metal white therefore. Lead for example is turned into white lead by acetic acid, and something similar happens in the case of zinc-oxide. Yellow and
20 yellowish red have an affinity with the acids, blue and bluish red with the alkalies. Not only metals change colour through chemical action however. Goethe ('Theory of Colours' part II p. 451) says, 'The juices of all blue and violet flowers are turned green by alkalies and so made brighter, while acids turn them a fine red. The decoctions of red woods, are turned yellow
25 by acids and violet by alkalies; the infusions of yellow plants are darkened by alkalies however, and almost lose their colour entirely through the
+ action of acids.' Similarly, on p. 201 he says, 'Litmus is a coloured material which can be specified into a reddish-blue by alkalies. It is very sensitive to acids, which turn it a reddish yellow, but an application of an alkali
+ will restore its bluish tinge.'

Here we are considering the particularization of the individual body, so that we can only present colour as a moment and a property which nevertheless has the possibility of becoming a substance. Colour does not concern us here in its separation and division as metal therefore. As properties,
35 colours are still held within individuality, although they may also be exhibited as substances. This is possible here because of the impotence of individuality, which is not yet the infinite form which is omnipresent within objectivity as its properties. But properties belong to the kingdom of death if, even in the organic sphere, they are still presented as sub-
40 stances. For since in living being infinite form is objective to itself in its

particularization and identical with itself in its properties, the particularization of this sphere is no longer separable; if it were, the wholeness here would be dead and decomposed.

Colour is now a property which presupposes that it is contained within a subjectivity; but as a particularity, it also has being-for-another, for every property as such only has being for the perception of a living creature. We, sentient subjects, constitute this other, our sense of sight being determined by colours. For sight there are only colours; shape belongs to touch, and is revealed to sight merely through the alternation of shade and brightness. Physical being has withdrawn into itself from touch and from determinate being lacking all quality; it is intro-reflected, and is in its otherness. Gravity, like heat, pertains to touch; colour is a general presence however, a being-for-other, a propagation which certainly resembles that in heat and gravity, but in which at the same time the property remains immediately objective. The nature which first developed itself as its sense of touch, now develops its sense of sight, and so passes over to smell and taste. As colour is for another than itself, this other must leave it to the body; consequently it merely relates itself to it theoretically, not practically. The sense of sight leaves the property as it is; the property certainly has being for it, but the sense does not seize it for itself. As the property belongs to nature however, this must also be a physical relation, it cannot be purely theoretical, as it is to the sense of a living being. Consequently, as it is a property which belongs to the thing itself, it must also be related to other things within the inorganic sphere. Light as a universal element is the other to which colour relates itself. In so far as light is not individualized, and precisely because it is free, it constitutes the other of colour, and so makes a single principle with it. The universal is then the power which forms and perpetually consumes this particular being; light causes all inorganic colour to fade. This is not so in the case of organic beings, which are perpetually renewing their colours. This fading is not yet a chemical process, but an unobtrusive theoretical process, the particular being unable to set anything in opposition to this its universal essence.

> For the elements are hostile,
> To the work of human hands,

as they are to anything individualized, which they decompose. In colour however, it is also the case that the abstract universal ideality of the element is always individualized.

2. Difference in particularized corporeality
(*The properties of opposition*)

§ 321

(*a*) **The principle of one of the members of this difference (being-for-self), is fire (§ 283), which is not yet a real chemical process (§ 316) within the individual body however, nor any longer a mechanical brittleness, but which is rather the implicit combusti-**
5 **bility of physical particularity. This principle, which is at the same time externally differentiated, constitutes the relationship with the negative aspect of elementary universality, i.e. the imperceptible destructiveness of air (§ 282). It is in fact the process of air on corporeality, specific individuality as s i m p l e theoretical**
10 **process, the imperceptible volatilization of the body in air, i.e. odour.**

Remark

+ **It is o d o r o u s m a t t e r, as something existing for itself (§ 126), and as an inflammable oily substance, which constitutes the odorousness of bodies. In the disagreeable smell of metals for**
15 **example, odour exists as a mere property.**

Addition. As it represents itself in the individual body, the opposition or second member of this difference consists of smell and taste, which are the senses of differentiation, and already belong to the self-developing process. They are very closely related, and are not distinguished in Swabia,
20 so that people there only have four senses. A flower is said to have a 'nice *taste*' instead of a 'nice *smell*', so that in so far as we also smell with our
+ tongue, the nose tends to be superfluous.

If we wish to grasp this *transition* more precisely, it is as follows. Since the metallicism or undifferentiated obscurity at which we have arrived is
25 chemically combustible and therefore completely oxidizable, it is a base or extremity which may only be brought into active opposition by an external agent, which must therefore be another corporeal differential such as oxygen etc. This abstract possibility of the combustible substance is
+ only combustible as calx, i.e. once the substance has been oxidized. Once
30 the acid has oxidized the metal, it enters into a state of neutrality with it. It is neutral with regard to the oxide however, not with regard to the

metal itself, i.e. in order to be neutralized, the metal must first be determined as one side of the opposition. Consequently, metal as such is able
to constitute one side of the chemical process; its undifferentiation is
merely a one-sidedness, an abstract determinateness, and precisely for that
reason, essentially related to the opposition. The opposition into which   5
we now enter from differentiation is, in the first instance total however,
for we have not yet reached the onesided opposition of the chemical process, both sides of which are themselves already real corporealities. As we
now have a total opposition, it is not possible to distingish only one side
of it within combustion, for we now have a material which is adequate   10
to the whole process. The combustibility of this material differs from that
of metal, which as it only constitutes one side of the different sides of the
process, is combustible in the ordinary sense of the word. As it forms the
whole possibility of the opposition, this material is the basic principle of
smell however. Smell is the sensation of this slow and immanent con-   15
sumption of the body in air. Air itself has no odour, precisely because it
simply decomposes odours, and everything loses its smell within it, just
as colours fade away in light. Whereas colour merely constitutes the abstract identity of bodies however, odour is their specific individuality as
concentrated within differentiation. It is their entire specificality as turned   20
outwards and consuming itself in this diffusion, for the body becomes
stale and dead if it loses its odour. This consumption of the body is process
which has no process; it is not a relationship to fire, as is a flame, which is
a consuming of an individuality itself within individual shape. It is usually
the case however, that in inorganic being, such a concentration occurs   25
only as fire. Fragrancy tends to occur only in organic being, in flowers
for example. Consequently, as metals are not total bodies, they do not
smell as such, but only in so far as they consume themselves by being
integrated into another body, and forming a certain atmosphere about
themselves. It is in this way that they become poisonous, and so also have   +
a disagreeable taste. This does not happen to the same extent with precious
metals however, simply because they do not lose their reguline shape so
easily. It is for this reason that eating utensils are so often made from them.
Just as light has a particular existence in metal, so fire has a particular
existence in odour. This is not the real existence of the independent   35
matter of sulphur however, it is merely the existence of an abstract   +
property.

§ 322

(b) **The other moment of the opposition,** *neutrality* (§ 284), individualizes **itself** into the specific **physical** neutrality of salinity, **and its determinations such as** acid etc. **This is the property
of** *taste,* **which at the same time remains in relationship with the
abstract neutrality of water, the element in which the merely
neutral part of the body is soluble. Conversely, the abstract
neutrality which is contained within this body is separable from
the physical constituents of its concrete neutrality, and may be
exhibited as water of crystallization, although this does not of
course exist as water in a neutral body which has not yet been
resolved. (§ 286 Rem.).**

Addition. The water of crystallization first comes into existence as water
in decomposition. It is supposed to be latent again in the crystal, but it is
certainly not there as water, for the crystal exhibits no trace of moisture.
Taste is the third particularity of the body, and as the result of its
neutrality, it has sublated this relationship to the element once again, and
drawn itself away from it. Consequently, the process here does not always
have immediate existence as it does in the case of odour; it rests rather
upon a chance encounter of the two sides. Water and salt therefore exist
in a state of mutual indifference, and taste is the real process in which
corporeal individualities pass into one another, and not into the elements.
Consequently, while combustible matter forms a process which is united
without difference in a single term, the neutral body may be decomposed
into acid and base (II. 161, 29). As abstract neutrality, water is tasteless
again; it is only with individualized neutrality that taste occurs as the unity
of opposites which have subsided into passive neutrality. It is therefore
only neutral bodies such as salts, which decompose into their opposites,
which have a definite taste. It is with reference to our sense that we call it
taste, but the other side here is still the element, and the precise condition
for bodies being tasted is that they should be soluble in water. Unlike salt,
metal is not the unity of opposites, and consequently it cannot dissolve
itself in water, but is in general an incomplete body which only regains
its completeness in ore for example. This will be treated as part of the
chemical process.
Colour, odour, and taste are the three determinations of the particularization of the individual body. With taste, the body passes over into the

reality of the chemical process, although this transition is by no means reached as yet. Here, in the first instance, these determinations are still related to the universal elements as the properties of bodies, and it is this which constitutes their incipient volatilization. The penetration and infection of the power of the universal meets no opposition, because the universal is itself the essence of the particular, and is already *implicitly* contained within it. In organic being, it is by means of the inner universality of the genus that the annihilation of the individual is brought about. We shall discover the same bodies in the chemical process, but there they will be independent entities in process *with one another* (see § 320 Add. II. 159, 31), they will no longer be in process with the elements. This begins already in electricity, and it is to this therefore that we have to make our transition. As individualities, these properties are of course also related to one another. As we posit their relation by comparing them, the matter appears at first to concern us alone; it has a further factor however, for the individual corporealities relate themselves to others precisely because they are particulars. Initially therefore, the individualized bodies do not merely subsist in a state of indifference, as in the immediate totality of the crystal, nor do they merely constitute physical differences as differentiations of the elements, for they also have a double relationship to one another. In the first instance, these particularizations are only superficially inter-related, and preserve their independence; as such, they therefore constitute that electric state, which appears throughout the totality of a body. The real relation is the passing of these bodies into one another however; it is this which constitutes the chemical process, and which expresses the deeper aspect of this relationship.

3. Totality in particular individuality; electricity
(*Electricity*)

§ 323

Bodies stand in relation to the elements in accordance with their determinate particularity; as shaped wholes however, they also enter into relationship with one another as physical individualities. They are *independent* **through a particularity which has not yet entered the chemical process, and** *preserves* **their mutual indifference within a wholly mechanical relationship. Within this mechanical relationship they manifest their self as sound, which is an** *internal* **oscillation, a motion of an ideal**

nature. Now however **it is as their light, in the** reciprocal **physical tension of their particularity, that they exhibit** the *real nature* of their selfhood. **Nevertheless, although this selfhood is at the same time an abstract reality, it is an intrinsically differen-**
5 **tiated light**—*electrical* relationship.

Addition. Electricity is a notable phenomenon. Like magnetism, it was formerly taken to be isolated, and was regarded as an appendage (see above § 313 Add. II. 109, 3). We have already indicated the connection between electricity and the phenomena most closely connected with it
10 (prec. § Add.), and we shall now compare it with the earlier stage of sound. It was with sound that we entered into shape. At the stage imme-diately preceding its dissolution within the chemical process, shape is pure and self-identical form, and it is this as electric light. It is the abstract soul of the body which appears in sound, although this revelation of its
15 selfhood belongs solely to the field of mechanical cohesion, for the body appears as a mechanical totality in the constant motion of its return–into-self. Here however, we find no such mechanical self-preservation, only a self-preservation as regards physical reality. The determinate being of electrical tension is a physical phenomenon. Just as sound depends upon
20 the striking of another body, so electricity too is certainly conditioned, for two bodies are necessary in order to produce it. The difference is however that in electricity, the two bodies are differentiated with regard to one another, so that the stimulant also enters into the differentiation. In sound on the contrary, there is either only one sounding body, or else
25 the sounds of both are mutually indifferent. The ground of this progress lies in the physically individualized bodies, as the totality of their proper-ties, having differentiatedly related themselves to one another. Although to our senses, these properties fall apart, they are united by the bond of the individual body in precisely the same way as our sensuous representation
30 of things reconnects them into a unity. It is now this individual totality which enters into relation, and it is from precisely this standpoint that we now have to consider this relationship. As a developed totality, the body is however a differentiated totality, and as this differentiation remains a totality, it is merely differentiation in general, and therefore requires the
35 reciprocal relation of two terms.
　　As the physical body is now before us as a physical totality, we have the immediate implication of a plurality of such bodies, for logic has clearly
+ demonstrated how the one multiplies itself into the many (§ 97 Add.). If this multiplicity of bodies is also in a state of mutual indifference, this

indifference will sublate itself, for the bodies are differentiated with regard to each other through their having to posit their totalities. In the relation which arises out of this positedness, they display themselves as physical totalities with regard to one another, and as they are these wholes, they must at the time remain what they are. It is precisely because they remain what they are that their relation is at first a mechanical one; the bodies touch and create *friction*. This takes place through external force, but as they are to remain totalities, this external relationship is not the kind of contact we had previously. It is not a shattering brought about by the resistance of cohesion; it does not produce sound, nor is it a force which breaks out into heat or flame, and consumes bodies. It is therefore only a slight friction or surface pressure, it is the impact by means of which *one* of the indifferent bodies posits itself where the other is. It can also arise when shape is struck and noise is created, so that determinate being has its pure inner negativity posited as vibration. It is through this that there is a positing of a sundered unity, of two terms which are independent and indifferent. This constitutes the magnet, both poles of which are the free shapes which divide its opposition between them; this they do so that its middle exists as a free negativity which in itself has no determinate being, and is only there on account of its members. Electricity is the pure consummation of shape, and so frees itself from it. It is shape which is beginning to sublate its indifference, for it is the immediate emergence of determinate being which is one the verge of leaving shape, but is nevertheless still conditioned by it. It is not yet the dissolution of shape itself; it is the superficial process, differentiations of which are leaving shape, although they still have it as their condition, and cannot yet stand alone. It is because its necessity is only implicit that this relationship appears to be contingent. It is not a difficult relationship to grasp, but it can be surprising at first to discover that it is electricity, and in order to demonstrate that it is so, we shall have to compare this determination of the Notion with the phenomenon.

§ 324

Mechanical contact **posits the physical** differentiation of **one body in another; as these differentials simultaneously preserve their mechanical independence of one another, their** mutual opposition constitutes a tension. **Consequently, the physical** nature of the body does not enter into this *tension* **in its concrete** determinateness; **it is** only **as the** reality of its *abstract* self **as** *light*, and indeed as an opposition, **that individuality**

manifests and adapts itself within the process. This sublation of
diremption, which is the other moment of this **superficial**
process, produces an undifferentiated light. As this light is
incorporeal it immediately disappears, and apart from this
5 abstract physical phenomenon, produces nothing of significance except the mechanical effect of a shock.

Remark

It is difficult to grasp the Notion of electricity, partly because
of the basic determination of an inertia, both physical and mechanical, ascribed to the individual body in this process. It is because of
10 this that electrical tension is attributed to another principle, i.e.
the matter which is the source of that light which comes forth
abstractly for itself, and distinguished from the concrete reality of
the body which remains independent of it. Secondly, there is the
general difficulty of the Notion as such, of grasping light in its
15 relatedness as a moment of the totality. What is more, light here
is no longer free, as sunlight is, but is a moment of the particular
body, for implicitly it is the pure self of the body, and enters
into existence as engendered within its immanence. The origin of
the primordial light of the sun (§ 275), takes place only in the No-
20 tion as such. This originating also takes place here (as in § 306),
but the light is differentiated, and arises out of an existence, in
which the Notion is existing as a particular body.

It is a familiar fact that through the completion of empirical investigation, the old distinction between *vitreous* and
25 *resinous electricity*, in which difference was defined in terms
of a specific and sensuous existence, has been idealized into
the *speculative distinction* between *positive* and *negative* elec-
+ tricity. Empiricism generally attempts to grasp and retain
the universal in *sensuous* form, here however we have a re-
30 markable instance of its having sublated its **sensuous** material.
There has been a lot of talk recently about the *polarization
of light*, but it would have been more fitting to have reserved this expression for electricity, instead of applying it
to the phenomena observed by *Malus*, in which transparent
35 media, various mutual positionings of reflecting surfaces,
**and many further circumstances, produce an external difference
in the appearance of light, but produce no difference in light**

itself (see § 278, § 319, **and** § 320). The conditions under which positive and negative electricity are produced, a smoother or rougher surface for instance, a puff of air and so on, are evidence of the *superficial* character of the electrical process, and of the minimal extent to which the concrete physical 5 nature of the body is involved in it. The faint colouring of both electric lights, their smell and taste, also indicate that electricity only constitutes the *incipient* corporeality of the abstract self of light. **The tension of its process is physical but not concrete, and** it is here that it maintains itself. The nega- 10 tivity which removes the oppositional tension is predominantly a *shock*. The self which posits its self-identity **through its diremption** also persists as **this totalization** in the **external** sphere of *mechanics*. Light occurs **in** the discharge-flash, but is scarcely able to materialize itself into *heat*, and according 15 to Berthollet ('Statique Chimique' pt. I sect. III n. XI), the *ignition* which can take place in this so-called discharge, is the direct *effect* of shock rather than the realization of light in fire. +

Electricity resembles magnetism (§ 314) **in that when both elec-** 20 **tricities are separated from one another and maintained in different bodies, Notional determination occurs, the activity of which consists of positing identity in opposition and opposition in identity. On the one side this is the mechanizing activity of spatial attraction and repulsion, which in so far as it can occur as** 25 **a separate phenomenon, establishes the connection between electricity and magnetism as such. On the other side, it is a physical activity, and manifests itself in the interesting phenomena of transmission, or of electrical conduction as such, and as induction.** 30

Addition. This electrical relationship is activity, but as it is not yet product, it is an abstract activity; it is only present where the contradiction of the tension is not yet resolved, so that each term, while maintaining its independence, contains its opposite.

This is not a simple internal mechanical tension between parts, for it is 35 essential that it should express itself. This expression must be different from the corporeality of the individual, which remains what it is in differentiation. Consequently it only occurs at first in its universal individuality, without its real corporeality entering into this process; that is why this

expression is still abstractly physical, so that the body only displays its differentiation by its general shining. Consequently, the body displays its physical soul as light; whereas the light of the sun is immediate and free however, this light is elicited by the force of another body. Here there-
5 fore, light is the mode of determinate being in mutually opposed bodies. This tensioned light has a tendency to differentiate itself on something else, yet precisely because the differentiation is not yet independent, but is merely abstract, the differentials only show themselves as light in their disappearance. In the flame produced by friction, light is the culminating
10 point in the destruction of the body; even the spark struck from a stone is a sublation of cohesion, and concentration of parts into a single point. Electric light is different however, for in this case ideality occurs as a preserving factor, a gentle fire; the spark is cold, a mere light, which as yet
+ has no nutriment. The reason for this is that the particular materiature of a
15 tensioned body has not yet entered into the process, but is merely deter- mined there in an elemental fashion as soul. As it is differentiated, light is no longer pure however, but is already coloured. The negative spark has a tinge of red, and the positive a bluish light. And since light is ideality breaking forth from physical being, the other physical determinations of
20 total individuality, odour and taste, also begin to appear, although in a completely ideal and immaterial way. Electricity smells, and when it is brought close to the nose for example it makes an impression similar to that created by a cobweb. Although it does so incorporeally, it also effects taste by means of its lights, one of which tastes more acid, and the other
+ more alkaline. Finally, figurations are formed. Positive electricity has an elongated radiation spark, while the negative spark is concentrated more into points. This may be observed when both sparks are brought to bear
+ upon powdered colophony.

Reflection habitually regards the corporeal individual as a dead being
30 which only enters into external mechanical contact or chemical relation- ship. Consequently, the expression of tension which we have here is ascribed not to the body itself, but to another body, of which the first is merely a vehicle. It is this second body which has been called *electrical*
+ *matter*. This conception implies that the body is merely a sponge which
35 allows matter of this kind to circulate within it, while it remains what it is, apart from its various degrees of receptivity. This would merely be transmission however, it would not be an activity which is immanent within the body. What is more, electricity is supposed to be the cause of everything in nature, and particularly of meteorological phenomena.
40 What electricity is supposed to have done cannot be indicated however.

Since it is neither matter nor a diffusion of things, it appears on the whole to resemble magnetism, in that it is somewhat superfluous. The activities of both appear to have an extremely limited effect; magnetism is the principle by which the iron needle points north, and electricity gives rise to the production of a spark. This occurs everywhere, but that is all, or almost all there is to it. Electricity appears then as an occult agent, and resembles the occult qualities assumed by the scholastics. If it occurs in storms, it is difficult to see why it should occur elsewhere. Vast natural phenomena such as storms should not be thought of on the analogy of our chemical kitchens however. How can clouds collide when they are even softer than a sponge? When there is lightning, and the rain is falling so that the whole sky is enveloped in a mantle of humidity, all electrical tension must be immediately neutralized, for the falling rain connects the clouds with the earth, and is a perfect conductor (see above § 286 II. 44, 22). Even if electricity is present here however, its significance, i.e. its necessary connection and relationship with corporeal nature, is not indicated. Electricity is in fact the universal scapegoat, everything is electric. It is an indeterminate word however, and does not indicate the function of the electricity. We, however, regard electrical tension as the intrinsic selfhood of the physical totality of a body which maintains itself in its contact with another body. What we see is an upsurge of anger in the body; there is no one there but the body itself, least of all any alien matter. Its youthfulness breaks out, it raises itself on its hind legs; in opposing its connection with another its physical nature gathers its forces into the abstract ideality of light. It is not only we who compare bodies, for they compare themselves, and in this comparison maintain their physical nature. This constitutes the initiation of organic being, which also maintains its distinctness from its means of sustenance. The main point here is that the activity of the body consists of its immanent physical refractoriness.

It should be noticed here that that which we had initially as an immediate determination, is now positive. As crystal, shape was immediately transparent, just as the independent heavenly bodies were immediate light. The individual body does not shine in an immediate manner however, and is not in itself light, because as shape it is not abstract ideality. As an explicated and developed unity, it includes the determination of the heavenly bodies in its individuality as a property, and in its immediacy it is therefore merely the shining of another individual body within it, which takes place by means of it. Through form, the crystal has certainly brought back the difference of material being-for-self into a unity. In its determinations, this unity of form is not yet physical identity, however,

but is merely a mechanical totality which is determined within itself. Light on the contrary is physical ideality. Crystal is this ideality, but only *implicitly*, because it is not self-illuminating, and only displays it in its reaction to another. That which it is implicitly now has to be posited however.
5 Posited within developed totality, this ideality will then no longer be the mere shining of that which is seen, an alien and incident light, but will be the simple totality of the shining of one self in the face of another. This means that as unity of form now posits its self-identity, crystal constitutes itself here as sun; the light which occurs within it as a differentiated self, dis-
10 plays its totality only in its specificality as a simple physical existence.

How does electrical differentiation arise? How is this opposition related to the physical properties of bodies? Electricity manifests itself wherever
+ two bodies come into contact, and especially when friction occurs. It is not only produced by the electrical machine therefore, for any pressure or
15 concussion will posit electrical tension, although contact is an essential condition. Electricity is not a specific or particular phenomenon which only occurs in amber or sealing-wax etc., it occurs in all bodies which are in contact with any other body. It is only necessary to make use of a very
+ sensitive electrometer in order to be convinced that this is so. The high
20 spirits of the body appear whenever it is stimulated, and all bodies display this vitality towards one another. Even if it is mainly positive electricity which appears in glass, and negative electricity in resin (Biot and the
+ French in general still speak of 'electricité résineuse et vitreuse'), this is still an extremely narrow distinction, for all bodies are electrical, including
25 metals, although they have to be insulated. What is more, negative electricity also occurs in glass; the kind of electricity produced depends upon a glass plate's being polished or rough. It is merely factors such as this
+ which exhibit the difference. *Hauy* ('Traité de minéralogie' vol. I p. 237) says, 'Electricity divides the mineral kingdom into three great sections,
30 which correspond to the general orders of minerals. Nearly all stones and salts of a certain degree of purity become positively electric when submitted to friction, while combustible substances such as resin, sulphur, and even diamonds become negatively electric. Metals are conductors.' Consequently, the neutral substance possesses positive electricity; the
35 differentiated substance which is for itself and belongs to fire and negative being, displays negative electricity; and the internally undifferentiated substance, which is completely uniform and internally fluid by nature, is conductive. Almost all liquids are therefore conductors, oil being the only exception on account of its combustibility. Broadly speaking, this consti-
40 tutes the general connection between electricity and specific natural

qualities; it is so superficial however, that the slightest modification of these bodies suffices to bring about an alteration in electricity. Wax and silk for example, are bad conductors; if the first is melted and the second heated however, they become good conductors, since the heat makes them fluid. Ice is a good conductor; dry air and gases on the other hand are very 5 bad conductors. If polished glass is rubbed with a woollen material, it becomes positively electric, while if it is rubbed with a catskin it becomes negatively so. If silk is rubbed with resin, negative electricity results, while if it is rubbed with polished glass, the result is positive. If two very similar glass tubes are rubbed together, one becomes positively and the 10 other negatively electric, and exactly the same takes place if two sticks of sealing-wax are used. If one takes two silk ribbons of the same kind and strokes one of them in a transversal direction, it becomes negative, while if the other is stroked lengthwise, it becomes positive. If two people are insulated—if they are not, their electricity will not be individualized from + that of the rest of the Earth—and one holds a catskin in his hand and rubs the other's clothes with it, the first will become positively electric, the second negatively so, the difference being due to the activity of the first party. If molten sulphur is poured into insulated metal vessels, the sulphur acquires positive, the metal negative electricity. *Biot* (vol. II pp. 356–359) + indicates a principal factor, 'When the surfaces of two bodies are rubbed + together, positive electricity seems to occur where the particles are least separated, and make fewer deviations from their natural position relative to one another. Conversely, that of the two surfaces whose particles are more scattered by the other's roughness, is more disposed to negative 25 electricity. This tendency increases if the surface undergoes a true expansion. When an animal or vegetable substance which is solid and dry is rubbed against a rough metallic surface, it becomes negatively electric because of the greater displacement of its parts. If such a substance is rubbed against very smooth metal however, so that there is very little altera- 30 tion in its surface, the effect being limited to pressure, and the removal of individual particles, it either shows signs of positive electricity, or of + none at all. When one rubs the hairy part of a catskin on a polished or unpolished metallic surface, the hairs have to give way to the pressure whole maintaining their relative position with regard to one another; 35 consequently, they are positively electric. If the same hairs are woven into a material, which involves their being displaced, twisted and pressed back on themselves, and are then rubbed against an unpolished (dépolie) metallic surface, they are not only compressed, but also separated from one another by the asperities of the surface. Unless the metallic surface has a 40

certain degree of smoothness, this will result in their becoming negatively electric.' Colour also makes a difference, 'If a new black silken material is rubbed against a white silk ribbon, it becomes negatively electric, the reason being evidently, that the black colouring of the material gives rise
5 to a greater roughness on its surface. If the black material has been used however, and its colour has rubbed off somewhat, it becomes positively electric when rubbed against a white ribbon. If a white (silk?) ribbon is rubbed against a white woollen material, it shows signs of negative electricity, while if it is rubbed against a woollen material which has been
10 dyed black, it shows signs of positive electricity.' The qualities which give rise to the difference can be either essential or superficial therefore.

Pohl, in his review of the first three volumes of '*Gehler's* Dictionary of Physics' edited by *Munke* ('Berlin Yearbooks for Scientific Criticism'
+ Oct. 1829 nr. 54 p. 430 ff.), writes, 'It has to be recognized that electrical
15 opposition, in almost the same way as the opposition of colours, gives nothing but faint indications of the extremely changeable chemical opposition of oxidation and disoxidation, which is frequently still quite independent of the conditions and the more solid internal qualitative relationships of the mass involved; also, that where there is a reciprocal inter-
20 action between substances under apparently identical conditions, and where the most meticulous and painstaking observation brings to light no further modifications, nature, in the nimble dalliance of its playful urge towards manifestation, casts the $+$ and $-$ of electrical opposition to one side or the other with an almost complete abandon. This activity might be
25 compared to the way in which it sends forth the same species, with either red or blue corollas, from the seed of a single plant.

The isolated subsistence of causal relationships is a false hypothesis, imported without question into phenomenology; it has been most widespread and pernicious and has been driven to its furthest extremes in
30 the treatment of electrical phenomena, where it has been bandied about as the conception of electrical motion and currents. That which is really no more than the faint stirring of an incipient chemical process, is regarded as a separate self-subsistent fluid X, which persists throughout all phenomenal change. Consequently, there is no thought of tracing the
35 process as such through its further development, and noting the natural context of its determinations. As the result of adherence to this conception, that which constitutes the true inner movement and development of the process itself, is immediately subsumed under the empty schema of the simply external movement attributed to this fictitious electrical fluid. It is
40 regarded as a current and treated exclusively, as if it constituted a second

kind of activity within the fundamental electrical substratum, complementary to the original form of the relation as it expresses itself in tension.

This view of the matter has obviated any just and natural assessment of the phenomena, and has proved to be a source of superficial and erroneous conclusions. It is as the result of it that the whole body of electric and galvanic theory propounded so far, as well as the individual observations which have been made, and including the errors and absurdities of all the various kinds of experimentation carried out recently by galvanists and electro-chemists, has lost direction.

Even before Ørsted's discovery, it was hardly reasonable to claim empirical evidence for the assumption that electricity was still actively present even when the most sensitive electrometer had failed to yield the faintest indication of it. Now however it is completely unjustifiable to make this claim if, in situations in which the electrometer has persistently shown no response, one now sees immediately that the magnetic needle indicates the presence, not of the electricity so long assumed to be there, but of magnetism.'

Electricity is infinite form differentiated within itself, and is the unity of these differentials; consequently the two bodies are inseparably bound together, like the north and south poles of a magnet. Magnetism is mere mechanical activity however, and is therefore merely an opposition in the activity of movement; as it has neither light, colour, odour, nor taste, it may be neither seen, smelt, tasted, nor felt. In electricity however these fluctuating differentials are physical, for they are in the light; any further material particularization of bodies would give rise to the chemical process. In so far as the differential is active in electricity, and remains active as a differential, it is true that this activity too can only subsist in mechanical being or motion. Like magnetism, it is an approach and a withdrawal, and it is this feature of it which explains playthings such as electric rain and electric chimes etc. Negative electricity is attracted by positive electricity, but repulsed by negative. In that the differentials unite themselves, they communicate themselves to each other; as soon as they have posited a unity, they fly apart again, and vice versa. Only one body, devoid as yet of physical determinateness, is necessary for magnetism, and it need only be the substratum of this activity. In the electrical process, each of the two distinct bodies has a differentiated determination which is only posited through the other, but in the face of which the further individuality of the body remains free and distinct. Consequently, the two electricities could not exist unless each had its own individual body. In other words, one electrical body only has one kind of electricity, but causes the body

174

outside it to be charged with the opposite kind; and where there is only one kind, the other is at once present. One and the same body does not determine its own polarity as in magnetism however. Like magnetism, electricity has the basic determination of the syllogism therefore, but in

+ electricity the *opposition* has an existence of its own. This is why *Schelling*
+ has called electricity a ruptured magnetism. Its process is more concrete than that of magnetism, but less concrete than that of chemism. Its tensioned extremities do not yet constitute the actuality of a total process, they are still independent, so that their process is still their abstract self. Their

10 physical differentiation does not constitute the whole of corporeality, and electricity is therefore only the abstract totality of the physical sphere. Consequently, magnetism is in the sphere of shape, what electricity is in the sphere of physical totality.

An electrically charged body can communicate its electricity, particu-
15 larly to conductors such as metals. When a metal is insulted however, it can equally well acquire its own electricity as self-differentiation: this is also the case with glass, although it is not a conductor. When electricity is communicated to various bodies it remains the same however, so that the bodies repulse one another. The physicists now make a further distinction

20 between the transmission of electricity, and electricity which displays
+ itself through induction. The second of these is as follows:—A is a body charged with positive electricity. If an insulated conducting cylinder B is then placed close to this electrically determinate body without actually touching it, it will also give evidence of electricity. The end of the cylin-
25 der closest to A will become negative, the opposite end positive, and the middle neutral however. Two further cases are to be noted here. (a) If B is removed from A's electric field its electricity disappears. (b) If B is not moved, and its positive end is brought into contact with a third body C, which through this transmission takes the positive charge from B, B
30 remains electric when removed from A's field, but only negatively so. The reason for this is that two individual bodies are needed in order to fix electricity, for positive and negative both need a body. As long as body B is not touched, tension and differentiation are within it as they are in magnetism, although this does not constitute its individual determinate-
35 ness. It only receives its determination by being brought into the proximity of another body, which already has its own determination. Consequently, as a conductor it remains undifferentiated, but as it is at the same time in the electrical sphere, it can, as extended, allow the different determinations to appear within it. Although it therefore possesses both
40 electricities, electricity does not exist within it as its own determination.

The individual existence of electricity first occurs when the body contains one electricity, and in order for this to be the case, it must be opposed by another body. As the undifferentiation of B is removed through this contact, and the opposite electricity to that which it turns to body A passes over into body C, with which it is in contact, body B becomes 5 charged with the other electricity. What is more, since the opposition of these bodies is already united through their proximity, the negative electricity of body B becomes stronger as its distance from A increases; conversely, its intensity weakens as this distance diminishes. If two glass plates are rubbed together, while their insulation is maintained, they will show 10 no trace of electricity when they are pressed close together, although they will do so when they are separated. The effect will not be the same with insulated metal plates, because their electricity also implicitly neutralizes itself. If two spheres of the same size and electricity are brought into contact, the electrical intensity at their point of contact is nil, and increases with 15 the distance from this point. If spheres of unequal size and the same electricity are used, the electricity at their point of contact is also nil; when they are separated however, the point of contact on the smaller sphere is negative. As the distance between them is increased, this determination disappears, and the whole of the smaller sphere becomes positive. It is 20 inequality in the amount of electricity which produces this opposition. +
Hauy ('Traité de Minéralogie' vol. I p. 237) also notices that when tourmaline and many other crystals whose forms are not symmetrical are placed in warm water or on hot coals, electric poles are formed at just those parts of their extremities which preclude symmetry, while their 25 middles remain undifferentiated. +

The *effects* of electricity are mainly to be seen in the removal of tension. If the electrified body is brought into contact with water, the tension ceases. The amount of electricity that a body can take up depends upon its surface. A bottle can be electrified until it breaks, for the tension can be- 30 come too great for the glass to bear. The primary removal of tension takes place when the two electricities come into contact. Each is incomplete without the other, and they want to totalize themselves. If they are kept apart they are in a state of force. The insubstantial opposites have no subsistence; they constitute a spontaneously self-sublating tension. As thus 35 collapsing into their unity, they are electric light, appearing in its disappearance. The essence of this light is however the negativity of the indifferent determinate being of shape, which itself has determinate being. The light breaks into shape, and by shattering its indifference, draws inner and outer form into a unity. The form which has become like itself is the light which bursts forth from within and 40

176

flows together with external light. It is the being-in-self of gravity which destroys itself, and which by its disappearance becomes precisely that powerless and simple light which is completely identical with its external counterpart.
+ Plato takes this fusion of internal and external light to be the principle of vision.
5 Through the connection set up between the tensioned bodies, one differentiation invades the other as both electricities integrate. This merely produces an ebullition however, the loss of both abstract determinations, and the compenetration of these sparks. The main result is the destruction of the bodies brought into contact. Electricity shatters pieces of wood, kills
10 animals, breaks panes of glass, heats and fuses metal wires, volatilizes gold
+ etc. Volta's pistol shows that the effects brought about by electricity may also be produced by mechanical pressure. This instrument is charged with two parts hydrogen to one part oxygen, and an electric spark then turns
+ these gases into water. The decomposition of water constitutes the chemi
15 cal aspect in the electrical process. It is precisely because the individuality of the body does not enter into the tension, that electrical activity can only display itself physically in the abstract neutrality of water. It has the power of decomposing water into hydrogen and oxygen. We already know however (see above § 286 Add. II. 46, 37), that these gases are not the in
20 gredients of water, but merely the abstract forms in which water appears, for in the galvanic process, there are no bubbles to be seen moving about in the glass tube, and if an acid is introduced into the middle of the tube it will also remain unchanged. This would not be the case if these gases
+ moved along the tube.

§ 325

25 The *particularization* of the individual body is not confined to the inert variety and separate activity of the various terms from which the pure abstract selfhood of the light-principle comes forth into process as the tension between opposites, and the resolution of the same into their undifferentiation. Since the
30 particular properties are merely the reality of this simple Notion, the body of the *light* which constitutes their soul, and since the complex of properties constituting the particular body is not truly independent, the *entire* corporeality enters into tension, and into a process which is at the same time the becom
+ ing of the individual body. Shape, which at first proceeded only from the Notion, and was therefore only posited implicitly, now also proceeds out of the existent process, and presents itself as posited existence. This is the *chemical process*.

Addition. We began with shape in its immediacy, and recognized it as a necessary moment of the Notion; it must also display itself at the end as existing however, i.e. as proceeding out of the process. The immediacy of the body presupposes the reality of the chemical process. Thus, although parents are the immediacy from which one begins, they then also deter- 5 mine themselves as being posited in the sphere of existence. Shape passes + into this third moment in accordance with the Notion; but the third moment is rather the first term from which that which was formerly the first term first proceeds. This is grounded in a deeper logical progres- sion. Particularization is not confined to difference as the tension of ab- 10 stract selfhood. The body in its particularity is not independent, and is not selfsubsistent, it is a link in the chain, and is related to another. This is the omnipotence of the Notion, which we have already seen in the elec- trical process. In this stimulation of one body by another, it is only the abstract selfhood of the body which is taken up and made manifest. 15 The process must become the essentially real process of corporeal deter- minations, which engages the whole of corporeality. The relativity of the body must appear, and it is this appearance which constitutes the alteration of the body within the chemical process.

C

The chemical process

§ 326

The moments of the developed totality of individuality are 20 **themselves determined as individual totalities, as wholly particu- lar bodies, and are at the same time only moments, related to one another as differentials. As the identity of non-identical indepen- dent bodies, this relation is a contradiction. It is therefore essen- tially a process, the determination of which conforms to the** 25 **Notion, in that it posits that which is different as identical and un- differentiated, and that which is identical as differentiated, acti- vated and separated.**

Addition. In order to understand the *general position* and *nature of the* 30 *chemical process,* we have to look forwards and backwards. The chemical process is the third moment of shape. The second moment was dif- ferentiated shape, and its abstract process or electricity. Before shape was

completed and neutral, it also had a process in magnetism. Just as shape is the unity of the Notion and of reality, so the mere primary abstract activity of magnetism is the Notion of shape. The second moment is electricity, or the particularization of shape in itself and with regard to
5 its other. The third moment is the self-realizing motivity of the chemical process, which is the true reality of the Notion in this sphere. Like magnetism, it is a single form, which divides itself into differentials and exists as a unity; yet it is not confined to this. Difference within a single body occurs in magnetism. In electricity each differential belongs to a distinct
10 body; each differential is independent, and the whole of shape does not enter into this process. The chemical process is the totality of the animation of inorganic individuality, for it exhibits whole and physically determined shapes. Bodies enter into the process not only on account of their having odour, taste and colour, but as odorous, gustable, or coloured
15 matter. Their relation is not motion, but the alteration of their entire material differentiation, the passing away of their distinguishing character. The light of the body, which constitutes its abstract relation, is not merely abstract, but is essentially particularized. Consequently, the whole corporeality enters into this process, and the chemical process is therefore
20 the reality of the electrical process. We have the whole shape therefore, as in magnetism, but it is not single, for there are now distinct wholes. The two sides into which form divides itself are the whole bodies therefore, such as metals, acids, and alkalies, the truth of which consists in their entering into relation. The electrical moment here consists of these sides
25 falling apart into a distinct independence which is not yet present in magnetism. The indivisible unity of magnetism is however the governing principle here; this identity of both bodies, whereby they return once more into the magnetic relationship, is lacking in the electrical process.

The chemical process is therefore the unity of magnetism and electri-
30 city; these constitute the abstract formal sides of this totality, and consequently do not constitute the same process. Every chemical process has magnetism and electricity implicit within it, but these moments are unable
+ to come forth in their distinctness within what one might call the saturated course of this process; they are only able to do so where the process itself
35 appears in an abstract manner, and does not attain its complete reality. This is the case in the universal individuality of the Earth. By itself, the chemical process constitutes the universal process of the Earth; but one has to distinguish here between the processes of special and of universal individuality. The second of these is self-maintaining, and despite its
40 animation even the chemical process can only appear within it in an

abstract universal manner. The Earth in its individuality is not a particular existence which can resolve itself and achieve self-neutralization of a real nature within another, for it persists in its universal individuality, and therefore does not enter into the chemical process which affects the whole + shape. It is only in so far as its existence is not universal, and so divides 5 itself into its particular bodies, that it enters into chemical process. We have seen the chemism of the Earth as the meteorological process. This is the process of the physical elements, which as universal determined matters are not yet individual corporealities. Since the chemical process exists here in this abstract manner, it is here too that its abstract moments 10 occur, and as this change takes place outside the Earth, it is also here that magnetism and the electrical tension of the storm make their appearance. Lightning and the northern lights etc. belong to the electricity of the Earth however, which *differs* from ordinary electricity, and is connected with completely different conditions (see above § 286 Add. II. 44, 22; 15 § 324 Add. II. 169, 38). Magnetism and electricity are merely carried by the chemical process, and are first posited through the universal process of the Earth itself. The Magnetism which determines the individual magnetic needle is a variable factor, and depends upon the internal process of the Earth, and upon the meteorological process. *Parry*, on his expedition to 20 the north pole, found that the magnetic needle became quite indefinite, so that if in a thick fog it pointed north for example, this was completely fortuitous. The activity of the needle ceased, and one could point it wherever one wanted to. Electrical phenomena such as the northern + lights etc. are considerably more variable. The northern lights have been 25 observed at midday, and to the south of England, and even of Spain. They + are therefore merely moments of the total process, upon which they are dependent. The chemical process, certainly produces electrical tension, particularly in its galvanic form, but it also carries a magnetic disposition. This dependence of magnetism upon the chemical process is one of the 30 most remarkable of recent discoveries. The north-south polarity of the Earth, the direction of its stationary axis, is determined by the east-west polarity of its general revolution as it turns upon its axis. *Oersted* discovered that in so far as electrical and magnetic activity are related to space as directions, they are also opposites which cross one another. The + direction of electrical activity is east-west, while that of magnetic activity is north-south, although this can also be reversed (cf. above § 313 Add. II. 109, 37). Magnetism however is, essentially, a merely spatial activity, while electricity is already somewhat more physical. The further importance of this discovery is that it also indicates the conjunction and 40 simultaneity of these moments within the chemical process of individual corporeality; the precise reason for its so doing so is that it shows that they issue from the galvanic process as the separate and distinct phenomena of electricity and chemism.

5 Philosophically systematic consideration differs from an empirical approach in that it presents the stages of determinations, and not the stages of the concrete existences of nature as totalities. Thus, when the Earth is, in the first instance, considered as a planet, this does not exhaust its concrete nature; on the contrary, the further determination of physical 10 moments is a further determination of the Earth, that is to say, in so far as the Earth as a universal individual is capable of further determination, for the finite relationships of individual bodies do not apply to it. The case is precisely the same with regard to these individual bodies. The progression of these stages and their inter-relatedness is one thing, body as such is 15 another. The individual body unites all these determinations within itself, and is as it were a bouquet in which they are bound together. If we apply these conditions to the case in question, it becomes evident that on the Earth as an independent individual opposed to the Sun, the chemical process does in fact display itself, although only as the process of the elements. 20 At the same time, the chemical process of the Earth is only to be grasped as belonging to the past, for separated into their own existence, these gigantic members remain at the stage of diremption, and do not pass over into neutrality. By appearing within them however, the process brings about the reduction of particular corporeal individualities to neutralities 25 which may be dirempted once again. This process is inferior to the universal process; we are restricted to it, while the meteorological process is the great chemical process of nature. On the other hand, it is also superior to it, because it is the immediate origin of the living process, and no member can subsist within the living process, or exist as part of it, with- 30 out having its subsistence in subjective unity. It is subjective unity which constitutes the actual being of the living process. The process of the heavenly bodies is on the contrary still abstract, because these bodies preserve their independence. Consequently, the individual chemical process is more profound, for the truth of particular bodies is actualized as they seek and 35 attain their unity within it.

This is the position of the chemical process within the whole. It is therefore to be distinguished from the process of the elements and the particular process, simply because the particular bodies are not only particular, but also belong to the universal elements. Consequently, it is 40 precisely because the universal meteorological process is universal, that it also has to appear within these elements when they are in process as particulars. All chemical processes are bound up with the general process of the Earth. The galvanic process is also determined by the seasons and time of day. Its action is displayed in particular by electricity and magnetism, each in its own manner. These activities have their periods apart   5 from the other variations, and these periodic changes have been carefully observed and reduced to formulae. Something of the kind has also been + observed in the chemical process, but not to the same extent; *Ritter* for example, discovered that a solar eclipse gave rise to variations. This con- + nection is more remote however, and it is not so constituted that the 10 elements as such enter into the process. Nevertheless, a determination of the universal elements does take place in every chemical process, for particular formations are merely subjectivizations of the universal elements, and do not cease to be related to them. Consequently, if the particular qualities operating in the chemical process are altered, this also 15 brings about a determination of the universal elements. Water is essentially either condition or product; similarly, fire is either cause or effect.

It is in this way that we reach the Notion of the totality of the chemical process in general, and have the concept of it as containing the Notion within the entirety of its differences; that is to say, as positing its negation 20 and yet remaining completely by itself. Consequently, each side constitutes the whole. Acidity is certainly not alkaline, and vice versa, and both are therefore exclusive. Implicitly however, each side is also the other, and is the totality of itself and of the other. This is the thirst of the alkali for the acid and vice versa. As soon as bodies are activated, they seize hold of one 25 another, and if they encounter nothing better, they enter into process with the air. The implicit identity of one with the other appears in its seeking the other, and it is by means of this that it contradicts itself. Everything has a tendency only in so far as it is this contradiction of itself. This contradiction commences in the chemical process, for it is here that *implicitly* 30 neutral being gives rise to the infinite tendency towards wholeness, which then makes a further *appearance* in life. The chemical process is therefore analogous to life, and the inner activity of life which may be observed there can cause surprise. If the chemical process could continue *of its own accord* it would be life, and this is why a chemical interpretation of life is 35 not so far-fetched.

§ 327

First of all we have to account for the formal process, i.e. a +
combination of elements which are merely different, not opposed,

and which do not require the existence of a third or middle
term in which to find their implicit unity. The determinateness
of their existence vis-à-vis one another is already constituted by
their common principle or genus. They are combined or separated
5 in an immediate manner, and the properties of their existence are
+ preserved. These combinations of bodies which are chemically
inactive with regard to one another, are found in the amalgamation and other interfusions of metals, mixtures and acids and the
like, of alcohol etc. with water, and so forth.

+ *Addition. Winterl* has called this process *synsomation*. The name does not
occur elsewhere however, and it has therefore been omitted from the
third edition. These synsomates are immediate compounds, and lack a
medium which would give rise to change and undergo change itself.
+ Consequently they do not yet constitute true chemical processes. Fire
15 certainly enters into metallic amalgams, but it is not yet a medium which
itself enters into the process. When various incomplete bodies are posited
within a unity, the question arises as to how they are changed, and we
have to answer it by saying that it is their particularization which is
changed. The primary and original determinateness by which they are
20 particularized, is their specific gravity, and then their cohesion. The compounding of such bodies of the same class is not merely a mixture therefore, for in their combination, their differentiation undergoes a modification. These determinatenesses belong to the universal particularity
of bodies however, and as they have no true physical differentiation, the
25 alteration of their particularity is not yet a specifically chemical change, but
an alteration in their substantial internality. Here change does not yet
reach the external existence of differentiation as such. Consequently we
have to distinguish this particular mode of alteration from the chemical
process, for although it takes place in every chemical process, it must also
30 have a free existence which is distinct and particularized. The mixture is
genuine combination, it is not external. When water and alcohol are
mixed, they permeate one another completely. The weight remains the
same as when they separate, but the specific density differs from that of
their merely quantitative unity, for when they are mixed, they occupy less
35 space than before. When gold and silver are melted together, they also
occupy less space. The goldsmith to whom Hiero gave gold and silver for
the making of a crown, was therefore suspected of having defrauded his
master by keeping some of the metal for himself, for Archimedes calculated the total weight of the alloy from the specific weight of its two

components. Archimedes may well have done the goldsmith an injustice however. Colour changes, just as specific gravity and cohesion do, so + that when brass is produced by the fusion of copper and tin, the redness of the copper changes into yellow. Quicksilver amalgamates easily with gold and silver, although not with iron and cobalt, and this gives rise to a 5 determinate relationship in which each metal saturates itself with the other. If there is not enough silver present for example, the unsaturated quicksilver will not enter into the relationship, and if there is too much silver, a part of it will remain unchanged. The combinations frequently + have a greater hardness and density than their component metals, for 10 differentiation represents a higher being-in-self, whereas the undifferentiated substance is less compact. At the same time, they are however more fusible than the metals of which they are composed, and for a corresponding reason, i.e. that that which has difference within it is more open to chemical changes and offers resistance to them; just as the most intense 15 personalities are most obstinate in the face of violence, but open themselves freely and unreservedly to a kindred spirit. *D'Arcet's* soft solder, which is a mixture of eight parts bismuth, five parts lead, and three parts tin, becomes fluid at a temperature which is lower than that of boiling water, and will even be fluidified by the warmth of the hand. There are + also earths which by themselves are non-fusible, but which become so when they are combined. This is important in metallurgy, for it makes foundary work easier. The refining of metals also has to be considered here, because it depends upon the different temperatures at which combinations will melt. Silver which is combined with copper, is refined out 25 with the help of lead for example. The lead becomes molten at a certain temperature, and takes the silver out with it; if gold also combined with the copper however, it will not be separated. Aqua regia is a mixture of muriatic and nitric acid; these acids only dissolve gold when they are combined, they cannot do so separately. These synsomates are, therefore, + merely alterations of internal and implicit differentiation. The true chemical process presupposes a more determinate opposition however, and it is from this that a greater activity and a more specific product issue forth.

§ 328

The real process relates itself at once to chemical differentiation 35 **(§ 200 ff.), for at the same time the whole concrete totality of the body enters into this process (§ 325). The bodies which enter into it**

are mediated by a third term which is not identical with them. The initial being of this third term is merely implicit as the abstract unity of these extremes; it is the process which posits its existence. Consequently, this third term is composed merely of elements, and these elements contain difference, for they are partly the unity of abstract neutrality in general, or water, and partly differentiated and divided as air. In nature the different moments of the Notion also exhibit themselves in particularized existence, and consequently, the concrete and abstract sides of the process give rise to a doubling of both its separation and neutralization. The separation is partly the breaking down of neutral corporeality into its corporeal component parts, and partly the differentiation of the abstract physical elements into the four chemical moments of nitrogen, oxygen, hydrogen, and carbon, which are still more abstract, and which together constitute the totality of the Notion, by whose moments they are determined. Chemical elements therefore have three moments: (1) the abstraction of undifferentiation, which is *nitrogen*; (2) the two moments of the opposition, which are (a) the element of differentiation which is for itself as the burning principle of *oxygen*, and (b) the element of the opposition's undifferentiation, which is the combustible principle of *hydrogen*; (3) the abstract moment of their *individual* element, which is *carbon*.

Similarly, combination is partly the neutralizing of concrete corporealities, and partly the neutralizing of these abstract chemical elements. What is more, although there is a difference between the concrete and the abstract determination of the process, there is to the same extent a union; for as the middle term of the extremities, the physical elements are the differentiations out of which the indifferent concrete corporealities are activated. In other words, it is through these elements that the corporealities achieve the existence of their chemical differentiation, which has a tendency towards neutralization, and passes over into it.

Addition. As a totality, the general nature of the chemical process is that of the double activity of parting, and of the reduction of that which is parted to unity. Since the shaped bodies which enter into the process have to come into contact with one another as totalities, so that their essential determinateness is contiguous (which is not possible in mere friction, when in a state of indifference they merely submit one another to force, as they do in the superficial electrical process), they must coincide in indifferent being, which as it constitutes their lack of differentiation, is an abstract physical element. This is water as the affirmative principle, and air as the principle fire, of being-for-self and negation. The elements which form this middle term enter into the process, and determine themselves as 5 differentials. Similarly, they fuse themselves together again into the physical elements. Consequently, the elementary principle here is either the active principle in which the individual bodies first display their activity with regard to one another, or it appears as passive determinateness through its being transformed into abstract forms. The extremes are either bound 10 to the middle, or they are neutrals like salts, and are therefore decomposed into extremes. The chemical process is therefore a *syllogism*, and it is not only its beginning, but also its entire course which is syllogistic; for it requires three terms, the two independent extremes, and a middle in which its determinateness meets and the terms differentiate themselves. In the 15 formal chemical process (see prec. §), we only made use of two terms however. Fully concentrated acid contains no water, and when it is poured on metal, it either fails to dissolve it, or only makes a feeble attack upon it. If it is diluted with water however, it makes a vigorous attack upon the metal, simply because the third term is then present. It is the same with air. 20 *Trommsdorff* says, 'Lead soon tarnishes, even in dry air, but when the air is humid, the process is even quicker. Pure water has no effect upon lead if the air is excluded, so that if a piece of freshly melted lead, which is still very bright, is dropped into a retort filled with freshly distilled water, and the retort is then sealed, the lead will remain completely unchanged. On 25 the other hand, lead immersed in water which is standing in an open container, and so has many points of contact with the air, soon tarnishes.' + Iron reacts in the same way, so that rust only occurs when the air is humid; if the air is dry and warm, iron will remain unchanged.

The four chemical elements are the abstractions of the physical elements, 30 which constitute a real existence in themselves. For some time it was thought that all bases consisted of such simple substances, just as they are now thought to have a metallic consistence. *Guiton* supposed lime to be composed of nitrogen, carbon and hydrogen, talc of lime and nitrogen, potash of lime and hydrogen, and natron of talc and hydrogen. *Steffens* + thought he had rediscovered the opposition between carbon and nitrogen in vegetables and animals etc. However, such abstractions only occur on + their own as chemical differentiation in individual corporealities, because process gives the universal physical elements, as a middle term, the character of existent differentiation, and so separates them into their abstractions. 40

It is in this way that water is dirempted into oxygen and hydrogen. The exposition of meteorology (§ 286 Add. II. 46, 17,) has already made it abundantly clear that the category of the physicists by which they suppose water to be *composed* of oxygen and hydrogen, is invalid. Similarly, the air is not composed of two gases oxygen and nitrogen, for they are also merely the forms in which the air is posited. These abstractions do not integrate themselves into one another therefore, but into a third term, in the extremes, which sublate their abstraction and complete themselves as the totality of the Notion. The chemical elements are called substances in accordance with the bases, regardless of their form. With the exception of carbon however, none of them may be separated out for itself, for they all occur in the form of gases. Yet taken as such, they are material and ponderable existences, for when metal is oxidized for example, it gains weight through the acquisition of oxygen. This is the case with lead for instance, for when lead is compounded with the abstract chemical element of oxygen, it weighs more than it does in its reguline state. *Lavoisier's* theory is based upon this. The specific gravity of the metal is reduced however, and it loses its character of undifferentiated compactness.

These four elements constitute a totality in that (*a*) nitrogen is the dead residue which corresponds to metallicism; it is irrespirable, and does not burn, but it may be differentiated and is oxidizable, for the atmospheric air is an oxide of nitrogen. (*b*) Hydrogen is the positive side of the determinateness in the opposition, it is differentiated nitrogen. It is incapable of supporting animal life, for animals suffocate quickly within it. Phosphorus does not catch fire within it, and a light or any other burning body lowered into it, is extinguished. In itself however, it is combustible, and may be lighted as long as atmospheric gas or oxygen has access to it. (*c*) Oxygen is the other moment here; it is negative and active, has its own odour and taste, and activates the former two elements. (*d*) The fourth element in this totality is carbon, which is a defunct individuality. This is ordinary charcoal, the chemical element of the earthy sphere. In its refulgent form it is the diamond, which is practically pure carbon, and which in its rigid earthy shape is crystalline. Carbon alone subsists for itself, the other elements only attain existence through force, and this existence is therefore merely momentary. It is these chemical determinations which constitute the forms in which the solidity of substance in general integrates itself. It is only nitrogen which remains outside the process; hydrogen and carbon are however the moments of differentiation which lose their onesidedness by becoming integrated as physically individual bodies.

§ 329

In its **abstraction**, the process is the identity of basic division and the unification of the differences posited by this division. As a **progression**, it is the return of totality into itself. It is **finite** however, in that its moments also possess bodily independence; it is therefore implicit within this totality, that the **immediate**   5 corporealities which it has as its **presupposition**, are to an equal extent only the products of the process. It is because of this immediacy, that the corporealities appear to subsist outside the process, which appears to come to them. What is more, the **moments of the course** of the process itself fall apart into their   10 immediacy and difference. Consequently, the real totality of this course becomes a cycle of **particular processes**, each of which has the other as its presupposition, but which for itself takes its beginning from without, and extinguishes itself in its particular product. It does this without continuing itself in the process,   15 from its own resources, and so passing immanently into the process which constitutes the next moment of the totality. The body enters into one of these processes as a condition, and into the other as a product, and its chemical character is determined by the particular process in which it has one or the other position. A   20 classification of bodies can only be based upon these positions within the particular processes.

The two sides of this course of the process are (i) from the undifferentiated body, through its activation, to neutrality; and (ii) from this union, back to a separation into undifferentiated   25 bodies.

Addition. The chemical process is still *finite* in comparison with the organic process, and for the following reasons; (a) The unity of the diremption and the diremption itself are simply inseparable within the living process, for the unity within it posits itself perpetually as object,   30 and perpetually appropriates that which it separates from itself, while in the chemical process this infinite activity still falls apart into two sides. To the chemical process it is an external matter, and a matter of indifference, that the diremptions may be brought together again; one process ceased with this diremption, and a new process can now begin again.   35 (b) The finitude of the chemical process also consists of each onesided chemical process only re-establishing the totality in a formal manner, as

for example in combustion, which terminates in diremption through the positing of differentiation or oxidation. In a onesided process of this kind, neutrality also occurs however, for water is also produced. Conversely, in the process which has the neutral principle as its end product, differen-
5 tiation also takes place, although only in an abstract manner through the development of gases. (c) Thus the shapes which enter into the process are in the first instance quiescent. The process consists of various shapes of this kind being posited in unity, or forced out of their indifferent subsistence into differentiation, without the body being able to preserve itself.
10 The implicit unity of the differences is certainly the absolute condition of this, but as they still occur as differences, they are only united through the Notion, and their unity has not yet entered into existence. Acid and caustic potash are implicitly identical; acid is implicitly alkali, which is precisely why it thirsts for it, just as caustic potash thirsts for acid. Each
15 has the tendency towards integration, for each is implicitly neutral, although it does not yet exist as such. Consequently, the finitude of the chemical process at this juncture consists of the Notion and existence constituting two sides which do not yet correspond to each other; in living being however, that which exists is also the identity of the differences.
20 (d) In the chemical process, the differences certainly sublate their onesidedness; this sublation is only relative however, for it falls into another onesidedness. Metals become oxides, and a substance changes to acid; these are neutral products, which are still onesided. (e) It follows from this that the entirety of the process falls apart into different processes. The pro-
25 cess whose product is onesided is itself incomplete, and does not constitute the total process. The process is finished when a single determinateness is posited in another; consequently, this process itself is not the true totality, but is merely one moment of the entire totality of process. Each totality is in itself the totality of the process, but this totality falls apart into dif-
30 ferent processes and products. The Idea of the chemical process in its entirety is therefore a series of sundered processes, which represent the different stages and transitional points of its course.

(f) Another feature of the finitude of the chemical process, is that it is precisely to the different stages of this process that the particular shapings
35 of the individual bodies belong; in other words, the particular corporeal individualities are determined in accordance with the particular stage of the entire process to which they belong. The superficiality of the electrical process is still very tenuously related to the individuality of the body, for the minutest determination is sufficient to make a body positively or
40 negatively electric. This relation first becomes important in the chemical

process. In the various chemical processes one has a number of sides and matters which may be distinguished. In order to grasp this complex, one has to distinguish between the active and inactive materialities of each process; these must not be placed on the same level, but must be well separated from one another. The nature of a body depends upon its po- 5 sition within the different processes, in which it is either generative, determinative, or product. It is certainly also capable of entering into further processes, but not as the determining factor. In the galvanic process for example, the regulus of the metal is the determining factor; it certainly also passes over into the process of fire as alkali and acid, but these do not 10 give its place within the whole. Sulphur also has a relationship to acid, by means of which it is effective, but in its relationship to fire, it is the determining principle, and it is through this relationship that it assumes its position. In empirical chemistry however, each body is described according to its reaction to all chemical bodies, and if a new metal is dis- 15 covered, the whole gamut of its reactions to other bodies is noted. If one looks through chemistry textbooks for the classifications employed there, one finds that the main distinction made is that between what are called simple bodies, and bodies which are combinations of these. In the first group one finds nitrogen, hydrogen, oxygen, carbon, phosphorus, sul- 20 phur, gold, silver, and the other metals lumped together. A merely cursory glance will show us that these things are quite heterogeneous however. What is more, although compounds are certainly products of the process, the so-called simple bodies are also the products of even more abstract processes. Finally, it is the dead product which emerges from this or that 25 process, which the chemists regard as the main thing to be described. The + truth is however that it is the process in its series of processes or stages which is the main thing; its course is the determining factor, and the determinatenesses of the individual bodies only find their significance in its various stages. This is however the finite formal process, in which each 30 body, through its particularity, displays a modified course of the entire process. It is precisely the particular behaviour of the body in its specifically modified process which constitutes the subject-matter of chemistry, and it presupposes that corporeal determinatenesses are given. Here on the contrary we have to regard the process in its totality, and the way in which 35 it divides bodies into classes, and defines them as the potentially fixed stages of its course.

As it fixes its stages in the particular corporeal individualities, the *totality* of the process allows these stages themselves to appear as processes of a particular kind. The totality which these constitute is a chain of particular 40 processes forming a rotation, the periphery of which is itself a chain of processes. The totality of the chemical process is therefore a system of particular modes of the process. (1) In the formal process of synsomation, which we have dealt with above (§ 327), the differentiation is not yet of a real nature. (2) In the actual process, it is the way in which activity exists which has to be discovered. (a) In galvanism, it exists as a variety of un-differentiated bodies. Here also, the differentiation is not yet present as a reality, for the variety is posited through the activity of the differentiation of the process. Consequently, we have metals here whose varieties touch one another, and as they are active in this combination as differentials, process is present. (b) In the process of fire, the activity exists for itself outside the body, for fire is this immanently consuming and negative being-for-self, the restless differential which is active as the positing of differentiation. This is initially an elementary and abstract process; its product is the corporealization of fire, which is the transition to caustic alkalies, active acids. (c) The third stage is the process of these activated bodies; the first was the positing of oxides, the second the positing of the acid. The differentiating activity now has a corporeal existence. This process is the reduction to neutrality occurring in the production of salts. (d) Finally, we have the return of the neutral substance to acid, to oxide and to radical, which constituted the point of departure. Undifferentia-tion comes first therefore; then comes the positing of the various bodies, then their opposition, and finally the neutral body as product. As the neutral body is itself one-sided however, it is reduced to undifferentiation is the presupposition of the chemical process, which has this presupposition as its product. In empirical investigation, the forms of the *bodies* are the prime consideration; but it is with the distinguishing of the particular forms of *process* that a beginning has to be made. This is the only way in which the empirically infinite multifariousness of the mere product may be grouped into a rational order, so that the abstract generality in which everything is flung together without order may be kept at bay.

1. Combination

a. Galvanism

§ 330

It is metallicism, a corporeality which with regard to its form is immediate and undifferentiated, and in which various properties are as yet undeveloped and held together in the simple

determination of specific gravity, which constitutes the initiation of the process, and so of the first particular process. Metals, as primary bodies, as merely different, and as not activated into mutual antagonism, stimulate the process by imparting their immanent determinateness and differentiation to one another 5 through the compact unity of their implicit fluidity, and their ability to transmit heat and electricity. As they are at the same time independent, they enter into a state of mutual tension, which is therefore still electrical. Their differentiation can however realize itself in the neutral and consequently separable medium of 10 water combined with air. Water is either pure, or capable of a more concrete effect on account of its salt content, and it is by means of its neutrality and its consequent susceptibility to differentiation, that an activity is initiated which is of a real nature and not merely electrical, and which arises out of the tensioned conflict of 15 metal with water. It is through this that the electrical passes over into the chemical process. The product of this process is + oxidation in general, and if it progresses so far, the disoxidation or hydrogenation of metal. It is at least the development of hydrogen; and likewise of oxygen gas, so that it is a positing of 20 differentials, in which the neutral element is dirempted and also enters into abstract existence for itself (§ 328); just as, at the same time, the combination of these differentials with the base enters into existence in the oxide or hydrate; this is the second kind of corporeality. +

Remark

In this exposition of the presence of the process at this first stage, it is easy to grasp the difference between electricity, the chemical state of the process in general, the galvanic state in particular, and the connection between them. Physics refuses to see anything in the galvanic process but electricity however, so that 30 the difference between the extremes and the middle term of the syllogism is regarded merely as the difference between a dry and a wet conductor, both alike being classed as conductors. Here, there is no need to consider more closely the modifications necessary in order that the extremes may also be differentiated fluid- 35 ities, while the middle is metal; in order that, as stated in this paragraph, the form of electricity may be maintained, and some-

times made to predominate, while at other times chemical action may be augmented; in order that in contrast with metals, which are so independent that they need water and more concrete neutralitites or the already developed chemical opposition of acids
5 or caustics to be differentiated and to pass over into their calxes, metalloids are so unstable, that when they are brought into contact with air, they may pass straight into their differentiation and become earths etc. These and many other particularities do not alter, but tend rather to confuse the treatment of the archetypal
10 phenomenon of the galvanic process, which we shall continue to call by its original and well-deserved name. Once the simple chemical form of this process had been discovered in the voltaic pile, the clear and straightforward consideration of it was muddled by the conception of wet conductors. It is mainly on account of
15 this conception that the plain empirical evidence of the activity manifested in and by water as the middle term, is disregarded and set aside. Water is regarded as a passive, not as an active conductor, with the result that electricity too is regarded as complete in itself, and as merely streaming through water as it does through
20 metals; for in this connection metals are also regarded as nothing but conductors, and as first class conductors in comparison with water. Despite this aberration, Mr. Pohl's 'The Process of the Galvanic Circuit' (Leipzig, 1826), displays the active relationship of galvanism from its simplest form onwards, that is
25 to say from the relationship between water and a single metal, to the multiple complexes which arise from the modifying of conditions. Mr. Pohl has carried out this work empirically, yet with the full energy of intuition, and with an awareness of the living
+ activity of nature. Perhaps it is simply because the overriding need
30 to grasp the general progression of the galvanic and chemical process as a totality of natural activity has tended to tax the rational intelligence too heavily, that the more modest task of examining the empirically presented factual element has hitherto been somewhat neglected.
35 An outstanding example of the ignoring of facts in this field is the conception of water as consisting of oxygen and hydrogen. When water is submitted to the active circuit of a pile, oxygen appears at one of its poles and hydrogen at the other. This is taken as evidence of decomposition: the hydrogen is considered to
40 be that part of the water left by the oxygen which has developed

around one pole, while the oxygen is thought to have left the pole at which the hydrogen has developed, and to have mysteriously found its way to the opposite side through a middle which continues to exist as water. In thus passing to their respective sides, the gases are also assumed to have passed through one another. It 5 is not only the intrinsically indefensible nature of this theory which goes unnoticed; it is also forgotten that given a separation of the materiality of two portions of water, which is however so constituted that one side continues to form simply a conducting connection through a metal, the development of oxygen at one pole 10 and of hydrogen at the other will also take place in the same way under conditions which make it impossible that there could be any completely external way in which this essentially groundless and mysterious migration of gases or molecules to their respective sides might take place. A similar disregard of evidence + occurs when an acid and an alkali are found to neutralize themselves on being brought to their respective and opposing poles. In this case too, a portion of the acid is said to neutralize the alkali by finding its way to it from the other side, while a portion of the alkali is said to neutralize the acid in the converse manner. 20 When a litmus tincture is placed between them however, this sensitive medium will show no trace of any action whereby one + might perceive the presence of the acid which is supposed to be passing through it.

Here one might also mention, that it is because water has been 25 regarded merely as a conductor of electricity, despite the fact that a pile mediated by water acts more weakly than one mediated by more concrete agents, that one encounters the extraordinary conclusion that, 'L'eau pure qui transmet une électricité forte, telle que celle que nous excitons par nos machines ordinaires, 30 devient presqu' isolante pour les faibles forces de l'appareil électromoteur,' (Biot 'Traité de Phys.' vol. II p. 506). 'Électro- + moteur' is the term used in this theory for the voltaic pile. It is only a theorizing which is obstinate enough not to be shaken by such a conclusion, which could have the audacity to assert that 35 water is an insulator of electricity.

The central feature of this theory is the identification of electricity with chemism, and if it is put out by the striking difference between them, consolation is sought in the conclusion that this difference is inexplicable. And it is of course, for if one 40

presumes their identity, one certainly makes it impossible to explain their difference. The mere equating of the chemical determinateness of the bodies with regard to one another with positive
and negative electricity, ought to be enough to make the super-
5 ficiality and insufficiency of the theory clear. Even though the
chemical relationship is deeply involved in external conditions
such as temperature, and is relative in other respects, the electrical
relationship is completely transient, movable, and capable of
being reversed by the slightest circumstance. What is more,
10 bodies of one side of the chemical relationship such as acids, may
be distinguished from one another by the exact quantitative and
qualitative ratios of their being saturated with an alkali ($\S$ 333),
but even if a merely electrical opposition is somewhat stabilized,
it will give rise to no trace of this kind of determinability. Yet
15 even if the entire visible course of the real nature of corporeal
change within the chemical process is disregarded, and one considers only its product, the difference between this product and
that of the electrical process is so striking, that if the identification
of these forms is assumed, it cannot fail to cause astonishment.
20 I shall confine myself to quoting Berzelius's naïve expression
of this astonishment in his 'Essai sur la théorie des proportions
+ chimiques etc.' (Paris 1819). On page 73 of this work he says, 'Il
s'élève pourtant ici une question qui ne peut etre resolue par
aucun phénomène analogue à la décharge électro-chimique
25 (the expression 'chemical combination' is dropped in favour of
electrical discharge), . . . ils restent dans cette combinaison avec
une force, qui est supérieure à toutes celles qui peuvent produire
une séparation mécanique. Les phénomènes électriques ordinaires . . . ne nous éclairent pas sur la cause de l'union per-
30 manente des corps avec une si grande force, après que l'état
d'opposition électrique est detruit.' In the chemical process,
changes take place in specific gravity, cohesion, shape, colour
etc., as well as in acid, caustic, alkaline and suchlike properties,
but all this is set aside and submerged into the abstraction of
35 electricity. If all these properties of corporeality can be forgotten
for the electrical positive and negative, philosophy should no
longer be reproached for its, 'abstracting from the particular, and
+ its empty generalities.' A now outmoded way of philosophizing
about nature 'potentialized', or rather dissipated and attenuated
40 the system and process of animal reproduction into magnetism,

and the vascular system into electricity; but this schematizing is
no more superficial than that perpetrated by this reduction of
concrete corporeal opposition. It is right that such a philosophical
procedure should have been rejected, for it merely epitomized
concrete existence, and because of its abstraction, was unable to   5
deal with singularity. Why should not the same procedure be
rejected in the case of this other theory?

There is however another point of difficulty in the difference
between the concrete process and the abstract schema, and that is
the strength of combination exhibited by substances such as   10
oxides and salts etc., which are the result of the chemical process.
Taken for itself, this strength certainly contrasts very sharply
with the result of mere electrical discharge, in which the bodies
which are stimulated into positive and negative electricity maintain precisely the same condition, so that each for itself remains   15
as unconnected as it was before and during the friction, while the
spark on the other hand disappears. The spark is the actual result
of the electrical process, and it is with this therefore that the result of the chemical process will have to be compared if we accept
the premiss that these processes are equivalents, and face the   20
difficulty presented by this assertion. It is not possible to remove
this difficulty by assuming that the force which combines the
positive and negative electricity of the discharge spark, is merely
the same as that which unites an acid and an alkali in a salt. The
spark disappears, and it is therefore no longer possible to compare   25
it. It is perhaps too obvious that the salt or oxide in the result of
the process, is a much more concrete thing than the electric
spark. What is more, the development of light and heat which is
apparent in the chemical process, has also been attributed to a
spark of this kind, although with an equal lack of justification.   30
Berzelius has something to say about the alleged difficulty, 'Est-ce
l'effet d'une force particulière inhérente aux atomes, comme la
polarisation électrique?'—i.e. is there not a certain difference
between chemical and electrical phenomena in bodies? Most
certainly and undoubtedly!—'ou est-ce une propriété électrique   35
qui n'est pas sensible dans les phénomènes ordinaires?', i.e.
in the strictly electrical phenomena we have already considered
(p. 195). This question may be answered quite simply in the affirmative, for as the chemical element is absent from electricity as
such, it may not be perceived there. The chemical element is   40

first to be seen in the chemical process. As regards the first possibility however, i.e. that of there being a difference between the
electrical and chemical determination of the body, Berzelius is
of the opinion that, 'La permanence de la combinaison ne devait
5 pas être soumise à l'influence de l'électricité'. This means that
on account of their difference, two of a body's properties must
be quite devoid of any inter-relationship, so that the specific
gravity of metal is unrelated to its oxidation, and its metallic
lustre and colour to its oxidation and neutralization etc. The
10 most rudimentary experience shows that the properties of the
bodies are essentially subject to the influence of the action and
change of other properties however. It is the dry abstraction of
the understanding which demands the complete separation and
independence of properties which are different, even when
15 they belong to the same body. As regards the second possibility,
i.e. that of electricity's having the power to dissolve strong chemical compounds, although this is not perceptible in ordinary
electricity, Berzelius observes that, 'Le rétablissement de la
polarité électrique devrait détruite même la plus forte combinaison
20 chimique'. In support of this he adduces the special instance of a
voltaic pile, which he calls an electric battery, which consists
of only eight or ten pairs of silver and zinc plates the size of a
five-franc piece, and which is able, with the help of quicksilver,
to decompose potash, i.e. to preserve its radical within amalgam.
25 The difficulty was caused by ordinary electricity not showing
the power in question, as distinct from the action of a galvanic
pile. The action of such a pile is now substituted for ordinary
electricity, the only difference being that it is now called a 'batterie
électrique' while in terms of the theory it was formerly (p. 194)
30 given the name of an 'appareil électro-moteur'. There is no difficulty in picking out the inconsistency here however, and the
argument will not bear inspection. In order to remove the difficulty which stood in the way of identifying electricity with
chemism, at this particular juncture, the galvanic pile is once
35 again presumed to be merely an electrical apparatus, and its
activity to be nothing but the generation of electricity.

Addition. Each single process starts with an apparent immediacy, which
at another point on the periphery of its circuit is however also a product.
Metal constitutes the true beginning, for it is inwardly stable, and only

appears to differ from another through comparison. Consequently, it is a matter of indifference to gold that it differs from zinc, for unlike neutral substances or oxides, gold is not differentiated within itself, and may not be decomposed into opposed sides. Consequently, metals in the first instance merely differ from one another; they are not merely different for us however, for they distinguish themselves from one another in so far as they touch one another, and this contiguity is for itself contingent. The activity of their differentiation, and the positing of themselves within another differentiation, is conditioned by the continuity of their metallicism. A third factor is necessary however, which is capable of differentiation of a real nature, and into which the metals are able to integrate. It is by this *third* factor that their differentiation is sustained. Metals do not have the brittleness of resin or sulphur, in which the posited determination is confined to a single point; determinateness is imparted to them as a whole, and they communicate their differentiation reciprocally by the one making it felt within the other. The *difference* of metals is therefore revealed in their relationship within the process; in itself this is precisely the general antithesis of their perfection, compactness, ductility, and fluidity, to their brittleness and their readiness to enter into oxidation. *Precious* metals such as *gold*, *silver* and *platinum* are not calcined by mere air through the principle of fire; their process in a free fire is to burn without burning away. They do not decompose into the extremes of basicity and acidity, so that they belong to neither of these sides. The only change which takes place is that from solidity to guttate fluidity, and this is not a chemical change. This is the result of their lack of differentiation. Gold appears to display the Notion of this solid metallic simplicity in its purest form; it does not corrode therefore, and old gold coins remain quite bright. *Lead* and other metals are attacked even by weak acids however. The still more numerous metals known as *metalloids*, are scarcely ever found in their reguline state, and oxidize merely by being exposed to the air. Even when they are oxidized by acids, gold, silver, and platinum do not require the addition of any combustible material such as charcoal in order to be restored to their original state; their reguline metallicism can be restored merely by putting them in the furnace and raising them to a red heat. It is true that *quicksilver* may be vaporized by heat, and that when it is shaken or rubbed while exposed to the air, it changes into an imperfect dark grey calx, which after continuous heating changes into a more perfect dark red calx having a sharp and metallic taste. *Trommsdorff* observes however, that when quicksilver is shut up in dry air and left to stand, no change takes place on its surface, and it does not corrode. He had however seen, 'a small flask of

quicksilver which had belonged to old *Büttner* for God knows how many years,' to which the air had had access through minute holes in paper, and which had calcined on top, where a thin film of red mercuric oxide could
+ be seen. This, and all other mercuric calxes, may be restored to the reguline
5 state of quicksilver by making them red hot, and without the addition of anything combustible. Thus, *Schelling* ('New Journal for Speculative Physics' vol. I sect. 3 p. 96) considers gold, silver, platinum and quicksilver to be the four precious metals on account of an indifference of essence
+ (gravity) and of form (cohesion) being posited within them. Metals such
10 as iron, in which form becomes most fully differentiated from essence, and in which selfhood or individuality predominate, are not to be regarded as precious metals however, any more than are metals such as lead, the imperfect form of which makes them impure and bad, and corrupts their essence. This is not an adequate division however. It is because of their
15 high specific gravity, as well as their continuity and compactness, that these metals are precious. Platinum certainly has a higher density than gold, but it
+ is a unity of the various metallic moments of osmium, iridium, and palladium. *Steffens*, even before *Schelling*, (cf. § 296 Add. II. 64, 12 note) maintained that the density of metals stands in inverse ratio to their cohesion; but
20 this is true only of some precious metals such as gold, which have a weaker
+ specific coherence than less perfect and more brittle metals. The more differentiated the metals are, the *greater* is the activity they give rise to. If we place together gold and silver, gold and copper, gold and zinc, silver and zinc, and add a third body such as water to the air which sur-
25 rounds them, this immediately gives rise to a process which generates considerable activity. This is a *simple* galvanic circuit. It was discovered by chance that its circuit has to be closed; if it is not closed, no action or
+ active differentiation will take place. Ordinarily, we regard bodies as being only where they are, and as only exerting pressure through contact
30 as weighted matters. We saw already in electricity however, that they work against one another in accordance with their physical determinateness. The case of the metals is similar, for it is their various natures or specific gravities which are in contact.

As the simple galvanic circuit is in general no more than the compound-
35 ing of two opposed elements by a third neutral dissolving element in which differentiation can enter into existence, metallicism is not the only *condition* of this activity. Fluids can also exhibit this form of the process, but as with the metals, it is always the simple determinateness by which
+ they are differentiated from one another, which is the active principle.
40 Although *Ritter* regarded it as a metal, charcoal is a burnt vegetable

material; it is able to enter into the galvanic process, and as a residuum in which determinateness has been extinguished, it also has an undifferentiated character. Even acids can give rise to the galvanic process on account of their fluidity. If soapy water is connected with ordinary water by a piece of tin, it gives rise to galvanic action. If one touches the soapy water with one's tongue, and the ordinary water with one's hand, one's sense of taste will be affected by the closing of the circuit. When the points of contact are changed over however, it is the breaking of the circuit which produces this effect. Mr. *von Humboldt* observed simple circuits produced by hot and cold zinc and humidity. *Schweigger* constructed similar piles from heated and cold copper bowls filled with a watery sulphuric acid. Even differentials such as these will give rise to galvanic action therefore; what is more, when this phenomenon appears in finely textured bodies such as muscles, the differentiation can be very much slighter.

The *activity* of the galvanic process is initiated by the emergence of an immanent contradiction, in which both particularities attempt to posit themselves in each other. The activity itself consists in the positing of the implicit inner unity of these internal differentials. Electricity continues to predominate heavily in the galvanic process, because the metals there are posited as differentials which are undifferentiated in their self-subsistence, and keep to themselves even when they are changing, and it is precisely this that characterizes electricity. There must be a negative pole on one side, and a positive pole on the other; chemically determined, oxygen must be developed at one pole and hydrogen at the other. This has given rise to the conception of electro-chemistry. There are physicists who have gone so far as to regard electricity as inseparable from chemical action. *Wollaston* has even said that electricity only occurs where there is oxidation. The catskin which brings forth electricity without oxidation when it is rubbed on glass, has been quite rightly cited as evidence to the contrary. When a metal is attacked chemically, it is neither dissolved nor decomposed into its component parts, so that it displays itself as a neutrality. The real differentiation displayed by a metal in oxidation, is a differentiation which comes to it from without through the metal's being combined with something else.

The initial combination of the two metals has no existent middle, for the middle which is present in their contact is merely implicit. The real middle is however that which differentiation has to bring into existence. In logic, this is the simple medius terminus of the syllogism, while in nature itself it is a duality. In this finite process, the mediating term, which is orientated towards the two one-sided extremes, and from which these

extremes are to integrate themselves, must be an existent and not only an implicit distinctness. The middle term must therefore have a break in its existence. Consequently, atmospheric air or oxygen is necessary for the initiation of galvanic action, and if the galvanic pile is insulated from
5 atmospheric air, it will not become active. *Trommsdorff* cites the following experiment by *Davy*: 'If the water between the plates is perfectly pure, and the air outside is kept from the water by a coating of resin, no gas will be given off by the water, no oxide produced, and the zinc in the pile will hardly be affected.' *Biot* (vol. II, p. 528) counters *Davy* with the
10 observation that even when it is under an air pump, a pile will still produce
+ gas, although not so abundantly. This is merely because it is impossible to remove all the air however. As the middle is a duality, the activity of the pile is increased considerably if instead of sheets of cardboard or cloth, hydrochloric acid or sal ammoniac etc. is placed between the metals, for
15 such a mixture is already implicitly complex chemically.

This activity is called galvanism because *Galvani* was the first to discover it, although *Volta* was the first to understand it. In the first instance, Galvani made use of the principle in a completely different way, and it was Volta who freed the phenomena from organic factors and reduced
20 them to their simple conditions, although he regarded them as nothing more than electricity. Galvani discovered that when one cuts a frog so as to lay bare its spinal nerves, and these nerves are then connected with its leg muscles by means of two metals, or simply by means of a silver wire, the contradiction of these differentials is expressed in the occurrence of
+ convulsive movements. *Aldini* used pure quicksilver to show that this effect may be produced by a single metal. He also showed that a damp hempen cord was often all that was needed in order to effect this active connection between the nerve and the muscle, and when he draped 250
+ feet of such a cord about his house, he was still able to produce this effect.
30 Someone else discovered that no armature was necessary with large and vigorous frogs, for mere contact of the leg with its nerve was enough to
+ produce jerks. According to *Humboldt*, where two similar metals are used,
+ the metallic stimulus may be evoked simply by breathing on one of them. If two different metals are brought into contact with a nerve in two
35 different places, and then connected by a good conductor, this will also give rise to the jerking phenomenon.

This was the first form of galvanism, and it was called animal electricity because it was thought to be restricted to organic being. *Volta* made use of metals instead of muscles and nerves, and constructed galvanic batteries
40 by joining quite a number of these pairs of plates. The determinateness of

G*

each pair is opposed to that of the pair following. The pairs are the sum of their activity however, so that at one extreme one has the sum of their negative activity, and at the other the sum of their positive activity; while the point of indifference is in the middle. *Volta* also distinguished between the wet conductors or water, and the dry conductors or metal, as if there were nothing present but electricity. The difference between water and metal is not the same however, and neither of them plays the part of a mere conductor. It is easy to separate electrical from chemical activity. The production of sparks gives rise to a brighter effect when the surface area of the plates is increased to eight square inches for example. The size of the surfaces seems to have little effect upon the other phenomena of the pile, while only three layers will produce sparks. If a pile is built out of forty pairs of zinc and copper plates of this size, and its silver pole is connected with its zinc pole by an iron wire, a fire-rose $3-3\frac{1}{2}$ inches in diameter appears as soon as the connection is made. Some of its individual rays are a good $1\frac{1}{2}$ to $1\frac{3}{4}$ inches long; in some places they are linked together, and they terminate in tiny stars. The communicating wires are so firmly welded by the spark, that a considerable force is required to separate them. In oxygen, gold and silver act as they do in atmospheric air, iron wires burst into flame and burn away, and lead and tin burn with great vigour and more vivid colours. If the chemical action here is diminished, it becomes distinct from combustion, for a vigorous combustion certainly occurred with electricity too, although it did so as a fusion through heat, not as a decomposition of water (see above § 324 II. 177, 5). Conversely, the chemical action becomes greater and electrical action weaker if the number of plates is increased to a thousand for example, while their size is reduced. Both actions do occur in conjunction however, for the decomposition of water will take place together with a powerful electric discharge. *Biot* has something to say on this ('Traité de Physique' vol. ii p. 436), 'Pour décomposer l'eau, on s'est d'abord servi de violentes décharges transmises à travers ce liquide, et qui y produisaient des explosions accompagnées d'étincelles. Mais Wollaston est parvenu à produire le meme effet, d'une manière infiniment plus marquée, plus sure et plus facile, en conduisant le courant électrique dans l'eau par des fils tressés, terminés en pointes aigues etc.' *Ritter*, the Munich academician, has constructed dry piles in which electrical activity is insulated. It has been noticed that water only gives rise to a feeble chemical action in a pile which, when differently constructed, could display powerful chemical action and high electrical tension. The chemists have concluded therefore that in this instance, water acts as an electrical insulator, and checks the transmission of electricity.

It has been argued that as there would be powerful chemical activity if this check were removed, and as the actual activity is feeble, the communication of the activity which brings about the chemical action must be hindered by the water. No more absurd conclusion could have been
5 reached, for water is the most powerful conductor, more powerful than metal; and this absurdity comes from attributing the action to electricity alone, and thinking only in terms of conductors.

Galvanic activity expresses itself both as *taste*, and as the *phenomenon of light*. If a strip of tinfoil is placed under the tip of the tongue so that it
10 touches the nether lip and projects beyond it, and one then touches the upper surface of the tinfoil and the tip of the tongue with silver, one finds that at the moment at which the two metals come into contact, one is aware of a distinctly caustic taste like that of iron sulphate. If I wet my hands, take hold of a tin beaker filled with alkaline lye, and bring the tip
15 of my tongue into contact with the liquid, I get an acid taste on that part of my tongue which touches this alkaline liquid. If, on the contrary, I take a tin beaker, or better still a zinc beaker, place it on a silver base, fill it with pure water, and then put the tip of my tongue into the water, I find that it is tasteless. As soon as I grasp the silver base with thoroughly
+ moistened hands however, I notice a weak acid taste on the tongue. If one sets a strip of zinc in one's mouth between the upper jaw and the left cheek, and a strip of silver between the lower right jaw and the right cheek, so that both strips project from the mouth, and then brings the ends together when the surroundings are dark, one becomes aware of a
+ light once the metals touch. The identity exists here subjectively within sensation, without the external production of a spark; this is also undoubtedly the case with strong batteries.

Now the *product* of galvanic activity is in general that which is implicit, i.e. the identity of the particular differentials, which in the metals are at
30 the same time bound up with their undifferentiated independence, attains existence, as does also the differentiation of one metal in the other. That which is undifferentiated is therefore posited as differentiated. Galvanic activity can not yet have a neutral product, for there are as yet no existent differentials present within it. As these differentials themselves are not yet
35 bodies, but are only abstract determinatenesses, the question arises as to the forms in which they should become existent here. The abstract existence of these differentials is something elemental, which we see in their aerial or gaseous appearances, and it is therefore the abstract chemical elements which have to be considered here. Water is of course the neutral element
40 which mediates between the metals, and through which their differentiality

can enter into contact. It is also the neutrality which dissolves the differentiality of two salts for example. Consequently, each metal takes its existent differentiation from water, and determines it twice, once as oxidation and once as hydrogenation. Since the general character of water is to be neutral however, the activating and differentiating principle is absent from it, and occurs in the air. The air certainly appears to be neutral, but it is the unrevealed principle of destructive activity, and the stimulated activity of the metals must therefore derive from the air. This accounts for its differentials appearing in an aerial form. In this process, oxygen is the activating and differentiating principle. The more specific result of the galvanic process is the *oxide*, a metal posited in differentiation, the first differentiation we have. Here the non-differentiated body becomes total, although not yet completely so. Although the product of the process also has a dual nature as oxidation and hydrogenation, the outcome is not two differentiated bodies. Oxidation occurs on one side, as for example when zinc is calcined. On the other side, the gold or silver etc. holds out as a compactness against its opposite, so that such a metal remains reguline. If it has already been oxidized, it will be disoxidized and restored to its reguline state. Since the activation of zinc cannot be the positing of a one-sided differentiation, and as the other side is probably incapable of disoxidation, the other side of the opposition appears only under the other form of water through the development of hydrogen. *Ritter* discovered that hydrogenized metals can be produced instead of oxidized metals, so that the other side of the product is also engendered. It is however acid and alkali which constitutes the specific differentiation, as opposition, and this is somewhat different from the abstract differentiation we have just dealt with. Yet even in this real differentiation, the opposition is due principally to the action of oxygen. The metal oxides which result from the galvanic process also include *earths* such as silica, lime, barytes, natron, and potash, for whatever appears as an earth generally has a metallic base. It has been possible to demonstrate the metallic nature of these bases, although there are many earths which only show faint traces of this metallicism. Although this metallic element cannot subsist for itself as in the case of metalloids, yet it will always appear in quicksilver amalgams, and it is only metallicism which can enter into an amalgam with quicksilver. In the metalloids, metallicism is only a moment therefore, for they oxidize themselves again immediately. It is very difficult to obtain reguline *wolfram* for example. *Ammonia* has a particular peculiarity, for on the one hand it can be demonstrated that its basis is nitrogen, its other constituent being oxygen, but that it also has a metallic base in *ammonium* (cf. § 328 Add.

II. 186, 30; § 330 II, 192, 25 note). Here therefore metallicism is also driven to appear in a gaseous form as a quite abstract chemical substance.

Oxidation is the result which terminates the process. The antithesis to this primary, abstract and general negation is free negativity, which is the negative being-for-self opposed to that negativity paralysed in the undifferentiation of metal. In conformity with the Notion, or implicitly, the antithesis is necessary, but in existence the occurrence of fire at this juncture is fortuitous.

b. Process of fire
(*The process of fire*)

§ 331

The activity of the preceding process was only implicit within
10 **the differentiated determinateness of the metals brought into rela-**
tion there. When this activity is posited as existing for itself, it is
fire. It is by means of fire that that which is implicitly combustible,
the third kind of corporeality, such as sulphur, is kindled into
flame. In general, it is therefore by means of fire that that which
15 **is still in a state of neutrality, of torpid and indifferent differen-**
tiation, is activated into the chemical opposition of acid and
caustic alkali. As these opposites cannot exist for themselves,
this opposition comes into being merely as the posited cor-
poreal moments of a third form, as a kind of corporeality with
+ **a real nature of its own.**

Addition. As the galvanic process ceases with the production of metallic oxide, of earth, the course of the chemical process is interrupted at this juncture. The chemical processes have detached existences; if this were not so they would constitute life, which is the circular return of the pro-
25 cess. If the product is now to make further progress, activity must come from without, just as the metals too were brought together by an external activity. It is only the Notion, the inner necessity, which carries the process further therefore; it is only the implicitness of the process which is continued into circular totality. Since the new form we introduce only
30 originates for us, within the Notion, or implicitly, we have to grasp the natural aspect of the factors entering into the process. The oxide which concluded galvanism does not constitute the existent product which is, so to speak, merely handled through other reagents. In its implicit determinateness, the object of the process is rather to be regarded as original.

It is not to be regarded as having become existent, but as having this determinateness of having become, through the simple inner determinateness of its Notion.

Fire as flame is one side of the process, and in it, the unity of differentiation which resulted from the galvanic process, now exists for itself in the form of the free restlessness of self-destruction. The other side is the combustible substance which is the object of fire, and which has the same nature as fire, although it is a physically subsistent body. The product of the process consists therefore on the one side, in the existence of fire as a physical quality, or conversely, in material being, which is already fire according to the determinateness of its nature, having fire posited within it. The primary process was that of gravity; here we have the process of levity, for it is here that fire embodies itself within acid. The physical body, as the possibility of being burnt and activated, is not merely a dead reduction to a state of passive undifferentiation, for it burns itself. Since the material activated in this way is in itself a plain opposition which contradicts itself, it requires its other, and has being only through the reality of its relation with its other. That which is combustible has two shapes therefore, for in so far as it enters into difference, this negative being-for-self posits itself in its own difference. One of these shapes is an ordinary combustible substance, sulphur, phosphorus etc., while the other is neutral. In both of these, quiescent subsistence is merely a mode of existence, it is not their nature. In the galvanic process however, undifferentiation constituted the nature of the metal. A remarkable feature of these substances is phosphorescence, which is a shining without burning, and which is displayed by a number of minerals. If these minerals are scratched, scraped, or even exposed to sunlight, they remain phosphorescent for a certain time. This transient light-phenomenon is the same as electricity, but lacks its dualism. Primary combustibility is not widespread; it embraces sulphur, bitumen, and naphtha. It is brittle, and lacks a firm undifferentiated base, so that it is not differentiated from without by compounding with a differential, but develops its negativity within itself as an integral part of itself. The indifference of the body has passed into a chemical differentiation. The combustibility of sulphur is this extinguished indifference, it is no longer the superficial possibility which *remains* possible within the process itself. That which is combustible burns, and fire is its actuality; it does not only burn however, it burns away, and so ceases to be indifferent and becomes an acid. Indeed, *Winterl* has maintained that sulphur is as such an acid. This is in fact true in that it neutralizes saline and earthy bases and metals without the help of the water base (hydrogen) required by other acids. Secondary

206

combustibility is the formally neutral body; its subsistence is also a mere form, and does not sustain the process by constituting the determinateness of its own nature. Salt is physically neutral; the formally neutral bodies are lime, barytes, and potash. These are in fact the earths, and as they are
+ nothing but oxides, they have a metallic base. The galvanic battery made
+ this clear by its disoxidation of alkaline substance. The alkalies are also
+ metallic oxides of an animal, vegetable, or mineral kind. The other aspect of the base is the carbonic acid which is found in lime for example, and which is produced by burning it with charcoal. This is an abstract chemical
10 substance, it is not an individual physical body however; lime is neutralized by the loss of it, but it does not become a real neutral substance, for its neutrality is only produced in an elemental and general way. It is not permissible to regard barytes or strontian as salts, for that which neutralizes them is not a real acid, but is this same chemical abstraction, which ap-
15 pears as carbonic acid. Here we have the two combustibilities which constitute the second side of the process.

The bodies which enter into conflict in the process of fire come together externally as conditioned by the finitude of the chemical process. The elements of *air* and *water* contribute as the mediating principle, so that in
20 order to produce acid from sulphur for example, the sulphur is placed in
+ air between wet walls. Consequently, the process in its entirety has the form of a syllogism, with two extremes and a divided middle. The approximate forms of this syllogism are now the modes of activity by which the extremes determine the middle in order to integrate themselves by
25 means of it. A more exact examination of this would require an extremely detailed discussion, and give rise to too great a digression. Every chemical process would have to be presented as a series of syllogisms, the terms succeeding one another as extremes and middles. What in general happens is that the combustibility of sulphur and phosphorus, or of some formally
30 neutral element is activated in the process. It is in this way that earths are brought to a caustic condition by fire; prior to this they are weak salts. Even metallic substances, and particularly poor metals such as metallic calxes, may be activated by combustion so that they are not oxidized, but transformed immediately into acids. The oxide of arsenic is itself arsenious
+ acid. In its state of activation, an alkali is corrosive and caustic, and an acid also attacks and destroys. Sulphur and similar substances contain no undifferentiated base; water therefore becomes their basic bond, and acid can then subsist for itself, although only momentarily. When an alkali becomes caustic however, the water which as water of crystallization was
40 no longer aqueous, and which constituted the bond of neutralization, loses

the formal neutrality of its shape through fire, for alkalinity already has its own undifferentiated metallic base.

Neutralization, the process of water
(*Salt formation*)

§ 332

That which is differentiated is simply opposed to its other, and as it is this which constitutes its quality, it has essential being only through its relation with this other. Consequently, it is only by means of violence that its corporeality has an independent and separate existence. This corporeality, in its onesidedness, constitutes the process in which it posits its identity with its negative. It only does this through the air however, in which acid and caustic alkali lose their strength, and are reduced to formal neutrality. The product here is the concrete neutrality of a salt, which is real, and is the fourth kind of body.

Addition. Metal only differs from its other implicitly; this other lies in the Notion of metal, and only in the Notion. Since each side now exists in opposition however, this onesidedness is no longer merely implicit, but is posited. Consequently, the individualized body tends to overcome its onesidedness and to posit the totality of what it is in accordance with its Notion. Both sides are physical realities, i.e. sulphuric, or some other acid except carbonic; and oxides, earths, alkalies. These are activated opposites, and do not need to be stimulated through a third term. Each has within itself the restlessness of self-sublation, of integration into its counterpart, and of self-neutralization. They are incapable of existing for themselves however, since they are incompatible with themselves. Acids get hot and enflamed when water is poured on them. Concentrated acids give off fumes, and absorb water from the air. Concentrated sulphuric acid increases its volume in this way for example, but becomes weaker. If acids are protected from the air, they attack their containers. Caustic alkalies are similar in that they become milder. These alkalies are said to absorb carbonic acid from the air, but this is an hypothesis, and the truth of the matter is that in order to neutralize themselves, they begin by making carbonic acid of the air.

That which enflames both sides is now a chemical abstraction; it is the differentiated abstraction of oxygen as a chemical element. Even if they

are only water, the bases are the bond of undifferentiated subsistence. The activating of both acids and caustic substances is therefore an oxygenation, although an acid and an alkali are relative to one another, and express the same opposition as that found between positive and negative. In arith-
5 metic, the negative is to be taken partly as implicitly negative, and partly as the mere negative of another, so that it is a matter of indifference which is negative and which is positive. The situation resembles that found in electricity, and in two paths which lead off in opposite directions, but which return to the same point whichever way one walks etc. Acid in itself is
10 certainly negative therefore, but its relationship passes over into relativity. That which is acid on one side is alkaline on another. Sulphuret of potash
+ is said to be an acid for example, although it is hydrogenized sulphur. In this case therefore the acid is hydrogenation. This is not always the case however, and here it is to be attributed to the combustibility of sulphur.
15 Sulphur becomes sulphuric acid through oxidation however, and is there-fore capable of both forms. The same is true of a number of earths, which fall into two series: (a) lime, barytes, and strontian, which are metal oxides of an alkaline nature, and (b) silica, alumina, and magnesia, which may also be accredited with this property, partly by analogy, and partly by the
20 traces of galvanic activity which they show in their amalgams. Steffens
+ contrasts alumina and silica with the alkaline series however. According
+ to Schuster, alum-earth also reacts to alkalies and is therefore acid. On the other hand, in its reaction to sulphuric acid it plays the part of a base. When alumina is dissolved in alkalies, it may be precipitated by acids, and
+ so acts as an acid. Berthollet confirms the double nature of alum-earth ('Statique Chimique', vol. II. p. 302) 'L'alumine a une disposition presqu'égale à se combiner avec les acides et avec les alcalis.' p. 308, 'L'acide nitrique a aussi la propriété de cristalliser avec l'alumine; il est probable que c'est également par le moyen d'une base alcaline'. 'Silica',
30 says Schuster, 'is an acid, although it is only a weak one, for when it combines with potash and natron to form glass, it neutralizes their bases',
+ etc. Berthollet (vol. II p. 314) notices however that it has a tendency to
+ combine with alkalies rather than acids.

Here also, air and water are mediatory, so that although acid can never
35 be wholly free from water, an acid in a predominantly anhydrous and fully concentrated state has a much weaker effect than dilute acid, and if it is also denied access to the air, its action can cease completely. The general abstract result of this is that an acid will combine with an alkali which has not been activated to form a neutral substance which is not an abstract
40 lack of differentiation, but a unity of two existent substances. They sublate

their opposition and contradiction because they cannot maintain it, and as they therefore sublate their onesidedness, they posit what they are in their Notion, both the one and the other. It is said that an acid does not act on a metal immediately, but first turns it into an oxide, which is one side of the existent opposition, and then neutralizes itself by combining with this oxide which, though differentiated, is not activated into causticity. The salt which is produced by this neutralization is primarily the middle term of chemical totality, but it is still not as yet the infinite totality of life; it is a totality which has come to rest, limited by others.

d. The process in its totality
(Elective affinity)

§ 333

These neutral bodies, entering again into mutual relation, form the chemical process in its complete reality, for it is real bodies such as this which constitute the sides of this process. Water is the abstract medium of neutrality, and these bodies need it in order to be mediated. As both sides are neutral on their own account however, they are not mutually differentiated. It is here that the particularization of universal neutrality occurs, together with the particularization of the differentials of bodies which are **activated** into mutual chemical opposition. This has been called *elective affinity*, **and is in fact the formation of further particular neutralities through the break-up of those already present.**

Remark

The most important advance towards a simplification of the details of elective affinity, is the law discovered by *Richter* and *Guyton Morveau*, which states that neutral compounds undergo *no alteration* in regard to their *state of saturation* when they are mixed in solution and between the acids there is a mutual exchange of bases. It is on the basis of this law that the particular relationships between acids and alkalies have been graded according to the specific quantity of each alkali needed to saturate each acid. **If one takes a certain acid, and grades the** *alkalies* **according to the quantities in which**

they have to be applied in order to saturate it, the *grading* will be the *same for every other acid*. The only factor which changes is the quantitative unit **of the acids combining with this constant series of alkalies.** The acids also have a constant grading relative
5 to the various alkalies.

Elective affinity itself is moreover merely an abstract relation of acid to base. The chemical body in general, and especially the neutral body, is at once a concrete physical body with a definite specific gravity, cohesion, temperature etc. The strictly physical
10 **properties, and the changes which they undergo in the process** (§ 328) **enter into relationship with the chemical moments of this process, and so modify its action by impeding, hindering, or facilitating it.** *Berthollet,* **while fully recognizing this grading of affinity** has, in his well-known 'Statique Chimique', brought
15 together and investigated the circumstances which produce an alteration in the results which have often **been attributed** exclusively to the onesided condition of **elective** affinity. He writes, 'The superficiality which has been introduced into science by these explanations, has in general
+ been regarded as a progress'.

Addition. The immediate self-integration of acid and alkaline opposites into a neutral substance, is not a process. The salt which is produced has no process, and so resembles the adherence of a magnet to the north and south poles, or the spark of an electric discharge. In order that the process
25 may be continued, the salts must be brought into an external relation once again, for they are indifferent and self-sufficient. They are not active in themselves, and only become so when they are submitted to accidental circumstances. That which is indifferent may only be brought into contact through a third term, which in this case is water once again. It is
30 principally at this juncture that figuration and crystallization occur. In general, the process consists of the sublation of one neutrality, and of its replacement by another neutrality. Consequently, neutrality is here engaged in a conflict with itself, for the neutrality which constitutes the product is mediated by the negation of neutrality. The neutralities of certain
35 acids and bases are therefore in conflict with one another. The affinity of an acid with a base is negated, and the negation of this affinity is itself the relation of an acid to a base. This negation is also an affinity therefore, and this affinity is that of the acid of the second salt with the base of the first, as much as it is that of the base of the second salt with the acid of the first.

Affinities of this kind are the negations of primary affinities, and are said to be elective, but this signifies nothing more than that acid and alkaline opposites posit their identity here in the same way as the opposites of magnetism and electricity. The way in which they exist, appear, and act, is the same. One acid expels another from a base, just as the north pole of a magnet repels the north pole, while each is related to the same south pole. Acids are compared through a third term however, and each acid is opposed by *its* opposite, which is *more its* base than another. The determination is not brought about by the general nature of mere opposition, for the chemical process is the realm in which kinds of substances are qualitatively active against one another. The *strength* of the affinity is therefore of prime importance. No affinity is onesided however, and another person is related to *me* to the extent that I am related to *him*. The acids and bases of two salts dissolve their combination and form fresh salts, for the acid of the second salt combines more easily with the basis of the first and drives out its acid, while the identical relationship exists between this acid and the base of the second salt, i.e.an acid abandons its base when it is presented with another base with which it has a greater affinity. Further real neutralities constitute the result, so that the product is of the same genus as the beginning, and is therefore a formal return of the neutral substance to itself.

In the remark, mention was made of the law of elective affinities discovered by *Richter*. This law was disregarded until Wollaston and Berthollet introduced Richter to the English and French, made use of his work, and so made it important. *Goethe's* theory of colour will suffer the same fate in Germany, and will not be accepted until a Frenchman or an Englishman takes it up, or expounds the same point of view and gains acceptance for it. There is no point in grumbling about this any more, for amongst us Germans it is always the same, unless it is trash such as *Gall's* phrenology which is being peddled. The principle of *stoichiometry*, which *Richter* expounded with a wealth of erudite reflections, may now be most conveniently elucidated by means of the following comparison. If I pay for certain goods in golden Fredericks, I might for example need one Frederick for a certain quantity of the first article, and two for the same quantity of the second article etc. If I pay in silver thalers, I shall need more of this sort of coin, $5\frac{2}{3}$ thalers instead of one golden Frederick, and $11\frac{1}{3}$ thalers instead of two Fredericks etc. The relative value of the goods is always the same, and that which is worth twice as much retains its relative value, regardless of the money in which its price is quoted. Similarly, as the different kinds of money also stand in a specific relationship

to one another, the portion of each article they will buy corresponds to their relative values. Thus, a golden Frederick is worth $5\frac{2}{3}$ times as much as a thaler, and if a thaler will buy three of a certain commodity,
+ the Frederick will buy $5\frac{2}{3} \times 3$ of the same commodity. *Berzelius* has kept
5 to the same point of view with regard to *degrees of oxidation*, and has tried to work it out into a universal law, for one substance is like another in making use of more or less oxygen. For example, one hundred parts of tin need to be saturated with 13.6 parts of oxygen in order to become a protoxide, 20.4 parts to become white deuteroxide, and 27.4 parts to be-
+ come yellow hyperoxide. *Dalton* was the first to investigate this, but he enveloped his determinations in the worst form of atomistic metaphysics by regarding the primary elements or the first simple aggregation as an atom, and then attributing weight and weight-ratios to these atoms, which he also supposed to be spherical, and to be partly surrounded by a more
15 or less dense atmosphere of caloric. He has since proceeded to expound the relative weights and diameters of these atoms, as well as the numbers
+ in which they came together to form compound bodies. *Berzelius* on the
+ other hand has created a jumble of electro-chemical relationships, which
+ has been complicated still further by *Schweigger*. The formal moments of
20 magnetism and electricity occur within this process in a limited way or not at all, for they are abstract forms, and can only come into prominence in an incompletely real process. *Davy* was the first to show that there is an electrical opposition between two materials which are *actively opposed*
+ *chemically*. If sulphur is melted in a crucible, an electrical tension is created
25 between the sulphur and the crucible since this is not real chemical process. We have already seen that the most determinate occurrence of electricity is in the galvanic process, for this also is not a real chemical process, and where it passes into the chemical sphere, the electricity disappears. Magnetism can only be produced in the chemical process where there is a
30 manifestation of spatial differentiation however, and this also occurs mainly in galvanism. Once again the precise reason for this is that galvanism is not the absolute activity of the chemical process.

3. Separation
(*The process of separation*)

§ 334

The dissolution of the neutral **body initiates the** reversion **to**
+ **the particular chemical form, i.e. through a series of partly**

particular processes, to the form of undifferentiated bodies. On the +
other hand, each and every separation of this kind is itself inseparably linked with a combination, while the processes classi-
fied as involved in the course of combination also contain the
other moment of separation (§ 328). In order to assign each 5
particular form of the process and each specific product to its
proper place, it is necessary to consider the concrete agents,
as well as the concrete products of the processes. Abstract processes in which the agents are abstract, such as the action of nothing but water on metal, or purely gaseous interactions etc., 10
certainly contain the totality of the process in an implicit manner, but they do not make an explicit display of its moments.

Remark

Empirical chemistry is mainly concerned with the *particularity* of *substances* and *products,* **and as it groups these**
in accordance with superficial and abstract determinations, 15
their particularity remains disordered. In this grouping, it brings
together metals, oxygen, hydrogen etc., **metalloids, which
were formerly known as** earths, sulphur, and phosphorus, and
places them on the same level as *simple* chemical bodies.
The great physical diversity of these bodies immediately gives 20
**rise to the incongruities of this sort of classification however, and
their chemical origin, or the process by which they are produced,
displays a similar lack of homogeneity. A similar** chaos reigns
where processes are assigned to a certain stage regardless of
their degree of abstraction or concreteness. If scientific 25
form is to **predominate** here, each product has to be assessed according to that stage of the **concrete and fully developed** process which essentially gives rise to it, and from which it
derives its particular significance. **In order to do this,** it is
equally essential to distinguish between the various stages 30
of abstraction or reality within the process. *Animal* and
vegetable substances belong moreover to quite another natural
order; the chemical process is so inadequate an expression
of their nature, that it tends mainly to destroy it, and can
merely make intelligible their relapse into *death.* These sub- 35
stances should principally serve to counteract the sort of
metaphysics **which** prevails in both chemistry and physics

however, and which employs thoughts or rather confused concepts such as the *immutability of substances* in all circumstances, and categories such as composition and *subsistence*, on the strength of which bodies are supposed to be formed from such
5 substances. It is generally admitted that when chemical substances combine, they lose the *properties* which they have in separation. Yet it is also generally asserted that they are the same things *with* or *without* these properties, so that both the things and the properties are not primarily the product of a
10 process. A metal is an undifferentiated body, and its affirmative determination is so constituted physically, that it displays its properties in an immediate manner. Bodies which are further differentiated may not be presupposed in this way however, and one is therefore unable to see how they comport themselves within
15 a process, for it is only from their place within the chemical process as a whole, that they derive their primary and essential determination. The empirical and completely specific particularity of a body may also be determined by means of its relation with all other particular bodies, but this knowledge may only be obtained
20 by reiterating the entire litany of the body's relation to all agents.

In this connection it is most surprising to find the four chemical elements of oxygen etc., regarded as substances, and put on the same level as gold, silver, and sulphur etc., treated in fact as if they had an independent existence like that of gold and sulphur
+ etc., or as if oxygen had an existence like that of carbon. Their place within the process indicates the degree of subordination and abstraction by which they are quite clearly distinguished in kind from metals or salts, and it is therefore utterly indefensible to place this genus on a level with concrete bodies. Its place has
30 already been determined (§ 328). Water and air are the two elements which belong to the internal division of the abstract middle term (cf. § 204 Rem.) On being abandoned as a middle term, they become the means by which the real extremes of the syllogism assume the existence of their original differentiation,
35 which is primarily merely implicit. When this moment of differentiation assumes determinate being for itself in this way, it constitutes the completely abstract moment of a chemical element. The word 'element' is usually taken to mean a basic substance or substantial principle, but the chemical elements are
+ rather the extreme limits of differentiation.

Here, as everywhere, the chemical process has to be taken in the completeness of its totality. The isolation of particular parts and formal and abstract processes, gives rise to the chemical pro- + cess in general being abstractly represented as nothing but the action of one substance upon another. As the result of this, many 5 other phenomena such as the abstract neutralization in which water is produced, and the abstract separation in which gas is developed, tend to be regarded as by-products or accidental consequences of the whole, or at least as merely connected with it in an external way, and not as the essential moments of its relation- 10 ships. A complete exposition of the totality of the chemical pro- + cess as a real syllogism would require moreover that it should be explicated as a triad of intimately inter-relating syllogisms. These syllogisms should not merely connect their termini however; they would have to be made explicit as activities which negate their 15 determinations (cf. § 198), and exhibit the interrelationship of combination and separation knit together in one and the same process.

Addition. Whereas the first process culminated in combination, in the processes of neutral bodies with one another, this combining occurs to- 20 gether with the diremptions or decompositions of the neutral bodies, and the separating out of the abstract bodies with which we began. It is in this way that the pure metal with which we began by considering it in its immediate existence, is now brought forth as a product of the total body towards which we were advancing. The salt is the real neutral substance 25 forming the concrete middle which is decomposed here, while in galvanism and the process of fire it was water and air which formed the formal middles and were decomposed. The means and stages of this reduction are various; principally they constitute the process of fire and the saline process. For example, a neutralized acid may be revived by raising 30 it to a red heat together with the requisite salt. Carbonic acid may be extracted from lime in the same way, since at this temperature the lime has a greater affinity with 'caloric' than with carbonic acid. This leads on to the reduction of metals; sulphur, which as acid is combined with a base, is driven off, leaving a reguline metal for example. Few metals occur 35 naturally in a pure state; most of them are refined by chemical action.

We have now presented the entire course of the chemical process, and in order that the individual bodies may be assigned to their appropriate stages, the determinate series of stages which constitutes the course of this process has to be established. If it is not, one is left with an unmanageable multitude of substances which, taken on their own, remain in a state of inorganic confusion. The individual bodies are the moments and products of the process, and as the concrete elements which are now determined in their individuality, they constitute the following system of determinately differentiated corporeality, and determine themselves within the process as follows:—

A. Air is individualized and differentiated into *various gases*, and forms a fourfold totality. (*a*) *Nitrogen* is here the abstract and undifferentiated form. (*b*) *Oxygen* and *hydrogen* are the opposed forms of air—the former kindling and activating, the latter positive and undifferentiated. (*c*) *Carbonic acid gas* is the earthy form, for it appears partly as an earth and partly as a gas.

B. One of the moments of the opposition is the *sphere of fire*, which is the realization of the individuality of fire, together with its counterpart, the *combustible substance*. This also forms a totality. (*a*) Its base is the implicitly combustible and inflammable factor, which is neither an undifferentiated substance only to be posited in a differentiation as a determination, nor a positive substance only to be limited by differentiation, but which is rather an implicit negativity. Fire itself may be regarded as time in *action*, and this negativity as inwardly realized and *dormant time*, the quiescent subsistence of which is mere form. Consequently, this negativity constitutes the quality of the base, and is not a mere form of its being, but the essential constitution of it. It is *sulphur* as the earthy base, *hydrogen* as the aerial base, and *naphtha* as the base of vegetable and animal oils etc. (*b*) *Acids* divide themselves as follows. (i) *Sulphuric* acid is the acid of combustible earthiness. (ii) *Aquafortis* or *nitric* acid, which has various forms. (iii) *Hydracid* or *muriatic* acid seems to me to have hydrogen as its radical; the undifferentiated moments of aerial individuality must be activated into acid, and are therefore already implicitly combustible. Unlike the metals, this is not merely due to their abstraction however, for as they are undifferentiated, the combustible material is within them, and is not external to them as it is to oxygen. (iv) The *earthy acids* are as follows; (1) *abstract*, earthy, *carbonic* acid; (2) *concrete* arsenic acid etc.; (3) vegetable and animal acids, such as citric acid, blood acid, and formic acid. (*c*) Finally there are the *oxides* and *alkalies* in general, which are opposed to acids.

C. The other moment of the opposition is the *realization of water* in *salts*, *earths* and *stones*, which are the neutralities of acids and oxides. It is here, strictly speaking, that the body appears in its totality. The various kinds of gas are airs, the sphere of fire has not yet reached the stability of totality, and sulphur dominates the other terrestrial bodies as the permeating base of this process. The *earths* are white, thoroughly friable, and individualized throughout; they are non-combustible, and lack both the continuity of metal, and its capacity for developing within a process. There are four main earths, and these neutral earthy substances divide themselves into 5 a double series. (*a*) Firstly, there are the neutral substances which have only the abstractness of water as the base of their neutrality, and which subsist in this neutrality by means of an acid as well as an alkali. The earths which form this transition are silica, alumina, and magnesia or talc. (*i*) Silica is as it were the earthy metal and perfectly brittle, and on account of 10 the abstraction of its singularity, enters into combinations; it does this in particular with potash, and becomes glass. In the process of fusion it displays singularity, just as metal displays colour and compactness. It is the colourless substance into which metallicism is annulled as pure form, and its internal discreteness is absolute. (*ii*) Silica is the immediacy and simplicity of the un- 15 disclosed Notion, and *alumina*, which has the possibility of being combustible, therefore constitutes the primary differentiated earth. Pure alumina will absorb oxygen from the air, but generally, together with sulphuric acid, it is an earthy fire, *porcelain jasper*. It is to fire that it owes its hardness or crystallization. + + Water gives rise to exterior cohesion rather than crystalline connectedness. 20 (*iii*) *Magnesia* or *talc* is the subject of salt, and accounts for the bitterness of sea water. It has the intermediate taste of a substance which has become the principle of fire and is precisely the return of the neutral substance to that principle. + (*b*) Finally, there is the antithesis to this first series. This is the genuinely real neutrality of *calcareous substances*, the alkalinity and differentiation which 25 dissolves its earthy principle anew, and needs only the physical element in order to become a process. It is here therefore that the extinguished process re-establishes itself. Lime is the principle of the fire which the physical body engenders within itself.

D. The metals are the earthy element to which all determinations except 30 weight are now external, and in which gravity is identical with light. Within light, this being-in-self is real in that gravity constitutes the being-in-self of indeterminate externality. Metals are coloured therefore, but on the other hand their lustre is a pure and indeterminate light which shines of its own accord, and effaces colour. The different states of metal, 35 its continuity and compactness, and then its readiness to enter into process, its brittleness, puncticity and capacity for oxidation are all exhibited within the compact metal itself. Thus, (*a*) some metals occur in their reguline state, while (*b*) others only occur in an oxidized or earthy state which is hardly ever reguline, and when it is, the metals appear in a completely powdery 40 form, like arsenic for example. Antimony and metals of its kind are similar, for they are so brittle and hard, that they may easily be pulverized. (c) Finally when metal occurs in a vitrified state as a scoria, it has the mere form of likeness of texture and resembles sulphur.

§ 335

In general, the chemical process is in fact *life*; in it the individual body in its immediacy is *sublated* as well as *produced*. Consequently, the Notion is no longer an interior necessity, but makes its *appearance*. **On account of the immediacy of the corporealities which enter into the chemical process however, it is generally encumbered with division. Its moments therefore appear as external** *conditions*, **and that which separates out here, disintegrates into mutually indifferent products; fire and activation die out in the** neutral body, **within which they do not revive. The beginning and end of the process are not identical, and it is this which constitutes the finitude of the chemical process, and separates and distinguishes it from life.**

Remark

In order to explain some chemical phenomena, **chemistry has had occasion** to use the determination of *teleology*. The phenomenon of an oxide being reduced to a lower degree of oxidation so that part of it may become more highly oxidized **by combining with the effective acid,** is an example of this. **In this** realization **of itself,** the Notion **displays the beginnings of a spontaneous** self-determination, **which is not therefore determined solely by the external conditions present.**

Addition. There is certainly an appearance of animation here, but it is lost in the product. If the products of the chemical process spontaneously renewed their activity, they would be life, and to some extent therefore, life is a perenniating chemical process. The determinateness of any species of chemical body is identical with the nature of the body's substantiality. Here therefore, we are still in the realm of fixed species. In living being on the other hand, the determinateness of the species is not identical with the substantiality of an individual, for although the individual is finite in its determinateness, it is also and equally infinite. In the chemical process, the Notion only displays its moments interruptedly. One side of the entirety of the chemical process contains fixed determinateness having being through its lack of differentiation, the other the tendency to have being as an opposition to that within it, an opposition in which this determinateness then falls away. This quiescent being and this tendency are different from one another however, and the totality is only posited implicitly or within the Notion. The unity in which both determinations are at once present does not attain existence. As existing, this unity is the determination of life, and it is towards this that nature drives. Life is implicitly present within the chemical process, but the inner necessity there is not yet an existent unity.

§ 336

The chemical process itself is so constituted however, that it posits as negated these immediate presuppositions forming the foundation of its externality and finitude. Within it, the properties of bodies appearing as the results of a particular stage are changed by the process from one stage to another, so that these conditions are reduced to products. In general therefore, the chemical process posits the relativity of the immediate substances and properties. Corporality which subsists as being indifferent is posited as a mere moment of the individuality therefore, and the Notion is posited in the *reality which corresponds to it*. This *concrete* unity with self, which brings itself forth from the particularization of the different corporealities into a whole, and by its activity negates the onesided form of its self-relatedness and leads the moments of the Notion back into unity while dividing and particularizing itself into them, is the organism. *The organism* is therefore the infinite self-stimulating and self-sustaining process.

Addition. We now have to make the *transition* from inorganic to organic nature, from the prose of nature to its poetry. In the chemical process bodies do not change superficially, all aspects of them change, and every property of cohesion, colour, lustre, opacity, ring, transparency etc. is effaced. Even specific gravity, which appears to be the profoundest and simplest determination, fails to hold out. It is precisely in this flux of accidents within the chemical process, that the relativity of the apparently indifferent determinations of individuality is realized as essence; the body displays the transience of its existence, and this its relativity is its being.

If one wants to say what a body is, one's description of it will only be complete once the whole cycle of its changes has been presented; for the true individuality of the body does not exist in any one of its states, and is only exhausted and displayed by the full cycle. It is precisely because
5 totality of shape is merely particular, that it is unable to survive, and as the individual body is finite, it receives its due and fails to endure. Thus, there are metals which run through the whole series of colours when they are oxidized or neutralized by acids, and which are also able to form neutral
+ transparent salts, for salts in general are the annihilation of colour.
10 Brittleness, compactness, smell, and taste also disappear; this is the ideality of the particularity which displays itself in this sphere. The bodies traverse the whole cycle of such possible determinations. For example, as a reguline metal, copper is red; copper sulphate is a blue crystal however, the precipitate of copper hydrate is mountain blue, and there is a muriatic copper
15 oxide which is white. Other copper oxides are green, dark grey, and
+ reddish brown etc., and azurite is yet another colour etc. The reaction varies according to the agent, and the chemical body is merely the sum of its reactions. Consequently, the totality of reactions is merely present as a sum, not as an infinite return of the body into itself. The body maintains
20 its determinateness in all the reactions in which it enters into relations with other bodies in synsomation, oxidation, and neutralization, but it maintains only the implicit being of its specific nature, not its existence. Iron is always implicitly iron, but it is also only implicitly so, for its mode of existence changes. Here we are concerned with the preservation of exis-
25 tence however, not with the preservation of implicitness; more precisely, our concern is that implicitness should be in existence, or rather that existence should be implicit. The cycle of particular reactions constitutes the universal particularity of the body; the existence of the particularity is merely implicit however, it is not universal. It is only in the process
30 of fire that activity is immanent, and as an individual moment of life and the activity of this moment, it merely hastens to extinction. It is here however that the immediate shape containing particular determinations becomes extinct, so that the transition takes place by which the implicit universality of determinateness is also posited within existence. This is
35 organic being in its self-conservation, by which it acts and reacts upon the most diverse powers, so that although it is differently determined in each reaction, it still maintains itself as a single unity. The implicit being of this kind of specific determinateness now also exists, and forms and breaks relationships. It does not neutralize itself in these relationships however,
40 but maintains itself within the process, which it determines together with

its other. Where infinite form is still materialized within shape as the soul of individuality, it is reduced to a unity which is not in itself infinitely free form, but which exists as an enduring being. Infinite form conflicts with this quiescence however, for it is restlessness, movement, and activity, and it is only as such that it comes forth as what it is in and for itself. The 5 persistence of its moments in shape, in which each can exist as an independent matter, is certainly also an occurrence of infinite form within existence; but here its unity is not yet in possession of the truth of its being. The chemical process now displays the dialectic by which all the particular properties of bodies are drawn into transitoriness however. It negates the 10 immediate presuppositions which are the principles of its finitude. It is therefore solely the being-for-self of infinite form which endures, the pure incorporeal individuality which is for itself, and for which material subsistence is simply a variable. The chemical process is the highest expression of inorganic being, for it annihilates itself within it, and shows 15 that its truth is nothing but infinite form. It is therefore through the sinking away of shape that the chemical process constitutes the transition to the higher sphere of the organism, in which infinite form assumes the reality of its nature. Infinite form is therefore the Notion, which here reaches reality. This transition is the raising of existence to universality. 20 Nature has here reached the determinate being of the Notion therefore, and the Notion is no longer merely implicit, and submerged within the extrinsicality of its subsistence. This is the free fire (a) as purged of all materiature, and (b) as materialized in determinate being. The moments + of that which subsists are themselves raised into this ideality, and do not 25 fall back into limited subsistence, but have their being solely within it. It is thus that we have objective time, an imperishable fire, the fire of life. *Heraclitus* also said that the soul was of fire, and that dry souls are the best. +

NOTES

10, 10

‚Hier ist der Begriff verborgen'. The exact sense in which Hegel is here using ‚verborgen' becomes clearer if we remember that in the physics and medicine of his day the word was also used to describe 'latent' heat and 'occult' inflammation. In general usage it has the meaning of hidden, concealed, secret or obscure.

11, 11

Hegel evidently takes the structure of his logic and of his philosophy of spirit as being parallel to that of his philosophy of nature. Consequently, the transition from being to essence, and from subjective to objective spirit, corresponds to this transition from mechanics to physics.

In § 112 of the 'Encyclopaedia' (tr. Wallace 'The Logic of Hegel' Oxford, 1963 p. 207) he explains the nature of the *logical* transition at this juncture, 'The terms in *Essence* are always mere pairs of correlatives, and not yet absolutely reflected in themselves: hence in essence the actual unity of the Notion is not realized, but only postulated by reflection. Essence,—which is Being coming into mediation with itself through the negativity of itself is self-relatedness, only in so far as it is relation to an Other,—this Other however coming to view at first not as something which is, but as postulated and hypothesized.'

In the 'Science of Logic' (tr. Johnston and Struthers, London, 1961) vol. II pp. 15–34 he takes the categories of show to be the initiation of essence, but in the 'Encyclopaedia', essence begins with the categories of identity and difference. J. M. E. Taggart, in 'A Commentary on Hegel's Logic' (Cambridge, 1910) p. 91 ff. discussed the relative merits of these attempts at formulating the transition.

12, 3

‚In der Natur daseyend.'

12, 12

Hegel entered the following note in the margin at this point ('Jenenser Realphilosophie' II p. 33 note 1), '(It has) become power, or passed *into itself* from immedate existence. (It is) *in itself*, (and has) emerged from the *self* of the *Idea* as *opacity*. Power (is) *simple being-in-self* which, by containing the unity of its opposite, is also absolute asunderness.'

12, 15

It was evidently the *integrality* (Gediegenheit) of motion in the solar system, and of light in space, which led Hegel to formulate this transition from one to the other. He had grasped the significance of this common feature as early as 1801/2, see 'Jenenser Logik Metaphysik und Naturphilosophie' (ed. G. Lasson, Leipzig, 1923) pp. 228–229 and 366–367, where light is characterized as 'the quiescence of motion in itself' ('das Ruhen der Bewegung in sich selbst').

The 1803/4 lectures on the philosophy of nature ('Jenenser Realphilosophie' I ed. Hoffmeister. Leipzig, 1932) open with a discussion of this, 'The solar system is the absolute totality and identity of the four motions which have been construed. Light is the manifesting essence, the absolute universality, the positive unity; the absolute rotatory motion constitutes its infinity, its absolute thought' etc.

12, 32

‚die Wirklichkeit als eine durchsichtige Möglichkeit'. This is Michelet's version, Hegel ('Jenenser Realphilosophie' II, ed. Hoffmeister, Leipzig, 1931) p. 34 wrote, ‚als reine durchsichtige Möglichkeit' i.e. 'as pure transparent possibility'.

13, 6

‚als die mit Allem zusammenfließende Möglichkeit'. This is Michelet's version, Hegel (op. cit. p. 34) wrote, ‚als mit allein zusammenfließende Möglichkeit'. Hoffmeister changes ‚allein' to ‚allem' in his version of text.

13, 36

Hegel deals at some length with 'the religion of the good or of light' in his lectures on the philosophy of religion (tr. Speirs and Sanderson, 3 vols. London, 1962) vol. II pp. 70–82: see also 'The Philosophy of History' (tr. Sibree, Dover Pub., 1956) pp. 173–181.

He evidently read the 'Zend-Avesta' in the translation published by A. H. Anquetil Duperron (1731–1805), 'Zend-Avesta, Ouvrage de Zoroastre' (3 vols. Paris, 1771). Thomas Hyde (1636–1703), in his 'Historia religionis veterum Persarum' (Oxford, 1700) was the first European scholar to direct attention to this document.

14, 28

‚ist das Vortreffliche nur im Sinne der Abstraction.' The usual meaning of 'vortrefflich' is 'excellent', 'exquisite', 'capital'. In Goethe and Schiller the word still occurs in its older form of ‚fürtrefflich', giving indication of its origin in ‚fürtreffen' i.e. 'strike home beyond something else'.

Hegel makes two points by using this word therefore: (i) he indicates the position of light in the dialectical progression as, 'the beginning of material manifestation', and (ii) he implies that light as such is invisible prior to the emergence of its 'limit' or 'deficiency'.

15, 22

This is a reference to the tales concerning the Man in the Moon and the Woman in the Sun, which are thought to have originated in the incident mentioned in 'Numbers' XV vv. 32–36. In English folk-lore the Man is said to have been banished to the Moon for stealing a dog and a bundle of thorns, and in the chancel roof of Gyffin church near Conway, he may be seen in the disk of the Moon, surrounded by the Sun and the Stars. Reginald Pecock (c. 1393–1461) mentions the tale in his 'The Repressor of Overmuch Wijting of the Clergy' (ed. Babington, 2 vols. Rolls Series, 1860): cf. 'A Midsummer Night's Dream' V i, 'The Tempest' II ii.

In German folk-lore the Man is said to have been a thief who went to work on a Sunday, a craftsman who bound brooms on Maundy Thursday, a farmer who erected a fence on Ascension Day, a peasant who stole coal at night, from his neighbour's yard. In the county of Mark, he is said to have been a thief, to whom God gave the choice of either burning in the Sun or rigidifying in the Moon: see J. F. L. Woeste 'Volksüberlieferungen in der Grafschaft Mark' (Iserlohn, 1848) p. 40.

Tales concerning the Woman in the Sun are not so common, but Karl Bartsch (1832–1888) records one in his 'Sagen, Märchen und Gebräuche aus Mecklenburg' (2 vols. Vienna, 1879–1880) I p. 460, II p. 198, 'It is not good to spin on a Saturday, in fact many say that it is sinful. Whoever does so will be sent to the Sun, where they will spin forever, like that godless woman who was punished in this way for spinning right through the winter, Saturdays and all. When the woman and girls come back with the water at Easter, they can easily see the godless sitting in the Sun and spinning.' Hegel probably knew the old Swabian saying:

> ‚Haun is daun so komm i in maun
> Haun i g'sponne so komm i in d'sonne'.

(If I've played the loon I'll end in the moon,
And if I've spun I'll be sent to the sun'.)

See 'Zeitschrift für deutsche Mythologie und Sittenkunde' (Göttingen, 1853–1859) I p. 169. Astronomers themselves have not been free from these superstitions. Tycho Brahe (1546–1601), in his 'Epistolarum Astronomicarum' (Uraniborg, 1596) entertains the possibility of there being people on the stars, saying that he will never believe that such huge bodies were made to no other purpose than to illumine the Earth. Sir William Herschel (1738–1822) thought himself, 'authorised *upon astronomical principles*, to propose the sun as an inhabitable world': see 'Phil. Trans. Roy. Soc.' 1795 pp. 46–72, 'The Scientific Papers of Sir William Herschel (ed. Dreyer, 2 vols. London, 1912) vol. I p. 479.

Cf. E. Hoffmann-Krayer and H. Bächtold-Stäubli 'Handwörterbuch des Deutschen Aberglaubens' (10 vols. Berlin und Leipzig, 1927–1942) especially vol. VI columns 510–513.

16, 5

The ballooning craze began in November 1782, when the Montgolfier brothers made their first experiments with hot air balloons at Avignon. By 1785 the novelty of such experiments had worn off, and ascents for purely scientific purposes were becoming more common. In Hegel's day, 'the art of navigating or floating in the air' was known in English as 'aerostation': see Charles Hutton (1737–1813) 'A Mathematical and Philosophical Dictionary' (2 vols. London, 1796). In German this term (‚Aerostatik‘) was confined to its proper and primary meaning, i.e. the science of weights suspended in the air, and 'the art of navigating or floating in the air' was known as ‚Aeronautik‘ or ‚Luftschiffahrtskunde‘. See J. S. T. Gehler 'Physikalisches Wörterbuch' vol. I pp. 219 and 258 (Leipzig, 1825).

Hegel may have had in mind the balloon ascent made by J. B. Biot (1774–1862) and L. J. Gay-Lussac (1778–1850) on September 16, 1804, accounts of which appeared in L. W. Gilbert's 'Annalen der Physik' (vol. XX pp. 19–37, 1805), W. Nicholson's 'Journal of Natural Philosophy' (vol. X pp. 278–288, 1805), and 'Journal de Physique' (vol. LIX pp. 454–461, 1804) etc. Gay-Lussac ascended from the Conservatoire des Arts in Paris, stayed up for six hours five minutes, and landed between Rouen and Dieppe. The temperature was 82°F at ground level in Paris, and after rising to a height of 23,000 feet, he found that it had fallen to 14.9°F. Cf. the account by John Jeffries (1744–1819) of Massachusetts, of ascents made at London, 'A Narrative of Two Aerial Voyages of Dr. Jeffries with Mons. Blanchard; with Meteorological Observations and Remarks' (London, 1786).

16, 8

‚die Erschütterung‘. The flash accompanying the discharge of electricity from the *Leyden jar*, and the electrical shock transmitted, were known as ‚die elektrische Erschütterung‘ (concussio, commotio electrica, commotion électrique). Two forms of illumination were recognized 'If the wire presented to the outside of the phial be pointed, it will be seen illuminated with a star; but if the pointed wire be connected with the coating of the phial, it will appear illuminated with a brush of rays': C. Hutton 'A Mathematical and Philosophical Dictionary' (2 vols. London, 1795) vol. II p. 25. Cf. J. S. T. Gehler's 'Physikalisches Wörterbuch, vol. IV pp. 377–378 (Leipzig, 1827). A. Masson (1806–1860) made various attempts to measure the intensity of this momentary light: see 'Comptes rendus' vol. XVIII p. 289, vol. XIX p. 325, J. C. Poggendorff's 'Annalen der Physik und Chemie' vol. LXIII p. 158, 'The Electrical Magazine' ed. C. V. Walker (2 vols. London. 1845–1846) I pp. 272–274, II pp. 6–7.

16, 18

This postulated explanation of the production of solar and stellar light bears some resemblance to that put forward by Johannes Hevelius (1611–1687) in his 'Cometographia' (Danzig, 1668) p. 380. Hevelius supposed the sun and stars to be surrounded with atmospheres, and thought that by whirling on their axes with great rapidity, they throw off great quantities of matter.

When he suggests that these luminous bodies may be self-frictionalizing (‚sich selber Ritzende‘), Hegel probably has in mind electrical machines such as that devised by Jesse Ramsden (1735–1800) in 1768, which generated *electricity* by means of *friction*. These machines were still used at the beginning of the last century, although they were being steadily replaced by 'influence' machines such as that described by William Nicholson (1753–1813) in 'Phil. Trans. Roy. Soc.' 1788 p. 403.

The rotation of the sun had been known to astronomers since the early seventeenth century, see David Fabricius (1546–1617) 'De maculis in sole observatis' (Wittenberg, 1611). Careful observation of the variable stars by Sir William Herschel (1738–1822), Nathanial Pigott (d. 1804), and the remarkable John Goodricke (1764–1786), see 'Phil. Trans. Roy. Soc.' 1786, gave rise to suggestions that the stars rotate on their axes. Goodricke's suggestion that the light-variation of Algol may be due to its being eclipsed by another star revolving around it was not confirmed until 1887. In Hegel's day it was generally supposed that the periodical stars have vast dark spots or sides, and that their apparent disappearance is due to a very slow rotation upon their axes. See the careful observations made by J. F. Wurm (1760–1833) and Luthmer, accounts of which appeared in 'Astronomisches Jahrbuch oder Ephemeriden für das Jahr. Nebst einer Sammlung der Neuesten in denastronomischen Wissenschaften: Beobachtungen, Nachrichten u.s.w.' (ed. J. E. Bode, Berlin, 1774–1825) 1801 p. 157, 1810 p. 140, 1814 p. 143, 1824 p. 243 etc.

16, 32

Jacques Alexandre Francois Allix (1776–1836) was the son of a mathematics teacher. He joined the army at the age of sixteen. By the age of twenty he had risen to the rank of colonel, and during the revolutionary and Napoleonic wars he saw service in the Rhineland, Italy, Westphalia, and Russia. He became a general in 1812. In 1815 he was arrested for supporting Napoleon during the hundred days, and for a while was under sentence of death, but he was released on July 24, 1815, and left France for Westphalia, the birthplace of his wife.

During his exile in Cassel, he occupied himself with scientific studies, and wrote the book referred to by Hegel: 'Théorie de l'univers ou de la cause primitive du mouvement et de ses principaux effets' (Paris, 1818, Italian tr. by G. Compagnoni, Milan, 1817). Laplace condescended to condemn the theories put forward in this work, but in general they attracted little attention from scientists, and Hegel probably read the book only because it contained a criticism of Newton.

On December 23, 1818 Allix was given permission to return to France, on probation. He answered the critics of his astronomical theories, as best he could, in 'De la Théorie de l'univers, lettres y relatives' (Paris, 1819). During the 1820's his displayed his versatility to the full by producing works on *agriculture*, 'Des effets du sulfate de chaux considère comme engrais' (Nevers, 1823), and *gunnery*, 'Système d'artillerie' (Paris, 1827), and, after the 1830 revolution, by publishing a *translation*, 'De la Tyrannie' (Paris, 1831), of a work by Vittorio Alfieri (1749–1803), whom he had met in Italy in 1800.

See C. Mullie 'Biographie des célébrités militaires' (Paris, 1851).

17, 2

,die Sonne ist also der Proceß des ganzen Sonnensystems, der in diese Spitze ausschlägt'. This statement draws together the whole argument of this paragraph. Solar light is not the same as the light of the flame, but resembles the integrated movement of the solar system, and is therefore an integral part of this system.

In his lectures on the philosophy of nature delivered in 1801 and 1803–4, Hegel took 'the system of the sun' to be the first major sphere. In 1801 he treated it as being comprised of the ether, space time motion, and light: ('Sämtliche Werke' ed. Lasson, Leipzig, 1923 vol. XVIII a pp. 195–239). In 1803–4 he treated it very sketchily, beginning with light, progressing to sun, earth and comet, and concluding with celestial motion: (op. cit. ed. Hoffmeister, Leipzig, 1932, pp. 3–12).

The key to his maturer views on the sun as the centre of the motion of the solar system, and as the source of light is to be found in the lectures of 1805–6 (op. cit. ed. Hoffmeister, Leipzig, 1931 pp. 34–35). Michelet made use of the exposition of light given here, but omitted what follows, 'As emergent being-for-self which fills space, light has not developed difference within itself, but has it only in a completely abstract manner, as a *plurality*. To be *one* constitutes its negative existence, and differentiation has being merely as this notionless multitude, which is devoid of self-limitation.' (i.e. the stars) . . . 'This power of light, which is impotent in its being-in-self, is essentially expressive however, and so has reality. As such it is sun, which as a celestial sphere is a centre of motion, and which as light is a source of life, although it is not life itself.'

17, 11

See the note on 13, 36.

18, 1

Newton. 'Opticks: or, a Treatise of the Reflections, Refractions, Inflections and Colours of Light' (4th ed. London, 1730, ed. Cohen, Dover Publications, 1952).

Bk. I pt. I def. i, 'By the Rays of light I understand its least Parts, and those as well Successive in the same Lines, as Contemporary in several Lines. For it is manifest that Light consists of Parts, both Successive and Contemporary; because in the same place you may stop that which comes one moment, and let pass that which comes presently after; and in the same time you may stop it in any one place, and let it pass in any other.' Bk. iii pt. I qu. 29, 'Are not the Rays of light very small Bodies emitted from shining Substances? For such Bodies will pass through uniform Mediums in right Lines without bending into the Shadow, which is the Nature of the Rays of Light . . . Nothing more is requisite for putting the Rays of Light into Fits of easy Reflexion and easy Transmission, than that they be small Bodies which by their attractive Powers, or some other Force, stir up Vibrations in what they act upon, which Vibrations being swifter than the Rays, overtake them successively, and agitate them so as by turns to increase and decrease their Velocities, and thereby put them into those Fits.'

Thomas Young (1773–1829), in a series of papers published in the 'Philosophical Transactions of the Royal Society' between 1800 and 1804 (1800 pp. 1, 106; 1802 pp. 12, 387; 1804 p. 1), revived the *wave* theory of light by showing that when two undulations from different origins coincide either perfectly or very nearly in direction, their joint effect is a combination of the motions belonging to each: See 'Miscellaneous Works of the late Thomas Young' (ed. G. Peacock, London, 1855). By the 1820's, A. J. Fresnel (1788–1827), by assuming the transversal nature of these waves, had produced explanations of interference, refraction and reflection; see 'Bulletin des Sciences de la Société Philomathique de Paris' 1822 p. 63, 'Mémoires de l'Academie' V, 1826, p. 339, W. S. Aldis 'A Chapter on Fresnel's Theory of Double Refraction' (Cambridge, 1870). When Hegel was delivering these lectures therefore, there was every reason to reject Newton's 'barbarous categories', even if one refused, as Hegel did, to accept Young's and Fresnel's. Twentieth century research has of course reinstated Newton's 'corpuscles' and 'particles' in the form of photons, which Planck and Einstein showed to be *units* of energy proportional in intensity to the *frequency* of the light waves.

18, 18

See the note on p. 238 Christian Huyghens (1629–1695), in his 'Cosmotheoros, sive De Terris Coelestibus, eorumque ornatu Conjecturae' (Hague, 1698) pp. 125–139, entered upon speculations of this kind. Edmund Halley (1656–1742), in 'Phil. Trans. Roy. Soc.' 1720 pp. 22–26 called attention to what he considered to be a paradox, i.e. that the number of fixed stars must be more than finite, and some of them more than a finite distance from others. 'And indeed, were the whole System finite: it, though never so extended, would still occupy no part of the *infinitum* of Space, which necessarily and evidently exists; whence the whole would be surrounded on all sides with an infinite inane' etc. Cf. Francis Roberts 'On the distance of the fixed stars' ('Phil. Trans. Roy. Soc.' 1694 p. 101); Jacques Cassini (1677–1756) 'De la grandeur des étoiles fixes et de leur distance à la terre' ('Mém. de l'Ac. des Sc. de Paris' 1717); Hegel's 'Logic' (tr. Wallace, Oxford, 1963) §§ 94, 95.

The distinction which Hegel draws here between 'the empirical appearances of the propagation of light', and its 'simple indivisibility' was probably due to some extent to the postulation of *ether* as the medium in which light appears: see Sir Edmund Whittaker 'A history of the theories of Aether and Electricity' (2 vols. London, 1951). Cf. Hegel's description of the ether in the lectures of 1801–1802 ('Sämtliche Werke' vol. XVIIIa ed. Lasson, Leipzig, 1923 pp. 196–201). In the lectures of 1803–1804 (op. cit. vol. XIX ed. Hoffmeister, Leipzig, 1932 pp. 3–4) he replaced the ether by light itself. He later (op. cit. vol. XX ed. Hoffmeister, Leipzig, 1931 pp. 33–34), rejected the ether entirely as a *physical* entity, but took many of its features to be characteristic of light.

For Hegel's views on memory, see §§ 452–454 of the 'Encyclopaedia' ('Sämtliche Werke' ed. Glockner, Stuttgart, 1958, vol. 10).

18, 29

This is evidently a reference to Newton's 'Opticks' Bk. I, pt. 1, axioms 6 and 7.

'Ax. vi. Homogeneal Rays which flow from several Points of any Object, and fall perpendicularly or almost perpendicularly on any reflecting or refracting Plane or spherical Surface, shall afterwards diverge from so many other Points, or be parallel to so many other Lines, or converge to so many other Points, either accurately or without any sensible Error. And the same thing will happen, if the Rays be reflected or refracted successively by two or three or more Plane or Spherical Surfaces.'

'Ax. vii. Wherever the Rays which come from all the Points of any Object meet again in so many Points after they have been made to converge by Reflection or Refraction, there they will make a picture of the Object upon any white Body on which they fall.'

In his exposition of these axioms, Newton defines a *focus*, and discusses the *refraction* of light by the eye. Hegel has difficulty in accepting the Newtonian account of refraction (see § 318), and is therefore forced into raising this objection to Newton's explanation of vision. Cf. Berkeley's confession, 'In vain shall all the *mathematicians* in the world tell me, that I perceive certain *lines* and *angles* which introduce into my mind the various *ideas* of *distance*; so long as I myself am conscious of no such thing'—'An Essay towards a New Theory of Vision' XII (Dublin, 1709).

Newton mentions, 'That vulgar Experiment of casting the Species of Objects from abroad upon a Wall or Sheet of white Paper in a dark Room' by means of a lens. Giovanni Battista della Porta (1538–1615) had given an account of the 'camera obscura' in his, 'Magiae Naturalis, sive de miraculis rerum naturalium' (Naples, 1558, 4th ed. 1589, Eng. tr. 'Natural Magick', London, 1658), and Kepler, in his 'Paralipomena ad Vitellionem' (Frankfurt, 1604) (cop. 5. Diopt. prop. 60), a commentary on the 'Perspectiva' (Nuremberg, 1535) of Witelo (c. 1230–1275), had accounted for it in substantially the same way as Newton. It is difficult to imagine how Hegel would have explained the phenomenon.

George Adams (1750–1795), in his 'Essay on Vision' (2nd ed. London, 1792) informs us that, 'Whatever is seen or beheld by the eye, is by opticians called an *object*. They consider every object as made up of a vast number of minute points, and that each of these points, by an unknown power, sends forth or reflects rays of light in all directions, and is thus the center of a sphere of light, extending indefinitely on all sides' (p. 39). On pp. 44–47 he goes on to give an elaborate account of the experiment just mentioned. Cf. William Porterfield's excellent 'Treatise on the Eye, the Manner and Phaenomena of Vision' (2 vols. Edinburgh, 1759) vol. I pp. 352–408.

18, 33

This 'representation', when applied to the study of gases gave rise to Avogadro's rule: see Amadeo Avogadro (1776–1856); articles in 'Memorie della R. Accademia di Torino' vols. 30 and 31, and 'Journal de Physique' 1811. It was used to explain transparency etc. by Robert Boyle (1627–1691), in his 'Experiments and Considerations about the Porosity of Bodies' (London, 1684), and by Peter van Musschenbroek (1692–1761), in his 'Introductio ad Philosophiam Naturalem' (2 vols. Leyden, 1762).

Hegel probably had in mind Newton's theory of colours when he mentioned the 'representation' so disparagingly. Cf. § 298 Remark. Newton had based this theory on the assumption that bodies of different colours absorb or reflect the various colours of the spectrum according to their *density*: see 'Opticks' (4th ed. London, 1730) Bk. II pt. iii: Biot 'Traité de Physique' (4 vols. Paris, 1816) vol. IV: Laplace 'Système du monde' (5th ed. Paris, 1824, 1824) vol. I, Cf. 'Philosophiae naturalis Theoria reducta ad unicam legem virium in natura existentium' (Vienne, 1758) by Roger Joseph Boscowich (1711–1787), in which matter is said to consist of physical points possessing the forces of attraction and repulsion.

19, 17

‚dieß scheint ein Widerspruch zu seyn, aber auf diesen Schein kann es uns nicht ankommen'. Hegel's point here is that the apparent contradiction *is in light itself*, light being the *most universal* manifestation of matter precisely because it is the most *immaterial* materiality.

19, 22

Eighteenth century attempts to weigh light originated in the desire to prove the materiality of Newton's 'corpuscles'. In 1708 William Homberg (1652–1715) claimed to have dispersed pieces of amianthus and set a watch spring moving by the impact of the sun's rays focused through a magnifying glass ('Mémoires de l'Academie royale des Sciences de Paris' 1708, p. 25). Peter van Musschenbroek (1692–1761) repeated Homberg's experiments without questioning his conclusions, and Peter Joseph Macquer (1718–1784), in his 'Dictionnaire de chymie' (Paris, 1766, Eng. tr. London, 1777, Germ. tr. Leipzig, 1806) gave an account of similar experiments, which he regarded as proving that light has weight. John Michell (1724–1793) and Joseph Priestley (1733–1804) carried out carefully regulated experiments which convinced Priestley that they had discovered the *weight* of the corpuscles and not merely observed their impact or movement: see his 'History and Present state of discoveries relating to vision' (2 vols. London, 1772, Germ. tr. Leipzig, 1776) pt. II sect. 6 ch. iii; pp. 282–283 of the German edition.

It was J. J. Mairan (1678–1771) who held that the movement of the balances used by these investigations was brought about by the heat concentrated in the focus, and by currents of air: see, 'Mémoires de l'Academie royale des Sciences' 1747 p. 630.

19, 33

Cf. the note on p. 224. In his 'Lectures on the Philosophy of Religion' (tr. Speirs and Sanderson, 3 vols. London, 1962) Hegel treats Zoroastrianism as being superior to Hinduism but inferior to the Greek religion in the dialectical progression. For an understanding of his regarding it as being 'more sublime' than these religions, see his analysis of Judaism (op. cit. vol. II pp. 170–224). He takes Genesis I v. 3 to be one of the *sublimest* passages in the Old Testament, ‚Das Wort ist das Müheloseste, dieser Hauch ist hier zugleich das Licht, die Lichtwelt, die unendliche Ausgießung des Lichts, so wird das Licht herabgesetzt zu einem Worte, zu etwas so Vorübergehenden'.

In Christian tradition, passages such as Milton's 'Hail, holy light, offspring of Heaven first-born' etc. ('Paradise Lost' II i ff.) are very common, and have the authority of Christ himself: see John VIII 12: cf. Isaiah XLII 6, Luke II 32.

19, 37

See the note III. 228.

20, 3

This is a reference to the doings of the Schildbürgers, the German equivalents of the Wise Men of Gotham, the inhabitants of Kampen in Holland, and the Danish Molboer.

In 1598, Hans Kremer (Mercator) of Zierenberg near Cassel published 'Wunderseltzamen, abentheuerlichen, unerhörten und bisher unbeschriebenen Geschichten und Thaten der Schiltbürger in Misnopotamia' (ed. Felix Bobertag in vol. 25 of 'Deutsche National-Litteratur' Stuttgart, no date). Hegel is evidently referring to the building of the Schildbürger town-hall. The architects had forgotten to give it windows, and so decided that the sunlight should be caught in sacks and carried into the building, 'So balb nun die Glocken eins geschlagen, da solte einer sein wunder gesehen haben wie sie alle angefangen haben zu arbeiten. Etliche halten lange Säcke, liessen die Sonne dreyn scheinen bis auff den Boden, knüpfften jn dann eilends zu und liessen damit ins Haus, den tag auszuschütten'.

The home of the Schildbürgers was taken to be Schildau near Torgau until J. H. Campe (1746–1818), in his 'Wörterbuch der Deutschen Sprache' (5 vols. Braunschweig, 1807–1811), took their name to be cognate with 'Spiessbürger' (a philistine, a square).

Cf. 'Merrie Tales of the Mad Men of Gotham' (ed. Cunningham, 1889), attributed to Andrew Boorde (c. 1490–1549): C. E. Mangor 'Beretning om de vidtbekendte Molboers vise Gerninger' (Viborg, 1771–1773): W. A. Clouston 'Book of Noodles' (London, 1888).

20, 17

See Newton 'Opticks' (4th ed. London, 1730) Bk. III pt. i, qu. 29, 'Are not the Rays of Light very small Bodies emitted from shining Substances? For such bodies will pass through uniform Mediums in right Lines without bending into the Shadow, which is the Nature of the Rays of Light'. In the preceding query Newton examines hypotheses in which light is supposed to consist in 'Pression or Motion, propagated through a fluid Medium', but rejects them because he has no evidence of the bending or crookedness of light, and because Huyghens had been unable to explain double refraction in Iceland spar by means of his wave theory.

Robert Hooke (1635–1702), in his 'Micrographia, or some Philosophical Descriptions of Minute Bodies' (London, 1665) pp. 57 and 221, had suggested that the waves in light might be transverse, i.e. at right angles to the direction of the rays, 'whence it necessarily follows, that all the parts of these Spheres undulated through an *Homogeneous medium* cut the Rays at right angles'. Christian Huyghens (1629–1695) however, in his Traité de la Lumière' (Leyden, 1690 Eng. tr. Thompson, London, 1912), ignored this suggestion, and postulated light waves resembling those of *sound*, 'composez de particules qui nagent dans une matière beaucoup plus subtile, qui les agite avec une grande rapidité, et les fait frapper contre les particules de l'ether, qui les environnent et qui sont beaucoup moindres qu'elles'. (p. 9).

By the middle of the eighteenth century, objections were being raised to Newton's account of this matter. Benjamin Franklin (1706–1790), in a letter dated April 23, 1752, objects to the doctrine that light consists of particles of matter emitted from the sun's surface. 'Must not the smallest portion conceivable, have, with such a motion, a force exceeding that of a 24 pounder discharged from a cannon? . . . Yet these particles, with this amazing motion, will not drive before them or remove, the least and slightest dust they meet with.' Cf. his 'Experiments and Observations on Electricity' (London, 1769) p. 264 Leonhard Euler (1707–1783), the famous mathematician, in his 'Nova Theoria Lucis et Colorum' which was printed on pp. 169–244 of his 'Opuscula varii argumenti' (Berlin, 1746) says that if Newton's hypothesis were correct, the sun would soon be exhausted, the matter emitted would disturb the courses of the planets, transparency would be difficult to explain, and it would be impossible to account for the rays' not interfering with one another. He therefore postulates an *ether*, and accepts a wave theory similar to Huyghens', 'Hoc igitur medium, per quod lumen diffundi pono, non erit diversum ab eo, quod apud philosophos aetheris nomine consideratur: quare uti sonus per aërem, ita simili modo lumen per aetherem propagatur. Est ergo aether fluidum subtile elasticum, quod omnia loca in mundo ab aliis corporibus relicta adimplet; perinde atque aër circa terram in omnia loca, quae ab aliis corporibus relinquuntur, penetrat.' (op. cit. ch. I § xxiii p. 181).

When Thomas Young (1773–1829) revived the wave theory at the beginning of the last century (note II. 229), he assumed, from a false analogy with sound waves, that the wave disturbance was longitudinal. Hegel is referring here to his discovery of *interference*, which he formulated as follows. 'Whenever two portions of the same light arrive to the eye by different routes, either exactly or very nearly in the same direction, the light becomes most intense when the difference of the routes is any multiple of a certain length, and least intense in the intermediate stage of the interfering portions; and this length is different for the light of different colours': see 'Miscellaneous Works' (ed. Peacock, London, 1855) I p. 202. In 1816 D. F. J. Arago (1786–1853) and A. J. Fresnel (1788–1827), while investigating the interference of polarized rays of light, discovered that two pencils of light, polarized in planes at *right angles* to each other never interfere under circumstances in which ordinary light shows interference phenomena: see 'Mémoire sur l'action que les rayons de lumière exercent les uns sur les autres' ('Annales de Chimie' vol. x pp. 288–306, 1819) cf. 'Quarterly Journal of Science' 1821 vol. XI p. 381. This discovery led to the assumption that the wave disturbance in light is transverse: see Young's letter to Arago dated January 12, 1817 ('Works' I p. 390). Josef Fraunhofer (1787–1826) confirmed this assumption at about the same time by discovering the dark lines in the solar spectrum: see 'Gilbert's Annalen der Physik' vols. 56 and 61. It was then left to A. J. Fresnel (1788–1827) to formulate these discoveries in mathematical terms (note II. 229).

20, 21

The classical exposition of this neurological theory is to be found in the 'Demonstrationes anatomico-pathologicae (Amsterdam 1760) vol. I, by Peter Camper (1722–1789). Ernst Gottlob Bose (1723–1788), in his 'Dissertatio de nervorum actione ex collisione' (Leipzig, 1762) refuted Camper's arguments in a competent manner.

21, 1

Galileo discovered four of Jupiter's satellites in 1610: see his 'Syderius Nuncius' (Venice, 1610). Cf. Simon Marius (1570–1624) 'Mundus jovialis anno 1609 detectus' (Nuremberg, 1614). Thomas Harriot (1560–1621) observed the satellites closely from Jan. 16, 1610 until Feb. 26, 1612: see Zach's article 'Berlin Royal Academy of Sciences' 1788. In the middle of the seventeenth century Jean Dominique Cassini (1625–1712) developed a method of determining longitude by means of them: see 'Éclipses des satellites de Jupiter dans les derniers mois de l'année 1676, proposées pour la détermination exacte des longitudes des lieux où elles sont observées' ('Journal des Savants' 17 Aug. 1676: cf. 16 Feb. 1666, 21 March 1672, 14 Sept. 1676 etc.). In 1671, the French Academy of Sciences sent Jean Picard (1620–1682) to Copenhagen to fix the exact position of Tycho Brahe's observatory, in relation to Paris. Picard observed the eclipses of Jupiter's satellites with the help of Rasmus Bartholin (1625–1698) professor at Copenhagen, whose assistant, *Ole Rømer* (1644–1710), was at that time working on an edition of Tycho Brahe's tables, the manuscripts of which had recently been acquired from Kepler's son, by the Danish king.

Rømer returned to Paris with Picard, in the hope of getting the tables published, and stayed there until 1681. In 1676 he published 'Demonstration touchant le mouvement de la lumière trouvé par M. Roemer' ('Journal des Savants' Dec. 1676), in which he described how he had calculated the speed of light from observations of Jupiter's satellites made during the course of several years. Rømer published very little, and it was not until the beginning of this century that any reasonably complete picture of his work became available: see 'Fysisk Tidskrift' 1908 p. 201, 1917 p. 169, 1936 p. 125: 'Det Kongelige Danske Videnskabernes Selskabs Forhandlinger' 1910, 1913, 1944: K. Meyer 'Om Ole Rømers Opdagelse af Lysets Tøven' (Copenhagen, 1915).

The method used by Rømer was as follows:—see I. B. Cohen 'Roemer and the first determinations of the velocity of light (1676)' ('Isis' 1939–1940 pp. 327–379): C. B. Boyer 'Early estimates of the velocity of light' ('Isis' 1941–1942 pp. 24–40):—

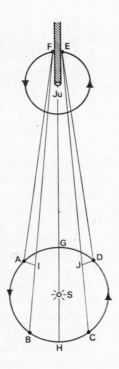

Let S be the sun, and A B C D the orbit of the earth. Let Ju be Jupiter, and F E the orbit of its satellite. When the earth is at A, the satellite may be seen emerging from Jupiter's shadow at F. If the earth stayed at A, the same would be seen again, $42\frac{1}{2}$ hours later. After 30 orbits of the satellite, the earth is at B however. Consequently, the time taken for light to pass from I to B must be *added* to the time calculated for the emergence of the satellite at F. Similarly, when the earth is at C, the satellite may be seen entering Jupiter's shadow at E, and when the earth is at D, the time taken for light to pass from J to C must be *subtracted* from the time calculated for the entry of the satellite into the shadow at E. The movement of Jupiter in its orbit has to be taken into consideration throughout of course. By this method, Rømer calculated that it must take light 16 minutes 26 seconds to pass from G to H.

The accuracy of this calculation was confirmed by James Bradley (1693–1762). Robert Hooke (1635–1703), in his, 'An attempt to prove the motion of the earth from observations' (London, 1674) noticed that γ Draconis, a star of the second magnitude, which passes practically overhead in the latitude of London, exhibits variations in position between July and October amounting to 23″. Bradley observed this star very carefully from December 1725 until August 1727, and found that the extreme range of its southerly and northerly positions was 40″. After satisfying himself that this apparent shift could not be explained by parallax, nutation of the earth's axis, or an irregular distribution of the earth's atmosphere, he took it to be evidence of the *aberration* of light, and communicated his discovery of this phenomenon to the Royal Society in January 1729 ('Phil. Trans.' vol. 35 p. 637).

Bradley's explanation of this appearance was as follows:—

Let S be a star, and the observer be carried along the line BA; let SB be perpendicular to AB. If the observer be stationary at B, the star will appear in the direction BS. If, however, he traverses the distance BA in the same time as light passes from the star to his eye, the star will appear in the direction AS. Since, however, the observer is not conscious of his own motion with the earth in its orbit, the star appears to have a *displacement*, which is at all times *parallel* to the motion of the observer.

In this diagram, BA is to BS as the velocity of the earth in its orbit to that of light. Bradley found that the twelve stars he was able to observe closely over a period of a year or more had a maximum shift of 40″. He therefore took the angle BSA to be 20″. The radius of a circle is equal to an arc of 57° 18″, consequently the velocity of the earth is to the velocity of light as 20″ to 57° 18″ or 1 to 10313. The time taken for the light of the sun to reach the earth will therefore be to $365\frac{1}{4}$ days as 20″ is to 360″, i.e. 8 minutes 7 seconds.

This calculation accorded so well with Rømer's, that in Hegel's day, the matter was considered to be settled. See 'Miscellaneous Works and Correspondence of James Bradley, D.D.' (ed. S. Rigaud, Oxford, 1832). There is an excellent account of Bradley's work in Charles Hutton's 'A Mathematical and Philosophical Dictionary' (2 vols. London, 1796).

In 1810 D. F. J. Arago (1786–1853) showed by experiment, that light coming from any star behaves in all cases of reflection and refraction precisely as it would if the star were situated in the place which appears to occupy in consequence of aberration, and the earth were at rest. From this he concluded that the apparent refraction in a moving prism is equal to the absolute refraction in a fixed prism. He did not publish the results of this work until 1839 however: see 'Comptes Rendus' viii p. 326.

21, 8

In his first lectures on the philosophy of nature ('Jenenser Logik, Metaphysik und Naturphilosophie' ed. Lasson, Leipzig, 1923, p. 201), Hegel takes the stars to be the punctualization of the 'absolute matter' of the ether, and says that, 'They are a motionless picture, a formal model, which represents an eternal past in dumb hieroglyphics, and which has life and a present only through the comprehension of these characters.'

He had himself been tempted to speculate upon 'these further consequences' therefore, and may have been led to do so by a translation of three of Herschel's papers ('Phil. Trans. Roy. Soc.' 1784 p. 437, 1785 p. 213, 1789 p. 212) published by G. M. Sommer as 'Über den Bau des Himmels, . . . nebst einem . . . Auszug aus Kants . . . Theorie des Himmels' (Königsberg, 1791). Sommer's translation of a passage from the second of Herschel's discourses is as follows (p. 31), ‚Optiſche Erſcheinungen. Von dieſer theoretiſchen Vorſtellung des Himmels, die, wie wir bereits bemerkt haben, aus einem nicht minder der Zeit als dem Raum nach entfernten Geſichtspunkt gefaßt iſt . . .' Cf. 'The Scientific Papers of Sir William Herschel' (ed. J. L. E. Dreyer, 2 vols. London. 1912): A. H. C. Gelpke (1769–1842) 'Allgemeinfassliche Betrachtungen über das Weltgebäude und die neuesten Entdekkungen, welche von Herrn Doktor Herschel darin gemacht worden sind' (Hanover, 1806).

Galileo was the first to suggest that the distances of the fixed stars might be computed by their parallax, and in 1782 ('Phil. Trans. Roy. Soc.' vol. 72 pp. 88 iii) Herschel gave an account of this method: 'Let OE be two opposite points of the annual orbit, taken in the same plane with two stars a, b, of unequal magnitudes. Let the angle aOb be observed when the earth is at O: and let the angle aEb be observed when the earth is at E. From the difference of these angles, if any should be found, we may calculate the parallax of the stars. These two stars ought to be as near each other as possible, and also to differ as much in magnitude as we can find them.'

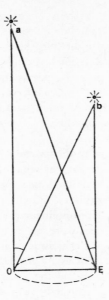

After announcing this method, Herschel continued to publish catalogues of these double stars for over thirty years, but his theory broke down under the weight of his observations, and in 1814 he wrote, 'I am still engaged in a series of observations for ascertaining a scale whereby the extent of the universe, as far as it is possible for us to penetrate into space, may be fathomed'.

23, 11

Christian Huyghens (1629–1695), in his 'Traité de la Lumière' (Leyden, 1690), was the first to show that the properties of a stream of light coming directly from a natural source are not alike on all sides of its direction of propagation. Huyghens knew of double refraction in Iceland spar from Rasmus Bartholin's 'Experimenta Crystalli Islandici Disdiaclastici' (Copenhagen 1669). He discovered that when the two emergent streams are divided by a *second* crystal, the intensity of each of the *subsequent* portions will depend upon the position with respect to one another of the principal planes of the faces of entry into the crystals, and that in certain cases one portion will vanish entirely. He also discovered however, that if the emergent streams overlap, they will have all the properties of common light. Cf. Newton's 'Opticks' (London, 1703) Book III pt. 1 query 25. In the following query Newton concludes from this experiment that every ray of light has two opposite sides.

Jean Baptiste Biot (1774–1862) was the originator of what Hegel calls 'the clumsy concept' of *fixed* polarization. Biot was led to formulate this concept as a result of the detailed investigations he made in the years 1812–1814, into the colours of crystalline plates, which he attempted to explain in terms of Newton's corpuscular theory: see 'Traité de Physique' (Paris, 1816) vol. IV pp. 254–316. Biot contended that the light corpuscles acquire *fixed* polarization by passing through a crystal which is thick enough to make their axes maintain a position with regard to the plane of polarization. He thought of this fixed polarization as being preceded by an *oscillation* of the corpuscles, set up by their having entered a doubly refracting body, and concluded from this that the colours of thin plates arise from an imperfect or *mobile* polarization, which would be *fixed* by a thicker crystal.

The most telling criticism of this theory came from J. F. W. Herschel (1792–1871), who pointed out that the *point* at which this mobile polarization passes over into fixed polarization, and the *reason* for its doing so, cannot be discovered: see 'Vom Licht' (tr. Schmidt, Stuttgart, 1831), a translation of his article on light in the 'Encyclopaedia Metropolitana' (London, 1817–1845). The theory tended to be dropped as advances were made in the formulation of the wave theory: see Fresnel's and Arago's criticisms of it in 'Annales de Chimie et de Physique' vol. XVII. Cf. the articles by Sir David Brewster (1781–1868) in 'Phil. Trans. Roy. Soc.' 1814–18 and the 'Edinburgh Philosophical Journal' vol. I p. 289 (1819). Brewster's attitude towards these phenomena is interesting because he did not take them to be a clear confirmation of either the corpuscular or the wave theory.

23, 27

Goethe attempted to avoid accepting both the corpuscular and wave theories of light and colour. Consequently, although he was intimately acquainted with the *history* of optics, he had very little influence upon the optical research of his day: see 'Zur Farbenlehre. Didaktischer Teil' (ed. Matthaei, Weimar, 1955): 'Zur Farbenlehre. Polemischer Teil' (ed. Matthaei, Weimar, 1958): 'Zur Farbenlehre. Historischer Teil' (ed. Kuhn, Weimar, 1957). The works Hegel refers to here appeared in Goethe's 'Zur Naturwissenschaft überhaupt' (Stuttgart and Tübingen, 1817). In the 1820 edition of this book (p. 126), Goethe acknowledges with thanks the assistance given him by 'distinguished' scientific friends, and adds that, 'Döbereiner, Hegel, Körner, Lenz, Roux, Schultz, Seebeck, Schweigger and Voigt have been particularly helpful'. See Goethe's 'Naturwissenschaftliche Hefte' (ed. Kuhn, 1962), which form pt. I vol. viii of the edition of Goethe's scientific works now being published by the German Academy of Natural Philosophy.

Hegel is evidently referring to the following passage on pp. 28–29 of this work, 'What now becomes apparent here is what everyone knows and admits, i.e. that the comparative strength of reflected light will only be at a maximum when that light proceeds on the same plane, and when, despite several reflections, it keeps to the original direction in passing from the sky to the surface, the mirror, and finally to the eye. In a case such as this, and on account of the smooth surface, sidelight is completely absent, and we see nothing but darkness.'

In the sections XVIII and XIX mentioned by Hegel, Goethe deals with 'The effect of the mirror with regard to brightness and darkness' and 'The effect of the mirror with regard to any image'. Goethe describes experiments with mirrors which illustrate the general principle just mentioned, and takes the phenomena of polarization to be evidence of 'obliquated' (obliquirte) light. Cf. Robert Hooke (1635–1702) 'Micrographia' (London, 1665) p. 221, 'This inflextion may be . . . an *obliquation* of the pulse of light whence the ruder part is continually promoted, and consequently refracted towards the perpendicular, which cuts the Orbs at right angles'.

23, 32

Hegel credits Johann Tobias Mayer (1752–1830) with this discovery: see the footnote II. 360. Mayer published two papers on the refraction and polarization of light in 'Commentationes Societatis Regiae Scientarum Gottingensis' vol. I and II (Göttingen, 1811 and 1813). Newton seems to have been the originator of such speculations: see 'Opticks' (4th ed. London, 1730) Bk. III pt. 1 query 26.

23, 40

Étienne Louis Malus (1775–1812) was born at Paris on June 23, 1775. In 1793 he was dismissed from the military engineering school at Mezières, and joined the army as a private. After distinguishing himself by his work on the fortifications of Dunkirk, he was made a member of the Polytechnic then being established under the direction of Gaspard Monge (1746–1818), one of the most outstanding French mathematicians and physicists of the day. In 1797 he joined the engineer corps, and from 1797 till 1801 saw active service in Germany and Egypt.

He began optical research soon after his return to Europe. After a period at Antwerp and on active service in Germany, he supervised the improvement of the defences at Strassburg (1806–8), and soon afterwards returned to Paris. In 1810 he became a major in the engineers, and in 1811 was appointed director of studies at the Polytechnic. He died in Paris, of phthisis, on February 23, 1812.

He discovered the polarization of light in 1808, and gave an account of the discovery in 'Sur une propriété de la lumière réfléchie par les corps diaphanes' published in 'Bulletin des Sciences de la Société Philomathique de Paris' vol. I pp. 266–269 (Dec. 1808): cf. 'Gilbert's Annalen der Physik' vol. 31 pp. 286–297 (1809), and W. Nicholson's 'Journal of Natural Philosophy' 1812 pp. 95–102. After working on the double refraction of light in Iceland spar, he happened to notice that the light of the setting sun reflected from a nearby window gave a less intense image than direct sunlight, 'I have found that this singular disposition,

which has hitherto been regarded as one of the peculiar effects of double refraction, can be completely impressed on the luminous molecules by all transparent solids and liquids . . . If we receive this reflected ray on any doubly refracting crystal, whose principal section is parallel to the plane of reflection, it
will not be divided into two beams as a ray of ordinary light would be, but
will be refracted according to the ordinary law.'

Defenders of the wave theory such as Thomas Young (1773–1829) still
regarded the waves as being longitudinal, and were therefore at a loss to
explain Malus's discovery. Consequently, the immediate effect of it was to
encourage the defenders of the corpuscular hypothesis, and Malus himself, in
his main work on the subject, 'Théorie de la Double Refraction de la lumière
dans les Substances Cristallisées' (Paris, 1810), tried to interpret the phenomenon
in the light of this theory. It was not until the idea of transverse waves had gained
currency that the mature work of Arago and Fresnel became possible (note
II. 233).

Hegel was therefore justified in criticizing Malus, although he was not
justified in ignoring the work of his successors. He seems to have in mind pp.
30–52 and pp. 205–241 of Malus's main work. For the subsequent development
of Malus's views on the subject see 'Sur les phénomènes qui dépendent des
formes des molécules de la lumière' ('Bull. des Sc.' I pp. 341–344 and 353–355:
'Gilbert's Ann.' 1809 pp. 463–477); 'Mémoires sur les phénomènes qui accom-
pagnent la réflexion et la refraction de la lumière' (Bull. des Sc.' II pp. 320–325:
'Gilbert's Ann.' 1811 p. 109–113, 1812 pp. 119–131); 'Mémoire sur l'influence
des formes des molécules de la lumière dans divers phénomènes d'optique'
('Mémoires de la Société des Sciences, Agriculture, et Arts, de Strassburg' vol.
I pp. 281–300 (1811)); cf. Thomson's 'Annals of Philosophy' vol. III pp. 81–84
(1814).

25, 5
The great solar furnace at Font Romeu in the eastern Pyrenees is built up of
8,000 small mirrors, and is able to heat two to three tons of material at a time
to a temperature of 3,500°C (6,300°F): see 'The Times' November 18, 1966.

25, 20
The *development* of Hegel's views on light is essential to an understanding of
these paragraphs. During the Jena period he was evidently searching for a
dynamical interpretation of light. It looked at that time as though Huyghens'
and Euler's theory of an ether might replace Newtonianism, and in the lectures
of 1801–1802 therefore, Hegel took light to be the 'absolute ether', the sublation
of ether, space, time and motion. Cf. Lars Regnér (1746–1810), professor of
astronomy at Uppsala. 'Versuch über die physische Ursache der Fortpflanzung
des Lichts bey den Himmelskörpern' (Zach's 'Monatliche Correspondenz' vol.
VI pp. 348–361 (Gotha, 1802)). Two years later he rejected the ether entirely,

and took celestial motion to be the sublation of light and the heavenly bodies. In the lectures of 1805–1806 he returned to some extent to his earlier view however, and treated celestial motion as the sublation of ether, space, time and mass, and light as the *initiation* of the *succeeding* sphere, which he took to include magnetism, electricity, heat, crystallization etc.

Throughout this development he takes light to be the sublation of motion, or at least, to be intimately connected with it, and he would certainly have welcomed Maxwell's electromagnetic theory had he lived to see it formulated. Much of the clumsiness and inaccuracy of § 276 would have been avoided if the physics of the day could have provided him with a confirmation of the brilliant characterization of light given in § 275. As it is, one has to admit that although he was right in thinking that the research of his day was *outdating* Newton's work, he was wrong in thinking that it was *disproving* it, just as he was wrong in rejecting the hypothesis of light waves and interference, and in regarding solar and stellar light as being essentially different.

The influence upon him of Goethe's optical writings was not entirely beneficial. It evidently helped him to realize the crudity of Malus's and Biot's attempts to explain polarization (§ 278), but it certainly kept him from appreciating the brilliant interpretations of this phenomenon put forward by Arago and Fresnel.

These paragraphs would still have been acceptable in 1815, and would have interested Maxwell in 1870, but they must have caused some raising of the eyebrows in 1830.

26, 2
Although Hegel goes on to speak mainly of the Moon, this is evidently a reference to all the satellites of the planets. At that time *fourteen* had been definitely identified (Earth 1, Jupiter 4, Saturn 7, Uranus 2). J. D. Cassini (1625–1712) in 1665 and 1678, and G. F. Maraldi (1665–1729) in 1707 and 1713 had noticed spots on the satellites of Jupiter, and from their movement it had been concluded that these bodies turn upon their axes: see William Herschel's paper 'Observations of the changeable brightness of the satellites of *Jupiter* and of the variation in their apparent magnitudes; with a determination of the time of their rotatory motions on their axes' (Phil. Trans. Roy. Soc. 1797 p. 332).

Iapetus was at that time taken to be the seventh and most remote of Saturn's satellites. Soon after its discovery, Cassini and Maraldi noticed its periodic disappearance, and concluded from this that it rotated upon its axis: see 'Mémoires de l'Academie des Sciences de Paris' 1705 Hist. p. 117 Mem. 20: 1707 p. 296. Herschel made careful observations of Saturn's satellitic system, and came to a similar conclusion: see 'On the satellites of the planet *Saturn* and the rotation of its ring on an axis' ('Phil. Trans. Roy. Soc.' 1790 p. 427: 'On the ring of *Saturn* and the rotation of the fifth satellite upon its axis' op. cit. 1792 p. 1): cf. J. H. Schroeter (1745–1816) 'Beiträge zu den neuesten astronomischen Entdeckungen' (Berlin, 1788).

Herschel discovered two of the satellites of Uranus in 1787 ('Phil. Trans. Roy. Soc.' 1787 p. 125), and after noticing the changes in their light, assumed that they also turn upon their axes ('Phil. Trans. Roy. Soc.' 1815 p. 298) cf. Bode's 'Astronomisches Jahrbuch' 1819 p. 232.

Hegel might be excused for not accepting this tenuous evidence of the turning of satellites upon their axes, but there seems to be no good reason for his having chosen to ignore the axial rotation of the *Moon*. 'The mean time of a revolution of the moon about the earth, from one new moon to another, when she overtakes the sun again, is 29 d. 12 h. 44 m. 3 s. 11th.; but she moves once round her own orbit in 27 d. 7 h. 43 m. 8 s. moving about 2290 miles every hour; and turns once round her axis exactly in the time that she goes round the earth, which is the reason that she shews always the same side towards us; and that her day and night taken together are just as long as our lunar month.' Charles Hutton (1737–1823) 'A Mathematical and Philosophical Dictionary' (2 vols. London, 1795).

26, 9

In the Heidelberg 'Encyclopaedia' (ed. Glockner, Stuttgart, 1956) § 223 p. 177, and in the 1827 edition of the book, Hegel added here, ‚ſo daß man von dieſen Körpern vermutete, daß die Nähe eines großen Planeten ihre Bahn ändern könne.‘ In the 1830 edition this sentence was removed, but Hegel failed to qualify the verb which followed.

26, 13

This was not a fashionable view in Hegel's day. J. N. de L'Isle (1688–1768), in his articles 'Sur l'atmosphère de la lune' ('Mém. de l'Acad. des Sciences de Paris' 1715 pp. 147, 166, 195, 220) held that the Moon has no atmosphere, and this view found an enthusiastic supporter in Johann Tobias Mayer (1723–1762) of Göttingen: see his 'Opera inedita' (ed. Lichtenberg, Göttingen 1775). Leonhard Euler (1707–1783), in his 'Sur l'atmosphère de la lune prouvée par la dernière eclipse annulaire du soleil' ('Mém. de Berlin' 1748 p. 103) held the opposite view however. Cf. Samuel Dunn (d. 1794) 'Certain reasons for a lunar atmosphere' ('Phil. Trans. Roy. Soc. 1762 p. 578). J. H. Schroeter (1745–1816), in his 'Selenotopographische Fragmente' (2 vols. Göttingen, 1791) cf. 'Phil. Trans. Roy. Soc.' 1792 p. 309, backed up the theories of Euler and Dunn with a wealth of observations, in which he claimed to have identified the obscuration of light by the lunar atmosphere, and his view of the matter predominated until well after Hegel's death: see J. S. T. Gehler's 'Physikalisches Wörterbuch' (vol. 6, Leipzig, 1837) pp. 2406–2409.

26, 15

This information is almost certainly drawn from J. H. Schroeter's 'Selenotopographische Fragmente' (2 vols. Göttingen, 1791). Schroeter was of the opinion that these mountains and craters are of volcanic origin, but that the volcanic activity of the Moon has now almost ceased. For a detailed account of contemporary knowledge of the Moon's surface see J. S. T. Gehler's 'Physikalisches Wörterbuch' (vol. 6, Leipzig, 1837) pp. 2409–2443.

26, 16

Johann Ludwig Heim (1741–1819) was born at Meiningen. He was educated by his father, a clergyman, and then at the town grammar school. Geology was his hobby, and although he read theology at Jena, he spent much of his spare time investigating the rock structure of the surrounding countryside. He took his degree in 1774, and soon afterwards accompanied Prince George of Meiningen to Strassburg, where he stayed long enough to make a geological survey of the area. On his return to Meiningen he began a career in local government, in the course of which he rose to become vice-president of the Protestant consistory, and finally, privy councillor to the Duke.

Heim's first work was 'Ueber die Bildung der Thäler durch Ströme' (Weimar, 1791), in which he attempts to show how valleys may be formed by the force of running water. His most important work is his 'Geologische Beschreibung des Thüringer Waldgebürgs' (3 pts. Meiningen, 1796–1812); see note III. 235. He left a fine collection of minerals and stones, which passed to the university of Jena at his death.

Hegel is referring here to his 'Ueber die Aehnlichkeit der ehemaligen Erd-Oberfläche mit der gegenwärtigen des Mondes', which was published in 'Monatliche Correspondenz zur Beförderung der Erd-und Himmels-Kunde' (Gotha, 1802) pp. 528–542, a periodical edited by F. X. von Zach (1754–1832). Heim's main point in this article is that, 'Astronomy and geology are sisters, and in the future they will perhaps walk together, hand in hand. At the present however, the latter is still a child, learning to spell in the school of the mineralogist, while the former is already grown-up and . . . fully educated.' He points out that more international surveys are needed before geologists can build up any comprehensive picture of world geology, but he thinks himself justified in regarding the distribution of the 'moribund sandstone formation' (note III. 241) as world-wide. He takes this formation to be the limit of the 'primitive' rocks, i.e. the last of the geological structures formed by chemical rather than 'mechanical' activity, and to be the transition to fletz-formations (note III. 221).

By studying the features of this sandstone, he built up a picture of the surface of the earth as it was before 'mechanical' erosion and transformation began. When he discovered something very similar described by J. H. Schroeter in his 'Selenotopographische Fragmente' (2 vols. Göttingen, 1791), he was encouraged to point out that the examination of this similarity might provide a useful field for research. Cf. J. Whitehurst (1713–1788) 'Inquiry into the original state and form of the Earth' (London, 1778).

For accounts of Heim's life and work see J. G. Meusel 'Das gelehrte Teutsch-land' (Lemgo, 1796–1834): J. S. Ersch and J. G. Gruber 'Allgemeine Encyclo-pädie der Wissenschaften' Sect. II (31 vols., Leipzig, 1827–1855).

26, 17

‚einer der geiſtvollen Geognoſten'. In the Heidelberg edition of the 'Encyclo-paedia' (ed. Glockner, Stuttgart, 1956) Hegel wrote, ‚einer der wenigen geiſtvollen Geognoſten' (§ 223 p. 177).

27, 4

G. C. Lichtenberg (1742–1799) thought that the comet of 1770 passed between the Moon and the Earth. This mistake seems to have given rise to late eighteenth century speculation on the possibility of a collision between the Earth and a comet. J. J. Lalande (1732–1807) dealt with the matter in his 'Ré-flexions sur les comètes, qui peuvent approcher de la terre' (Paris, 1773), and P. A. Dionis de Séjour (1734–1794), in his exhaustive 'Traité analytique des mouvemens apparens des corps célestes' (2 vols. Paris, 1786/9) vol. II pp. 291–644, came to the conclusion that although the possibility exists, its dangers are negligible.

H. W. M. Olbers (1758–1840), in his 'Ueber die Möglichkeit, dass ein Comet mit der Erde zusammen stossen könne' ('Zach's Monatliche Correspondenz' vol. XXII pp. 409–450, Gotha, 1810) gives a survey of eighteenth century views on this subject, and comes to the conclusion that there is a 439 million to 1 chance of such a collision taking place. Cf. H. C. Schumacher (1780–1850) 'Astronomische Nachrichten' nr. 128 (Altona, 1823 et seq.).

William Whiston (1667–1752), who is remembered mainly as the original of the Vicar of Wakefield and on account of his translation of Josephus, but who was known in his own day as a great popularizer of Newtonianism, a prolific scribbler, and a religious crank, ranks very high among those who concerned themselves with speculation regarding cometary collision. His 'A New Theory of the Earth' (London, 1696) was so praised by Locke and Newton, that in 1703 he succeeded the latter as Lucasian professor of mathematics at Cambridge. It is only fair to remember however, that when he was proposed to the Royal Society as a member by Sloane and Halley in 1720, Newton, as president, refused him admittance. In this work, which had reached its fifth edition by 1736, Whiston put forward the view that the Earth had originated in a cometary collision, and in the course of his subsequent eschatological surmisals, stated that it was likely to end as it had begun. He created havoc in London by suggesting that the comet of October 1736 would bring about the end of the world. People streamed out of the city, and the banks had to close on account of their funds being inadequate to the sudden demand for withdrawals. See Whiston's 'The Astronomical Year: or, on account of the many remarkable celestial phenomena of the great year 1736' (London, 1737).

27, 13

,ihre ſelbſtändig gewordene Atmoſphäre, ein bleibendes Meteor'. Hegel wrote ,Luft' not ,Atmoſphäre' ('Jenenser Realphilosophie' II p. 77). Michelet also inserted the reference to § 287.

27, 18

Michelet's version is as follows, ,ſo daß er der Regent ihres Proceſſes bleibt, als des einzelnen, wie die Sonne des allgemeinen' Hoffmeister ('Jenenser Realphilosophie' II p. 77) inserts ,Prozeſſes' after ,allgemeinen'. This certainly clarifies the meaning of the sentence.

27, 20

In the margin at this point ('Jenenser Realphilosophie' II p. 77 note 2) Hegel wrote, 'Aeriformity moon, meteor comet, isolated- thunder-storm the real electric explosion'.

27, 32

The changing marks on Mars, and the stripes across Jupiter and Saturn had been observed at that time, and were taken as evidence that these planets possess atmospheres. Hegel probably mentions the atmosphere of Mercury on account of his having read J. H. Schroeter's 'Hermographische Fragmente zur genauern Kenntniss des Planeten Mercur' (Göttingen, 1816), and the atmosphere of Venus on account of Schroeter's 'Aphroditographische Fragmente' (Helmstedt, 1796): cf. 'Phil. Trans. Roy. Soc.' 1792 p. 309, 1795 p. 117.

27, 37

This does not contradict the statement made on II. 26 (see note). The Moon may well lack the meteorological *process* of an atmosphere, without being devoid of the 'element' *air* (see § 282). On these supposedly volcanic eruptions see W. Herschel 'An account of three volcanos in the moon' ('Phil. Trans. Roy. Soc.' 1787 p. 229): William Wilkins 'An account of an appearance of light, like a star, seen in the dark part of the moon' ('Phil. Trans. Roy. Soc.' 1794 p. 429).

28, 9

Pierre Simon Laplace (1749–1827), 'Exposition du système du monde' (2 vols. Paris, 1796, Germ. tr. 2 vols. Frankfurt-on-Main 1797, Eng. tr. J. Pond 2 vols. London, 1809) bk. I ch. xiii p. 141, 'Les heures des maries sysigies ou quadratures, varient avec les distances du soleil et de la lune à la terre, et principalement avec les distances de la lune. Dans les sysigies, chaque minute d'accroissement ou de diminution dans le demi diamètre apparent de la lune, fait avancer ou retarder l'heure de la pleine mer de 354. Ce phénomène a également lieu dans les quadratures; mais il y est trois fois moindre.'

28, 17

,Der Komet ist ein durchleuchtender, durchsichtiger Wasserkörper'.

28, 22

Hegel is here expressing the generally accepted opinion of his day. H. W. M. Olbers was convinced by his observation of the comets of December 1798 ('Astronomisches Jahrbuch' 1802 p. 200) and June 1825 ('Astronomisches Jahrbuch' 1828 p. 151), that if these bodies had nuclei, they were merely nebulous. Stars were often observed through the centres of comets: see Herschel's articles in 'Phil. Trans. Roy. Soc.' 1795 p. 60 and 1807 p. 266.

There were claims that comets which had passed before the sun had shown opaque centres, but they were not well substantiated: see 'Astronomisches Jahrbuch' 1804 pp. 185, 208: 1823 p. 138: H. C. Schumacher (1780–1850) 'Astronomische Nachrichten' no. 87 (Altona, 1823 et seq.).

The question was complicated by faulty *historical* data. Jakob Pontanus (1542–1626) had mistranslated an account of the comet of 1454 given by George Phrantza (1401—c. 1477) in his 'Chronicle': see 'Propovestiarii Chronicon' (Ingolstadt, 1604) bk. IV ch. 16. It was not until the original Greek text of this chronicle was published (Vienna, 1796), and attention was drawn to the ordinary eclipse of the Moon on May 12, 1454, that text-books dropped this example of a comet causing a total eclipse of the Moon: see F. C. Kries (1768–1849) 'Über die angebliche Verfinsterung des Mondes durch einen Cometen im Jahre 1454' ('Zach's Monatliche Correspondenz' vol. XXIII pp. 196–202, Gotha, 1811).

28, 29

Edmund Halley (1656–1742), having noticed that the elements of the comet of 1682 were nearly the same as those of the comets of 1531 and 1607, concluded that all those orbits belonged to the same body, the periodic time of which was about seventy years. He predicted therefore, that the comet would return in 1758, 'Unde ausim ejuisdem reditum sidentur praedicere, anno scil 1758' ('Phil. Trans. Roy. Soc.' 1705 pp. 1882–1899). This was a bold prediction at the time, but it was justified by the event, for the comet made its appearance as was expected, although it did not pass through its perihelion until March 1759. A. C. Clairault (1713–1765), in his 'De l'aberration de la lumière des planetes, des comètes et des satellites' ('Mém. de l'Ac. des Sc. de Paris' 1746 pp. 539 and 816) had predicted a retardation of 618 days due to the attraction of Jupiter and Saturn. Cf. 'Phil. Trans. Roy. Soc.' 1759 pp. 93–94, 1765 p. 294.

It passed through its perihelion again on November 15, 1835, and was well observed in almost every observatory, although its brightness was found to be disappointing.

Four appearances of the comet were known in Hegel's day, 1759, 1682, 1607 and 1531. It is also recorded as having appeared in 1066 and 1456. See E. F. McPike 'Halley's Comet: its past history and 1910 return' (Washington, 1905).

28, 34

When Milton likened Satan to a *comet* which 'from his horrid hair shakes pestilence and war', he was expressing a widespread popular fear of this phenomenon. The Anglo-Saxon Chronicle records the appearance of Halley's comet in 1066 as a fitting prelude to the catastrophes of the year, 'At that time, throughout all England, a portent such as men had never seen before was seen in the heavens. Some declared that the star was a comet, which some call "the long haired star": it first appeared on the eve of the festival of Letania maior, that is on 24 April, and shone every night for a week.'

Schiller captures the popular attitude very well in the fine lines of the opening speech in scene 8 of 'Wallenstein's Lager':

,Es ist eine Zeit der Tränen und Not,
Am Himmel geschehen Zeichen und Wunder,
Und aus den Wolken, blutigrot,
Hängt der Herrgott den Kriegsmantel runter.
Den Kometen steckt er wie eine Rute
Drohend am Himmelsfenster aus,
Die ganze Welt ist ein Klagehaus . . .'

In the late eighteenth century however, it became fashionable to satirize these superstitions: see Goethe's 'Gedichte Parabolisch' nr. 13

,Der Philister springt zur Tür heraus
,Der Stern steht über meinem Haus!
O weh!' etc.

Hegel's attitude toward the fear of a collision between the Earth and a comet is evidently a rationalization of this satire.

29, 20

This paragraph throws light upon Hegel's meaning on p. 27: see the note II. 27, 18.

29, 30

,daß wir schlafen und wachen, des Morgens anders gestimmt sind als des Abends'. Hegel does not use the word ,Laune' (mood) here, although it would have underlined his meaning, as it originates from Middle High German ,Lune', which meant a psychic changeableness related to the phases of the *Moon*. Cf. Goethe's "Maximen und Reflexionen" no. 1005 ("Werke" ed. Petsch, 1932 vol. 14): ,Die Laune ist ein Bewußtloses und beruht auf der Sinnlichkeit. Es ist ein Widerspruch der Sinnlichkeit mit sich selbst'.

29, 39

See F. A. Mesmer (1734–1815) 'De planetarum influxu in corpus humanum' (Vienna, 1766): Andrew Wilson 'Short Remarks upon autumnal disorders of the bowels' (Newcastle-on-Tyne, 1765): Alexander Wilson 'Observations relative to the influence of climate on vegetable and animal bodies' (London, 1780, Germ. tr. Leipzig, 1781): H. W. Dirksen 'Die Lehre von den Temperamenten' (Nuremberg, 1804): J. A. M. Gouffès 'Dissertation sur l'influence des climats et de l'atmosphère en particulier' (Paris, 1804): Francis Balfour 'Observations respecting the remarkable effects of Sol-lunar Influence on Fever'— Asiatick Researches' VIII pp. 1–33 (Calcutta, 1805).

For a *comprehensive* treatment of this subject in English see the remarkable collection of curious observations in, 'Remarks on the Influence of Climate' etc. 'on . . . Mankind' (London, 1781), by William Falconer (1744–1824).

29, 40

Johann Ehlert Bode (1747–1826) was born at Hamburg, and devoted himself to astronomy from his earliest years. His first published work was 'Berechnung und Entwurf der Sonnenfinsternis vom 5. August 1766' (Hamburg, 1766). His facilities at that time consisted of a home-made telescope and a garret. Two years later he published 'Anleitung zur Kenntniss des gestirnten Himmels' (Hamburg, 1768, 10th ed. 1844) and it was the success of this work which led to his being summoned to Berlin in 1772 for the purpose of computing ephemerides on an improved plan. He worked at first under Johann Heinrich Lambert (1728–1777), and in 1774 began to prepare the 'Berliner astronomisches Jahrbuch' for 1776. After Lambert's death he took over the sole responsibility for this work, which he continued to compile until 1825 (i.e. the volume of 1829). In 1786 he became director of the Berlin observatory.

His works were highly effective in diffusing throughout Germany a taste for astronomy. His 'Uranographia' (2 pts. Berlin, 1801), which is a collection of twenty star-maps accompanied by a catalogue of 17,240 stars and nebulae is one of the finest works of its kind ever published, and in order to help the general public make use of his yearbooks, he issued 'Erläuterungen für die Besitzer (meiner) astronomischen Jahrbücher' (Berlin, 1817).

He is mainly remembered on account of his making known 'Bode's Law' which was actually formulated by Christian Wolff (1679–1754), and later by Johann Daniel Titius (1729–1796): see 'Gilbert's Annalen der Physik' vol. 15 p. 169; von Zach's 'Monatliche Correspondenz' vol. VI p. 504 and vol. VII p. 75. This law states that if the distances of the planets from the Sun are expressed in tenths of the Earth's distance from it, Mercury=4, Venus=7 Earth=10, Mars=16, Jupiter=52, Saturn=100, Uranus=196, and that if 4 is then subtracted from each number, one is left with the series 0,3,6,12,48,96,192. The gap between Mars and Jupiter naturally led to the supposition that a planetary body might be looked for in this region, and on January 1, 1801

Guiseppe Piazzi (1746–1826) confirmed this by his discovery of *Ceres*, the largest of the minor planets: see F. X. von Zach 'Monatliche Correspondenz' vol. III pp. 602–607, vol. IV p. 559: 'Phil. Trans. Roy. Soc.' 1802 p. 213. About two thousand of these minor planets have since been identified.

Bode probably sighed at Hegel's suggestion on account of the labour he had expended upon attempts to explain cometary orbits: see His 'Allgemeine Untersuchungen und Bemerkungen über die Lage und Austheilung aller bisher bekannten Planeten und Kometenbahnen' (Berlin, 1791, French tr. Berlin, 1801): 'Erläuterungen der Sternkunde' (3rd ed., Berlin, 1808) § 756. Cf. A. H. C. Gelpke (1769–1812) 'Neue Ansicht über den merkwürdigen Naturbaus der Kometen und besonders desjenigen von 1811' (Leipzig, 1812).

30, 19

In the Heidelberg 'Encyclopaedia' of 1817, Hegel referred here to his inaugural dissertation 'De Orbitis Planetarum' (Jena, 1801), at the end of which he had attempted to reduce the distances between the planets to a numerical sequence ('Erste Druckschriften' ed. Lasson. Leipzig, 1928) pp. 399–401. Knowledge of the discovery of Ceres in January 1801 (see the previous note), reduced the acceptability of these calculations, and in 1817 Hegel wrote that, ‚Was ich in einer frühern Dissertation hierüber versucht habe, kann ich nicht mehr für befriedigend ansehen,' (op. cit. § 224 p. 179).

30, 25

Pierre Simon Laplace (1749–1827), 'Exposition du système du monde' (2 vols. Paris, 1796) vol. II p. 263, 'Led astray by his fiery imagination . . . Kelper explained the order of the Solar System by means of the laws of musical harmony. It is evident, even from his mature writings, that he was so taken by these fantastic speculations, that he regarded them as the life and soul of astronomy.'

30, 31

This is a reference to Kepler's 'Harmonice Mundi' (Linz, 1619, ed. M. Caspar, Munich, 1940), which clearly played a large part in the formation of Hegel's early ideas on astronomy: see His 'Dissertatio philosophica de Orbitis Planetarum' (Jena, 1801).

This work of Kepler's is remembered in the history of science mainly because it contains the formulation of his third law, 'That for all planets, the squares of the time of revolution round the sun are the cubes of their mean distances from it' (bk. V ch. III, Caspar's ed. p. 302). As Hegel notes however, it is intrinsically interesting as an attempt to grasp the order of the solar system as a series of numerical relationships, and so to interpret it according to the laws of musical harmony.

In his 'Prodromus Dissertationum cosmographicarum continens Mysterium cosmographicum' (Tübingen, 1596 tr. M. Caspar, Munich, 1938), Kepler attempted to explain the solar system *stereometrically*. Six planets were known at that time—Mercury, Venus, Earth, Mars, Jupiter and Saturn, and the five spaces between them led him to think of the five regular figures of stereometry. Beginning with the spherical projection of the Earth's orbit, he drew around it the twelve-sided figure, and around this the sphere of Mars. Around the sphere of Mars he drew the four-sided figure, and around that the larger sphere of Jupiter, which was followed by the cube or six-sided figure, and finally by the sphere of Saturn. Inside the Earth's sphere came the twenty- and eight-sided figures around the spheres of Venus and Mercury. In this way he reduced the order of the solar system to the numerical progression 8,20,12,4,6. The discovery of Uranus in 1781, and the discovery of the minor planets after 1801 made this interpretation obsolete, and Kepler himself found it necessary to supplement it in his later writings.

The theory of planetary *harmony* is expounded in book three of Kepler's 'Harmonice Mundi'. Vincenzo Galilei (c. 1520–1591), in his 'Dialogo della musica antica et della moderna' (Florence, 1581, cf. O. Strunk 'Source Readings in Music History' New York, 1950) initiated the modern method of adjusting the intervals of the scale by slight variations of the pitch of the notes from the 'just' intonation, in order to make these notes available in different keys. He took the tone to be related to the semitone as 18 to 17, and so put forward a flexible method of chromatic tuning which came very close to that employed today (99:100).

Kepler accepted this temperament of Galilei's as establishing the correct interrelationship of the various keys, and taking 21600, or the number of minutes in a circle, as the numerical definition of G, worked out a progression which gives the following values from C:

C	C♯	D	E♭	E	F	F♯	G	A♭	A	B♭	B	C
1.0	.9444	.8919	.8424	.7956	.7514	.7096	.6702	.6330	.5978	.5646	.5332	.5000

He then applied the numerical relationships of the scales to the movements of the planets, taking the movement of Saturn as the basis of his tonal progression (G). By this method he discovered:

(i) That the relation between the movements of the radius vector, i.e. the line joining the Sun and the planet, in aphelion and perihelion, may be expressed as a harmony.

(ii) That the relationships between all the planets in respect of these movements in aphelion and perihelion may also be expressed as harmonies.

(iii) That in certain circumstances, the motions of the planets outside the aphelia and perihelia also form an harmonious whole. J. W. A. Pfaff (1774–1835) noticed that Kepler's musical theory approximated very closely to that put forward by J. P. Kirnberger (1721–1783) in his 'Die Kunst des reinen Satzes in der Musik' (Berlin, 1771) and his 'Wahren Grundsätze zum Gebrauch der Harmonie' (ed. J. A. P. Schulz, Berlin and Königsberg, 1773) cf. G. L. T

'Gedanken über die Temperatur Herrn Kirnbergers' (Berlin, 1775). He applied Kepler's principles to the newly discovered planet Uranus, and found that the relation between its daily movement in perihelion and that in aphelion comes close to being as 1 to .842, i.e. the minor third. He also discovered that the movement of Saturn in perihelion is to that of Uranus in perihelion as 1 to .682, i.e. almost the fifth. After making similar discoveries with the minor planets, he worked out a revised table of planetary harmonies, taking the movement of Uranus as its basis ('Schweigger's Neues Journal für Chemie und Physik' 1814 vol. X pp. 36–43).

31, 3

Newton 'Opticks' (4th ed. 1730 ed. Cohen, Dover Publications, 1952). Newton makes use of this analogy on several occasions: see Bk. I pt. II prop. iii exp. 7, prop. vi prob. 2: Bk. II pt. I obs. 14; pt. III prop. xvi; pt. IV obs. 5, obs. 8. The analogy is certainly not without interest, although Newton makes no attempt to work out the tonal sequences with any precision, and also makes use of different progressions (cf. op. cit. pp. 128, 154, 295).

31, 24

,Ist von einem Stolz die Rede, so müssen wir die Erde, das Gegenwärtige, als das Hohe betrachten.'

31, 27

> 'Of man, what see we but his station here,
> From which to reason, or to which refer?
> Through worlds unnumber'd though the God be known,
> 'Tis ours to trace him only in our own.'
>> Alexander Pope (1688–1744) 'Essay on Man' epist. i.

> 'An ocean of infinities
> Where all our thoughts are drowned.'
>> Isaac Watts (1674–1748) 'The Infinite'.

31, 31

Henrik Steffens (1773–1845). Of all Schelling's followers he was the most intimately acquainted with the natural science of the day. He was born in Stavanger, and brought up, on Rousseauistic principles, in Elsinore and Copenhagen. N. F. S. Grundtvig (1783–1872), the Danish Carlyle, was his cousin. From his father, who came of a Holstein family, he seems to have inherited impulsiveness, restlessness and curiosity, from his mother, who was Norwegian, depth of character, intellectual poise, and a basically religious tone of mind. Niels Treschow (1751–1833), his headmaster in Elsinore, seems to have given him his first lessons in philosophy.

He matriculated in 1790 and then studied mineralogy, botany and zoology at Copenhagen University. He lodged with his mother's family during these years, and 'while walking in the streets of Copenhagen often felt as though he wanted to push people from behind in order to make them move quicker'. In 1796 he went down to Kiel to study Natural Science under the geologist, geographer and entomologist J. C. Fabricius (1748–1808). In 1797 he took his doctorate at Kiel in mineralogy. It was in the spring of 1798 that Schelling's 'Ideen zu einer Philosophie der Natur' (1797) fell into his hands, and this, as he later acknowledged, proved to be the turning point of his life. He found in Schellingianism a way of thinking which enabled him to organize his already wide knowledge of the natural sciences into a coherent system.

From 1798 until 1802 he travelled widely in Germany, financed by a Danish scholarship. He heard Werner lecture on geology at Freiberg, and Fichte and Schelling lecture at Jena; he also met Goethe, Novalis and A. G. Schlegel. He contributed to Schelling's Journal, and in 1801 published his 'Beyträge zur innern Naturgeschichte der Erde', under Schelling's auspices.

In the spring of 1802 he left Germany for Copenhagen, and in the hope of getting a university appointment there, delivered his famous lectures at Elers' College during the winter of 1802–1803. Grundtvig, Oehlenschläger, Ørsted and the Mynster brothers were among those who heard him, and it was at these meetings that the romantic movement in Denmark was launched. See 'Indledning til philosophiske Forelæsninger' (ed. B. T. Dahl, Copenhagen, 1905); C. I. Scharling 'Grundtvig og Romantiken' (Copenhagen, 1947). The university authorities were bewildered, assumed that as he was clearly not an ordinary Lutheran he must be an atheist, and elected Niels Treschow to the vacant professorship in philosophy.

The rest of Steffens' life was spent in Germany. He was professor of philosophy, mineralogy, physiology and natural history at Halle 1804–1811, professor of physics at Breslau, 1811–1832, and then professor at Berlin. He took part in the War of Liberation, and was present at the battle of Leipzig and the capture of Paris, although he described himself as 'der ungeschickteste Seconde-Lieutenant in der preussischen Armee.'

Hegel seems to have studied the text-book on the philosophy of nature which Steffens published as basis for his lectures at Halle; see 'Grundzüge der philosophischen Naturwissenschaft' (Berlin, 1806) and to have referred to his early works on geology; see 'Ueber Mineralogie und das mineralogische Studium' (Altona, 1797), 'Beyträge zur innern Naturgeschichte der Erde' (pt. I, Freiberg, 1801), 'Geognostische-geologische Aufsätze' (Hamburg, 1810). As he began work on his logic however, he seems to have lost interest in the *intuitive* approach to the natural sciences championed by the Schellingians, and he never seems to have concerned himself with Steffens' mature work in this field, which is distinguished by its comprehensiveness and exactness; see the magnificent 'Handbuch der Oryktognosie' (4 vols. Halle, 1811–1824).

Hegel never mentions Steffens' weighty contributions to the wider culture of post-war Germany; see 'Anthropologie' (2 vols. Breslau, 1822; ed. H.

Poppelbaum, Stuttgart, 1922); 'Die gegenwärtige Zeit' (2 pts. Berlin, 1817); 'Über die Idee der Universitäten' (Berlin, 1809: ed. Spranger, Leipzig, 1910); 'Karikaturen des Heiligsten' (2 pts. Leipzig, 1819–1822); 'Von der falschen Theologie und dem wahren Glauben' (Breslau, 1823). Steffens' autobiography, though not always reliable on details, is one of the main sources for the history of the German romantic movement; see 'Was ich erlebte' (10 vols. Breslau 1840–1844 tr. W. L. Gage, Boston, Mass., 1863). S. T. Coleridge made a close study of many of Steffens' works.

See Harald Beyer's article in 'Norsk Biografisk Leksikon' vol. XIV pp. 457–471 (Oslo, 1967); Wilhelm Rudloff 'Heinrich Steffens pädagogische Anschauungen' (Diss. Jena, 1914); Else Huesmann 'Heinrich Steffens in seiner Beziehung zur deutschen Frühromantik' (Kiel, 1929). Martin Meissner 'Heinrich Steffens als Religionsphilosoph' (Breslau, 1936); Elisabeth Achterberg 'Heinrich Steffens und die Idee des Volkes' (Würzburg, 1938); V. Waschnitus 'Heinrich Steffens' (Neumünster, 1939). Ingeborg Møller 'Henrik Steffens' (Oslo, 1948).

32, 1

'Betrachtungen über die besondere Bildung und die inneren Verhältnisse unseres Planetensystems' ('Schellings Werke' ed. M. Schröter, Munich, 1962) first supplementary volume pp. 502–560.

On account of some supposed analogy between the planets and the metals, the same signs were used for both, i.e. ☿ for Mercury and quicksilver: ♀ for Venus and copper: ♂ for Mars and iron: ♃ for Jupiter and tin: ♄ for Saturn and lead. There were many variations of this analogy. Philostratus the Athenian (c. 170–245), in his 'The Life of Apollonius of Tyana' (tr. Conybeare 2 vols., London, 1903), tells how Apollonius got into philosophical conversation with someone who gave him, 'seven rings, named according to the planets, and to be worn on the days belonging to them. The golden ring was to be worn on Sunday, the silver ring on Monday, the iron ring on Tuesday, the mercurial ring on Wednesday, the tin ring on Thursday, the copper ring on Friday, and the lead ring on Saturday.' See J. C. Wiegleb (1732–1800), 'Geschichte des Wachsthums und der Erfindungen in der Chemie in der ältesten und mittlern Zeit' (Berlin, 1792) p. 106. This work was a translation of two Latin treatises by Torbern Bergman (1735–1784) 'De primordiis Chemiae' (Uppsala, 1779), and 'Historiae Chemiae' (Uppsala, 1782), and was the best source for the early history of chemistry easily available to Hegel. Cf. Rudolf Koch 'The Book of Signs' (tr. V. Holland, Dover Publications, no date).

32, 14

See the note III. 275.

32, 15

See the note III. 361.

32, 19

Hegel evidently has in mind the use *Ptolemy* made of Pythagorean principles: see I. Düring 'Ptolemaios und Porphyrios über die Musik' ('Göteborgs högskolas årskrift' vol. 40, 1934): L. van der Waerden 'Die Harmonielehre der Pythagoreer' ('Hermes' 58, Berlin, 1944): C. v. Jan 'Die Harmonie der Sphären' ('Philologus' 52, Göttingen, 1894): T. H. Martin 'Hypothèse astronomique de Pythagore' ('Bullettino di . . . storia della scienze' vol. V 1872).

Kepler mentions Pythagoras seventeen times in 'Harmonice Mundi' (Linz, 1619, ed. Caspar, Munich, 1940).

32, 20

Michelet took this passage from Hegel's notes of 1805/6, see 'Jenenser Realphilosophie' II (ed. Hoffmeister, Leipzig, 1931) pp. 31–32. As *Hegel* makes no mention of Paracelsus but speaks merely of 'the ancients', as he also makes no reference to the four cardinal virtues, and as Michelet changed the rest of the passage quite considerably, it may be worthwhile to give the original, ‚Die Alten sagten, der irdische Körper bestehe aus Merkurius, Schwefel, Salz und aus der jungfräulichen Erde. Der Merkurius ist die Metallität, die irdische Farbe, flüssige Sichselbstgleichheit, an welcher der Prozeß sich äußerlich verläuft und die Substanz unberührt läßt, der Schwefel die Verbrennlichkeit, daß das Feuer ihm nichts Fremdes, sondern er die sich verzehrende Wirklichkeit desselben ist. Das Salz (ist) sein Aufgelöstsein (in das) gleichgültige Reale, Zerfallen des Feuers in Selbständige, die jungfräuliche Erde, endlich die einfache Unschuld dieser Bewegung, das Subjekt, das die Vertilgung dieser Momente ist'.

Both Michelet and Hegel are probably confusing the writings of various authors. J. R. Partington, in 'A History of Chemistry' vol. II pp. 115–151 (London, 1961) says that Paracelsus recognized the four Aristotelian elements of fire, air, water and earth, but thought that they appeared in the form of the three *principles* of sulphur, mercury and salt.

Hegel's *general* interpretation of these 'elements' is clearly the correct one. Paracelsus for example regarded sulphur as the principle of combustibility (fire and air), mercury as the principle of fusibility and volatility (water), and salt as the principle of fixity and incombustibility. If Hegel did have Paracelsus in mind here, his inaccuracy in matters of detail is probably due to the contradictions in Paracelsus's own writings, the confused doctrines of his followers, such as Peter Severinus (1542–1602), Jospeh Du Chesne (1544–1609), and Oswald Croll, see 'Basilica Chymica' (Frankfurt, 1609, Eng. tr. London, 1670), or vagueness in the general accounts of iatrochemistry available to him. See T. A. Rixner and T. Siber 'Leben und Lehrmeinungen beruehmter Physiker am Ende des XVI. und am Anfange des XVII Jahrhunderts' (7 vols. Sulzbach, 1819–1826; 2nd ed. 1829): articles by R. Hooykaas in 'Janus' 1935 pp. 175–187: 1937 pp. 1–28.

32, 36

Hegel presents a full-scale assessment of Jacob Boehme in his 'Lectures on the History of Philosophy' (tr. Haldane and Simson, 3 vols. London, 1963) vol. III pp. 188–216. See 'Boehmes Sämtliche Schriften' (11 vols. ed. A. Faust, Stuttgart, 1942 f.).

Most of Boehme's works were translated into English during the course of the seventeenth century, and had a great influence upon English writers: see W. Struck 'Der Einfluss Jakob Boehmes auf die englische Literatur des 17. Jahrhunderts' (Berlin, 1936). Newton studied the 'Life of Jakob Boehme' (London 1654) by Durant Hotham (c. 1617–1691) with great care, and took extensive notes on Boehme's works (see L. T. More 'Isaac Newton' New York, 1962 pp. 25 and 159).

John Pordage (1607–1681), the rector of Bradfield in Berkshire, attempted to evolve a consistent *physical* doctrine out of Boehme's writings, see 'Theologia Mystica' (London, 1683, Germ. tr. 1698), 'A Treatise of Eternal Nature' (London, 1770). Mrs. Jane Leade (1623–1704), who helped Pordage to form the Philadelphian Society on Boehmenist principles in 1670, acquired Francis Lee (1661–1719) of St. John's College Oxford as a son-in-law, and it was through Lee, who later studied medicine at Leyden, that the writings of this group became known in Germany. See F. Roth-Scholtz (1687–1736) 'Ein gründlich Philosophisch Sendschreiben vom rechten und wahren Steine der Weissheit' in 'Deutsches Theatrum Chemicum' (Nuremberg, 1728). Cf. J. F. Pierer 'Medizinisches Realwörterbuch' vol. 8 pp. 237–239 (Altenburg, 1829): G. A. Alleman 'A critique of some philosophical aspects of the mysticism of Jakob Boehme' (Philadelphia, 1932).

34, 12

Cf. Hegel's 'Lectures on the History of Philosophy' (3 vols. tr. Haldane and Simson, London, 1963) vol. I p. 298 and pp. 310 to 139: F. G. Sturz 'Empedocles Agrigentinus' (Leipzig, 1805). Hegel also knew of Empedocles from Aristotle's works: see for example the 'Physics' (tr. Wicksteed and Cornford, 2 vols. Loeb, 1929, 1934): see I iv (187^a 12–188^a 19), 'The other school to which Empedocles and Anaxagoras belong, start from the first with both unity and multiplicity, for they assume an undistinguished confusion, from which the constituents are sifted out . . . Empedocles has only his four so-called elements . . . (and) was . . . sounder in assuming a small limited number of prime substances.' W. D. Ross, in his 'Aristotle's Physics' (Oxford, 1936) p. 487 comments as follows on this passage, 'Apart from being true to the facts, the theory that ὁμοειδῆ can be produced out of simpler elements distinct from themselves has the scientific advantage that it enables us to do with a smaller number of ultimate elements, as Empedocles in fact does. The principle enunciated is the ancestor of Occam's razor.'

The fragment in which Empedocles propounds his theory of the elements is to be found in Hermann Diels' 'Die Fragmente der Vorsokratiker' (2 vols. Berlin, 1906, 1910) vol. I p. 175.

'Hear the four roots of all things:
Shining Zeus, life-bringing Hera, Aidoneus,
And Nestis, whose tear-drops are a well-spring to mortals.'

J. Burnet, in his 'Early Greek Philosophy' (London, 1908) pp. 263-266 discusses the significance of the deities mentioned, and comes to the conclusion that Zeus is air, Hera earth, Aidoneus fire, and Nestis water. Cf. Jean Bollack 'Empédocle. Introduction à l'ancienne physique' (Paris, 1965).

34, 17
'und es ist dann das Interesse des Gedankens'. Cf. the note III. 382.

35, 21
In his 'Lectures on the History of Philosophy' (tr. Haldane and Simson, London, 1963) vol. II pp. 176-179, Hegel discusses *Aristotle's* treatment of the elements of earth, fire, air and water, and praises him for attempting to assess them dialectically. He criticizes *Empedocles'* interpretation of these elements (op. cit. I pp. 313-316) because it tended to call in question the reality of process. He takes *Anaxagoras'* interpretation of the elements to be substantially the same as that of early nineteenth century organic chemists (op. cit. I pp. 334-339). The treatment of the elements by the *Stoics* he regards as being merely derivative, and of no philosophic interest (op. cit. II pp. 245-246).

35, 28
'z.B. Pflanzensäfte, noch mehr das Animalische.' See the notes III. 277, 284, 329, 336, 337 etc.

35, 31
‚Aber die Mitte, das physikalische individuelle Anorganische, ist das Hart=näckigste'. ‚Hartnäckig' has the meaning of 'stiffnecked', 'stubborn', 'obstinate'. It was given wide currency in German through Luther's translation of the Bible: see II Kings XVII 14, Isaiah XLVIII 4.

35, 34
The various meanings attached to this word by the physicists of Hegel's day, the great advances made in pneumatics, pneumatic chemistry and microbiology since that time, and Hegel's reference to Greek theories when introducing this subject, make it very easy to misinterpret this paragraph.

In section (*a*), Hegel deals very vaguely with the general properties of gaseousness as they were understood at that time. In contemporary English terminology the gaseous state as such was referred to as 'elementary air' which was taken to have the 'mechanical properties and effects' of fluidity, weight, and elasticity:

see for example Charles Hutton's 'A Mathematical and Philosophical Dictionary' (2 vols. London, 1796); cf. Newton's 'Opticks' (4th ed. London, 1730) quest. 31. There is an excellent survey of this branch of the subject as it was treated in Germany towards the end of the 1820's in 'Gehler's Physikalisches Wörterbuch' vol. IV (Leipzig, 1828) pp. 1012–1074.

In section (b), Hegel deals with the particular properties of gaseousness. Joseph Priestley (1733–1804), in his 'Experiments and observations on different kinds of air' (London, 1772, Germ. tr. 3 pts. Leipzig and Vienna, 1778, 1779), and John Pringle (1707–1782), in his 'A discourse on the different kinds of air' (London, 1774) laid the foundations of modern pneumatic chemistry. By the end of the 1820's, twenty four separate gases had been identified, but Hegel refused to regard these discoveries as affecting his theory of gaseousness. Much of the corrosion, disintegration and dispersion described by him would now be explained chemically or in the light of microbiology.

In section (c) Hegel deals with the characteristics of gaseousness which should have been presented in section (a), and uses an experiment with *atmospheric air* to illustrate the transition to fire.

As so many of the characteristics of gaseousness are dependent upon temperature, this § should have been *preceded* by §§ 303–306. Cf. John Dalton (1766–1844) 'On the expansion of gases by heat' ('Memoirs of the Manchester Literary and Philosophical Society' 1802), 'Upon the whole therefore I see no sufficient reason why we may not conclude, that all elastic fluids under the same pressure expand equally by heat—and that for any given expansion of mercury, the corresponding expansion of air is proportionally something less, the higher the temperature.'

36, 4

‚die verdachtlose, aber schleichende und zehrende Macht'.

36, 22

Cf. 'Hegel's Science of Logic' (2 vols. tr. Johnston and Struthers, London, 1961) II pp. 460–465: 'Hegel's "Philosophy of Right"' (tr. Knox, Oxford, 1962) pp. 86–104: 'The *good* is the Idea, as unity of the *Notion* of the will with the *particular* will.'

37, 5

As late as 1811 Sigismund Hermbstädt (1760–1833) had to make the point that there is no such thing as a general *odorous matter* (Riechstoff, spiritus rectus) modified into the various smells, but that all odours are particular, and are in fact *effluvia*, disseminated by the air ('Magazin der Berliner Gesellschaft naturforschender Freunde' Berlin, 1811. IV s. III vol. IV): cf. G. F. Hildebrandt (1764–1816) 'Anfangsgründe der Chemie' (3 vols. Erlangen, 1794–1802) vol. III pp. 895 and 958: K. G. Hagen (1749–1829) 'Grundsätze der Chemie' (Königsberg, 1796) p. 99.

Johann Georg Steinbuch in his 'Beitrag zur Physiologie der Sinne'(Nuremberg, 1811) p. 304, considers the possibility of there being 'odorous rays' (Riechstrahlen), by means of which smells are propagated.

Robert Boyle (1627–1691) seems to have initiated research into the *rate* at which bodies dissipate into the air. He notices for example that a grain of musk will perfume a room for twenty years despite constant changes of air. ('Essays of Strange Subtilty' London, 1673): cf. A. von Haller 'Elementa physiologiae corporis humani' (Lausanne, 1757–1760) vol. V bk. 14 sect. 2 § 3.

37, 23

Hegel deals at some length with the philosophy of identity in his 'Logic' (tr. Wallace, Oxford, 1963) §§ 103, 118: cf. 'Hegel's Science of Logic' (tr. Johnston and Struthers, London, 1961) vol. II pp. 37–43, and Hegel's treatment of Schelling in 'Lectures on the History of Philosophy' (tr. Haldane and Simson, 3 vols. London, 1963) esp. pp. 524–540.

Hegel may well have in mind the following passage in Schelling's 'Fernere Darstellung aus dem System der Philosophie' (1802) ‚Die ewige Natur also oder die ewige Materie hält alle Formen ebenso in sich, wie die absolute Einheit überhaupt alle Formen, nämlich so, daß in jeder für sich Einheit und Vielheit eins, jede also für sich ein Universum ist.' ('Schellings Werke' ed. M. Schröter. Erster Ergänzungsband, Munich, 1962 p. 477).

In German philosophical terminology 'matter' is generally regarded in the Aristotelian manner as the still unshaped and primary substance opposed to form: see C. Baeumker 'Das Problem der Materie in der griechischen Philosophie' (Münster, 1890); F. Liebe 'Vorstellungen vom Aufbau der Materie im Wandel der Zeiten' (Vienna, 1953). Cf. B. Russell 'The Analysis of Matter' (Dover Publications, 1962).

37, 25

‚Die Luft reinigt sich, verwandelt Alles in Luft, ist nicht Sammelsurium von Materien'. A ‚Sammelsurium' is a hotchpotch, a mish-mash, a gallimaufry, a hash, a medley. The word was coined by North German university students about 1650, and originally meant a meal consisting of sour or pickled oddments.

37, 34

Jean Baptiste Biot (1774–1862) began his investigations on gases in 1806, when he worked with D. F. J. Arago (1786–1853) on their refractive properties. The passage quoted by Hegel is taken from his 'Traité de physique expérimentale et mathématique' (4 vols. Paris, 1816) vol. I p. 188. In it, Biot in his turn is quoting a conclusion reached by L. J. Gay-Lussac (1778–1850) after much experimentation (see the following note).

38, 12

As early as 1662, Robert Boyle (1627–1691) had shown that the pressure of a given mass of gas varies inversely as the volume provided that the temperature remains constant. In 1802 ('Annales de Chimie' vol. 43 p. 137 ff: 'Gilberts Annalen der Physik' vol. XII p. 255) John Dalton (1766–1844) and L. J. Gay-Lussac (1778–1850), by investigating the expansion of gases with change of temperature, discovered that the volume of a gas under constant pressure increased by 1/267th part of its volume at 0°C for each 1°C rise in temperature.

F. Delaroche (1743–1812) and J. E. Bérard (1789–1869) experimented with air, oxygen, hydrogen, carbon monoxide, carbon dioxide, nitrous oxide and ethylene, and discovered that equal volumes of the *permanent* gases have the same thermal capacity, but that the thermal capacities of compound condensable gases vary. From experiments on air at pressures of 740 mm. and 1000 mm., they found the specific heats to be 269 and 245 respectively, and concluded that the *specific heat diminished with increase of pressure*. ('Annales de chimie' 1813 vol. 85 p. 72).

P. L. Dulong (1785–1838), building on Laplace's suggestion ('Annales de chimie' 1816 p. 238) that the rapid compressions and rarefactions occurring in the propagation of sound are perfectly *adiabatic* and that it is therefore necessary to take account of the rise of temperature due to compression in calculating the velocity of sound, compared the velocities of sound in different gases ('Annales de chimie' 1829 p. 156). As the result of these experiments and observations, he discovered that the changes of temperature at the same compression, stand in inverse ratio to the specific heats of a constant volume, and concluded from this that equal volumes of all gases under the same conditions evolve on compression the same quantity of heat. By this means he showed that the heat evolved in the compression of a gas is proportional to the *energy* expended in compressing it. This confirmed the conclusion reached theoretically by N. L. S. Carnot (1796–1832), and published in his 'Réflexions sur la puissance motrice du feu et les machines propres à developper cette puissance' (Paris, 1824 Germ. tr. Leipzig, 1892, Eng. tr. Thurston, London, 1890), 'The motive power obtainable from heat is independent of the agents employed to realize it. The efficiency is fixed solely by the temperatures of the bodies between which, in the last resort, the transfer of heat is effected.'

By the end of the 1820's therefore, scientists were well on the way to laying the foundations of modern thermodynamics. Hegel evidently ceased to follow developments in this branch of science after about 1810, when the caloric theory of heat had still not been conclusively refuted (see 'Annales de chimie' 1813 p. 72).

The pneumatic tinder-box or tachopyrion which he mentions here, was first devised by a worker in the munitions factory at Étienne. Joseph Izarn (1766–c. 1834) gave an account of the gadget in his 'Lithologie atmosphèrique'

(Paris, 1803), and Joseph Mollet (1758–1829), professor of physics at the university of Lyons published a short note on it in 'Journal de Physique' vol. 58 p. 457 (Paris, 1804). M. A. Pictet (1752–1825), in 'Sur l'échauffement des projectiles par leur frottement contre l'air' ('Bibliothèque Britannique' vol. 23 pp. 331–336, Geneva, 1803) mentioned an earlier English version of this gadget. A certain M. Dumotiez of Paris gave it the name of 'briquet pneumatique' ('Journal de Physique' vol. 62 p. 189 Paris, 1806), and put it into commercial production. The transparent cylinder mentioned by Hegel was one of Dumotiez's gimmicks. He also manufactured a miniature model, which fitted into the top of a walking cane. It was realized that the piston had to be forced in *rapidly*, but no particular attention was paid to this fact in the early attempts at explaining the phenomenon. Paul Erman (1764–1851) performed various experiments with different kinds of tinder, some of which were repeated by L. W. Gilbert (1769–1824): see 'Gilbert's Annalen der Physik' vol. 18 pp. 240–249 and p. 407 (Halle, 1804). U. R. T. Le Bouvier-Desmortier (1739–1827) reported that given a certain kind of tinder, when the cylinder is filled with hydrogen, carbon dioxide, nitrogen, or oxygen, no combustion takes place. ('Journal de Physique' Aug. 1808).

39, 12

‚Die erste Allgemeinheit ist todte Affirmation'. This characterization of air should be compared with § 282.

39, 19

Cf. §§ 257–259: also § 350 and § 351. See 'De combustionis lentae phaenomenis, quae vitam constituant' (Jena, 1804) by J. F. Ackermann (1765–1815).

39, 23

Cf. § 334 Addition sect. b.

39, 34

John Mayow (1640–1679), in his 'Tractatus quinque medico-physici' (Oxford, 1674, Germ. tr. Jena. 1799, Eng. tr. Edinburgh 1907) put forward ideas on combustion which are very similar to modern ones. He noticed the similarity between the processes of respiration and combustion, and showed that one constituent of the atmosphere, which he termed 'spiritus nitro-aereus' is essential to combustion and life, and that the second constituent, which he termed 'spiritus nitri acidi', inhibits combustion and life. See J. A. Schere 'Beweis, dass J. Mayow vor hundert Jahren den Grund zur antiphilogistischen Chemie und Physiologie gelegt hat' (Vienna, 1793).

Georg Ernst Stahl (1660–1734), in his 'Zymotechnia fundamentalis' (Halle, 1697) postulated 'phlogiston' in an attempt to explain fire. According to his theory, combustibility is due to this 'element', which is present in all combustible bodies in an amount proportional to their degree of combustibility. All substances which can be burnt he therefore regarded as being composed of phlogiston and some other substance, and the operation of burning he took merely to be a liberation of phlogiston.

In 1774 J. Priestley obtained *oxygen* by igniting mercuric oxide, and gave it the name 'dephlogisticated air'. A. L. Lavoisier repeated Priestley's experiment and then showed that combustion is simply an oxidation, the oxygen of the atmosphere combining with the substance burnt. These discoveries should have put an end to Stahl's theory, but it lingered on. Charles Hutton (1737–1823) could still write in 1796 that, 'Fire is a distinct fluid, capable of being transferred from one body to another.' ('A Math. Phil. Dict,' 2 vols., London, 1796), and Hegel's treatment of fire as an *element* might have passed muster in certain circles as late as 1815.

Nevertheless, if this definition of combustion is closely considered, it will be found to be not incompatible with Lavoisier's discovery, and not irretrievably at odds with Carnot's definition of heat (note II. 261). Hegel is probably attempting to avoid a purely *chemical* explanation of combustion, and in so far as this exposition is preceded by a consideration of gaseousness and superseded by a treatment of liquidity, it has its merits.

39, 35

‚Das andere (Element) ist das Neutrale'. This version is suggested by Nicolin and O. Pöggeler in their edition of the 'Enzyklopädie' (Hamburg, 1959). They have taken it from § 228 of the Heidelberg Encyclopaedia (ed. Glockner, Stuttgart, 1956) p. 180. Michelet's version: ‚Das andere ist das Neutrale'.

40, 15

Cf. The assessment of Thales in 'Lectures on the History of Philosophy' (tr. Haldane and Simson, 3 vols. London 1963) I pp. 171–185; see also pp. 191, 194, 291–2, 313–315.

41, 12

In regarding the formation of steam and ice from water as a change in *chemical* quality, Hegel was evidently influenced by the experiments performed by G. C. Lichtenberg (1742–1799). Lichtenberg boiled water to remove the air from it, and then froze it in a vacuum. He discovered that it formed a spumescence full of large bubbles, and concluded that the gas must have originated from the breakdown of the water: see J. C. P. Erxleben (1744–1777) 'Anfangsgründe der Naturlehre' (6th edit. ed. G. C. Lichtenberg, Göttingen, 1794) § 426 Zusatz. Cf. the note II, 268. G. F. Parrot (1767–1852) performed similar experiments and came to the same conclusion as Lichtenberg: see his 'Grundriss der theoretischen Physik' (3 pts. Riga and Leipzig, 1809–1815) pt. 2 p. 66. G. W.

Muncke (1772–1847) however, in his 'Ueber das Schiesspulver' (Marburg, 1817) described a number of experiments of this kind in which water from melted snow always gave rise to ice with bubbles in it, while boiled water did not.

In Hegel's day, the difference between these results was usually ascribed to the different temperatures of the ice. Lichtenberg said that the ice was 'very cold', and Parrot that it was reduced to —18°R, while Muncke supplied no details as to temperature. Cf. 'Gehler's Physikalisches Wörterbuch' vol. III p. 112 (Leipzig, 1827).

41, 13

The pressures exerted by steam, gunpowder and freezing water constituted the most powerful expansive forces known at that time: see P. van Musschenbroek (1692–1761) 'Tentam experimentorum in Acad. del Cimento captorum' (Leyden, 1731); G. F. Parrot (1767–1852) 'Grundriss der theoretischen Physik' (3 pts. Riga and Leipzig, 1809–1815) pt. 2 p. 59; 'Transactions of the Royal Society of Edinburgh' vol. II.

Parrot (op. cit. II p. 67) attributed this expansion to the air contained in the water, but this was questioned by G. W. Muncke (1772–1847) in his 'Ueber das Schiesspulver' (Marburg, 1817) p. 97, who found that ice devoid of air still expanded at the same rate. John Dalton (1766–1854), in his 'A new System of Chemical Philosophy' (London, 1808, Germ. tr. 1808 vol. I p. 155), tried to explain this expansion as a change in the aggregation of the constituent parts of water and ice. The maximum density of water occurs at about 4°C. Above this point water continuously expands, and at no temperature is it less dense than ice. In 1849 James Thomson (1822–1892) showed that ice can be melted by increase of pressure, and calculated that every additional atmosphere of pressure the freezing point of water is lowered by .0075°C.

41, 21

Hegel only deals with *water* in this paragraph, but if these remarks are taken to apply to the *liquid state* in general, the reason for his treating water as an 'element' becomes more apparent.

John Dalton (1766–1844), in his 'On the Force of Steam or Vapour from Water and various other Liquids' (1801) came to the conclusion that, 'There can scarcely be a doubt entertained respecting the reducibility of all elastic fluids of whatever kind into liquids; and we ought not to despair of effecting it in low temperatures and by strong pressures exerted on the unmixed gases'. Cf. Michael Faraday's experiments, 'Phil. Trans. Roy. Soc.' 1823 pp. 160–165 and 189–198, and his 'Historical statement respecting the liquefaction of gases' ('Quarterly Journal of Science' 1824 pp. 229–240).

Nevertheless, there was still no certainty with regard to the *principle* involved in liquidity. Faraday failed to liquefy hydrogen, oxygen, fluoboric and phosphuretted hydrogen gases; T. von Grotthuss (1785–1822) attempted to explain fluidity by means of the influence of Galvanism upon atoms ('Gilbert's Annalen der Physik' vol. 61 p. 63); Laplace postulated the three forces of attraction, heat, and repulsion in accounting for the arrangement of the 'molecules' in solid, fluid or gaseous states ('Annales de Chimie et Physique' vol. XXI p. 22); H. F. Link (1767–1851) tentatively put forward theories involving attraction and repulsion etc: see 'Ueber Naturphilosophie' (Leipzig, 1806) p. 175, and 'Gilbert's Annalen der Physik' vol. 47 p. 1.

Hegel seems to have accepted the main point, i.e. that there is an 'element' of liquidity, and then merely illustrated this basic state from its most common natural occurrence as water.

41, 35

In the ordinary terminology of Hegel's day this 'element' was known not as ‚Erdigfeit, but as ‚Feſtigfeit' (soliditas, solidity). The relation between solidity and the other 'elements' was generally treated as a matter of cohesion and elasticity: see Gehler's 'Physikalisches Wörterbuch' vol. IV pp. 198–199 (Leipzig 1827).

44, 18

See for example Thomas Charles Hope (1766–1844). 'Observations on the contraction of water by heat, at low temperatures' ('Transactions of the Edinburgh Royal Society' 1805 vol. V pp. 379–405). Cf. Thomas Birch (1705–1766) 'History of the Royal Society' (4 vols. London, 1756–7) iv pp. 253–263.

44, 24

'shift into another genus.' See Aristotle 'De Caelo' (tr. Stocks, Oxford, 1922) Book I i, 268b I, 'We cannot pass beyond body to a further kind . . . For if we could, it would cease to be true that body is complete magnitude.'

44, 27

This is a reference to the *frictional* electrical machines, the first of which was devised by Otto von Guericke (1602–1686) about 1663: see his 'Exper. nova de vacuo spatio' (Amsterdam, 1672) p. 240. These machines were usually operated manually, and transformed mechanical work into electric energy in the form of electrostatic charges of opposites sign delivered to separate conductors. Jesse Ramsden (1735–1800) and Edward Nairn (1726–1806) designed the most popular English versions of these machines. After William Nicholson (1753–1815) had described his 'influence' machine ('Phil. Trans. Roy. Soc.' 1788 p. 403), these frictional machines rapidly became obsolete. See J. Gray 'Electrical Influence Machines, their Development and modern Forms' (London, 1903): J. Clerk Maxwell 'Treatise on Electricity' (2nd ed. Oxford, 1881) vol. I p. 294; 'Gehler's Physikalisches Wörterbuch' vol. III pp. 413-473 (Leipzig, 1827).

I*

44, 33

As early as 1708, a certain Dr. Wall suggested that the light and crackling produced when amber is rubbed, might constitute the same phenomenon as lightning and thunder ('Phil. Trans. Roy. Soc.' XXVI 1708 no. 314). J. A. Nollet (1700–1770), in his 'Leçons de physique expérimentale' (6 vols. Paris, 1743:1750, Germ. tr. 3 pts. Leipzig, 1771) vol. IV p. 314 showed approval for the hypothesis that thunder and lightning are in the hands of nature what electricity is in the hands of man, and that the clouds correspond exactly to man's electrical machines. J. H. Winkler (1703–1770) put forward a very similar view in his 'Von der Stärke der elektrischen Kraft des Wassers in gläsernen Gefässen' (Leipzig, 1746).

Benjamin Franklin (1706–1790), by flying a kite from a wire string in a thunderstorm, and by charging phials etc. by means of the electricity conducted by the wire, showed that the clouds change from positive to negative electricity several times in the course of one thunder-gust, and that atmospheric electricity is essentially the same as that produced in the laboratory: see: 'New experiments and observations on electricity' (London, 1751, Germ. tr. Leipzig, 1758): 'Dr. Benjamin Franklins nachgelassene Schriften' (3 vols. Weimar, 1818).

It is not at all clear why Hegel should have chosen to ignore this evidence, although there was no distinct idea at that time of the nature of the electric potential in the atmosphere. Hegel is thinking perhaps of the 'Neue Ideen über Meteorologie' (Berlin, 1788), by J. A. Deluc (1727–1817), in which it is suggested that lightning is not stored in the clouds and then discharged, but is engendered at the very moment at which it appears.

45, 9

Aristotle 'The Physics' (tr. Wicksteed and Cornford, 2 vols. Loeb, 1929, 1934): see esp. 205[a], 'It is impossible that all the universe, even if it be limited, should be or should become any single one of the elements as Heraclitus supposed, when he said that all things sometime become fire. Against this the same argument can be urged as applies to the undifferentiated unity or matrix such as some physicists have assumed in addition to the elements; for things always change from one term of an opposition to the other, from hot to cold, for instance.' Aristotle gives a more fully worked out account of this in 'De Generatione et Corruptione' (tr. Forster, Loeb, 1955) 328b–334b.

F. E. D. Schleiermacher (1768–1834), Hegel's colleague at Berlin, first collected the fragments of Heraclitus in a systematic manner: see his 'Herakleitos der dunkle, von Ephesos' (F. A. Wolf and P. Buttmann 'Museum der Alterthumswissenschaft' vol. I, Berlin, 1808). Hegel probably has in mind the following fragments:

20. This world, which is the same for all, no one of gods or men has made; but it was ever, is now, and shall be an ever-living Fire, with measures kindling, and measures going out.

21. The transformations of Fire are, first of all, sea; and half of the sea is earth, half whirlwind.

22. All things are an exchange for Fire, and Fire for all things, even as wares for gold, and gold for wares.

23. It becomes liquid sea, and is measured by the same tale as before it became earth.

24. Fire is want and surfeit.

25. Fire lives the death of air, and air lives the death of fire; water lives the death of earth, earth that of water.

26. Fire in its advance will judge and convict all things.

The numbering given here is that found in I. Bywater's 'Heracliti Ephesii Reliquiae' (Oxford, 1877). Hermann Diels' 'Die Fragmente der Vorsokratiker' (ed. Kranz, Berlin, 1934) gives the generally accepted order of these fragments. Cf. G. S. Kirk 'Heraclitus. The Cosmic Fragments' (Cambridge, 1954): P. Wheelwright 'Heraclitus' (Princeton, 1959).

45, 30

Friedrich Albrecht Karl Gren (1760–1798) was born at Bernburg, where his father, a Swede by birth, had been settled long enough to have become naturalized. He was educated for the ministry, but after his father's death, he took up apothecary work, and by 1779 was in charge of his own apothec at Offenbach.

In 1780 W. B. Trommsdorff (1738–1782), of Erfurt, advised him to take up medicine. In 1782 therefore, he began his university studies at Helmstädt. In 1783 he moved to Halle, where he studied under W. J. Karsten (1732–1787), and took his doctorate in 1787. He subsequently married Karsten's daughter, and settled down in Halle as a university teacher. His 'Systematisches Handbuch der gesammten Chemie' (4 pts. Halle, 1787–1791) proved to be very serviceable, and had run to a fourth edition by 1819. It is a lucid and thorough work, and contains useful bibliographies covering the whole field of chemistry.

Hegel is here referring to his 'Grundriss der Naturlehre zum Gebrauch akademischer Vorlesungen' (Halle, 1788), which has all the merits of the former work, and ran to six editions. As is usual with Hegel, this quotation is not word-perfect, but seems to have been taken from the *fourth edition* of the book (Halle, 1801). E. G. Fischer (1754–1831) edited the fifth edition (Halle, 1808), and made certain changes in the terminology. In the sixth edition (ed. K. W. G. Kastner, Halle, 1820), the numbering of the paragraphs was completely changed.

The work by *Horace Bénédict de Saussure* (1740–1799) mentioned by Gren is 'Essais sur l'Hygrométrie' (Neuchâtel, 1783, Germ. tr. Leipzig, 1784). A critical edition of this book has been published by A. J. von Oettingen: 'Versuch über die Hygrometrie' (Leipzig, 1900).

Saussure was born at Geneva, and under the influence of his father, Nicolas de Saussure (1709–1790), an eminent agriculturalist, and his maternal uncle,

Charles Bonnet (1720–1793), devoted himself in his early years to botany. In 1762 he published his first botanical work, and in the same year was appointed professor of philosophy at the academy of Geneva, a post which he held until 1789. In the autumn of 1768 he visited England, and was elected Fellow of the Royal Society.

From 1773 onwards he began a systematic study of the geology and topography of the Alps, and gave an account of his expeditions and observations in 'Voyages dans les Alpes' (4 vols. Geneva 1779–1796). His geological observations made him a firm believer in the neptunian theory (note III. 218).

In his 'Essais sur l'Hygromètrie', se Saussure describes a new hygrometer of his own construction, based on the fact that a hair will stretch when it is moistened, and contract when dried. J. A. Deluc (1727–1817), in his 'Idées sur la météorologie' (2 vols. London, 1786/7), and in two papers read to the Royal Society ('Phil. Trans.' 1791 pp. 1 and 389), pointed out the unreliability of this instrument. Gren and Hegel were evidently unaware of this criticism.

According to de Saussure, water vapour is essentially a combination of water and heat. He assumes however, that this vapour is *dissolved* in the air, and that it reappears as soon as the air is saturated, through the agency of electricity.

45, 39

As the result of the controversy between James Hutton (1726–1797) and J. A. Deluc (1727–1817) concerning the *cause of rain* (see the following note), the Berlin Academy chose this topic as subject for a prize essay. Johann Diedrich Otto Zylius (1764–1820), a private tutor from Mecklenburg, was awarded the prize for his 'Prüfung der Theorie des Herrn Deluc vom Regen' (Berlin, 1795). For further details relating to Zylius, see J. G. Meusel 'Das gelehrte Teutschland' (Lemgo, 1796–1834).

In this work Zylius defended Hutton's dissolution theory (Auflösungstheorie), against Deluc's theory of *transformation*. He had already criticized Deluc's doctrine of evaporation and rain in an article published in Gren's 'Journal der Physik' (vol. VIII, 1794), and Lichtenberg's objections to the critics of the phlogiston theory in an earlier article (Gren's 'Journal' vol. VI, 1792). Consequently, Lichtenberg had good reason to pitch into his prize essay once it was published.

Georg Christoph Lichtenberg (1742–1799): physicist, satirist, aphorist, humorist, traveller, art critic, linguist, philologist, Lichtenberg was one of the most brilliant and many-sided figures of the German enlightenment. There is an excellent characterization of him by Martin Cooper in 'The Listener' (October 15, 1964): cf. 'Lichtenberg's Commentaries on Hogarth's Engravings' (ed. Herdan, Cresset Press, 1966). He dealt most fully with Zylius' work in 'Vertheidigung des Hygrometers und der Luc'schen Theorie vom Regen' (ed. L. C. Lichtenberg and F. Kries, Göttingen, 1800). He evidently had some doubt as to the advisability of publishing this work, partly on account of the uncertainty of his own views (see pp. 200–201), and partly on account of the boisterous and acid nature of his criticism. The best account of his views on rain is to be found in his edition of the 'Anfangsgründe der Naturlehre' (6th ed. Göttingen, 1794) by J. C. P. Erxleben (1744–1777). As Hegel notes, Lichtenberg, in the main, accepted Deluc's theory, mainly because he was convinced of the incompetence of those who had questioned it (see p. xliv), but also because it accorded well with the phlogiston theory (see pp. 378–381). Despite the literary brilliance of Lichtenberg, Zylius' doctrine won the day; his 'Über den gegenwärtigen Zustand unserer Kenntnisse von den wässrigen Lufterscheinungen' (Haarlem, 1804), was crowned by the Pieter Teyler (1702–1778) Institute a decade after his first attempts to refute Deluc, and by the early 1830's the theories of his opponents were no longer regarded as worthy of serious consideration: see 'Gehler's Physikalisches Wörterbuch' vol. VII pp. 1212–1220 (Leipzig, 1834).

46, 5

Jean André Deluc (1727–1817), the Swiss geologist and meteorologist. In 1773 he came to England, and received the appointment of reader to Queen Charlotte, which he continued to hold for forty four years, and which afforded him both leisure and a competent income. He died at Windsor on November 7, 1817.

As a philosopher, he was a great admirer of Francis Bacon: see his 'Bacon tel qu'il est' (Berlin, 1800). As a geologist he was a determined opponent of the vulcanists: see his 'Lettres physiques et morales sur les montagnes' (La Haye, 1778), and 'Traité élémentaire de geologie' (Paris, 1809, Eng. tr. London, 1809).

James Hutton (1726–1797), in a paper read to the Royal Society of Edinburgh in 1784, put forward the view that the amount of moisture which the air can retain in solution increases with augmentation of temperature, and concluded from this that when two masses of air of different temperatures mix, a portion of the moisture must be condensed and appear in visible form. After investigating available data regarding rainfall and climate in various regions of the globe, he came to the conclusion that rainfall is everywhere regulated by the humidity of the air and the causes which promote mixtures of different aerial currents in the higher atmosphere: see 'The theory of rain'—'Transactions of the Royal Society of Edinburgh' vol. I p. 41 (Edinburgh, 1788): F. A. C. Gren's 'Journal der Physik' vol. IV pp. 413–471 (Leipzig, 1791).

Hutton initiated the modern view of rain in this paper, but he had called in question the theory put forward by Deluc in his 'Recherches sur les modifications de l'atmosphère' (2 vols. Geneva, 1772), and in his 'Idées sur la météorologie' (2 vols. London, 1786/7). He was therefore obliged to defend his argument in 'Answers to the objections of Deluc, with regard to the theory of rain' ('Trans. Roy. Soc. Edin.' vol. II p. 39).

Deluc contended that the *amounts* of water discharged by the air on certain occasions are too great to be explained from Hutton's hypothesis. He objected strongly to the theory that water is *dissolved* in the air, and contended that when water evaporates, it changes into a new kind of gas, which cannot be detected hygroscopically, but which can change back into water.

To the meteorologists of the day, this contention appeared to be confirmed by the *synthesis* of water from 'dephlogisticated air' and 'inflammable air' by Henry Cavendish (1731–1810), see his 'Experiments on Air' ('Phil. Trans. Roy. Soc.' Jan. 1784, lxxiv pp. 119–153), and by Lavoisier's famous 'Mémoire ou l'on prouve par la décomposition de l'eau, que ce fluide n'est point une substance simple' ('Mémoires de l'Academie des Sciences' April, 1784).

In 1787 the Dutch chemist Martin van Marum (1750–1837), working with the great frictional machine in the Teyler Institute at Haarlem, managed to *decompose* water by means of electric sparks. As the oxygen combined with the metal wire however, he thought he had produced only hydrogen: see 'Verhandelingen uitgegeeven door Teylers Tweede Genootschap' (Haarlem, 1787) Stuk iv p. 144. Soon afterwards J. R. Deiman (1743–1808), Adrien Paets van Troostwyk (1752–1837) and John Cuthbertson (d.c. 1845) showed that both hydrogen and oxygen are produced by the decomposition of water: see Rozier's 'Observations sur la Physique' Nov. 1789, vol. xxxv pp. 376–380: Gren's 'Journal der Physik' 1790 ii p. 131: Nicholson's 'Journal of Philosophy' 1797 i p. 241.

Deluc called these discoveries to witness in support of his theories (see his 'Neue Ideen über die Meteorologie' Berlin and Leipzig, 1797 pt. i p. 186 ff), and was enthusiasticially backed by Lichtenberg and W. A. Lampadius (1772–1842). Lampadius proceeded to put the theories to the test in a number of very detailed observations: see his 'Versuche und Beobachtungen über die Elektrizität und Wärme der Atmosphäre' (Berlin and Stettin, 1793). Their work evidently convinced Hegel, although during the first decades of the new century the opposing views steadily gained recognition: see especially John Dalton (1766–1844) 'Meteorological Observations and Essays' (London, 1793, 2nd ed. London, 1834).

46, 40

Johann Wilhelm Ritter (1776–1810). Vera ('Philosophie de la Nature, de Hégel' I p. 434) takes Hegel's description of Ritter as 'a physicist who died in Munich' to be 'somewhat crude'. There seems to be no reason why Hegel should have intended it to be derogatory however.

Ritter was born at Samitz near Hainau in Silesia, and died in Munich on January 23, 1810. Before going up to Jena in 1795, he worked as a pharmaceutist. Novalis and Herder were two of his closest friends. After university he lived as a private gentleman in Gotha and Weimar, and in 1804 was called to Munich as a regular member of the Bavarian Academy. In his short period as a teacher and research worker he was very active, and made discoveries of lasting importance in the spheres of galvanism and physiological electricity. His work was little recognized in his own day however. Cf. note II. 285.

Hegel has probably taken the account of this experiment from Ritter's 'Beyträge zur nähern Kenntniss des Galvanismus' (4 vols. Jena, 1800–1805) vol. II pp. 1–54. Ritter first described it in an article published in 'Voigt's Magazin für den neuesten Zustand der Naturkunde' vol. II art. 2 (Sept. 1800). Hegel's account is not quite accurate: plate I figure i in Ritter's book makes it quite clear the wires do not *join* through the mercury, and in describing the experiment, Ritter speaks of ‚das Verbindungsmittel beyder Enden a und b' etc.

Alessandro Volta (1745–1827) discovered the electric battery in 1800, and so placed in the hands of investigators the means of maintaining a steady electric current. Before that date they had been restricted to the study of the isolated electric charges given by frictional electric machines. It was not long before this technical advance gave rise to the first discoveries relating to electrolysis. At almost the same time as Ritter, William Nicholson (1753–1815) and Anthony Carlisle (1768–1840) found that hydrogen and oxygen were evolved at the surfaces of gold and platinum wires connected with the terminals of a battery and dipped in water. The volume of the hydrogen was about double that of the oxygen, and, since this is the ratio in which these elements are combined in water, it was concluded that the process consisted essentially in the *decomposition* of water. ('Tilloch's Phil. Mag.' 1800 VII pp. 337–347: 'Nicholson's Journal' 1801 IV pp. 179–187).

The conclusion that Ritter drew from his experiment, i.e. that water is a chemically simple body, was plausible enough under the circumstances. He should however have taken into account the impurities in the water, and the chemical changes effected in the mercury and the wires. The first exact quantitative study of electrolytic phenomena was made about 1830 by Michael Faraday (1791–1867): see his 'Experimental Researches' (London, 1833). Cf. Sir Humphry Davy (1778–1829) 'Chemical Agencies of Electricity' ('Phil. Trans. Roy. Soc.' 1807 pp. 1–56).

Cf. J. R. Partington 'A History of Chemistry' vol. 4 p. 21 (London, 1964). Partington does not discuss this experiment, but mentions another made by Ritter, in which the two quantities of water in the tube were separated by concentrated sulphuric acid. In this case he was able to criticize the conclusions drawn by pointing out that Ritter was not aware that hydrogen could pass through the acid.

47, 6

Alexander von Humboldt (1769–1859) and Louis Joseph Gay-Lussac (1778–1850) published the results of the joint researches mentioned here by Hegel in 1805: see 'Gilbert's Annalen der Physik' vol. xx pp. 38–95 (Halle, 1805):

'Journal de Physique' vol. LX pp. 129–168 (Paris, 1805). The samples of air were taken from the Théatre français however, not from a dancing-hall (Gilbert, pp. 87–88, Journal p. 155), and the conclusion drawn was that 'die Luft nur sehr geringe Verschiedenheiten in ihrer Mischung (zeigt)' not that there was 'no difference'. By using the eudiometer they found that the air contained about 21% oxygen, a negligible amount of hydrogen, and that there was very little variation in its composition.

47, 20

See note II. 227.

47, 34

This attack is evidently directed at the work of Joseph Black (1728–1799) of Edinburgh. Black noticed that if a piece of ice below freezing-point is gradually heated at a uniform rate, its temperature may be observed to rise regularly till the freezing-point is reached. He also noticed that at this point, its temperature ceases to rise, and that during the period in which the melting takes place, heat may be supplied without producing any rise in temperature, although the same quantity of heat supplied to an equal mass of *water* would raise its temperature to nearly 80°C. It was this heat absorbed in producing a *change of state* without a rise of temperature that Black called 'latent': see his 'Lectures on the Elements of Chemistry' (2 vols. ed. J. Robinson, Edinburgh, 1803, Germ. tr. Crell, 4 vols. Hamburg, 1804–5) II op. 108.

Hegel can hardly be questioning the facts of this and similar experiments. He is probably questioning Black's assumption (op. cit. II p. 4) that heat is an imponderable *fluid*.

48, 34

Hegel notes in his diary that he discussed this with his teacher at the Stuttgart Grammar School, Heinrich David von Cless (1741–1820), when out walking with him on July 4, 1785, ‚Unter andern machte ich die Frage: warum es im Julius und August heißer sei, als im Juni, wo doch die Sonne uns sich am meisten nähere.' See Karl Rosenkranz 'Hegel's Leben' (Berlin, 1844) pp. 433–434; J. Hoffmeister 'Dokumente zu Hegels Entwicklung' (Stuttgart, 1936) pp. 10–11. Cless explained the phenomenon by stating that the stimulation by the sun reached a maximum at midsummer, that this set off a reaction in the earth which only reached its maximum a month or so later, and that the heat could therefore only be attributed indirectly to the sun itself.

48, 36

Sir William Edward Parry (1790–1855), on his second expedition to discover the North-west Passage (May 1821–October 1823) recorded the following temperatures:—

July 1821	76°W 54°N	Mean 1°7R
Dec. 1821	65°W 66°N	Mean −20°R
Jan. 1822	65°W 66°N	Mean −24°5R
June 1822	65°W 66°N	Mean 0°9R
July 1822	65°W 66°N	Mean 2°R
Dec. 1822	64°W 69°N	Mean −18°6R
Jan. 1823	64°W 69°N	Mean −21°8R
June 1823	64°W 69°N	Mean 0°2R
July 1823	64°W 69°N	Mean 3°6R

See 'Journals of a Voyage' etc. (London, 1821–1828), published by the authority of the Admiralty. This did not constitute information as to the temperature at the 'poles' however, cf. 'Gehler's Physikalisches Wörterbuch' vol. 9 pp. 654–656 (Leipzig, 1828). What is more, Parry noticed an interesting *difference* in the *diurnal* changes of temperature, 'The times of maximum and minimum altitude appear, however, decidedly to lean to four and ten o'clock, and to follow a law directly the reverse, as to time, of that found to obtain in temperate climates, the column being *highest* at *four*, and *lowest* at ten o'clock, both A.M. and P.M.' See 'Narrative of an attempt to reach the North Pole . . . in the year 1827' (London 1829) pp. 53–54.

Cf. 'Analysis of a Journal of a Voyage' etc. in 'The Edinburgh philosophical Journal' vol. V pp. 177–208 (Edinburgh, 1821).

49, 10

‚Die Wolkenbildung ift ein Spiel der Reduction der Luft zu Neutralität.'

49, 29

Cf. Michelet' note II. 60.

49, 37

This passage is taken from Goethe's 'Meteorologische Nachschrift' to 'The Climate of London' (2 vols. London, 1818) by Luke Howard (1772–1864), which is to be found in 'Goethe, die Schriften zur Naturwissenschaft) sect. I vol. 8 pp. 320–322 (ed. D. Kuhn, Weimar, 1962). This volume also contains lines by Goethe in honour of Howard (pp. 233–9), and Howard's account of himself, which he sent at Goethe's request (pp. 287–195).

50, 3

‚fich als die auf die Spitze getriebene Negativität aufhebt'.

50, 17

See the notes II. 268–270.

50, 31

Hegel, in a marginal note ('Jenenser Realphilosophie' ii p. 78 note I) characterizes this 'extreme point of opposition' as 'electrical tension' („Spannung als Elektrizität').

51, 1

On the original text ('Jenenser Realphilosophie' II p. 78), it is 'purely electrical phenomena' („reiner Elektrizitäten'), not 'the unity', which have these 'pure fluidities' and not 'material forms' („gestaltete Materie') as *their* moments.

51, 12

See the note III. 218.

51, 21

See the note III. 234.

51, 25

Interest in animals as weather prophets increased greatly after D. B. Quatremère d'Isjonval (1754–1830) forecast, from his observation of spiders, that the winter of 1794–5 would be particularly severe. This prophecy had an important effect on the fate of Holland. Charles Pichegru (1761–1804), at the head of the French army of the Rhine-and-Moselle, crossed the Meuse on October 18, 1794, and after taking Nijmwegen, drove the Austrians beyond the Rhine. In accordance with the ordinary tactics of the time, he should then have taken up winter quarters, but acting on Quatrèmere d'Isjonval's advice, he prepared for a winter campaign. Beginning this at the end of December, he crossed the Meuse and the Waal on ice, and driving the English troops before him, took Utrecht and Amsterdam, and soon occupied the whole of Holland. The Dutch ships were frozen in the Helder, and were easily taken. See D. B. Quatremère d'Isjonval 'L'Aranéologie' (La Haye, 1797): W. C. Orphal (1773–1823) 'Die Wetterpropheten im Thierreiche' (Leipzig, 1805): K. L. Scharfenberg 'Wetteranzeige' (Vienna, 1819): J. Weber 'Die Spinnen sind Deuter des kommenden Wetters' (Landshut, 1800): Luke Howard (1772–1864) 'The Climate of London' (2 vols. London, 1818) vol. I table 29. Cf. III. 146, 34.

52, 9

Cf. the notes III. 215, 218.

52, 12

See Goethe's 'Meteorologische Nachschrift' to Luke Howard's 'The Climate of London' (2 vols. London, 1818): 'Goethe, die Schriften zur Naturwissenschaften' sect. I vol. 8 (ed. D. Kuhn, Weimar, 1962) pp. 330–331, „Wie wir nun oben die Ursachen der Barometer-Veränderungen tellurisch genannt haben, so möchten wir hinwieder die Gewitterzüge topisch d.i. örtlich

nennen, und können daher nicht anders als billigen, daß eine Hallische Gesellschaft auf die Gewitter im besonderen zu achten unternommen hat.'

Goethe is here referring to the programme for a systematic investigation of the
paths of storms proposed by the Halle Natural Science Society in 1820: see
'Schweigger's Neues Journal für Chemie und Physik' vol. 27 article 4 (Nuremberg, 1820). Cf. F. W. Remer 'Göthe's Witterungs-Deutung' (Berlin, 1834):
W. Wasielewski 'Goethe's meteorologische Studien' (Leipzig, 1910).

52, 22

See Edmund Halley (1656–1742) 'A historical Account of the tradewinds'
('Phil. Trans. Roy. Soc.' no. 183 p. 152). In German these winds are known as
,Passatwinde' (Spanish viento de pasada). Their English name evidently origi-
nates from the phrase 'to blow trade', i.e. in constant course or way. In Hegel's
day, in both German and English, they were often not distinguished from the
Monsoons: see J. C. P. Erxleben (1744–1777) 'Anfangsgründe der Naturlehre'
(ed. Lichtenberg, 6th ed. Göttingen, 1794) 717: T. Forrest (1729?–1802?) 'A
Treatise on the Monsoons in East India' (London, 1784).

52, 23

Francis Balfour (fl. 1812) and John Farquhar (1751–1826) took barometer
readings in Bengal in 1795, and found that there was no change from 6 a.m.
until 7.30 a.m., that there was a rise from 7.30 until 8.00, a fall from 8 a.m.
until 3 p.m., no change from 3.00 until 8 p.m., a rise to the level reached at
9 a.m., and then no further change until sunrise: see 'Asiatick Researches' vol.
IV p. 217 (Calcutta, 1792). George Wright claimed that the barometrical
oscillations on Ceylon were so regular, that one could tell the time from them:
see 'Tilloch's Philosophical Magazine' 1822 pp. 386–389. Cf. William Roxburgh
(1751–1815) 'Meteorological Diary kept at Fort St. George on the coast of
Coromandel' ('Phil. Trans. Roy. Soc.' 1780 p. 246).

52, 29

See Sir William Edward Parry (1790–1855), 'Journals of the First, Second and
Third Voyages for the discovery of a North-West Passage' (5 vols. London,
1828). These journals contain many descriptions of the aurora borealis see I p.
227, III p. 169, IV pp. 209–210, V pp. 45–46 and 172–176.

The last of these passages, in which Parry describes the displays seen between
Sept. 15, and Oct. 5, 1825, as he was sailing down Davis's Strait to the
Orkneys, is by far the best. Hegel probably has in mind the description of the
display of Dec. 22, 1824 however (V pp. 45–46), 'At seven (in) the morning, it
became more brilliant, and stationary, describing a well-defined arch, extending from the E.S.E. horizon to that at W.N.W., and passing through the zenith.
A very faint arch was also visible on each side of this, appearing to diverge

from the points in the horizon,* and separating to twenty degrees distance in the zenith. It remained thus for twenty minutes, when the coruscations from each arch met, and after a short but brilliant display of light gradually died away.'

The auroras are now thought to be caused at heights varying between forty and six hundred miles, by jets of atomic matter, shot from the sun, and deflected towards the north and south poles by the magnetic field of the Earth. 'American scientists plan to create this summer an artificial auroral display, as bright as a full moon, by firing an electron accelerator on board an Aerobee rocket . . . The underlying purpose of the experiment . . . is to help the mapping of the earth's magnetic field, by tracing the field line.' 'The Times' January 6, 1967. A close approximation to the modern theory is to be found in the 'Traité physique et historique de l'aurore boréale' (Paris, 1733) by J. J. de Mairan (1678–1771).

Benjamin Franklin (1706–1790) put forward the view that the sea consists of non-electric water and electric salts, and that the clouds in the equatorial regions take up this electricity and transport it to the poles, discharging it as a luminescence when they come in contact with the colder and damper air-streams of those regions: see his 'Experiments and observations on Electricity' (London, 1769) p. 49; cf. 'Phil. Trans. Roy. Soc.' vol. 48 pp. 358, 784, vol. 51 p. 403.

Richard Kirwan (1733–1812), in an article published in 'Transactions of the Royal Irish Academy' vol. II 1788, revived an older theory by suggesting that the aurora is formed by the *combustion* of matter: (hydrogen formed at the equator).

Hegel is evidently rejecting these theories in favour of the electromagnetic hypothesis put forward by John Dalton (1766–1844) in his 'Meteorological observations and essays' (London, 1793), and supported by J. B. Biot (1774–1862), 'Journal de Physique' vol. 93, 'Gilberts Annalen der Physik' vol. 67— and C. Hansteen (1784–1873), 'Magazin for Naturvidenskaberne' (Christiana, 1824) p. 85: 'Edinburgh Philosophical Journal' vol. 23 p. 83, vol. 24 p. 235: 'Schweigger's Journal' vol. 16 p. 188.

52, 35

This is a reference to several passages on clouds to be found in 'Goethe, die Schriften zur Naturwissenschaft' pt. I vol. viii (ed. D. Kuhn, Weimar, 1962). Goethe distinguishes *four* main types of clouds: stratus, cumulus, cirrus and nimbus (op. cit. pp. 73–93).

Goethe's views on this subject, as he warmly acknowledges, were greatly influenced by the writing of Luke Howard (1772–1864): see 'The Times' March 21, 1964. Howard first gave detailed descriptions of the cloud-types in his 'On the modifications of Clouds' (London, 1803), a work which also contains three plates illustrating his categorization. His main work on the subject was however 'The Climate of London' (2 vols. London, 1818), and it was this book

---

*'I am aware that this appearance is usually referred to the effect of viewing the phenomenon in perspective, but I here describe *appearances* only.'

which so impressed Goethe, Howard's descriptions of the various clouds are to be found in the second volume (pp. 329–338):—

'1. The Cirrus. A cloud resembling a lock of hair, or a feather.

2. The Cumulus. A cloud which increases from above in dense, convex or conical heaps.

3. The Stratus. An extended, continuous, level sheet of cloud, increasing from beneath.

4. The Cirrocumulus. A connected system of small roundish clouds, placed in close order, or contact.

5. The Cirrostratus. A horizontal or slightly inclined *sheet*, attentuated at its circumference, concave downwards, or undulated. Groups or patches having these characters.

6. The Cumulostratus. The Cumulus flattened at top, and overhanging its base.

7. The Nimbus. A dense cloud, spreading out into a crown of Cirrus, and passing beneath into a shower.'

Cf. 'Gilbert's Annalen der Physik' vol. XXi pp. 137–159 (1805).

Cf. Elizabeth Fox Howard 'Goethe and Luke Howard, F.R.S.' (Leominster, 1932, Germ. tr. Hennigsdorf, 1932): 'The Friends' Quarterly Examiner' (July, 1932), James Boyd 'Goethe's Knowledge of English Literature' (Oxford, 1932) pp. 125–128.

53, 6

At Veii and near S. Sabina in 207 B.C.: see XXVII 37, 'Before the consuls set out (for their provinces) there were nine days of rites, because stones had rained from the sky . . . Then again the nine days of rites were repeated, because in Armilustrum it seemed to rain stones.'

At Cumae in 202 B.C.: see XXX 38, 'At Cumae the orb of the sun seemed diminished, and a shower of stones fell'.

At Remens in 173 B.C.: see XLII 2, 'At Lanuvium the vision of a great fleet was said to have been seen in the sky, and at Privernum it was said, dark coloured wool had grown from the earth. In the Veientine country about Remens there was said to have been a shower of stones.'

At Reate in 169 B.C.: see XLIII 13, 'Reate imbri lapidavit.'

See 'T. Livi Patavini Historiarum Libri qui supersunt, ex editione G. A. Ruperti' (20 vols. London, 1828). Cf. J. F. H. Dalberg (1760–1812) 'Ueber Meteor-Cultus der Alten, vorzüglich in Bezug auf Steine, die vom Himmel gefallen sind' (Heidelberg, 1811).

The stones fell at Aigle in Normandy on April 26, 1803. J. B. Biot (1774–1862) was sent by the French Institute to investigate the matter, and his report constitutes the best account of the incident: see 'Relation d'un voyage fait dans le département de l'Orne pour constater la réalité d'un météore observé à l'Aigle' (Paris, 1803): cf. 'Mémoires de l'Institut' vol. VII.

This occurrence was widely publicised, but it was not the first of its kind to change the views of the scientists of Hegel's day. On June 16, 1794 stones fell at Siena: see A. Soldani (1733–1808) in 'Atti dell' Accademia di Siena' vol. IX: D. Tata (1723–c. 1800) 'Memoria sulla pioggia di pietre nella Campagna Sanese' (Naples, 1794). On December 13, 1795 a large stone smelling of sulphur landed near Woodcottage in Yorkshire: see 'The Gentleman's Magazine' (Feb. 1796): cf. 'Phil. Trans. Roy. Soc.' 1802: 'Gilberts Annalen der Physik' vol. XIII p. 291.

53, 19

Ernst Florens Chladni (1756–1827), in his 'Ueber Feuer-Meteore und über die mit denselben herabgefallenen Massen' (Vienna, 1819) collected accounts of all the instances of aerolites then known, and initiated the modern approach by suggesting that these bodies were extra-terrestrial in origin. J. A. Deluc (1727–1817) denied their extra-terrestrial origin, questioned the possibility of their being atmospheric formations, and insisted on the necessity of their having been ejected by volcanoes ('Gilberts Annalen der Physik' vol. VI p. 13). J. T. Mayer (1752–1830), in his 'Lehrbuch der physischen Astronomie' (Göttingen, 1805) p. 334 put forward the theory of their atmospheric origin accepted here by Hegel, and C. J. Diruf 'Ideen zur Naturerklärung der Meteor- oder Luftsteine' (Göttingen, 1805), and W. von Freygang 'Idées sur le phénomene des Aéro-lithes' (Göttingen 1804) developed it.

The theory that 'the Moon has dropped something' was put forward by H. W. M. Olbers (1758–1840) in 'Zach's Annalen der Physik' vol. XIV p. 38. It was repeated by A. J. P. von Scherer (1783–1835) in Oken's 'Isis' 1833 sect. IV–VI p. 481.

For descriptions of fire-balls which Hegel may have consulted see: 'Phil. Trans. Roy. Soc.' vol. 30 p. 978—Worcester, March 19, 1719: 'Phil. Trans. Roy. Soc.' 1741 p. 870, 1742 pp. 1,188—southern England, Dec. 11, 1741: 'Phil. Trans. Roy. Soc.' 1759 pp. 218, 259—the north country, Nov. 26, 1758: 'Mém. de l'acad. des sciences' 1771 p. 670—Paris, July 10, 1771: 'Phil. Trans. Roy. Soc.' 1784 pp. 112, 201—Great Britain, Aug. 18, 1783.

53, 21

,unreife Monde'.

53, 30

,in biefen Urtheilen'.

53, 40

Hegel entered a long note in the margin at this juncture, part of which is as follows ('Jenenser Realphilosophie' II p. 79), 'Universality: all moments sublated—division. In its implicit state, gravity is a falling from unity, then a projection, then a vibration, motion; then it is singularity in general, character, shape, electricity, dissolution of heat—heat, expansion, expansible fluidity, chemical, physical element. Shape *divides* or *determines* itself: intensity, hostility.'

This is part of his attempt to rationalize the transition from 'Formation and Chemism' (op. cit. pp. 33–79) to 'Physics' (op. cit. pp. 79–103).

For the state of German meteorology at the time, of Hegel's death, see Ludwig Friedrich Kämtz (1801–1867) 'Grundzüge der Meteorologie' (3 vols. Halle, 1831–1836): G. Schübler (1787–1834) 'Grundsätze der Meteorologie' (Leipzig, 1831), 'Correspondenzblatt des würtembergischen landwirtschaftlichen Vereins' (1825–1834) etc.

57, 29

'No body is absolutely or perfectly dense; or no space is perfectly full of matter, so as to have no vacuity or interstices; on the contrary, it is the opinion of Newton, that even the densest bodies, as gold etc. contain but a small portion of matter, and a very great portion of vacuity; or that it contains a great deal more of pores or empty space, than of real substance'. Charles Hutton 'A Mathematical and Philosophical Dictionary' (2 vols. London, 1796) I p. 366. Cf. Newton's 'Opticks' (4th ed. London, 1730) bk. III pt. 1 question 31.

58, 30

Kant 'Metaphysische Anfangsgründe der Naturwissenschaft' (Riga, 1786). See especially the second main part of this work, in which Kant postulates attraction and repulsion as being basic forces, without which matter could not exist. He was not the first to do this however. Newton's hypothesis (see the previous note), led Godwin Knight (1713–1772) to put forward similar views almost forty years before Kant ('Phil. Trans. Roy. Soc.' 1748). Cf. Thomas Young (1773–1829) 'Phil. Trans. Roy. Soc.' 1805 I p. 82: John Robison (1778–1843) 'System of Mechanical Philosophy' (ed. Brewster, 4 vols. Edinburgh, 1822) IV vol. 4 I. 258.

59, 34

See 'Goethe, die Schriften zur Naturwissenschaft' pt. I vol. 8 (ed. Kuhn, Weimar, 1962) pp. 328–330, 'Meteorologische Nachschrift'. This data for December 1822 was evidently collected by Heinrich Ludwig Friedrich *Schrön* (1799–1875), see his 'Meteorologische Jahrbücher' (Jena, 1822–1827), who succeeded J. F. Posselt (1794–1823) as director of the astronomical department at Jena. Goethe had encouraged his meteorological studies since about 1819, when he first arrived in Jena.

Goethe writes 'Tepl', not 'Töpel'. The place referred to is evidently the spa Teplitz, which is situated in the southern Erzgebirge, some twenty seven miles S.S.E. of Dresden.

60, 26

See Goethe (op. cit. pp. 321–322). These remarks were evidently written down in the summer of 1822, after Goethe had read 'The Climate of London'

(2 vols. London, 1818–1820) by Luke Howard (1772–1864). Schrön's observations seemed to Goethe to confirm the conclusions he had reached from reading this English work.

61, 8

‚Solche leere Vorstellungen sind das cheval de bataille der Reflexion'.

62, 28

Schelling 'System der gesammten Philosophie und der Naturphilosophie insbesondere' (Manuscript from 1804).

'§ 147 Der absoluten Cohäsion als Form des in=sich=selbst=Seyns entspricht als Form der Bewegung der Magnetismus. Oder: die absolute Cohäsion selbst, aktiv, lebendig angeschaut ist Magnetismus.'

See 'Schellings Werke' (ed. Schröter, Munich, 1962) supplementary volume no. 2 pp. 252–258.

63, 32

Friedrich Albrecht Karl Gren (1760–1798), see the note II. 267. Hegel is evidently referring to his 'Grundriss der Naturlehre' (4th ed. Halle, 1801).

In § 149 of this work, Gren discusses the cohesive properties of *uniform* (not necessarily homogeneous) bodies, and mentions the experiment with the glass plates cited here by Hegel, ‚Aus verschiedenen bisher angestellten Versuchen scheint das Gesetz zu folgen: daß die Stärke der Cohäsion bey verschiedenen Paaren von einerley Körpern, sowohl von gleichartigen als ungleichartigen, mit der Menge der Berührungspuncte im Verhältniß stehe.'

He adds (§ 150), that no law had yet been discovered for the cohesion of dissimilar bodies, ‚Es ist noch kein Gesetz bekannt, nach welchem sich die Größe der Kräfte des Zusammenhanges bey Körpern von ungleicher Art richtete'.

64, 17

Cf. §§ 265–266. When surfaces were considered merely with regard to adhesion and cohesion, no reference being made to *mass*, their properties were taken to be the result of certain *forces*. The English and French physicists of Hegel's day had no ready-made term for these phenomena, and spoke merely of the 'attraction' and 'repulsion' of a surface. In German, the term 'Flächenkraft' was widely used, and had a considerable literature centred around it: see G. F. Parrot (1767–1852) 'Entretiens sur la Physique' (6 vols. Dorpat, 1819–1824) vol. I p. 93 f.: K. W. G. Kastner (1783–1857) 'Grundriss der Experimentalphysik' (2nd ed. Heidelberg, 1820–1822), vol. I p. 76 f.: J. F. Fries (1773–1843) 'Mathematische Naturphilosophie' (Heidelberg, 1822) p. 450 f., 'Lehrbuch der Naturlehre' (Jena, 1826) vol. I 7.

Kastner and Fries postulated two forces (attraction and repulsion), and Fries attempted to treat the subject mainly as a matter of geometry. Cf. Gehler's 'Physikalisches Wörterbuch' vol. IV (Leipzig, 1827) pp. 350–353.

64, 27

Schelling 'Zeitschrift für spekulative Physik . . . Zweyter Band zweytes Heft' (Jena und Leipzig, 1801). This quotation is taken from Schelling's 'Darstellung meines Systems der Philosophie'. Hegel alters the punctuation of the passage slightly, and omits Schelling's references to §§ 56 and 58 of the same work.

Schelling is here summarizing a part of Steffens' 'Beiträge zur innern Naturgeschichte der Erde' (pt. I Freiberg, 1801), which was then about to be published.

65, 36

Michelet's version of these two sentences is shortened, and differs somewhat from the original, which is as follows, ‚Es ist zu bemerken, daß diese Momente nur einzelne Dimensionen sind, deren jeder Moment des realen Körpers als eines gestalteten ist. Luft, Wasser, Feuer sind das Gestaltlose oder die aufgehobene Gestalt, Körperlichkeit überhaupt, das einen Charakter überhaupt hat. Die Gestalt ist nicht ohne eine derselben, so wenig als die Masse ohne Weichheit, oder Schwere, oder Elastizität ist.' ('Jenenser Realphilosophie' II p. 47).

67, 19

See the note I. 320.

67, 24

In the 1827 edition of the 'Encyclopaedia', this paragraph began with the following sentence, '*Sound* is the *continued* changing of these determinations, the oscillation of the moments of elasticity.' Michelet noted the deletion of this sentence, but misplaced it: see the errata.

69, 10

At the beginning of the last century, this transition from *cohesion* to sound, rather than from *air* to sound, would not have been accepted without dispute. In making it, Hegel was evidently influenced by the work of E. F. F. Chladni (1756–1817): see 'Die Akustik' (Leipzig, 1802) p. 4, 'In most text-books of physics sound is treated in connection with the air, but this is a completely inept procedure, for other elastic bodies sound, and transmit the sound of alien bodies, quite as well as the air does, and many sound more readily than the air. It would therefore be more fitting if this part of natural science were treated as a matter of motion, and more precisely, if it were considered in connection with the oscillations of the pendulum, to which it is very closely related.'

69, 10

‚Der Klang', in § 300 Hegel deals with sound in general and with noise. In the terminology of his day these were known as 'der Schall' and 'das Geräusch'. In § 301 he deals with musical sounds, which were known as ‚der Klang'

Strictly speaking therefore, the correct heading for this section would be ‚ber Schall'. See the definitions of these terms given by Gustav Schilling (1805–1881) in 'Encyclopädie der gesammten musikalischen Wissenschaften, oder Universal-Lexicon der Tonkunst' (6 vols. Stuttgart, 1834–1838).

E. F. F. Chladni, in the preface to his 'Neue Beyträge zur Akustik' (Leipzig, 1817), mentions the trouble he had had with the French translator of his 'Die Akustik' (Leipzig, 1802) on account of there being only one word in French for ‚Schall', ‚Klang' and ‚Ton' (son), ‚Ein übrigens sehr einsichtsvoller Mann, den ich fragte, wie eine gewisse etwas verwickelte Idee wohl konnte ausgedrückt werden, wo aber das, was er mir vorschlug, immer nicht ganz das ausdrückte, was ich eigentlich sagen wollte, äußerte endlich: Notre diablesses de langue ne veut pas se prêter à l'expression de toutes les idées possible. Il faut même quelquefois sacrifier une idée aux caprices de la langue'. Cf. 'Traité d'Acoustique par E. F. F. Chladni' (Paris, 1809).

69, 19
‚Seelenhaftigkeit' cf. the note III. 318. 'I will not say, with Plato, the soul is an harmony, but harmonical, and hath its nearest sympathy unto musick.' Sir Thomas Browne (1605–1682) 'Religio Medici' (London, 1643) pt. II sect. ix.

70, 29
‚hiermit . . . haben die Instrumente ihren eigenthümlichen Klang und timbre'. E. F. F. Chladni, in his 'Neue Beyträge zur Akustik' (Leipzig, 1817) p. 58 notes that, ‚Einigen Ersatz hat die französische Sprache darin, daß man die qualitative Verschiedenheit des Klanges in Hinsicht auf die Würkung, wofür man im Deutschen keinen bestimmten Ausdruck hat durch das Wort timbre bezeichnen kann'. By the 1830's however, the German term ‚Klangfarbe' had come into use: see Gustav Schilling (1805–1881) 'Encyclopädie der gesammten musikalischen Wissenschaften' (6 vol. Stuttgart, 1834–1838) vol. VI p. 647.

71, 18
See Peter van Musschenbroek (1692–1761) 'Introductio ad philosophiam naturalem' (2 vols. Leyden, 1762) vol. II p. 2191. It was mainly this work which spread the idea that sound consists of a tremulation of minute particles, 'in motu tremulo partium minimarum'.

71, 19
‚Der natürliche Mensch': see I Corinthians ii 14, 'But the natural man receiveth not the things of the Spirit of God: for they are foolishness unto him: neither can he know them, because they are spiritually discerned'.

71, 32
At the beginning of the last century, nearly all German books and articles on sound (Schall) made this point. J. F. Pierer, in his 'Medizinisches Realwörterbuch'

vol. VII p. 193 (Altenburg, 1827) gives fifty three German words meaning much the same as 'noise'.

72, 4

Thomas Young (1773–1829) thought otherwise. See his 'A Course of Lectures on Natural Philosophy (2 vols. London, 1807) I p. 378, 'The origin of a simple sound, without any alteration, requires very little investigation: it appears that the only condition necessary for its production is a sufficient degree of velocity in the motion or impulse which occasions it'.

72, 20

‚Bei schlechten Instrumenten hört man so das Klappern das mechanische Anschlagen'.

‚Klappern', as applied to musical instruments, was at that time a purely technical term, and referred to the sounds produced by *key-board* instruments, in which there was a *scraping* of the keys, due to their being too close together, or a *knocking*, due to the fillets on which the keys rested, or which they struck when they were played, being inadequately covered with leather or cloth. See Gustav Schilling (1805–1881) 'Encyclopädie der gesammten musikalischen Wissenschaften' (6 vols. Stuttgart, 1834–1838) vol. IV p. 119.

72, 39

See the note III. 327.

73, 7

Ernst Florens Friedrich Chladni (1756–1827) was born at Wittenberg, where his father was professor of law. He tells us ('Die Akustik' p. xiv), that as a small child he was not allowed to leave his father's house, and that this awoke his interest in geography *books*, and his desire to travel.

At university he wanted to study medicine, but his father persuaded him to read law at Wittenberg, and he later took his doctorate in this subject at Leipzig. After his father's death, he felt free to follow his natural bent and study the natural sciences. At the age of nineteen he began to play the piano, and this led him on to the study of musical theory. His first important publication was 'Entdeckungen über die Theorie des Klanges' (Leipzig, 1787); see the note II. 285.

After making various attempts to improve upon the glass harmonica, he finally constructed a new instrument between June 2, 1789 and March 8, 1790, which he called a 'Euphon' ('Leipziger allgemeine musikalische Zeitung' 1821 p. 529, 1822 p. 805). During the 1790's he attempted to construct a key-board instrument having the qualities of wind and stringed instruments, and in 1799 finally succeeded in doing so ('Leipziger allgemeine musikalische Zeitung' 1824 p. 825). He called this second invention a 'Clavicylinder'.

These instruments and a number of articles on musical theory ('Neue Schr. der Gesellsch. Naturf. Freunde zu Berlin' vol. I pp. 102, 125, vol. II p. 274, 'Acta Acad. Moguntinae' 1794-5 no. 5), had made him known by the turn of the century, but it was his 'Die Akustik' (Leipzig, 1802), the book quoted here by Hegel, which brought him fame. In this book, he gave accounts of many novel experiments, and presented a survey of the phenomena of sound which, together with the supplementary 'Neue Beyträge zur Akustik' (Leipzig, 1817), remained the standard work on the subject until well after Hegel's death: see 'Gehler's Physikalisches Wörterbuch' vol. VIII pp. 178-505 (Leipzig, 1836).

In 1808 Chladni visited Paris, and was well received by Laplace and Berthollet etc., who arranged for an interview with Napoleon. This meeting lasted for almost two hours, during which Chladni gave an account of his discoveries. The main result of the interview was that the Emperor made a grant of 6000 francs towards the translation of Chladni's main work into French ('Traité d'Acoustique' Paris, 1809).

In the spring of 1810 Chladni left Paris for Switzerland and Italy, and finally returned to Wittenberg in the summer of 1812. In the winter of 1815-1816 he lectured on acoustics and meteors at Berlin (see the note III. 245). He died at Breslau in 1827, just as the hall of the Berlin Singing Academy, which he had designed, was being completed. On account of the excellence of its acoustics, this hall was in great demand for broadcasting and gramophone recordings until only twenty years ago. It was destroyed by bombing in 1944.

V. Kohlschütter 'E. F. F. Chladni', in R. L. C. Virchow's and F. von Holtzendorff-Vietmansdorf's 'Sammlung gemeinverständlicher wissenschaftlicher Vorträge' New Series, pamphlet 261 (Berlin, 1897).

73, 9
'Die Akustik' (Leipzig, 1802) pp. 107-108. As part of his investigation of longitudinal vibrations, Chladni cut the following substances into two foot rods, the thickness of which he found to be a matter of indifference, and elicited the following notes:—

Whalebone, approximately	A
English tin	B
Fine silver (15 löthig)	D an octave higher
Nutwood, Yew	F
Brass, Oak, Plumwood	F♯
Clay pipe shanks (Cologne pipes)	E–G
Copper almost	G
Pearwood, Red beech, Maple	A♭–A
Mahogany, almost	B♭
Ebony, Beech, Elm, Alder, Birch	B♭
Lime, almost	B

Cherry	B
Willow, Pine	C two octaves higher
Glass, Iron, approximately	C$\sharp$
Deal, a little higher than	C$\sharp$

Chladni suggested that these differences in pitch and tone might be due to the various degrees of brittleness and specific weight.

Hegel probably referred to this table in the French version of it given by J. B. Biot in his 'Traité de Physique' (Paris, 1816) vol. iv p. 85. He misquotes Chladni on the note given by glass, and refers to his ‚Thönerne Tobakspfeifenstiele' as ‚Kölnische Pfeiffen'. See M. H. Klaproth and F. Wolff 'Chemisches Wörterbuch' vol. v p. 167 (Berlin, 1810), 'A clay suitable for the making of pipes is found in the former archbishopric of Cologne and in the Liège area. It is transported from these areas and worked in Holland.'

73, 13

Johann Wilhelm Ritter (1776–1810), see the note II. 270. These experiments were probably inspired by the teaching of Franz Joseph Gall (1758–1828), see the note II. 430. Most of Ritter's published writings are sober works concerned with *galvanism*; see 'Galvanismus' Weimar, 1798) 'Beyträge zur . . . Galvanismus' (4 vols. Jena, 1800–1805); 'Das Electrische System der Körper' (Leipzig, 1805). His collected papers 'Physische-Chemische Abhandlungen' (3 vols. Leipzig 1806) show no signs of flippancy or eccentricity. The 'Fragmente aus dem Nachlasse eines jungen Physikers' (2 vols. Heidelberg, 1810) contains a delightful collection of fantastic speculations, observations and experiments however. As it also contains a considerable amount of material relating to sound (I pp. 221–8, II pp. 225–269), and there is also evidence that Hegel had read the book (see the note II. 297), the attribution of these experiments to Ritter was not entirely unwarranted. I have discovered no direct evidence of his having performed them however.

Georg Heinrich Ritter (1765–1823), who studied at Göttingen, Würzburg, Vienna and Strassburg, was court physician and spa doctor at Wiesbaden for some years, and put forth works on the cultivation of vines and domestic animals, as well as a number of ordinary medical treatises, published 'Cranologie und Cranoskopie, nach Englischen Schriften' in 'Ausländische medicinische Litteratur' (Berlin, 1823) vol. XIII p. 460. It is unlikely however that Hegel had this article in mind.

See A. C. P. Callisen 'Medicinisches Schriftsteller-Lexicon' (33 vols. Copenhagen and Altona, 1830–1845) vol. XVI pp. 154–160, vol. XXXI pp. 474–479.

73, 20

Jean Baptiste Biot (1774–1862), the French physicist. At the age of only twenty three, he was appointed professor of mathematics at Beauvais. In 1800 he became professor of physics at the Collège de France, and only three years later, he was elected member of the Academy of Sciences. In 1856 he was elected member of the French Academy. He was an extremely prolific writer, and his researches extended to almost every branch of physical science.

Hegel is here quoting his 'Traité de Physique expérimentale et mathématique' (4 vols. Paris, 1816) vol. II p. 4, 'Enfin le son se transmet aussi à travers les corps solides. Le mineur, en creusant sa galetie, entend les coups du mineur qu'on lui oppose, et juge ainsi de sa direction. Si l'on se place à l'une des extrémités d'une longue file de tuyaux métalliques, comme on peut le faire dans les aquéducs, on entend très-distinctement les coups de marteau frappés à l'autre extrémité, et même on entend ainsi distinctement deux sons, l'un plus rapide, transmis par le métal, l'autre plus lent, transmis par l'air.'

73, 25

Hegel is underestimating these distances. The cannonade at Mainz in 1792 was heard very clearly near Einbeck, 165 miles away. In 1809, the cannonading of Heligoland was heard near Hanover, 175 miles away. On December 4, 1832, during the siege of Antwerp, the French artillery was heard in the Saxon Erzgebirge, 400 miles away (see the contemporary 'Leipziger Zeitung'). Cf. Thomson's 'Annals of Philosophy' Jan. 1816 p. 3.

73, 29

See the note II. 282.

74, 12

J. W. Ritter (1776–1810) uses this phenomenon to illustrate the transition from sound to heat, see 'Fragmente' (2 vols. Heidelberg, 1810) vol. II p. 252, ‚Die schwingende Saite z.B. wird in den Lagen: ⌒ und: ⌣ wärmer seyn, als in der Lage: —'.

74, 20

See Chladni's 'Entdeckungen über die Theorie des Klanges' (Leipzig, 1787), 'Die Akustik' (Leipzig, 1802), and 'Neue Beyträge zur Akustik' (Leipzig, 1817). All these books contain illustrations of the famous 'figures'.

Chladni discovered that thin metal plates may be used to *illustrate* regions of vibration and rest. As his experiment is usually performed, the plate is screwed to the top of a firm upright post, the plate being horizontal, and the screw in the middle of it. White sand is then scattered over its surface. The plate is then *bowed* at the edge, and thrown into vibration between nodal lines or curves. The sand is thrown from the moving parts or ventral segments into these lines, so forming the 'figures'. It soon becomes apparent that, as in the case of a musical *string*, the pitch of the note given is higher in accordance with the greater number of ventral segments into which the plate is divided. Historically, the main importance of Chladni's discovery was the impetus which it gave to research into the nature of elasticity: see R. J. Hauy's researches into the laws of vibrating surfaces ('Journal de Physique' vol. 88 p. 125); M. Faraday's article in 'Phil. Trans. Roy. Soc.' 1831 p. 299; F. Savart in 'Annales de Chimie et Physique' vol. 36 p. 187 and vol. 40 pp. 1 and 113.

74, 28

See the note II. 294.

75, 12

Hegel is here referring to the *monochord*.

75, 22

See Leonhard Euler (1707–1783) 'Tentamen novae theoriae musices' (St. Petersburg, 1739); Daniel Bernoulli (1700–1782) in 'Mémoires de l'Academie' 1762 p. 467; E. F. F. Chladni 'Die Akustik' (Leipzig, 1802) pp. 26–37; P. Dulong (1785–1838) in 'Annales de Chimie et Physique' vol. 41 p. 113. These writers also deal with the vibrations of the air in pipes. Their work prepared the way for the 'Théorie analytique de la chaleur' (Paris, 1822) of J. B. J. Fourier (1768–1830).

75, 29

Pythagoras is said to have discovered the significance of the harmonic proportion 12:8:6, in which 12:6 is the octave, 12:8 the fifth and 8:6 the fourth: see Plato's 'Timaeus' 36a (ed. Archer-Hind, London, 1888 pp. 107–111). The stories that have come down to us about his having observed the harmonic intervals in a smithy, and then weighed the hammers that produced them etc. are absurd, and were recognized as such in Hegel's day: see Charles Burney (1726–1814) 'A General History of Music' (4 vols. London, 1776–1789), E. F. F. Chladni 'Die Akustik' (Leipzig, 1802) p. 102, M. C. P. Schmidt 'Kulturhistorische Beiträge zur Kenntniss des griechischen und römischen-Altertums' (Leipzig, 1906–12) vol. I p. 78 f. As genuine popular tales however, they bear witness to the existence of a real tradition, in which Pythagoras was regarded as the author of this momentous discovery. It is clear that the early Pythagoreans studied proportion, and it is by no means unlikely that Pythagoras himself discovered these intervals: see E. Zeller 'Die Philosophie der Griechen' (7th ed. Leipzig, 1923) vol. I pp. 507–510.

Cf. C. E. Ruelle 'Collection des auteurs grecs relatifs à la musique' (Paris, 1870).

75, 30

The frequency with which Hegel refers to the *soul-like* nature of harmony in these paragraphs, and this reference to *symmetry*, seem to indicate that he had read the fascinating effusions published by Johann Friedrich Hugo Dalberg (1752–1812) in his 'Fantasien aus dem Reiche der Töne' (Erfurt, 1806). Verbal descriptions of the 'feelings and passions' aroused by 'harmony and melody' are very rarely successful, but Dalberg's book contains some fine passages. ‚Ordnung, Symmetrie, Uebereinſtimmung iſt die Seele des Geiſtes, ift das, wobei er das reinfte Vergnügen empfindet' (p. 37). ‚Die Seele ift ein Ton, der fich immer reiner ftimmen foll; jeder Ton hat etwas vom Grundton in fich, je mehr er fich diefem nähert, je reiner und geiftiger wird er. Die Seele muß erft ihre Laufbahn durchwandern, wie der Ton des Monochords die Octav, eh fie zur Vollendung gelangt. Darum hat fie einen doppelten Trieb zur Thätigkeit und Ruhe, zur Trägheit und Bewegung, beide ihr wefentlich nöthig'.

76, 14

‚darum ift die Quarte auch ein frifcherer Ton'. See Gustav Schilling (1805-1881) 'Encyclopädie der gesammten musikalischen Wissenschaften' (6 vols. Stuttgart, 1834–1838) vol. V pp. 586–590.

76, 22

See the article by J. G. Voigt of Halle in F. A. C. Gren's 'Neues Journal der Physik' (Leipzig, 1796) vol. II pp. 352–357, 'Einige Bemerkungen über die Schwingungsknoten bey klingenden Saiten'.

‚Man theile AB die Saite des Monochords in irgend eine Anzahl gleicher Theile, z.B. in 4 durch die Punkte C, D, E, und ftelle den beweglichen Steg in E.

C D E

A·———·—·———·B

Man lege in die Punkte C, D, und einige andere der Saite, wo man will leichte Körnchen, z.B. Papierftückchen. Nun ftreiche man mittelft einem mit Colo= phonium beftrichenen Violinbogen, den Theil E A an, fo wird der Ton gehört, der dem Theile E A korrefpondiert und fich zum Grundtone der Saite A B verhält, wie 4:1, und alle Papierftückchen, ausgenommen die in den Punkten C und D lagen, werden durch die Erfchütterung der Saite herunter geworfen. Die beiden Punkte C und D heißen Schwingungsknoten'. Voigt describes four other simple experiments of this kind.

76, 31

This is discussed at length in Hegel's 'Lectures on the History of Philosophy' (tr. Haldane, 3 vols. London, 1963) vol. I pp. 194–239.

The Pythagoreans swore by the τετρακτύς or tetrad which consists of the first four integers ($1+2+3+4=10$) represented by pebbles or dots arranged in an *equilateral triangle*. For them, this figure symbolized the 'elements of number', which they thought to be the elements of all things. They regarded it as containing the concordant ratios of musical harmony, and by some of them (e.g. Iamblichus), it was taken to be identical with cosmic harmony. In the Pythagorean oath it was described as, 'containing the root and fountain of everflowing Nature,' See Aristotle 'Metaphysica' (Oxford, 1924) vol. I pp. 145–150: F. M. Cornford 'Mysticism and Science in the Pythagorean Tradition' ('The Classical Quarterly' 1923 pp. 1–12, 1924 pp. 137–150).

In the second sentence Hegel seems to have in mind the following passages in Aristotle's 'Metaphysics' (986a 15), '(The Pythagoreans) say that the elements of number are the even and the odd, the latter limited, the former unlimited, and that unity is made up of both even and odd, that numbers come from unity and, to repeat, that the whole heaven is numbers,' Cf. the Pythagorean definitions given by Aristoxenus in H. Diels 'Die Fragmente der Vorsokratiker' (2 vols. Berlin, 1906) vol. I p. 270. Plutarch gives a fuller explanation of these doctrines in 'The E at Delphi' 388 ('Moralia' tr. Babbitt V pp. 217–222, Loeb, 1936). Cf. J. E. Raven 'Pythagoreans and Eleatics' (Cambridge, 1948) ch. X.

W. A. Heidel is of the opinion that this subsumption of the even under the indefinite, the odd under the finite, marks the meeting of the ethico-religious and the mathematico-scientific streams of interest in Pythagoreanism ('Archiv für Geschichte der Philosophie' vol. XIV p. 390).

76, 38

See Alexander Malcolm 'A treatise of musick, speculative, practical and historical' (Edinburgh, 1721, corrected ed. London, 1779); J. N. Forkel (1749–1818) 'Allgemeine Geschichte der Musik' (Leipzig, 1801); Fr. von Drieberg 'Die mathematische Intervallehre der Griechen' (Berlin, 1819); Thomas Busby (1755–1838) 'A General History of Music, from the earliest times to the present' (2 vols. London, 1819, Germ. tr. C. F. Michaelis, 2 vols. Leipzig, 1821–1822); C. E. Ruelle 'Collection des auteurs grecs relatifs à la musique' (Paris, 1870).

77, 13

This was a much debated point at that time. For later views on the subject see K. W. J. H. Riemann (1849–1919) 'Geschichte der Musiktheorie' (Leipzig, 1898).

Johann Ulrich Sponsel (1721–1782), in his 'Orgelhistorie' (Nuremberg, 1771 ed. Smets, Cassel 1931), pointed out that organs did not assume their 'modern' form until the pedal was invented at the end of the fifteenth century, and that instruments comparable with those used by J. S. Bach were not built before 1600. Genesis IV 21 and Psalm CL 4 had given rise to claims of immense antiquity for the instrument, and it was generally assumed that these original organs had spread throughout Europe after the Greek Emperor Constantine V had presented one to Pippin III in 756: see Archibald Bower (1686–1766) 'History of the Popes' (7 vols. London, 1748–1766) vol. V § 158 p. 248. Sponsel disputed these claims, but to little purpose. Cf. 'Journal zur Kunstgeschichte' vol. V p. 121 1777.

Johann Friedrich Hugo Dalberg (1752–1812) in his 'Untersuchungen über den Ursprung der Harmonie und ihre allmählige Ausbildung' (Erfurt, 1800) shows some knowledge of Old Scottish, Chinese, Greek, Assyrian, Arabic,

Egyptian and Indian music, and comes to the conclusion that, 'Temperament has no foundation in *nature*, but is a product of *art* and of need, and of the limited capabilities of our instruments'. (p. ix). On pages 47–48 of this work he suggests that, 'Of all the instruments, it is the organ, and next to the organ the piano, which has contributed most to the perfection of harmony'.

Cf. G. U. A. Vieth (1763–1836) 'Anfangsgründe der Mathematik' (Leipzig, 1824) pt. II sect. i p. 451. Musical theorists were aware of the possibility of *enharmonic* music at this time: J. N. Forkel (1749–1818) 'Allgemeine Geschichte der Musik' (2 vols. Leipzig, 1788–1801). Cf. the account of Indian music, with its 25 note scale in 'Asiatick Researches' vol. IX no. 9. J. D. Berlin (1711–1787), in his 'Anleitung zur Tonometrie' (Copenhagen and Leipzig, 1767) suggested a 36 note scale, and even in the seventeenth century, A. Kircher (1601–1680), in his 'Musurgia universalis' (2 vols. Rome, 1650) drew attention to the importance of the enharmonic techniques employed by Galeazzo Sabbatini (1597–1662): see for example Sabbatini's motet 'Derelinquat impius viam suam'.

78, 6

In the scale of C, given by Hegel on p. 76, the frequency ratios and successive frequency ratios are as follows:

Note	C	D	E	F	G	A	B	C
Freq. ratio	1	$\frac{9}{8}$	$\frac{5}{4}$	$\frac{4}{3}$	$\frac{3}{2}$	$\frac{5}{3}$	$\frac{15}{2}$	2
Succ. freq. ratio		$\frac{9}{8}$	$\frac{10}{9}$	$\frac{16}{15}$	$\frac{9}{8}$	$\frac{10}{9}$	$\frac{9}{8}$	$\frac{16}{15}$

Starting from C, the subsequent frequency ratios required for the diatonic scale of G for example, may be easily discovered by writing down the eight notes from G to g in the key of C, together with their frequency ratios to C, and the frequency ratios required for the new scale:

Note on scale of C	G	A	B	c	d	e	f	g
Freq. ratio with C=1	$\frac{3}{2}$	$\frac{5}{3}$	$\frac{15}{8}$	2	$\frac{9}{4}$	$\frac{5}{2}$	$\frac{8}{3}$	3
Freq. ratio of diat. scale with G=1		$\frac{9}{8}$	$\frac{5}{4}$	$\frac{4}{3}$	$\frac{3}{2}$	$\frac{5}{3}$	$\frac{15}{8}$	2
Freq. ratio with C=1, G=$\frac{3}{2}$	$\frac{3}{2}$	$\frac{27}{16}$	$\frac{15}{8}$	2	$\frac{9}{4}$	$\frac{5}{2}$	$\frac{45}{16}$	3

It will be apparent from this, that six of the eight notes on the scale of G *coincide* with those on the scale of C. Instead of A=$\frac{5}{3}$ however, we now have A=$\frac{27}{16}$, and instead of f=$\frac{8}{3}$, we now have f=$\frac{45}{16}$. The interval between $\frac{5}{3}$ and $\frac{27}{16}$ is $\frac{27}{16} \div \frac{5}{3}$, i.e. $\frac{81}{80}$. This is the 'comma' mentioned by Hegel, and it is so small, that on an instrument, the same note will serve for both keys.

In the case of f however, the interval between $\frac{8}{3}$ and $\frac{45}{16}$ is $\frac{45}{16} \div \frac{8}{3}$, i.e. $\frac{135}{128}$. This is quite *perceptible*, and on the piano therefore, a *separate string* has to be provided above f, i.e. f sharp. Taking the successive key-notes D, A, E, B, one finds that besides these 'commas', each scale introduces a *new sharp*. This is the origin of the five sharps C, D, F, G, A, which, as Hegel observes, are very closely represented by the *black notes* of the pianoforte.

78, 40

The first effective diatonic chromatic harp was devised by Fray Juan Bermudo (c. 1510–1560): see his 'Comiença el libro llamado declaración de instrumentos musicales' (Ossuna, 1555). During the seventeenth century, double and triple harps were devised, and the Welsh triple harp, for example, was still in use at the beginning of this century: see E. Roberts 'Instruction for Welsh harp' (1904); H. J. Zingel's article in 'Die Musik in Geschichte und Gegenwart' vol. V pp. 1507–1563 (Cassel and Basel, 1956).

These double and triple forms were clumsy however, and the first effective attempt to build a completely harmonic harp was made in the Tyrol towards the end of the seventeenth century, when *hooks* were screwed into the neck of the instrument. These appendages could be turned down to fix the desired semitone at pleasure, so that it was no longer necessary for the player to shorten the strings with his fingers: see Nauwerk 'Die Hakenharfe' ('Allgemeine musikalische Zeitung' Leipzig, 1815 p. 545).

Georg Hochbrucker (c. 1670–1763) of Donauwörth in Bavaria made the next important improvement, by inventing the *pedal* harp. There were five pedals to his instrument, which enabled the player to govern the stopping with his *feet*, and to play in no less than eight major scales. This instrument was so common in Germany at the beginning of the last century, that it was known as the 'German harp'.

Pierre Joseph Cousineau (c. 1753–1824) and François Joseph Dizi (1780–1835) effected further improvements in Hochbrucker's design, but the harp which Hegel has in mind here is almost certainly the famous 'double movement' instrument produced by Sébastien Erard (1752–1831) in 1810. This instrument was first built at Erard's London workshop in Great Marlborough Street. It was so successful, that between 1810 and 1811 he is said to have sold harps of this kind to the value of £25,000, and his design has never been substantially improved upon. See Pierre Erard (1796–1855) 'The Harp in its present improved state compared with the original pedal Harp' (London, 1821): W. H. Grattan Flood 'The Story of the Harp' (London, 1905).

79, 8

Vincenzo Galilei (c. 1520–1591) was the first to use the modern method of adjusting the intervals of the scale in order to make the notes available in different keys. By taking the tone to be related to the semitone as 18 to 17, he was able to put forward a flexible method of chromatic tuning which came very close to that employed today (99:100). See his 'Dialogo della musica antica et della moderna' (Florence, 1581); cf. O. Strunk 'Source Readings in Music History' (New York, 1950).

In Hegel's day, the predominant *temperament* was that suggested by J. P. Kirnberger (1721–1783) in his 'Die Kunst des reinen Satzes in der Musik' (Berlin, 1771), cf. G. L. T. 'Gedanken über die Temperatur Herrn Kirnbergers' (Berlin, 1775).

79, 23

Joseph Sauveur (1653–1716) was for some years thought to have been the first to discover these *overtones*: see his article in 'Mémoires de l'Academie de Paris' 1701. However, John Wallis (1616–1703), in 'Phil. Trans. Roy. Soc.' 1677 p. 839, and in his 'Treatise of algebra, both historical and practical' (3 pts. London 1684–1685) vol. II p. 466, mentions their having been discovered at *Oxford*, by William Noble (d. 1681) fellow of Merton, and Thomas Pigot (d. 1686) fellow of Wadham, who communicated their discovery to Narcissus Marsh (1638–1713) as early as 1676. See Anthony Wood (1632–1695) 'Athenae Oxonienses' (Oxford, 1721); C. G. Jöcher 'Allgemeines Gelehrten–Lexicon' (4 vols. Leipzig, 1750–1751); Sir John Hawkins (1719–1789) 'History of Music' (5 vols. London, 1776) vol. III p. 134; Matthew Young (1750–1800) 'Enquiry into the principal phaenomena of sounds and musical strings' (Dublin, 1784) pt. II sect. v.

These tones are caused by vibrations not occurring in their simplest forms; when a string vibrates for example, *distinct* vibrations are also set up in the separate parts of it.

80, 14

Giuseppe Tartini (1692–1770), the Italian violinist, composer and musical theorist. After his clandestine marriage with the niece of the archbishop of Padua, he spent some time in a monastry at Assisi, and it was there that he learnt the rudiments of musical theory from the organist, Padre Boemo.

In 1721 he was appointed solo violinist at the church of San Antonio in Padua. Two years later he was called to Prague for the coronation of the Emperor Charles VI, and stayed in the city for a further two years as conductor of Count Kinsky's private band. In 1728 he founded a school for violin in Padua, and subsequently taught, played and conducted at Rome and Bologna. His fame as a violinist was so great, that although Lord Middlesex offered him £3,000 p.a. in 1744, he was unable to entice him to London.

Tartini's main work on the theory of music is his 'Trattato di musica secondo la vera scienza dell' armonia' (Padua, 1754). The *combination* tones mentioned here by Hegel are discussed in the first part of this book, in which Tartini attempts to expound the *physical basis* of harmony. The second and third parts of the treatise include mathematical calculations and geometrical demonstrations by means of which Tartini attempts to prove the *harmonic* nature of the *circle*, and to derive from it the major and minor tonal systems, diatonic and chromatic dissonances, and even an enharmonic scale. The last two parts of the work are concerned with the derivation of the diatonic scale, and a discussion of the intervals found in the music of the time.

The 'Trattato' is a long and complicated work, but Tartini also published what is in fact a summary of its main arguments: see 'De principj dell'armonia musicale contenuta nel diatonia genere' (Padua, 1767). Jean Adam Serre (1704–1788) criticised these arguments in his 'Observations sur les principes de l'harmonie' (Geneva, 1763, Germ. tr. Leipzig, 1767). Cf. E. R. Jacobi 'Jean-Adam Serre. Ein vergessener Schweizer Musiktheoretiker' ('Schweizerische Musikzeitung' vol. 98 p. 145 ff. 1958). Tartini replied in 'Risposta di Giuseppe Tartini alla critica del di lui Trattato di musica di Monsieur le Serre di Genevra' (Venice, 1767).

Most English translations of Tartini's works are hard to come by, but there are several in existence: see 'Principles and power of harmony' (tr. Stillingfleet, London, 1771); 'A letter from the late Signor Tartini' (tr. Burney, London, 1771); 'A Treatise on the ornaments of music' (tr. Babitz in 'Journal of Research in Music Education' IV 1956 pp. 75–102).

See also: A. Rubeli 'Das mathematische System Giuseppe Tartinis' (Winterthur, 1958): A. E. Planchart 'A study of the theories of Giuseppe Tartini' ('Journal of Music Theory' vol. IV no. 1 pp. 32–61, Yale, 1960): Dale Jorgensen 'A Résumé of Harmonic Dualism' ('Music and Letters' vol. 44 no. 1 pp. 31–42, Oxford, 1963). This last article is also interesting on account of its making mention of *Hegel*, and of Goethe's theory of music.

80, 27

Jean Baptiste Biot's 'Traité de Physique expérimentale et mathématique' (4 vols. Paris, 1816) vol. II pp. 47–48 is the source of the explanation of combination tones given here by Hegel, 'Supposons, par exemple, que l'on fasse résonner à la fois, par deux cordes placées près l'une de l'autre, les deux sons ut$_2$ et sol$_2$ d'une même octave. Les nombres des vibrations de ces sons dans un même temps sont 2 et 3; il y aura donc des époques où elles arriveront ensemble à l'oreille, et d'autres ou elles y arriveront séparées. Pour les distinguer, représentons les instans qui répondent aux milieux des vibrations, par des points également espacés sur une même ligne:

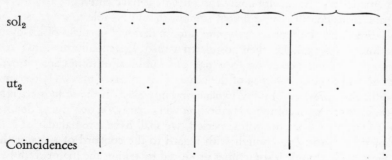

Les époques des coincidences sont évidentes; les intervalles qui les séparent sont doubles de ceux qui séparent les vibrations de ut$_2$. L'oreille sera donc affectée par leur retour périodique, comme elle le serait par un son ut, plus grave d'une octave que ut$_2$. C'est en effet ce qui arrive, et la découverte de ce beau phénomène est attribuée au célèbre musicien Tartini'.

Cf. D. C. Miller 'The Science of Musical Sounds' (New York, 1926).

80, 35

Tartini, in his 'Trattato di musica' (Padua, 1754) says that he first observed these tones in 1714. The first to *publish* an account of them was Georg Andreas Sorge (1703–1778) however, see his 'Anweisung zur Stimmung der Orgel-werke und des Claviers' (Hamburg, 1744) p. 40, and his 'Vorgemach der musikalischen Composition' (3 pts. Lobenstein, 1745–7) ch. V §§ 4–5. Sorge does not treat them as a *discovery* however. As A. Kircher (1601–1680) in his exhaustive 'Phonurgia Nova' (Kempten, 1673) makes no mention of them, it seems likely that they first became generally known early in the eighteenth century.

Robert Smith (1689–1768), in his 'Harmonics, or the Philosophy of Musical Sounds' (Cambridge, 1749) p. 105 explained these tones from the hypothesis that *different* particles of air move through space in different directions, 'Different particles of the air at the ear will keep moving constantly opposite ways at the same time. And in so rare a fluid as air is, where the intervals of the particles are eight or nine times greater than their diameters, there seems to be room enough for such opposite motions without impediment: especially as we see the like motions are really performed in water.' Matthew Young (1750–1800) referred to them as 'grave harmonic tones', and attempted to explain them in pt. II sect. vi of his 'Enquiry into the principal phaenomena of sounds and musical strings' (Dublin, 1784). On the continent, J. L. Lagrange (1736–1813) dealt with them in 'Recherches sur la propagation du son', a paper published in 'Miscellanea philosophico-mathematica Societas Privata Taurinensis' vol. I § 64 (Turin, 1759). In a paper read to the Royal Society on January 16, 1800 ('Phil. Trans.' 1800 pt. I pp. 106–150), Thomas Young (1773–1829) criticised an essential part of Smith's explanation of the tones, 'It is surprising that so great a mathematician as Dr. Smith could for a moment have entertained an idea, that the vibrations constituting different sounds, should be able to cross each other in all directions, without affecting the same individual particles of air by their joint forces' (p. 130). He then postulated a theory essentially the same as that accepted by Hegel, according to which the combination tones are formed by what he called the coalescence of the beats of the primary tones. He recognized the difficulties presented by this explanation however, 'If the sounds are related as 7:8, or as 5:7, each compound vibration will occupy $\frac{2}{15}$, or $\frac{2}{12}$; and deducting 5 or 4 vibrations from the whole period, we shall have a remainder of $\frac{1}{3}$. This explanation is satisfying enough with regard to the concord of a major third; but the same harmonic is sometimes produced by taking the major sixth below the key note: in this case it might be supposed that the superior octave, which usually accompanies every sound as a secondary note, supplies the place of the major third, but I have found that the experiment succeeds even with stopped pipes, which produce no octaves as harmonics. We must therefore necessarily suppose that in this case, if not in the former, the sound in question is simply produced as a grave harmonic, by the combination of some of the acute harmonics, which always accompany the primitive notes.' Young reprinted this paper in 'A Course of Lectures on Natural Philosophy' (2 vols. London, 1807) vol. II pp. 531–554. It is apparent from this work that his belief in the existence of an analogy between the structure of *light* and sound led him to interpret combination tones in this way (cf. the note II. 234).

When Hegel goes on to say that, 'in the consideration of harmony one should not confine oneself solely to hearing' etc., he is evidently referring to Young's controversy with John Gough (1757–1825) of Middleshaw near Kendal. Gough first questioned Young's theory in 'The Theory of Compound Sounds' a paper published in the 'Memoirs of the Literary and Philosophical Society of Manchester' vol. V pt. ii pp. 653–665 (1802), and the subsequent controversy may be followed in 'Nicholson's Journal' of 1802/3 (see vol. II pp. 264–7, vol. III pp. 39–41 etc.). Gough's main point is that the tones are the result not of an *objective coalescence* which may be calculated mathematically, but of *mixtures* of sounds apprehended *subjectively*. 'I profess to maintain compound sounds to be mixtures of elementary sounds, not aggregates by coalescence . . . Now I know, by observation, that when an extensive surface is made to vibrate it sounds to a great distance; for when the shear-men of Kendal beat the tenters on a calm morning, the strokes may be heard for two miles, or more; though the ear of a by-stander is not much affected by them, the operation being performed by striking the stretched cloth with a stick not thicker than a man's finger. Seeing then a number of sounds which are nearly in unison, forms an aggregate of more power than any one of its constituents, it follows, that when a multiplicity of instruments contains a strong combination of unisons, that combination determines the range of the concert.' (Op. cit. vol. III p. 41 August 19, 1802.)

Hegel probably knew of this controversy from the excellent account of it published by G. U. A. Vieth (1763–1836) in 'Gilbert's Annalen der Physik' vol. XXI pp. 265–314 (1805). Until the middle of the 1820's the explanation of the tones given by Biot and accepted by Hegel was generally regarded as the correct one. In 1826 however, J. Purkynje (1787–1869) published an article in 'Kastner's Archiv' (sect. I p. 39) reviving the theory that they may be purely subjective phenomena. This view was generally rejected at the time, but it was later given careful consideration by Hermann von Helmholtz (1821–1894) in 'Die Lehre von den Tonempfindungen' (Braunschweig, 1863, Eng. tr. Ellis, London, 1875) app. xii; cf. J. W. S. Rayleigh (1842–1919) 'Theory of Sound' (2nd ed. 2 vols. London, 1894–6) § 386. A. F. A. Blein (1767–1845) revived one of the problems mentioned by Young in 1800 by giving accounts of a series of combination tones which could not be readily explained from the generally accepted hypothesis; see 'Exposé de quelques principes nouveaux sur l'acoustique' (Paris, 1827).

80, 40

Georg Joseph Vogler (1749–1814) is generally known to English readers on account of Browning's poem, with its fine characterization of the master extemporizing upon 'this instrument of his invention'.

Vogler, whose father was a violin maker, was born at Pleichach near Würzburg, and was educated by the Jesuits. Like J. C. Bach and W. A. Mozart, he studied the history and theory of music under Giovanni Battista Martini (1706–1784) at Bologna, but was dissatisfied with his teacher. In 1773 he was ordained priest in Rome, made a knight of the Golden Spur, and appointed protonotary and chamberlain to the Pope. It was on account of these appointments that he was later known as 'Abbot' (Abt) Vogler.

In 1775 he was appointed court chaplain and deputy director of music to the Elector Palatine, and soon made himself known as an eccentric but extremely effective teacher. In his 'Tonwissenschaft und Tonsetzkunst' (Mannheim, 1776), he put forward a new system of musical theory. He also invented a new system of fingering for the harpsichord, which gave rise to a considerable controversy, and which was condemned as 'miserable' by no less a person than Mozart.

Soon after the elector's court moved to Munich in 1780, Vogler left for Paris, where his organ concerts in the church of St. Sulpice attracted considerable attention. He subsequently held appointments at Stockholm and Darmstadt. Gänsbacher, Weber and Meyerbeer were among his pupils, and their affection for their old master was unbounded. Until he settled down in Darmstadt in 1807, he travelled widely and continuously, and visited Spain, Greece, Armenia and even Greenland, in search of uncorrupted forms of national melody. From 1786 until 1789 he was working in St. Petersburg and Stockholm on the construction of his 'orchestrion', the instrument mentioned here by Hegel. Once it was finished, he toured Europe with it, and in 1790 performed upon it with great effect at the Pantheon in London.

The orchestrion was built into a case having a capacity of only nine cubic feet. It had four manuals, each consisting of sixty three notes, and thirty nine pedal notes. By a system of shutters, Vogler acquired a forte and piano for each separate pipe, so that the instrument had the same *volume* range as a great organ. By making use of Tartini's discovery of combination tones, Vogler also gave his instrument the same *range of notes* as a great organ, while dispensing with the larger pipes. Tartini had discovered for example, that if the fundamental tone of a triad is played together with its fifth, the octave below this fundamental tone is heard. Vogler assumed therefore, that if a pipe of sixteen feet is combined with that of its fifth (i.e. ten feet eight inches), the note produced by

the great thirty two feet pipe would be heard; he discovered that this note is produced from the fundamental tone, the major third and the perfect fifth.
This discovery was soon utilized, and led to a general *simplification* of organ
building.

Vogler supervised the building of simplified organs in the St. Peterskirche
and the Michaelshofkirche at Munich and elsewhere, but although he was
able to handle these instruments with astonishing virtuosity and effect, they
were found by others (including Mendelssohn) to be unplayable, and were
subsequently rebuilt.

For the state of German organ-building at the time of Hegel's death, see
Gottlob Töpfer 'Die Orgelbau-Kunst' (Weimar, 1833). On Vogler's organ-
building see: E. Rupp 'Abbé Vogler als Mensch, Musiker und Orgelbauthe-
oretiker' (Augsburg, 1922); H. Spies 'Abt Vogler und die von ihm 1805
simplifizierte Orgel von St. Peter in Salzburg' (Mainz, 1932); H. Schweiger
'Abbé Vogler's Simplifikationssystem' (Kirchenmusikalisches Jahrbuch, vol. 29,
1934, pp. 72–123); H. J. Moser 'Orgelromantik' (Ludwigsburg, 1961).

81, 26

‚fo ift das Erhalten feiner felbft nur die Eine Saite'. ‚Saite' (string), must
be a misprint for ‚Seite' (side, aspect).

82, 3

‚wie denn fchon der Klang bis zum Springen oder Schmilzen fortgehen'.
The verb here should be singular (fortgeht). The phrase has been corrected in the
translation.

82, 8

This transition from sound to heat may well have been influenced by
the treatment of the subject in J. W. Ritter's 'Fragmente aus dem Nachlasse
eines jungen Physikers' (2 vols. Heidelberg, 1810) vol. II pp. 225–269. Ritter
discusses the influence of sound upon the *structure* of bodies, and illustrates his
argument in much the same way as Hegel; see pp. 255–256, ‚Ein aus
Oscillationsgluth leuchtender Körper muß eigentlich in dem Augenblicke
fchmelzen, in welchem jedesmal die Compreffion ftatt hat ... Durch
diefe momentanen Schmelzungen und Wiederfeftwerdungen müffen
Aenderungen von Bedeutung im fchwingenden Körper hervorgebracht werden,
befonders in der Conftellation feiner Theile. Ob hierher fchon das fogenannte
Ausfpielen von Inftrumenten gehören mag? — Das Glaferzerfchreien ift auch
wohl Folge eines Brechens wegen Schmelzung.'

82, 16

In Michelet's version of this sentence, heat appears formally 'in that it sublates' (indem fie ... aufhebt) this boundedness. In Nicolin and Pöggeler's
version it appears formally 'as sublating' (als aufhebend) this boundedness. As

they give no reason for this emendation (cf. 'Encyklopädie' Hamburg, 1959, pp. 250 and 485), Michelet's version has been preferred.

83, 25

,die tropischen Vögel, deren Selbstischkeit, nach Pflanzenweise, in ihre vege‐ tative Hülle, das Gefieder, durch das Licht und die Hitze ihres Klima's heraus‐ gerissen wird'. Cf. the note III. 335.

Although these remarks may at first sight seem somewhat fantastic, the views they express were quite common at the beginning of the last century. J. F. Meckel (1781–1833) for example, in his 'Ueber die Federbildung' ('Reil's Archiv für die Physiologie' vol. xii pp. 37–96, Halle, 1815) makes much of the similarity between feathers and plants (p. 60), and notes that, 'The brightest colours always occur at the ends of the feathers and are brought forth through the influence of the sunlight.' (p. 70) etc. J. M. Bechstein (1757–1822), in his delightful 'Gemeinnützige Naturgeschichte Deutschlands' (4 vols. Leipzig, 1801–7) vol. ii p. 36, 'For although there are also beautifully coloured birds in a temperate country such as Germany, and undistinguished birds enough within the tropics, it is nevertheless quite clearly in the hot regions of the earth that the most beautiful birds such as Peacocks, Colibris, Parrots etc. are to be found, as well as the Leopard and Zebra and the most beautiful butterflies and flowers'.

83, 31

Johann Baptist Spix (1781–1826) was born at Höchstadt in Upper Franconia, and was the son of a chirurgeon. He began to study theology, but in 1804, under the influence of Schellingianism, took up medicine, and was awarded his doctorate in this subject at Würzburg. He worked at Bamberg for a few years as a general practitioner, but in 1811, through the influence of Schelling, was taken into the employ of the Munich Academy. He was subsequently elected member of this Academy, and keeper of its zoological collection. In 1815 he was chosen by the Bavarian government to lead the expedition to Brazil, probably on account of an earlier expedition to the Mediterranean, which he had undertaken on behalf of the Academy.

His 'Cephalogenesis' (Munich, 1815) was a valuable contribution to literature on the comparative anatomy of the skull, and his 'Geschichte und Beurtheilung aller Systeme in der Zoologie' (Nuremberg, 1811) was highly praised, but his inability to concentrate *exclusively* upon the solution of *specific* problems prejudiced the quality of his purely scientific work. He was never able to clear his mind of Schellingianism. His health was seriously impaired by the Brazilian expedition, and he only lived to help Martius with the first volume of the work quoted here by Hegel.

Karl Friedrich Philipp Martius (1794–1868) was born at Erlangen, and from his earliest years, trained by his father in the natural sciences. Even as a boy, he had a fine command of Greek and Latin, and the study of the classical languages and literatures always remained his favourite hobby.

In 1810 he went up to the university of Erlangen and began to study botany. In 1814 he was awarded his doctorate for his work in cataloguing the plants in the botanical garden of the university; see his 'Plantarum horti academici Erlangensis enumeratio' (Erlangen, 1814). Soon afterwards he was appointed one of the supervisors of this garden, and it was in this capacity that he became acquainted with the king of Bavaria, who was a keen botanist and often visited the garden, and who recommended him for the Brazilian expedition.

He became professor of botany at Munich at the early age of thirty two, and later gained a European reputation on account of his botanical works. Mount Martius in New Zealand was named after him.

Hegel is here quoting 'Reise in Brasilian auf Befehl Sr. Majestät Maximilien Joseph I Königs von Baiern in den Jahren 1817 bis 1820 gemacht' (3 pts. Munich, 1823, 1828, 1831), most of which is the work of Martius. H. E. Lloyd (1771–1847) published an English translation of the first part of this work; see 'Travels in Brazil in the years 1817–1820' (2 vols. London, 1824). The passage cited differs somewhat from the original in punctuation. The hyphen was evidently inserted to indicate the deletion of a curious speculation regarding the influence of melody made by man upon the musical productions of animals. Hegel has taken the passage from a chapter in which a journey from Rio de Janeiro to São Paulo in December 1817 is described (I pp. 179–217). The *Santa Cruz* he mentions is the royal palace, some 37 miles west of Rio, where Spix and Martius stayed for a few days. After climbing the jungle-clad granite hills beyond this palace to a height of some three thousand feet, they descended somewhat into clayey country, and it was here that they heard this bird.

The whole expedition to Brazil lasted just over three years. They left Trieste on April 7, 1817, with the Austrian party accompanying the archduchess Leopoldina, who was to be married to Don Pedro the son of John VI of Portugal and later emperor of Brazil (I p. 12), and arrived at Rio de Janeiro on July 15th (I p. 85). After making several expeditions in southern and central Brazil, they travelled up to Bahia (Salvador), São Luis and Pará (Belém) (bk. II). They then set out to explore the Amazon, and on September 18, 1819 reached Santarém (III p. 1030). In order to get as full an impression as possible of the upper Amazon and of the foothills of the Andes, they separated at Villa de Ega (Tefé) on December 7, 1819 (III p. 1181). Spix crossed the Brazilian frontier at Tabatinga on January 9, 1820 (III p. 1188). They met again at Pará on April 16, 1820 (III p. 1327), and spent the next two months packing their collection, which consisted of 85 mammals, 350 birds, 130 amphibia, 116 fishes, 2700 insects, 80 arachnida, 80 crustacea and 6500 plants (III p. 1387). Only 57 animals reached Munich alive, most of them being monkeys and parrots. Martius subsequently published several works on the flora of Brazil, see 'Nova genera et species plantarum' (3 vols. Munich, 1824–1829), 'Icones selectae

Plantarum Cryptoganicarum' (Munich, 1827), and 'Flora brasiliensis' (2 vols. Stuttgart, 1829, 1833).

Cf. J. R. Moore 'Goldsmith's degenerate song-birds, an eighteenth century fallacy in ornithology.' ('Isis' 1942–1943 pp. 324–327): O. Goldsmith (1728–1774) 'An History of the Earth and Animated Nature' (London, 1774) V pp. 324–325.

85, 10

Benjamin Thompson (1753–1814) count Rumford, was born at Woburn, Massachusetts, and apprenticed to a warehouseman at the age of thirteen. He married well however, fought for Britain during the rebellion, and left America for London in March 1776. From then on his social rise was rapid. George Germain gave him a post at the colonial office, Sir Joseph Banks had him elected fellow of the Royal Society, and in 1784 George III knighted him. A tour of the continent in 1783 brought him into contact with the Elector of Bavaria, and further honours followed in quick succession. In 1788 he became a major general in the Bavarian army, privy councillor, and head of the Bavarian war department. The king of Poland conferred the order of St. Stanislaus upon him, scientific societies at Berlin, Munich and Mannheim elected him to membership, and in 1791 he was made *count* of the Holy Roman Empire.

In Munich he did a great deal of good work. He improved conditions in the Bavarian army, cleared the city of beggars by establishing workhouses, organized the distribution of cheap food to the poor, and laid out the 'English garden', which still flourishes there. He returned to Britain in 1795, and occupied himself with improving conditions in the workhouses and hospitals of Dublin, and installing improved heating and cooking facilities in well over a hundred London houses, including those of Lord Palmerston, Sir Joseph Banks and the Marquis of Salisbury. He was back in Munich in 1796, preventing the French and Austrian armies from entering the city. In May 1802 he finally left England, married Lavoisier's widow in 1805, separated from her in 1809, and in 1811 settled, with a daughter by his first marriage, at Auteuil near Paris, where he lived a retired existence, spending much time in his garden.

He is mainly remembered for the experiments with heat mentioned here by Hegel, but he also did much for the general furthering of science. In 1796 for example, he gave £1,000 to the Royal Society, the interest on which was to provide a prize and a medal for, 'the most important discovery, or useful improvement, in any part of Europe during the preceding two years, on heat or light'. At the same time he granted $5,000 to the American Academy of Arts and Sciences to provide a similar award for work of this kind done, 'in any part of the Continent of America, or in any of the American Islands'. It was Rumford's inspiration which led to the founding of the *Royal Institution* in Albemarle Street, and in 1801 he helped to organize the Bavarian Academy of Arts and Sciences. He also endowed a professorship at Harvard, the holder of which should deliver lectures on, 'the utility of the physical and mathematical sciences for the improvement of the useful arts, and for the extension of the industry, prosperity, happiness and wellbeing of society'. See J. A. Thompson 'Count Rumford' (New York, 1935).

85, 28

,und zwar in Gestalt von Allgemeinheit, Gemeinsamkeit'.

85, 35

Marc Auguste Pictet (1752–1825) was appointed professor at Geneva in 1786, and was later president of the Genevan Academy. When the city was annexed to France in 1798, Pictet was member (1802), and then secretary (1803) of the governing council. In 1807 he was one of the fifteen inspectors appointed for reforming the public education of the city.

He was a founder member of the Genevan 'Société de physique et d'histoire naturelle', director of the Genevan observatory, and a fellow of the Royal Society. He visited Great Britain in 1801, and between 1796 and 1816 issued his 'Bibliothèque britannique', which provided accounts of current British scientific research for the French-reading public.

Hegel may have remembered this experimentation with cold from his reading of F. A. C. Gren's 'Grundriss der Naturlehre' (4th ed. Halle, 1801) § 545 (see the note II. 267). Pictet gave an account of it in his 'Essais de physique' (Geneva, 1790) p. 82; see the German translation of this work 'Versuche über das Feuer' (Tübingen, 1790) ch. 6. James Hutton (1726–1797) called Pictet's conclusions on the matter in question in his 'On the philosophy of light, heat, and fire' ('Edin. Roy. Soc. Trans.' vol. IV (Hist.) pp. 7–16). Benjamin Thompson (1753–1814) drew Pictet's attention to this article in a letter sent from Munich on January 12, 1797: see 'The Complete Works of Count Rumford' (4 vols. Boston, 1870–1875) vol. IV pp. 736–738.

Thompson repeated Pictet's experiment at Edinburgh in 1800, in the presence of T. C. Hope (1766–1844), John Playfair (1748–1819) and Dugald Stewart (1753–1828), and gave the following account of it in his 'Historical Review of the various experiments of the author on the subject of heat' (1805), 'Two metallic mirrors, fifteen inches in diameter, with a focal distance of fifteen inches, were placed opposite each other, sixteen feet apart. When a cold body (for example, a glass bulb filled with water and pounded ice) as was the case on this occasion, was placed in the focus of one of the mirrors, and a very sensitive air thermometer was placed in the focus of the other mirror, the latter thermometer began immediately to fall. If, instead of being placed directly in the focus, the thermometer was removed a short distance from it to one side, the cooling power which in the former case the cold body had exerted upon it was no longer perceptible.' See, 'The Complete Works of Count Rumford' (4 vols. Boston, 1870–1875) vol. II p. 222; C. A. Gerhard 'Benjamin Grafen von Rumford Abhandlungen über die Wärme' (Berlin, 1805) p. 36.

86, 18

,Die Annahme einer Wärmematerie, wie die des Schallstoffs, ruht auf der Kategorie, daß, . . .'.

86, 22

Peter van Musschenbroek (1692–1761), in his 'Introductio ad philosophiam naturalem' (2 vol. Leyden, 1762) vol. II p. 632, noticed that metals increase in weight when 'calcinated' by fire, and concluded from this that heat has weight.

As the attack on the phlogiston theory gathered momentum at the close of the eighteenth century, some curious hypotheses were put forward. F. A. C. Gren (1760–1798), in his 'Systematisches Handbuch der gesammten Chemie' (Halle, 1787) took phlogiston to consist of heat and light and to constitute a *negative weight*. From this hypothesis he explained why materials became heavier on being burnt, by assuming that they *lose* phlogiston. See his subsequent controversy with J. T. Mayer (1752–1830) in Gren's 'Journal der Physik' (Leipzig, 1790–93) vol. I pp. 205 and 359, vol. II p. 198.

86, 31

For early views on the materiality of heat see Athanasius Kircher (1601–1680) 'Mundus subterraneus' (Amsterdam, 1665) tome I, lib. IV, sect. i, cap. 2; Christian Wolff (1679–1750) 'Nützliche Versuche' (3 pts. Halle, 1721–3) vol. II ch. IX § 206. By the middle of the eighteenth century the materiality of heat was a generally accepted proposition, see George Martine (1702–1741) 'Medical and philosophical Essays' (London, 1740), Benjamin Franklin (1706–1790) 'Philosophical Works' (5th ed. Dublin, 1802) p. 351, William Hillary (d. 1763) 'The nature and laws of fire' (London, 1760).

The postulation of material *inflammability* or *phlogiston* was of course closely connected with these theories of material heat, see G. E. Stahl (1660–1734) 'Zufällige Gedanken . . . über den Streit von dem sogenannten Sulphure' (Halle, 1718). Adair Crawford (1748–1795) 'Experiments and observations on animal heat and the inflammation of combustible bodies' (London, 1779, Germ. tr. Leipzig, 1785). The 'Anfangsgründe der antiphlogistischen Chemie' (Berlin, 1792), by C. Girtanner (1760–1800) was the first important German work to call these theories in question.

On later phlogiston theory see J. R. Partington 'A History of Chemistry' vol. 3 ch. xiii (London, 1962).

86, 39

Hegel is here referring to 'An Inquiry concerning the Source of the Heat which is excited by Friction', a paper which Rumford read to the Royal Society on January 25, 1798. See 'Phil. Trans. Roy. Soc.' 1798 pt. I pp. 80–102; 'The Complete Works of Count Rumford' (4 vols. Boston, 1870–1875) vol. I pp. 471–493.

In this article Rumford calls in question the existence of an 'igneous fluid', and describes experiments he performed while superintending the boring of brass cannon in the workshops of the military arsenal at Munich.

(i) By using a blunt steel borer with a pressure of 10,000 lb. revolving 32 times a minute for 41 minutes, he obtained 837 grains Troy of metallic dust, which constituted $\frac{1}{948}$th of the cylinder. He then asks, 'Is it possible that the very considerable quantity of heat that was produced in this experiment . . . could have been furnished by so inconsiderable a quantity of metallic dust? and this merely in consequence of a *change* of its capacity for heat?'

(ii) He then performed the same experiment in a *vacuum* to show that it was not the air which had engendered the heat.

(iii) He encased the cylinder being bored in a watertight deal box, which he then filled with $26\frac{1}{2}$ lbs. of water having a temperature of 60°F. After $2\frac{1}{2}$ hours of boring the water boiled, and he discovered that $8\frac{2}{3}$ oz. Troy of metallic powder had been produced.

(iv) He showed that the metallic powder required the same amount of heat to raise its temperature 1°, as an equal amount of the original metal.

He concluded from these experiments that the source of the heat generated was apparently '*inexhaustible*', and that it is, 'extremely difficult, if not quite impossible, to form any distinct idea of any thing, in the manner the heat was excited and communicated in these experiments, except it be *motion*'.

Hegel's statement that these experiments 'told heavily' against theories of the materiality of heat is strictly accurate, for these theories were not *refuted* by them. It was still possible for supporters of the caloric theory to argue that although Rumford had proved that the powder and the solid metal required the same quantity of heat to raise the temperature of equal masses of either one degree, he had not proved that they *contained equal quantities of heat*, and this to the physicists of the day was the main point at issue. In 1799 Sir Humphrey Davy (1778-1829) provided a more direct refutation of the calorists' view when he melted ice by rubbing two blocks of it together. It was a well-known fact that ice requires to have a quantity of heat *added* to it to convert it into water, so that it had to be admitted that the water produced by the friction contained more heat than the ice. Davy concluded from this experiment that 'friction . . . does not diminish the capacity of bodies for heat'. See the 'Essay on Heat, Light and the Combinations of Light' in 'Contributions to physical and medical knowledge' (ed. T. Beddoes, Bristol, 1799) vol. I p. i; cf. Davy's 'Collected Works' (London, 1836) vol. II.

88, 14

‚Die Reibung von zwei Hölzern (bei den Wilden)', Nicolin and Pöggeler, in their edition of the 'Encyklopädie' (Hamburg, 1959) p. 252, omit the words in parenthesis, but make no mention of this in their notes (cf. p. 485).

89, 17

In Hegel's day the investigation of specific heat or thermal capacity was already strictly divided into the study of gases, fluids and solid substances; see the exhaustive survey of the subject in Gehler's Physikalisches Wörterbuch' vol. X pp. 666–836 (Leipzig, 1841). See also J. F. W. Herschel's article 'Heat' in the 'Encyclopaedia metropolitana' (London, 1829–1845). Forerunners of the table printed by Herschel (p. 338) are to be found in J. H. Magellan (1723–1790) 'Essai sur la nouvelle Théorie du feu élémentaire' (London, 1780), F. X. Baader (1765–1841) 'Vom Wärmestoff' (Vienna and Leipzig, 1786), Jacob Gadolin (1719–1802) 'De theoria caloris corporum specifici' (Åbo. 1784), and John Murray (d. 1820) 'Elements of Chemistry' (4th ed. 2 vols. Edinburgh, 1816).

In Pierre Louis Dulong (1785–1838) and Alexis Thérèse Petit (1791–1820) announced their famous discovery that the specific heats of thirteen solid elements which they had investigated were very nearly proportional to their atomic weights, i.e. that the atoms of simple substances have equal capacities for heat, the specific thermal capacity of a substance being equal to ·375 divided by its atomic weight; see 'Recherches sur quelques points importants de la théorie de la chaleur' ('Annales de Chimie' vol X pp. 395–413; cf. 'Tilloch's Philosophical Magazine' vol LIV pp. 267–275, 1819, 'Thomson's Annals of Philosophy' vol. XIV pp. 189–198, 1819).

89, 40

See the note II. 272. See also William Irvine (1743–1787), who assisted Black in his experiments, 'Essays, chiefly on Chemical Subjects' (London, 1805), and William Irvine the younger (1776–1811); the article in 'Nicholson's Journal' vol. vi. pp. 25–31 (1803). Cf. 'Experimental determinations of the latent heat of Spermaceti, Bees' Wax, Tin, Bismuth, Lead, Zinc and Sulphur' ('Nicholson's Journal' IX, 1804, pp. 45–52; 'Gilbert's Annalen der Physik' vol. 38 pp. 305–317, 1811).

90, 27

At about 11 p.m. on April 20, 1781, thick smoke was seen to be pouring from a cabin on the war frigate 'Maria', which was anchored off Cronstadt, the great Russian naval station on the island of Kotlin near the head of the Gulf of Finland. As a similar fire had broken out during the previous spring, sabotage or foul play was suspected. Sir Samuel Greig (1735–1788), who had entered Russian service in 1764, had appointed many *Scottish* officers in the course of reforming the navy, and in his capacity as governor of Cronstadt. After the matter had been thoroughly investigated by Count Ivan Czernischev however, the Empress Catherine (1729–1796) was satisfied that the fire had started by a process of *spontaneous combustion*, 'in a hammock, rolled up and tied with string, and containing smoke-black mixed with the oil used for applying it,' and that the previous fire could have started in the same manner in 'hemp, rolled up in greasy mats'. See Czernischev's report of July 23, 1781 in 'Acta Academiae Scientiarum Imperialis Petropolitanae' vol. III pt. i p. 311.

Johann Gottlieb Georgi (1729–1802) gave an account of these fires and of many related experiments proving the existence of spontaneous combustion of this kind in 'Neue Nordische Beyträge zur physikalischen und geographischen Erd- und Völkerbeschreibung, Naturgeschichte und Oekonomie' vol. III pp. 37–83, vol. IV pp. 309–324 (St. Petersburg and Leipzig, 1782–3). Cf. J. C. Wiegleb (1732–1800) 'Handbuch der allgemeinen und angewandten Chemie' (2 vols. Berlin, 1781); Charles Rivington Hopson (1744–1796) 'A General System of Chemistry' (London, 1789) p. 629 note; Thomas B. Woodman, 'Account of a spontaneous Inflammation' ('Phil. Trans. Roy. Soc.' 1794 pp. 426–428).

90, 40

Hegel is referring to the 'Göttingsche gelehrte Anzeigen unter der Aufsicht der königl. Gesellschaft der Wissenschaften. Der dritte Band auf das Jahr 1817'. The article he is quoting is an anonymous review of the 'Memoirs of the American Academy of Arts and Sciences', and appeared as no. 161 on pp. 1801–1808 (October 9, 1817).

The American article which gave rise to this observation by the German reviewer was, 'On the origin and formation of ice islands' by A. Fothergill, M.D., F.R.S., A.P.S. etc. (op. cit. vol. III pt. i pp. 69–81, Cambridge, Mass., 1809). Fothergill questions the accepted theory that icebergs are formed only in the polar regions, 'If it be true, according to some late observations, that the temperature of the sea decreases from its surface downwards so far as has yet been determined by the deepest soundings, where its coldness reaches the freezing point even of salt-water, is it not probable that, at greater depths out of soundings it may be many degrees below the freezing point, and that where congelation is constantly going on, these enormous masses of ice, may be gradually formed *stratum super stratum*, attaching themselves to the bottom till, loosed by currents or tides, they are detached, and being specifically lighter than water, like air balloons increasing in buoyancy in proportion to the increase of their surface, they will gradually rise, and at length rear their heads far above the surface?'.

91, 9

‚Holz dagegen wird verzehrt, weil es ein Material ist, das die Hitze fortsetzen kann' On the generation of heat by burning wood see K. Wagenmann (1787–1867) 'Über die Heizung mit erwärmter Luft' (Berlin, 1827). Cf. 'Gehler's Physikalisches Wörterbuch' vol. V pp. 141–221 (Leipzig, 1829).

92, 9

In the 1827 edition of the 'Encyclopaedia', Hegel inserted the following passage here, 'it disappears only by *being conditioned*, and the different determinations have lost their immediacy, and therefore their capacity for being conditions'.

92, 29

‚Daß der Klang, als Seele, der Materiatur nicht entfliehe . . .'. Cf. the note II. 282. By using the unusual word 'materiature', Hegel is evidently referring to the scholastic doctrine according to which form is rendered inherent in a particular 'materiate' by means of 'materiation'. Aristotle's treatment of matter and form is evidently the ultimate origin of this concept: see W. D. Ross 'Aristotle' (London, 1923) p. 167 et seq.

J. H. Stirling (1820–1909), in the first Gifford lectures, published as 'Philosophy and Theology' (Edinburgh, 1890) p. 349, uses the word to mean that which constitutes materiality, 'As you may wash away all colour from a clot of blood, and be left at last with a pure transparent ultimate, a pure transparent web which held the colour, so you may discharge *materiature* from any particle of dust, or sand, or mud, and be left at last with a pure diamond of fibres intellectual'.

Sir Thomas Browne (1605–1682), in 'Pseudodoxia Epidemica' (London, 1646, Germ. tr. Christian Rautner, Frankfurt and Leipzig, 1689) bk. vii ch. i, discusses the treatment of creation in Aristotle's 'De Caelo' and then continues, 'But herein we remain sufficiently satisfied from Moses, and the Doctrin delivered of the Creation; that is, a production of all things out of nothing, a formation not only of matter, but of form, and a *materiation* even of matter it self.' Cf. Richard Burthogge (1638?–1694?) 'An Essay upon Reason' (London, 1694) pp. 157–158; Marcus *Vitruvius* Pollio 'De Architectura Libri Decem' (ed. Rose, 2nd ed., Leipzig, 1899) Bk. 4 ch. 2 ii; 'Thesaurus Linguae Latinae' (8 vols. Leipzig, 1900–1966) vol. 8 col. 467.

95, 4

Nicolin and Pöggeler, in their edition of the 'Enzyklopädie' (Hamburg, 1959), alter this paragraph somewhat without explaining why. They omit 'the Notion of' (‚in ihrem Begriffe') in (a), and by reconstituting Hegel's sentence structure, disrupt the syntax of (b). Their general lay-out of the text has been adopted, but the translation has been made from Michelet's version.

95, 7

In the second edition of the 'Encyclopaedia' (1827) Hegel added 'for the senses' (‚für die Sinne') after 'difference', but the words were removed in the third edition (1830).

96, 11

In the first edition of the 'Encyclopaedia' (1817), Hegel added the following passage at this juncture (see Michelet's version), 'The form of shape and of individuality in general is not to be thought of as an external mechanism or composition. There is no point in attempting to understand the determinateness of shape by dragging in external division and an external application of parts, for the essential element of it is always the characteristic differentiation which appears within these parts, and which constitutes the determinate and self-identical unity of their relation'.

96, 28

‚weil die Individualität sich hier noch nicht gegenständlich ist'. Cf. § 337.

97, 20

For the state of knowledge, at the beginning of the last century, with regard to the physical and chemical factors determining crystal structure, see § 315. When Hegel takes the decisive factor to be this 'invisible germ' or 'constructive force' in water, he is merely characterizing the general position of crystallo-graphic research at that time. See J. B. L. de Romé de l'Isle (1736–1790), 'Cristallographie ou déscription des formes propres à tous les corps du règne mineral' (3 vols. Paris, 1783) vol. I p. 13, 'Nulle cristallisation ne peut s'opérer sans le concours d'un fluide, qui, par son interposition, mette les molécules intégrantes des sels à portée de s'unir'. John Murray (d. 1820), in his 'System of Chemistry' (4 vols. Edinburgh, 1819) admits (vol. I p. 42) that, 'The theory of crystallization is still obscure, so far as relates to the cause of the regular forms to which it gives rise'. Cf. Jacob Green (1790–1841) 'On an instance of instantaneous Crystallization' ('The American Journal of Science' 1821 vol. III pp. 93–4). Froriep 'Notizen aus dem Gebiete der Naturwissenschaften' (Weimar, April 1825 no. 254).

98, 7

Jacob Nicolai Møller (1777–1862) was the son of the well-known Norwegian doctor Hans Møller (1736–1796), and was born at Åkre in Gjerpen (Norway). In 1791 he came down to study law at Copenhagen University, and after taking his degree in this subject in 1795, worked for a while in the Danish chancellery. He soon found office work irksome however, and in 1797 he left for Berlin, with the object of studying mineralogy. It was in Berlin that he met his country-man Henrik Steffens (1773–1845), who travelled with him to Freiberg in Saxony to hear A. G. Werner (1750–1817) lecture on the earth sciences. In 1800 they met Schelling in Jena, and the article referred to here by Hegel, Møller's second published work, was written soon afterwards, and appeared in Schelling's 'Neue Zeitschrift für speculative Physik' (Tübingen, 1802) vol. I pt. iii pp. 1–66. It has as its title 'Über die Entstehung der Wärme durch Reibung nebst Folgerungen für die Theorie beyder Phänomene'.

Hegel evidently has in mind the following passage (p. 45), 'I concluded, further, once I had discovered this curved line, that I had as it were discovered the original type of the organization, and that all organizations would perhaps consist of numbers of such curved lines standing in various relationships to one another, just as all crystals consist of straight lines joining in all directions . . . It was thus that I discovered that this line is in fact the model in accordance with which the artist had moulded every part, not only of the human form, but also of forms such as vases etc., and that for this reason I might well call it the line of beauty. When I looked at all the other forms of organic nature in the light of this discovery, I found the curved line reoccurring everywhere: in plants, nearly all the forms of which fall between the line and the surface; in the minute world of insects; in the dumb fishes of the sea, in the light-winged inhabitants of the air, and in the creatures dwelling upon the firm-set earth.'

Møller adds that he is aware of the lenticular form in crystals cf. A. G. Werner 'A Treatise on the External Characters of Fossils' (tr. Weaver, Dublin, 1805) pp. 112, 303: plate I figs. 23, 24, but assures us that he would be able to explain it in the light of his general principle.

Møller fell ill in Hamburg in 1803 and was nursed back to health by Charlotte Elisabeth Alberti, the daughter of Lessing's clerical friend, who was also related to Steffens and Ludwig Tieck (1773-1853). On January 27, 1804 he married this young lady in the chapel of the Austrian embassy at Hamburg, and on the same day abandoned his Lutheran faith and was received into the Roman church. When he returned to Copenhagen later that year he was unable to get employment in a silver works because of his new religion. He therefore left Scandinavia for good, and spent the next thirty years wandering about Germany, working as an estate manager, hotel keeper, private tutor and schoolmaster. In 1812 he was appointed teacher at the grammar school in Nuremberg where Hegel was headmaster, but the pay was so bad that he did not stay long.

In 1834 his son was appointed professor of philosophy at Louvain, and in 1835 he was granted a similar honorary appointment. He died in Louvain on November 30, 1862.

The religious aspect of his intellect entirely overshadowed his scientific interests in his later years. His 'Speculative Darstellung des Christenthums' (Leipzig, 1819), 'Das absolute Princip der Ethik (Leipzig, 1819), 'Johannes Scotus Erigena und seine Irrthümer' (Mainz, 1844) and 'Aus der Scholastik des St. Thomas von Aquin' were published under the name of Nicolaus Møller, by which he chose to be known after his conversion. By 1822-1826, when he was in Vienna, he had almost completely forgotten his mother tongue.

See: H. Steffens 'Was ich erlebte' (10 vol. Breslau, 1840/4): D. A. Rosenthal 'Konvertitenbilder aus dem 19. Jahrhundert' (3 vols. Schaffhausen, 1866-70) I i p. 62 et seq., p. 409 et seq.: F. Boetzmann 'De la science à la foi' (Malines, 1909): T. Menge 'Graf F. L. Stolberg und seine Zeitgenossen' (Gotha, 1862) II p. 245 et seq. Cf. the articles by F. Nielsen in 'Dansk Biografisk Lexikon' vol. XII pp. 79-81 (Copenhagen, 1898), and by K. Kjelstrup in 'Norsk Biografisk Leksikon' vol. IX pp. 573-574 (Oslo, 1939), J. B. Halvorsen 'Norsk Forfatter-Lexikon 1814-1880' (7 vols. Kristiania, 1885-1908) vol. iv pp. 225-228.

Møller published two further scientific articles: 'Om Anvendelsen af Steenkul' (C. G. Rafn's 'Bibliotek for Physik, Medicin og Oeconomi' xvii pp. 177–236, Copenhagen, 1800), and 'Forsøg til en Characteristik af de fire Verdensdele' (C. Molbech's 'Athene II' pp. 322–344, Copenhagen, 1814, Swedish tr. Stockholm, 1815).

While living in Belgium he published several works criticizing recent German philosophy: 'De l'état de la philosophie moderne en Allemagne' (Louvain, 1843), 'La sophistique de Hegel' (Louvain, 1846), first published in the 'Revue catholique de Louvain' III, 1845–1846, 'Foi et science' ('Revue de Bruxelles' nouv. série I, 1842), and three articles in the 'Katholische Zeitschrift der Universität Bonns' 1845: 'Die Theodicée Schellings', 'Parmenides und Hegel', and 'Ueber die Dialectik Hegels'.

98, 26

J. C. Scaliger (1484–1558), in his 'Exotericarum Exercitationum' (Paris, 1557) exerc. 88, mentions a kind of metal found in Mexico which could not be liquefied by fire or by the arts of the Spaniards, 'inter Mexicum et Dariem fodinus esse orichalci: quod nullo igni, nullis Hispanicis artibus hactenus liquescere potuit.' This was undoubtedly platinum, but it was not until the middle of the eighteenth century that the Swedish chemist H. T. Scheffer (1710–1759) made an accurate examination of the metal: see 'Kungliga Svenska Vetenskapsakademiens Handlingar' 1752 vol. xiii pp. 269, 276: 1757 vol. xviii p. 314.

As the metal was practically immune to any form of corrosion, it was used for making chemical apparatus after W. H. Wollaston (1766–1828) had discovered how to make it *malleable*: 'On a method of rendering platina malleable' ('Phil. Trans. Roy. Soc.' 1829). Wollaston discovered how to do this as early as *1804*, but he kept the process a secret, and probably earned about £30,000 from it. He dissolved native platinum in aqua regia, precipitated ammonium chloroplatinate with ammonium chloride, decomposed this by heat, washed the finely divided residue of platinum, compressed a mud of the moist powder, raised this to a white heat, and hammered it into an ingot which could be beaten into foil or drawn into wire.

When Hegel says that platinum is *granular* he probably has in mind the state in which it occurs naturally, and also, perhaps, its *rigidity*, i.e. the great difficulty formerly experienced in melting it or making it malleable. In his day Peru and Colombia produced most of the platinum marketed. The rich deposits of the metal at Verkhniy-Isetsk in the Urals were not discovered until 1819 and not extensively exploited until 1822. In 1831 platinum ore was recognized in the gold-bearing deposits of Borneo, where it was known to the natives as 'mas kodok' (frog gold), and had previously been regarded as worthless. A *nugget* of platinum weighing 310 ozs. was later discovered at Nizhe Tagisk.

99, 10

‚und iſt in dieſer noch abſtrakten Strenge — der Magnetismus.' In normal usage 'die Strenge' merely means strictness ‚sharpness, keenness. Hegel's meaning becomes clearer here if we remember that metals which are hard to melt, such as platinum, were said to be 'ſtrengflüſſig', i.e. refractory.

100, 6

See the note III. 228.

100, 8

See 'Schellings Werke' (ed. Manfred Schröter, Munich, 1958) vol. II pp. 257–261, first supplementary volume pp. 163–173, second supplementary volume pp. 255–276.

In 1799 Schelling wrote ‚Wenn nun allgemeine Analogien überhaupt beweiſende Kraft haben, ſo iſt kein Zweifel, daß dem Magnetismus dieſelbe Funktion für die allgemeine Natur zugeſchrieben werden muß, die wir der unbekannten Urſache der Senſibilität für die organiſche zuſchreiben'. He then goes on to assert that all oppositions in nature have their root in the phenomenon of magnetism.

In 1804, in a fuller exposition of this doctrine, he writes, ‚Die Elektricität iſt ebenſo wie der Magnetismus nicht die Wirkung eines beſonderen Princips, ſondern eine allgemeine Kategorie der Materie'.

101, 21

‚der ſpröde Punkt'. Literally translated this would be 'the brittle (hard, inflexible) point'.

101, 33

René-Just Hauy (1743–1822) discovered for example that the *electricity* of tourmaline decreases rapidly from the summits or poles towards the middle of the crystal, where it is imperceptible, and that if a tourmaline is broken into any number of fragments, each fragment, when excited, has two opposite poles. He found that Siberian and Brazilian topaz, borate of magnesia, mesotype, sphene and calamine also possess this property. See his 'Traité de minéralogie' (4 vols. Paris, 1801, Germ. tr. Karsten, 3 vols. Leipzig, 1803): cf. P. F. Mottelay 'Bibliographical History of Electricity and Magnetism' (London, 1922) pp. 286–288.

102, 1

See Schelling, 'Ideen zu einer Philosophie der Natur' (1797, 'Werke' ed. Schröter, 1st suppl. vol. p. 172), ‚Dieß iſt eine der erſten Lehren der Naturphiloſophie, die im Entwurf des Syſtems dieſer Wiſſenſchaft ſo ausgedrückt iſt: „Der Magnetismus iſt ſo allgemein in der allgemeinen Natur, als die Senſibilität in der organiſchen, die auch der Pflanze zukommt.

Aufgehoben iſt er in einzelnen Subſtanzen nur für die Erſcheinung; in den ſogenannten unmagnetiſchen Subſtanzen verliert ſich bei der Berührung unmittelbar in Elektricität, was bei den magnetiſchen noch als Magnetismus unterſchieden wird, ſowie bei den Pflanzen unmittelbar in Zuſammenziehungen ſich verliert, was beim Thier noch als Senſation unterſchieden wird. Es fehlt alſo nur an den Mitteln, um den Magnetismus der ſogenannten unmagnetiſchen Subſtanzen zu erkennen u.ſ.w." '.

102, 34

Sir George Leonard Staunton (1737–1801) has left an account of the eighteenth century Chinese compass in his 'An Authentic account of the Earl of Macartney's Embassy from the King of Great Britain to the Emperor of China' (2 vols. London, 1797 Germ. tr. M. C. Sprengel, 2 pts. Halle 1798). 'The nature and cause of the qualities of the magnet have at all times been subjects of contemplation among the Chinese. The Chinese name for the compass is ting–nan–chin, or needle pointing to the south; and a distinguishing mark is fixed on the magnet's southern pole, as in European compasses upon the northern one'. (Vol. I p. 445).

Cf. J. A. M. de Moyria de Maillac (1679–1748) 'Histoire générale de la Chine' (13 vols. Paris, 1777–1785) vol. i p. 316: Julius Klaproth (1783–1835) 'Lettre à M. le Baron Humboldt sur l'invention de la boussole' (Paris, 1834).

As early as 2637 B.C. Hoang-ti, in order to help his military campaigning, is said to have constructed a chariot upon which stood a prominent female figure which indicated the four cardinal points, and which always turned *to the south* whatever might be the direction taken by the chariot: see P. F. Mottelay 'Bibliographical History of Electricity and Magnetism' (London, 1922) pp. 1–3.

103, 3

André Marie Ampère (1775–1836), building on H. C. Ørsted's famous discovery of the magnetic field surrounding an electric current ('Gilbert's Ann. der Physik' 1820, VI p. 295), investigated in an experimental and theoretical manner the mutual action of electric currents, and the equivalence of a closed circuit to a polar magnet. It was this latter investigation which suggested his celebrated hypothesis that *molecular currents* are the cause of magnetism. See 'Receuil d'observations électrodynamiques' (Paris, 1822); 'Théories des phénomènes électrodynamiques' (Paris, 1826).

These investigations laid the foundation of modern *electrokinetics*: see M. Faraday 'Experimental Researches in Electricity' (3 vols. London, 1839–1855): J. Clerk Maxwell 'Electricity and Magnetism' (2 vols. Oxford, 1892): E. F. Fournier d'Albe 'The Electron Theory' (London, 1906).

103, 19

This probably became generally known during the fifteenth century: see the article by G. Hellmann in 'Meteorologische Zeitschrift' (ed. Hann and Hellmann) 1906 vol. 23 p. 145. The first accurate measurement of the declination of the needle was made by Robert Norman of Wapping, a manufacturer of compass needles: see his 'The Newe Attractive' (London, 1581), in which he states that the dip, 'for this citie of London, I finde, by exact obseruations to be about 71 degrees 50 mynutes' (ch. 4).

Henry Gellibrand (1597–1637), Gresham professor of astronomy, discovered the secular change in the declination; see his 'Discourse Mathematical on the Variation of the Magneticall Needle together with its Admirable Diminution lately discovered' (London, 1635). George Graham (1675–1751), the London instrument maker, discovered a diurnal variation of 35' in the needle; see 'An Account of Observations Made of the Horizontal Needle at London, 1722–1723' ('Phil. Trans. Roy. Soc.' 1724–5 p. 332 and pp. 96–107). John Canton (1718–1772), by observing declination-changes on 603 days between 1756 and 1759, was able to draw the distinction between *regular* and irregular diurnal variation in declination ; see 'An attempt to account for the regular and diurnal variation of the horizontal magnetic needle'. ('Phil. Trans. Roy. Soc.' 1759).

By measuring the oscillations of a vertical needle in the magnetic meridian, Jean Charles Borda (1733–1799) was able to determine correctly the differences in the *intensity* of terrestrial magnetism. J. J. D. Cassini (1747–1845), by observations made between 1782 and 1791, was able to show that the magnetic needle is also subject to an *annual* periodical fluctuation depending on the position of the sun with regard to the equinoctial and solstitial points.

In Hegel's day there was some doubt as to the date at which declination had first been discovered: see Tiberius Cavallo (1749–1809) 'Treatise on Magnetism' (London, 1787) supplements; cf. P. F. Mottelay 'Bibliographical History of Electricity and Magnetism' (London, 1922) pp. 45–54 on the identity of Petrus Peregrinus (Cavallo's 'Peter Adsiger'), and the authenticity of the Leyden manuscript dated August 8, 1269.

103, 26

See 'Jenenser Realphilosophie' II p. 51 (ed. Hoffmeister, Leipzig, 1931), ‚wie am magnetiſchen Eiſen an den Polen der Eiſenfeilſtaub ſtärfer angezogen wird als an dem Mittelpunfte'. Michelet substituted ‚attrahirt' (attracted) for ‚angezogen'.

103, 28

William Gilbert (1540–1603), in his 'De Magnete Magneticisque Corporibus' (London, 1600, Eng. tr. Mottelay, Chicago, 1952) bk. II ch. 27, appears to put forward a curious anticipation of the theory mentioned here by Hegel.

Hegel could well be referring to 'Untersuchungen über den Magnetismus der Erde' (Christiania, 1819), by Christopher Hansteen (1784–1873), which was the standard work on this subject during his period at Berlin. As this passage dates from the Jena period however, it is almost certainly a reference to the theory put forward by J. B. Biot (1774–1862) in 1804, according to which the laws governing the declination of the needle and magnetic intensity may be deduced from the hypothesis of a magnet situated at the centre of the earth having its poles infinitely close to each other and directed to opposite points on the surface of the globe; see 'Sur les variations du magnétisme terrestre à differentes latitudes'; 'Journal de Physique' LIX 1804 pp. 429–450; 'Tilloch's Philosophical Magazine' XXII 1805 pp. 248–257, 299–308; 'Gilberts Annalen der Physik' 1805 pp. 257–298, cf. Sir Edward Sabine (1788–1883) in the Report of the Seventh Meeting of the British Association; K. B. Mollweide (1774–1825) in 'Gilbert's Annalen der Physik' vol. XXIX pp. 1–35, 251–267.

The theoretical background to this idea is to be found in two papers published in 'Histoire de l'Academie royale de Berlin' (1757 p. 175, 1766 p. 213) by Leonhard Euler (1707–1783). Euler adopted the theory of Descartes that the 'magnetic fluid' moves from the equator to the poles, and then attempted to explain mathematically the course of the magnetic needle over the earth's surface by announcing that the horizontal needle is a tangent to the circle passing through the place of observation and through the two points on the earth's surface where the dipping needle becomes vertical or the horizontal needle loses its directive power. His theories were based upon the 'Variation Chart' published by Edmund Halley (1656–1742) in 1700, revised versions of which were published by William Mountaine and James Dodson (d. 1757) in 1744, 1756 and 1757 ('Trans. Roy. Phil. Soc.' 1757). Cf. P. C. Le Monnier (1715–1799) 'Les lois du Magnétisme (2 vols. Paris, 1776–1779).

Charles Augustin de Coulomb (1736–1806) had also contributed to Biot's theory through his investigation of the distribution of electricity upon the surface of spheres; see 'Mémoires de l'Academie Royale des Sciences' 1784, 1785. It was the information collected by F. H. A. von Humboldt (1769–1859) during his voyage to the Americas in 1799–1804 which provided Biot with his *data* regarding the variation in the declination of the needle and the *intensity* of the earth's magnetic force; see Humboldt's 'Voyage aux régions équinoxiales du Nouveau Continent fait en 1799–1804' (30 vols. Paris, 1807 etc.).

The method used at this time for comparing the force at different places consisted in taking the time of *oscillation* of the dipping needle. This probably accounts for Hegel's referring to declination as 'an oscillation of a more universal nature'.

103, 29

See 'Jenenser Realphilosophie II' (ed. Hoffmeister, Leipzig, 1931) p. 51, ‚Sondern der Magnetismus ist dies ganz Allgemeine der Erde, das allenthalben als dies Ganze ist'. Michelet's version of this sentence changed the meaning, ‚Sondern der Magnetismus ist dieß ganz Allgemeine der Erde, die allenthalben der ganze Magnetismus ist'. 'Magnetism is however completely general to the Earth, and the Earth therefore constitutes the completeness of magnetism throughout the whole of its being'.

103, 35

Jeremias Benjamin Richter (1762–1807); for an account of his life and work see the note II. 428. Hegel is here referring to his article 'Ueber die bis jetzt sicherste Reinigungsmethode des Kobalts und Nickels vom Wismuth, Arsenik, Eisen und Kupfer; vozüglich aber die Methode der Scheidung des Kobalts vom Nickel oder des Nickels vom Kobalt in grossen Quantitäten', which appeared in A. F. Gehlen's 'Neues allgemeines Journal der Chemie' vol. XX pp. 61–72 (Berlin, 1804). Cf. 'Annales der Chemie vol. 53 p. 107. A summary of this article was published in 'Tilloch's Philosophical Magazine' vol. XIX pp. 51–54 (1804). Cf. the account of Richter's supposed discovery of 'nickeline' in Nicholson's 'Journal of Natural Philosophy' vol. XII pp. 261–165 (London, 1805), and the article by Wilhelm Hisinger (1766–1852) 'Undersökning af Niccolan' in 'Afhandlingar i Fysik, Kemi och Mineralogi' vol. III pp. 105–112 (Stockholm, 1810), summarized in 'Thomson's Annals of Philosophy' vol. I pp. 116–120 (1813), in which Hisinger showed that 'nickeline' was in fact an alloy of nickel with cobalt, plus a little iron and a trace of arsenic.

Cobalt had been discovered by Georg Brandt (1694–1768), see his 'Cobalti nova species examinata et descripta' (Stockholm, 1748), and soon afterwards Axel Fredrik Cronstedt (1722–1765) had established the fact that nickel is a distinct metal, see his 'Rön och forsök gjorde med en malmart från Los kobalt grufvor' (Stockholm, 1751). Great difficulty was encountered in obtaining these metals in their pure state however, and Torbern Olaf Bergman (1735–1784), who investigated them with great care, came to the conclusion that it was impossible to obtain pure nickel, see his 'Opuscula Physica et Chemica' (6 vols. Uppsala, 1779–1784). It was Bergman who first discovered the magnetic property of nickel (op. cit. II p. 240). F. A. K. Gren (1760–1798), in his 'Systematisches Handbuch der gesammten Chemie' (4 pts. Halle, 1787–1791) notes that cobalt has magnetic properties.

For some years, as Hegel notes, many chemists attributed the magnetic properties of these metals to their impurities (i.e. their iron content). L. J. Thénard (1777–1857) showed however that the magnetic property of nickel *increases* when it is purified ('Tilloch's Philosophical Magazine' vol. XX p. 63), and Richard Chenevix (1774–1830) showed that its loss of magnetic power was due to its arsenic content ('Nicholson's Journal' vol. V p. 287). W. A. Lampadius (1772–1842) subsequently calculated its magnetic energy as in the ratio of 35 to 55 to that of iron.

See also W. A. Lampadius 'Annales de Chimie' vol. XXVI p. 89: J. B. Trommsdorff (1770–1837) 'Nicholson's Journal' vol. xii p. 258: C. F. Bucholz (1770–1818) 'Tilloch's Philosophical Magazine' vol. xxiii p. 193: Richard Chenevix 'Observations on the supposed magnetic property of nickel'

('Nicholson's Journal' III p. 286, 1802): Richard Phillips (1778–1851) 'On the purification of nickel' ('Tilloch's Phil. Mag.' vol. xvi p. 312, 1803).

104, 20

At the beginning of the last century, the term 'metalloid' was new, and was not yet clearly defined. It was not always synonymous with 'semi-metal' (Halbmetall), and this probably accounts for Hegel's keeping to the older term, the meaning of which was quite clear. As he indicates, *shape* or *structure* was taken to be the basic factor in the distinction between metals and semi-metals.

Georg Brandt (1694–1768), in an article published in the 'Acta Sveciae Upsaliae publicata' (1735), classed mercury, antimony, bismuth, cobalt, arsenic and zinc as semi-metals, and rejected cinnabar, vitriols etc. from this class. He regarded true metals as those which *solidify* from fusion with a *concave surface*, and semi-metals to be metallic in appearance but *brittle* under the hammer. J. G. Wallerius (1709–1785), in his 'Elementa Metallurgiae speciatim Chemicae conscripta' (Stockholm, 1768, Germ. tr. Leipzig, 1770) vol. II pt. iii classes mercury, arsenic, cobalt, nickel, bismuth antimony and zinc as semi-metals, and (pt. iv) iron, copper, lead, tin, silver, gold and platinum as complete metals. John Murray (d. 1820), in his 'System of Chemistry' (4 vols. Edinburgh, 1819) vol. iii p. 455 notes that, 'Nickel has been placed among what are named Semi-metals, from appearing to have little *ductility* or *malleability*'.

Paul Erman (1764–1851), in an article published in 'Gilberts Annalen der Physik' vol. 42 p. 45 (1812) was evidently the first to use the term 'metalloids', which he applied to the metals of *alkalies* and *earths*. At almost the same time, Berzelius also used the term for *any ponderable elements* which are not metals: see 'Kungliga Svenska Vetenskaps-Academiens Handlingar' (Stockholm, 1812) vol. 33 pp. 28–74, and his 'Lehrbuch der Chemie' (tr. Wöhler, Dresden, 1825) vol. I pt. i p. 166. It was only later that this term was applied to semi-metals like arsenic.

104, 27

‚der Magnet-Eisenstein scheint aber das Specifische zu seyn, woran sich der Magnetismus offenbart.' Hegel is referring to *magnetite*, which was known to the ancients as Magnesian stone on account of its having been found in large quantities in the district of Magnesia near the Aegean coast. See W. A. Tiemann 'Systematische Eisenhüttenkunde' (Nuremberg, 1801) § 304.

104, 29

Alexander von Humboldt (1769–1859); see 'A letter from M. de Humboldt to M. Pictet, on the Magnetic Polarity of a Mountain of Serpentine' in 'Nicholson's Journal of Natural Philosophy' vol. I pp. 97–101 (June, 1797).

'I traversed the chain of mountains of the High Palatinate and the margraviate of Bayreuth; and I found, in the bottom of the Fichtelgebirge, between Munichberg and Goldcronach, an isolated hill, which rises to elevation of fifty toises' (320 ft), 'above the surrounding plain. Its height above the level of the sea may be estimated at two hundered and eighty, or three hundred, toises' (1790–1920 ft). 'This hill extends in length from west to east, and forms a pyramid extremely obtuse. The rocks which crown the summit or ridge are composed of serpentine of considerable purity . . . The action of this mountain of serpentine upon the magnet shews itself in a very curious manner. The uncovered rocks which are seen on the northern slope, and those on the declivity towards the south, have poles directly opposite. The former exhibits only south poles, the latter north poles. The whole mass of foliated serpentine does not therefore possess a single magnetical axis, but presents an infinity of different axes perfectly parallel to each other. This parallelism also agrees with the magnetic axis of the globe, though the poles of serpentine are inverted; so that the northern pole of the hill is opposed to the south pole of the earth. The east and western slopes present what in the theory of magnetism would be called the points of indifference . . . Two points, of which the action is very strong, are joined by rocks which do not exert the least attraction. The chemical analysis of these compounds affords the same results; and it would be no less difficult to discover any difference of aggregation between them, than between iron which has received the touch, and other iron which had never acquired the magnetic power.'

104, 32

In support of this statement, Hegel cites an observation made in 'Reise in Brasilien' (3 pts. Munich, 1823–1831) by J. B. Spix (1781–1826) and K. F. P. Martius (1794–1868); see the note II. 298. The expedition landed at Funchal on June 7, 1817. In vol. I pp. 64–65 there is a description of the hills of Madeira. Hegel quotes from the following passage, 'The phenomenon of the attraction and repulsion of the magnetic needle is very marked in the basalt of Madeira . . . Evidence of polarity was more marked in this wacke than in the lower-lying basalt, which bears out the observation made by Giesecke that higher-lying basalt is more magnetic than that at lower levels. Incidentally, basalt which on account of its height is more insulated from the ground, becomes polarized earlier for the same reason that every stone capable of magnetism, even magnetite, only becomes magnetic when it is brought out of the depths into the air and light, just as a weather-vane only becomes magnetic when it is set on a steeple, or an iron rod when it is placed upright'.

Spix and Martius are referring here to a paper 'On the mineralogy of Disko Island', written by Sir Charles Giesecke (1761–1833) in 1814, and published in the 'Edinburgh Philosophical Journal' vol. I pp. 117–120 (1819). They knew of this paper (see their footnote) from a notice which appeared in the 'Edinburgh Philosophical Journal' vol. V p. 221 (1821), and Hegel also quotes this reference. 'Sir Charles Giesecke observed similar effects in Greenland. All the basalt of Disco Island is magnetic. That which is found in the most elevated situations is most so, the fallen masses dispersed around the base of the mountains having more power over the needle than the others.'

Colonel George Gibbs (1776–1833), who had recently donated a magnificent collection of 12,000 minerals to the University of Yale, gave an account of a similar observation in, 'On the connexion between magnetism and light' ('The American Journal of Science' ed. B. Silliman vol. I pp. 89–90, New York, 1818). He visited a magnetic iron mine belonging to the governor of New Jersey, 'The ore in the upper part of the bed is magnetic and has polarity; but that raised from the bottom has no magnetism at first, but acquires it after it has been sometime exposed to the influence of the atmosphere . . . I could only account for this circumstance by supposing that magnetism existed not in the interior of the earth, as was supposed, but only on the surface, and in such bodies as received this principle from atmospheric, or celestial influence'.

During the two decades preceding Hegel's death, the nature of this connection between light and magnetism was a matter of controversy. Some attributed the 'stimulation' as he calls it, to the *light* itself, others attributed it to the *heat* generated. In the summer of 1812 D. P. Morichini (1773–1823), professor at Rome, claimed to have demonstrated the *direct* magnetizing of steel needles by the violet rays of the solar spectrum: see his 'Sopra la forza magnetizzante del lembo estremo del raggio violetto' (Rome, 1812): cf. 'Bibliothèque britannique' vol. 52 pp. 21–35 (1813): 'Gilbert's Annalen der Physik' vol. 53 p. 212 (1813). Sir Humphry Davy (1778–1829) saw Morichini's experiments performed in Italy in 1813, and was convinced by them, as was John Playfair (1748–1819), when he saw Dr. Carpi perform similar experiments in Rome in 1817. S. H. Christie (1784–1865), in 'On magnetic influence in the solar rays' ('Phil. Trans. Roy. Soc.' 1826 pp. 219–239, 1828 pp. 379–396) defended Morichini's hypothesis and suggested that terrestrial magnetism is probably derived from solar influence, but A. von Baumgartner (1793–1865) contended that the influence of light upon the movement of the needles was due to the heating of the air about them; see 'Zeitschrift für Physik und Mathematik' I pp. 200–209, 263–281 (1826), III pp. 96–103, 157–174 (1827): 'The Edinburgh Journal of Science' VI pp. 202–204 (1827). Cf. Gehler's 'Physikalisches Wörterbuch' vol. VI pp. 873–903 (Leipzig, 1836): Emil Wilde 'Geschichte der Optik' (2 vols. Berlin, 1838–1843) II pp. 241–248: Mary Somerville (1780–1872) 'The Connection of the Physical Sciences' (London, 1834 tr. Klöden, Berlin, 1835): P. F. Mottelay 'Bibliographical History of Electricity of Magnetism '(London, 1922) pp. 423–424.

104, 35

This was the ordinary method by which bodies were demagnetized in Hegel's day. The metal was raised to a bright red heat, and then carefully guarded from magnetic influence while it cooled. This was a troublesome operation however, and was open to the objection that it was almost sure to produce a material but uncertain change in the physical constitution of the metal. It was subsequently discovered, (see Brit. Assoc. Report, 1890, 145), that ordinary magnetizable iron is in many respects an essentially *different substance* from the non-magnetizable metal into which it is transformed when its temperature is raised to this critical point. Abrupt alterations take place in its density, specific heat, thermo-electric quality, electrical conductivity, temperature-coefficient of electrical resistance, and in some at least of its mechanical properties.

Consequently Hegel is completely justified in pointing out the connection between the magnetic properties of iron and the processing to which it is submitted. It was J. A. Ewing (1855–1935) who introduced the method of demagnetizing a specimen by subjecting it to a succession of magnetic forces which alternate in direction and gradually diminish in strength from a high value to zero; see 'Phil. Trans. Roy. Soc.' vol. 176 p. 539; cf. 'Magnetic Induction in Iron and other Metals' (3rd ed. London, 1900).

105, I

The iron and steel industry did not take on its modern form until the middle of the last century, when Henry Bessemer (1813–1898) invented his extraordinary process of making the heat developed by the rapid oxidation of the impurities in pig iron raise the temperature above the exalted melting-point of the resultant purified steel.

The most thoroughgoing and comprehensive eighteenth century work on the processing and properties of iron and steel is 'Forsök till järnets historia' (Stockholm, 1782, Germ. tr. by Georgi, 2 vols. Berlin, 1785) by Sven *Rinman* (1720–1792). See also 'Mémoire sur le fer considerée dans ses différents états métalliques' ('Mém. de l'Acad. roy. des Sciences' 1786 p. 204; Germ. tr. Crell's Chem. Annal. 1794 vol. I) by Charles Auguste Vandermonde (1735–1796), Gaspard Monge (1746–1818) and C. L. Berthollet (1748–1822). When Hegel was delivering these lectures the best discussion in German of the various theories relating to the different structures, properties and chemical impurities of iron and steel was to be found in the works of Wilhelm Albrecht *Tiemann*: see his concise 'Bemerkungen und Versuche über das Eisen' (Braunschweig, 1799), his 'Systematische Eisenhüttenkunde mit Anwendung der neuern chemischen Theorie' (Nuremberg, 1801), which contains a very useful bibliography, and his 'Abhandlung über die Förmerie und Giesserei auf Eisenhütten' (Nuremberg, 1803).

In England, it was David *Mushet* (1772–1847), who by his experience at the Clyde Iron Works, the Alfreton Iron Works in Derbyshire, and the iron works at Coleford in the forest of Dean, made himself the greatest expert of his day in this field; see the forty articles on iron and steel published in 'Tilloch's Philosophical Magazine' 1798–1823, and collected in his 'Papers on Iron and Steel' (London, 1840).

Cf. the curious theory put forward by Timothy Lane (1734–1807) in 'On magnetic attraction of oxides of iron' ('Phil. Trans. Roy.' Soc. 1805 pp. 281–284), and the chemical analysis of steel by L. N. Vauquelin (1763–1829) in 'Nicholson's Journal' vol. I pp. 248–256.

105, 12

William Gilbert (1540–1603), in his 'De Magnete' (London, 1600, Eng. tr. Mottelay, Chicago, 1952) bk. III ch. 12 quotes 'Of the Compounding of Antidotes' by Philip Costa of Mantua as evidence of this, 'At Mantua, an apothecary showed me a piece of iron completely turned to loadstone, so attracting other iron that it might be compared to a loadstone. But this piece of iron, after it had for a long time supported a terracotta ornament on the tower of the church of San Agostino at Rimini, was at last bent by the force of the winds and so remained for ten years. The friars, wishing to have it restored to its original shape, gave it to a blacksmith, and in the smithy Master Giulio Cesare, a prominent surgeon, discovered that it resembled loadstone and attracted iron. The effect was produced by long-continued lying in the direction of the poles'.

About 1722, the rusty base of an iron cross which had been on a church spire in Delft for two hundred years was found by Antonius Leeuwenhoek (1632–1723) to be highly magnetized; cf. the letter from Arnould Marcel ('Phil. Trans. Roy. Soc.' 1731–1732 pp. 294–298).

105, 17

Anton Brugmans (1732–1789) was born at Hautum in the Netherlands, and was the son of a clergyman. At the early age of fourteen he left the Grammar School at Dokkum and continued his studies at the University of Franeker. Only two years later he took his M.A. with a thesis 'De Essentiarum idearumque absoluta necessitate' (Franeker, 1748), and in 1749 was awarded his doctorate for 'Recherches sur quelques principes de connoissances humaines' (Leyden, 1756).

In 1756 he began to teach 'philosophy' at Franeker, most of his courses being concerned with the natural sciences. In 1766 he was appointed professor of natural science at Groningen and his post at Franeker was taken by Jan Hendrik van Swinden (1746–1823), who was to continue Brugmans' work on the nature of magnetism (see the following note).

Hegel is referring here to Brugmans' 'Tentamina philosophica de materia magnetica ejusque actione in ferrum et magnetem' (Franeker, 1765). C. G. Eschenbach (1753–1832) published a German translation of this work 'Philosophische Versuche über die magnetische Materie, und deren Wirkung in Eisen und Magnet' (Leipzig, 1784). Brugmans gives the following account of these points of indifference and supplies the following diagram (op. cit. Germ. tr. pp. 69–76, and table II fig. 11):—

'In a rod such as AC, be it of iron or steel, there are two points M and N which are so constituted, that if one begins at one end, such as A, to stroke this rod with a powerful magnet, and finishes the stroking at these points, no magnetic power will be brought forth, first at A and then at C. That is to say, that if one has stroked as far as M, no magnetism will be apparent at A, and that if one strokes on to N, it will be lacking at the other end (C). However, if one stops stroking either before or after these points (M and N), magnetism will be brought forth at both ends.

So far as I know, these points M and N have hitherto remained unnoticed, and I shall therefore take the opportunity of calling them the *points of indifference*. This seems to me to be a not entirely unsuitable name, for the ends of the rod which has been stroked up to these points have an *indifferent* effect upon the poles of the magnetic needle.'

Brugmans' 'Magnetismus seu de affinitatibus magneticis observationes academicae' (Leyden, 1778, Germ. tr. Eschenbach, Leipzig, 1781) is his best known work. He supposed that a magnet contains minute invisible particles of iron, each of which possesses by itself the properties of a separate magnet. He also assumed that there are two *distinct fluids*—the 'austral' and the 'boreal'— which reside in each particle of iron. These fluids he supposed to be inert and neutral when combined, as in ordinary iron, but he went on to assume that when they are decomposed, the particles of the 'austral' attract those of the 'boreal', and vice versa, while they each repel their like.

Brugman's great contribution to practical affairs was his invention of a *hydrometer* by which the strength of spirits could be easily determined. His instrument was widely used on the continent. In England however, it was the instrument devised by Bartholomew Sikes which was prescribed for the customs; see 'Phil. Trans. Roy. Soc.' 1794; 56 George III c. 40.

105, 20

Jan Hendrik van Swinden (1746–1823) was born at 's Gravenhage in the Netherlands, and was the son of a lawyer. In 1763 he began his studies at the university of Leyden where he took his doctorate in 1766. On February 18, 1767 he took over the post previously occupied by Brugmans at Franeker, his opening lecture being concerned with the causes of mistakes in matters of philosophy (zaken van wijsbegeerte). For the next eighteen years he lectured on physics, logic and mathematics at Franeker.

His research during these years was concentrated mainly upon meteorology. Brugmans' 'Tentamina philosophica' (Franeker, 1765), by drawing his attention to the points of indifference (see the previous note), led him, as Hegel notes, to the discovery of *culmination*. He noticed that if an iron wire is stroked in one direction with the north pole of a magnet for example, the end from which the stroking begins becomes the south pole of the wire, and the other end becomes its north pole. He noticed also that the power of the north pole increases steadily when the stroking is done along a certain stretch of wire, but that a point is reached at which the power of the north pole reaches a maximum. Van Swinden called this the point of culmination (puctum culminans), for if the stroking stops either before or after it, the power of the wire's north pole will not be so great. See his 'Tentamina Theoriae mathematicae de phaenomenis magneticis. Specimen Primum, sistens principia generalia ad novam punctorum indifferentiæ et puncti culminantis Theoriam', which was published in vol. XIX p. 458 (1772) of 'Commentatii de Rebus in Scientia Naturali et Medicina gestis' (44 vols. Leipzig, 1752–1798).

In 1777 van Swinden was awarded a gold medal by the Paris Academy for his essay on changes in the magnetic needle: see 'Recherches sur les aiguilles aimantés et sur leurs variations régulières' ('Mémoires savants étrangers' VIII, 1780). In 1780 his essay on the relationship between electricity and magnetism was awarded a prize by the Bavarian Academy: see 'De analogia electricitatis et magnetismi' ('Neue Abhandlungen der Baierschen Akademie der Wissenschaften' vol. II, Nuremberg, 1780). This essay is quite remarkable, for although he was not yet aware of the analogy of the magnet and the solenoid, he is mainly concerned with comparing the 'animal magnetism' of Mesmer etc. (see the note III. 381) with electricity. Two other important works in this field appeared while he was teaching at Franeker, 'De paradoxo magnetico' ('Neue Abhandlungen der Baierschen Academie' etc. vol. I 1778), and 'Receuil de mémoires sur l'analogie de l'électricité et du magnetisme' (3 vols. La Haye, 1784).

In 1785 van Swinden was appointed professor of philosophy, physics, mathematics and astronomy at the Athenaeum in Amsterdam. In 1795 he turned down an invitation to teach at Leyden, but accepted ten years later when the offer was renewed at the wish of the king. His most famous work was 'Beschrijving van een . . . volledig bewegelijk Hemelsgestel' (Franeker, 1780, Germ. tr. by F. Meyer, Leipzig, 1807). He published a nautical almanack, helped to found a training school for navigators, and spent the period from July 1798 until October 1799 in Paris helping Tralles, Delambre and Legendre to formulate the metric system; see his 'Précis des opérations qui ont servi à déterminer les bases du nouveau système métrique' (Paris, 1799).

Cf. 'The Edinburgh Journal of Science' (ed. Brewster, vol. I 1824); P. F. Mottelay 'Bibliographical History of Electricity and Magnetism' (London, 1922) pp. 271–274.

105, 32

See Sir William Edward Parry (1790–1855), 'Journal of a Voyage for the discovery of a north-west Passage . . . performed in the years 1819-20' (London, 1821). Appendix V of this work contains details of the magnetic observations made during the voyage. Appendix VIII contains, 'an account of experiments to determine the acceleration of the pendulum in different latitudes'. When Hegel treats these subjects as being closely related therefore, he may well have been influenced by these appendices. Cf. 'Phil. Trans. Roy. Soc.' 1819 pp. 196–199.

Hegel is evidently referring to events which took place on August 7, 1819 (op. cit. pp. 37–38), 'Since the time we first entered Sir James Lancaster's Sound, the sluggishness of the compasses, as well as the amount of their irregularity produced by the attraction of the ship's iron, had been found very rapidly, though uniformly, to increase, as we proceeded to the westward; so much, indeed, that, for the last two days, we had been under the necessity of giving up altogether the usual observations for determining the variation of the needle on board the ships. This irregularity became more and more obvious as we now advanced to the southward . . . It was evident, therefore, that a very material change had taken place in the dip, or the variation, or in both these phenomena. . . . which rendered it not impossible that we were now making a very near approach to the magnetic pole. This supposition was further strengthened on the morning of the 7th; when, having decreased our latitude to about 73°, we found that no alteration whatever in the absolute course on which the Hecla was steering, produced a change of more than three or four points in the direction indicated by the compass, which continued uniformly from N.N.E. to N.N.W., according as the ship's head was placed on one side or the other of the magnetic meridian. We now, therefore, witnessed, for the first time, the curious phenomena of the directive power of the needle becoming so weak as to be completely overcome by the attraction of the ship; so that the needle might now be properly said to point to the north pole of the ship.'

Cf. William Bain (Royal Navy), 'An Essay on the Variation of the Compass, shewing how far it is influenced by a change in the direction of the ship's head.' (Edinburgh, 1817).

105, 35

‚Der Magnet als Masse und als Hebel vorgestellt'. ('Jenenser Realphilosophie' II p. 52). Michelet changed this to ‚Der Magnetismus, als Masse und als Hebel vorgestellt'.

105, 40

When Hegel was lecturing at *Berlin*, the standard work on terrestrial magnetism was 'Untersuchungen über den Magnetismus der Erde' (Christiania, 1819) by Christopher Hansteen (1784–1873). There is a review of this work in the 'Edinburgh Philosophical Journal' vol. IV pp. 295–300 (1821), where Hansteen's world chart of the variations and dip of the needle is also reproduced.

106, 3

In the manuscript ('Jenenser Realphilosophie' II p. 52 note 3) Hegel added a remark here at a later date, ‚wie am Hebel; aber diese haben das

Allgemeine nicht an ihnen selbst; ihr Schwerpunkt ist nicht das absolut Negative'.

106, 10

,Indem in dem Pendel die Größe der Masse als bewegende Kraft eintritt, so muß an ihm dasselbe Volumen, das eine größere spezifische Schwere hat, stärkere Bewegungskraft haben — so ist es näher den Polen zu'. (Jenenser Realphilosophie II' p. 52).

Michelet's version ,. . . so muß an ihm dieselbe Masse stärkere Bewegungskraft haben, je näher den Polen zu'. This is excusable, as Hegel actually wrote, ,. . . die eine größere spezifische Schwere hat, stärkere Bewegungskraft hat — so näher den Polen zu'.

106, 18

On the geodetical use of the pendulum at this time see Sir Edward Sabine (1788–1883) 'An Account of Experiments to determine the figure of the Earth' (London, 1825): F. W. Bessel (1784–1846) 'Untersuchungen über die Länge des einfachen Secundenpendels' (Berlin, 1828): J. B. Biot (1774–1862) and D. F. Arago (1786–1853) 'Receuil d'observations géodésiques' (Paris, 1821): Petrus van Galen 'Disputatio mathematica inauguralis de Pendulo, eiusque adplicatione ad telluris figuram determinandam' (Amsterdam, 1830).

106, 27

In the terminology of the time 'chemism' (Chemismus) was taken to mean *chemical relationship,* i.e. 'everything in natural phenomena and mixed transformations which is determined by chemical factors and may be explained in the light of chemical principles'. See J. F. Pierer 'Medizinisches Realwörterbuch' (8 vols. Altenburg, 1816–1829) vol. II p. 122. In the addition to this §, Hegel defines it as 'the totality into which bodies enter in accordance with their specific particularity'. The best account he gives of the general significance he attaches to it is to be found in 'The Logic' (tr. Wallace, O.U.P. 1963) §§ 200–203 where he takes it to be the category presupposing 'mechanism', and anterior to 'teleology'. For the *development* of his views on it during the Jena period see 'Jenenser Logik' etc. (ed. Lasson, Leipzig, 1923) pp. 268–273: 'Jenenser Realphilosophie I' (ed. Hoffmeister, Leipzig, 1932) pp. 28–73: 'Jenenser Realphilosophie' II (ed. Hoffmeister, Leipzig, 1931) pp. 57–79, 95–103.

Typical of the experiments illustrating the connection between electricity and chemism was that performed in Amsterdam by A. P. van Troostwyk (1752–1837) and J. R. Deiman (1743–1808), in the course of which they managed to decompose water by means of electricity: see Rozier's 'Journal de Physique' Nov. 1789: Gren's 'Journal der Physik' II vol. i p. 132: cf. 'Phil. Trans. Roy. Soc.' 1797 pp. 142–158.

After Alessandro Volta (1745–1827) had suggested that the electric current which brings forth certain phenomena in living beings is also the prime cause of chemical and magnetic activity, changes in temperature etc. ('Gilbert's

Annalen der Physik' vol. XII p. 509), the relation between magnetism, electricity and chemism became the subject of much research. See Sir Humphry Davy (1778–1829) 'Chemical Agencies of Electricity' ('Phil. Trans. Roy. Soc.' 1803 pp. 1–56).

For a recent survey of developments in early electrochemistry, see J. R. Partington 'A History of Chemistry' vol. iv pp. 3–28 (London, 1964).

107, 10

,daß die Identität dieſer Erſcheinungen in der Vorſtellung anerkannt worden iſt'.

107, 31

See for example Schelling's 'System der gesammten Philosophie und der Naturphilosophie insbesondere' (1804), published by Manfred Schröter in 'Schelling's Werke' (Munich, 1962) second suppl. volume pp. 61–506. §§ 166–169 of this work have the following headings:—

§ 166 ,Die Elektrizität iſt ebenſo wie Magnetismus nicht die Wirkung eines beſonderen Princips, ſondern eine allgemeine Kategorie der Materie.

§ 167 Weder durch Magnetismus noch durch Elektrizität iſt die Totalität des dynamiſchen Proceſſes geſetzt.

§ 168 Die Totalität des dynamiſchen Proceſſes iſt nur im chemiſchen Proceß dargeſtellt.

§ 169 Der chemiſche Proceß iſt ſowohl durch Magnetismus alſo durch Elektrizität vermittelt'.

108, 35

Alessandro Volta (1745–1827) discovered that all conductors of electricity might be divided into *two classes*: those such as metals and carbon in its conducting form, in which a difference of potential is created by mere contact, one of the conductors being positively electrified and the other negatively, and those such as water, aqueous solutions of various kinds, and those conductors now known as electrolytes.

Volta discovered that if a *series* of bodies of the first class, such as disks of various metals, is brought into contact, the potential difference between the first and the last is precisely the same as it would be if these bodies were in *immediate* contact. He showed in fact, that in this case there is no *accumulation* of potential. He also showed however, that if metallic disks are *alternated* with disks of cloth wetted with a conductor of the second class, the effect of the feeble potential difference between one pair of metal disks is added to that of the potential difference between the next pair, so that any required difference of potential can be accumulated by a sufficiently long series of pairs.

These discoveries led him to devise the 'voltaic pile' mentioned here by Hegel. It consisted of disks of copper and zinc or other metals, with wet cloth placed between the pairs. Volta's description of his pile was communicated in a letter written to Sir Joseph Banks (1743–1820) on March 20, 1800; see 'On the

Electricity excited by the mere contact of conducting Substances of different Kinds' ('Phil. Trans. Roy. Soc.' vol. 90 pt. i p. 402, 1800).

The analogy between the polarity of the voltaic pile and that of the magnet was soon noticed, but it was not until 1819 that H. C. Ørsted (1777–1851) discovered that when a wire joining the end plates of a voltaic pile is held near a pivoted magnet or compass needle, the latter is deflected and places itself more or less transversely to the wire, the direction depending upon whether the wire is above or below the needle and on the manner in which the copper or zinc ends of the pile are connected to it. He recognized the existence of what is now called the magnetic field round the conductor. See 'Experimenta circa effectum conflictus electrici in acum magneticam' (Copenhagen, July 21, 1820): there is a translation of this work, 'Experiments on the Effect of a Current of Electricity on the Magnetic Needle' in 'Thomson's Annals of Philosophy' vol. XVI pp. 273–6 (1820): cf. Gilbert's 'Annalen der Physik' LXVI, 1820 pp. 295–304.

At about the same time Sir Humphry Davy (1778–1829) and D. F. Arago (1786–1853) discovered the power of the electric current to magnetize iron and steel. See 'Annales de Chimie et Physique' vol. XV pp. 93–103 (1820). 'Thomson's Annals of Philosophy' 1821, II pp. 81–88.

These discoveries opened up research in the field of *electromagnetism*: see C. H. Pfaff (1773–1852) 'Der Elektro-Magnetismus, eine historisch-kritische Darstellung der bisherigen Entdeckungen' (Hamburg, 1824).

109, 3
Hegel is evidently referring here to his Jena lectures, which were delivered soon after Volta's discovery and some fifteen years before Ørsted's. In the lectures of 1803 ('Jenenser Realphilosophie I' p. 80 cf. p. 255), he notes that, 'We have recognized true cohesion in formal shape as magnetism, i.e. as a being of various specific weighted entities in a *single* unity, in shape as totality'. In the lectures of 1805–6 this idea is developed ('Jenenser Realphilosophie II' pp. 50–54), and as in Hegel's later lectures, magnetism is regarded as forming the transition from shape to the crystal, 'Magnetism is therefore the formal determinate being of differences within the unity of the subject; it is pure direction or line' etc.

109, 28
See the note on Schelling II. 310.

110, 3
Paul Erman (1764–1851) was appointed professor of physics at Berlin when the university was founded in 1810. For further details concerning him see the note III. 311.

The original account of the experiment with the 'rotation circuit' described here by Hegel is to be found in Erman's 'Umrisse zu den physischen

Verhältnissen des von Herrn Professor Ørsted entdeckten elektrochemischen Magnetismus' (Berlin, 1821). This work falls into three main parts: (i) observations on the free-moving electro-magnetic circuit, (ii) observations on the dipping needle of the box-compass, and (iii) observations on the azimuth compass.

The experiment mentioned is to be found in the first part (pp. 7–36). Hegel's quotation is taken from p. 14. Erman supplies the following diagrams of his apparatus:

(*a*) The strip of cardboard or whalebone and the container:

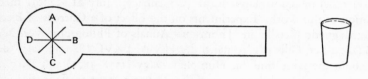

The cardboard is cut at AC,DB etc. and the container is fitted into it.

(*b*) The container is filled with a weak acid and the circuit is brought into contact with it by means of a piece of zinc:

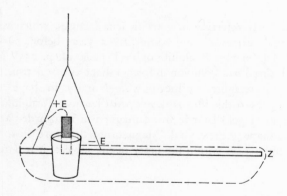

The whole apparatus is suspended by means of four threads. The magnet is brought to bear on it at Z.

112, 26

,Das Anziehen ist eben Machen, daß das Andere ebensogut selbst geht, als das Machende'.

112, 30

Hegel formulated the transition from magnetism to the crystal as early as 1805–6 ('Jenenser Realphilosophie' II p. 54). In the lectures of 1803–4 ('Jenenser Realphilosophie' I p. 70) he took the embryonic crystalline forms of hail, sleet and snow to be, like aerolites, a synthesis of the fluidity of air and the punctiformity of earth. It was probably the discovery of the *chemical* action involved in the functioning of the *voltaic pile* which clarified his views on this transition; see for example Sir Humphry Davy's numerous papers on this subject in 'Phil. Trans. Roy. Soc.' 1807–1810.

Hegel regarded water as being essential to crystallization (see the note II. 307). He seems to have supposed that once the 'invisible germ' or 'constructive force' giving rise to crystallization had been traced in water, it would prove to be similar to the figuration of a magnetic field. The discovery of magnetic 'lines of force' by Michael Faraday (1791–1867), see his 'Experimental Researches in Electricity' (3 vols. London, 1839, 1844, 1855) § 3237, and the recognition of the similarity between these lines and the 'watering' of metal mentioned by Hegel II. 116, 14 and C. N. Haldat du Lys (1770–1852), see 'Annales de Chimie et de Physique' vol. XLII pp. 33–45, 1829, seemed to confirm this supposition.

This theoretical background evidently accounts for Hegel's mentioning the *ice-spicula* at this juncture, the formation of ice being the most basic form of crystallization. The best investigation of this aspect of ice available to him was 'Dissertation sur la Glace' (Paris, 1715, improved ed. Paris, 1749), by J. J. Dortous de Mairan (1678–1771); cf. C. M. Marx (1794–1864) 'Geschichte der Crystallkunde' (Carlsruhe and Baden, 1825) pp. 82–84. De Mairan observes that, 'Il faut donc reconnaître, dans les particules de glace qui forment les étoiles de la neige, comme dans les globules du sang une autre cause, une cause active, un mécanisme plus caché, plus compliqué'. (p. 168).

See the account of the huge hail-stones which fell at Bonn on May 7, 1822 in 'The Edinburgh Philosophical Journal' vol. XI pp. 326–329 (1824), 'The masses had a concentric lamellar structure; in the centre was a white nearly opaque, nucleus, of a round or elliptical form, around which were arranged concentric layers, which increased in translucency from the innermost to the outermost'. A letter sent by a certain Robert Lindsay of Aberdeen, and containing a description of hail stones he had observed in the Orkneys in 1818, was read to the Wernerian Society on Nov. 29, 1823: Lindsay observes that 'The regularity in form may have been occasioned by laws of fracture in *crystallized* bodies . . . The probable cause of fracture may be found in the expansion of air in the opaque nucleus, in electricity, or in centrifugal force.'

Cf. J. S. C. Schweigger's 'Journal für Chemie und Physik' vol. XXXII pp. 1–25 (Nuremberg, 1821): John Murray (d. 1820) 'System of Chemistry' (4 vols. Edinburgh, 1819) vol. I p. 36. Jacob Green (1790–1841) 'On the crystallization of snow' ('The American Journal of Science' vol. II no. 2 pp. 337–339, 1820).

113, 7

‚im Durchgang der Blätter', d.h. in der Kerngestalt'. Hegel is here equating two theories of crystal structure prevalent at the beginning of the last century.

A. G. Werner (1750–1817), in his 'Von den äusserlichen Kennzeichen der Fossilien' (Leipzig, 1774) §§ 156–159 took the 'folium' (Blatt) to be the fundamental feature of crystal structure, and foliated fractures to be distinguished in accordance with the 'Größe, Richtung und Lage der Blätter'. In the lectures which he subsequently delivered at Freiberg however, his terminology changed somewhat. Thomas Weaver (1773–1855), when he published his 'Treatise on the External Characters of Fossils' (Dublin, 1805), supplemented Werner's original text with corrections and notes, and in this work (§§ 195–197 and pp. 274–276) there is a full account of Werner's mature views on the 'passage of the folia' and foliated fractures.

Hegel was clearly justified in regarding this theory of Werner's as approximating very closely to that put forward by R. J. Hauy (1743–1826) in his 'Essai d'une Théorie sur la Structure des Crystaux' (Paris, 1784). Hauy, in his attempt to explain crystal structure, postulated what he called 'une molécule constituante'. It is this that Hegel calls 'Kerngestalt', and which is generally known in English as the 'cleavage nucleus'. Hauy defines the basic problem of crystallography in the introduction to this work (p. 25), 'Tout consiste à resoudre, dans chaque cas particulier, ce problème général; Étant donné un crystal, déterminer la forme précise de ses molécules constituantes, leur arrangement respectif, et les loix que suivent les variations des lames dont il est composé.'

113, 13

‚Der Ton des Magnets geht zuerst . . .' ('Jenenser Realphilosophie' II p. 54). Michelet changed this to ‚Der Magnetismus geht zuerst . . .'

113, 19

P. N. de Changeux (1740–1800) in Rozier's 'Observations sur la Physique' vol. VII p. 482 (Paris, 1776) noticed the influence of *electricity* upon crystallization, 'Un chymiste très-instruit m'a assure, qu'ayant soumis à l'électricité les dissolutions des sels neutres la crystallization avoit été favorisée; les sels étoient beaucoup plus réguliers et plus gros'.

In Gilbert's 'Annalen der Physik' 1824 there is an article by L. N. Seeber (1793–1855) of Freiburg on the influence of magnetism upon crystallization, but Henry James Brooke (1771–1857) in 'On Crystallization', an article published in the 'Edinburgh Philosophical Journal' n. 23 (Jan. 1825) calls the conclusions reached in question.

The influence of magnetism upon crystallization is also discussed by K. A. Weinhold (1782–1829) in 'Physikalische Versuche über den Magnetismus. (Meissen, 1819) pp. 32, 38, 41: John Murray (1786–1851) in 'Philosophical

Magazine' (Nov. 1821 pp. 380–382): T. J. Seebeck (1770–1831) in 'Berzelius Jahrbuch über den Fortschritt der physikalischen Wissenschaften' (tr. F. Wöhler, 1825) vol. IV pp. 16, 45 etc. Cf. A. G. Lüdicke (1748–1822) 'Ueber den Einfluss des magnetischen Wirkungskreises auf die Krystallisation einiger Salze' ('Gilbert's Annalen der Physik' vol. 68 pp. 76–83, 1821).

113, 25

The translation of this sentence has been made from Michelet's version of it. As the original differs quite considerably however, it may be of interest to give it ('Jenenser Realphilosophie' II p. 54), ‚Es ist dies die Geometrie der Natur, die ihre Bestimmtheit zu Kristallen ausbildet, eine stille sprachlose Regsamkeit, die zeitlos ihre Dimensionen gleichgültig — ohne Licht — darlegt. Es ist dabei keine äußerliche Bestimmung und Formung, sondern das eigne stille Lebensprincip der Natur, das tatlos sich exponiert, und von dessen Gebilde man nur sagen kann, daß es da ist'.

113, 37

See the note II. 327.

114, 6

‚Es ist daher die Zweckmäßigkeit der Natur selbst hier zuerst vorhanden'. In the original ('Jenenser Realphilosophie' II p. 54) explains this by adding that 'The previous forms are not yet purposeful, but merely constitute a *determinate being*, which as such does not have its relation to another within itself'.

114, 23

‚Die getrennten Stücke bleiben gleichgültig liegen'. Thomas Weaver (1773–1855) in his 'A Treatise on the External Characters of Fossils' (Dublin, 1805) gives two equivalents for ‚Stücke'. In connection with the 'external appearance' of 'fossils', he translates Werner's ‚eckigen Stücken' as 'angular *pieces*' (p. 254). In connection with the 'form of fragments', he translates Werner's ‚abgesonderten Stücke' as 'distinct concretions' (p. 278). Hegel evidently has in mind this second use of the word.

114, 28

This is evidently a reference to a remark made by R.-J. Hauy (1743–1826) in his 'Traité de crystallographie' (3 vols. Paris, 1822) vol. II p. 291 'Nous devons concevoir que les molécules du cristal générateur sont douées d'une vertu analogue à celle qu l'on a désignée par le nom de *polarité*. Chacune d'elles à deux pôles sollicités par des forces contraires'.

See the article by J. J. Berhardi (1774–1850) on the 'magnetic axes' of crystals in 'Schweigger's Journal' vol. XXV pp. 99–100, 247–253 (1819). Cf. the article by G. F. Pohl (1788–1849) in which the internal structure of crystals is treated from an electro-magnetic point of view and taken to be the result of 'polari-zation lines'. ('Kastner's Archiv' 1824 III i p. 47 et seq.). There is a survey of work in this field by P. L. Dulong (1785–1838) and L. J. Thénard (1777–1857) in 'Schweiggers Journal für Chemie und Physik' vol. XXX pp. 229–246 (Halle, 1824). John Murray (d. 1820) mentions the subject in his 'System of Chemistry' (4 vols. Edinburgh, 1819) vol. I p. 42, 'The theory of crystallization is still obscure, so far as it relates to the cause of the regular forms to which it gives rise. This has been accounted for, on the supposition that the particles of bodies have different figures, and that they have a polarity or tendency to arrange themselves, in obeying the law of cohesion, by certain sides in preference to others; whence the uniformity of crystallization in each individual, and the difference in the figure of its crystals from that in others.'

114, 35

R.-J. Hauy (1743–1826), in his 'Essai d'une Théorie sur la Structure des Crystaux' (Paris, 1784) had explained the outer form of crystals by taking it to be built up from regular or irregular aggregations of its cleavage nucleus (op. cit. chs. I and II).

In 1809 W. H. Wollaston (1766–1828) invented the first reflecting goniometer (the vertical-circle model). This enabled the angles of crystals to be measured with much greater precision than they had been by the old hand-goniometer. At almost the same time, Christian Samuel Weiss (1780–1856), a colleague of Hegel's at Berlin, began to attack the problem of crystalline form from a purely *geometrical* point of view, without reference to any theory of structure; see his 'De indagando Formarum crystallinarum charactere Geometrico principali' (Leipzig, 1809), and 'Uebersichtliche Darstellung der verschiedenen natürlichen Abtheilungen der Crystallisationssysteme' ('Abhandlungen der Berliner Akademie der Wissenschaften' 1814–1815 pp. 290–336). Weiss considered the faces of crystals by their intercepts on co-ordinate axes, which were drawn join-ing the opposite corners of certain forms. In this way he was able to group the various forms described by Hauy into four classes, cubic, tetragonal, hexagonal and orthorhombic.

114, 36

‚Der (sic) Wachsthum des Krystalls geht schichtenweise vor sich'.

This is probably a reference to the doctrine mentioned in R.-J. Hauy's 'Traité de crystallographie' (3 vols. Paris, 1822) vol. I pl 54, 'Le cristal naissant est déjà semblable à celui, que la nature nous présente entièrement formé, et il ne fait ensuite que s'accroître par une succession de couches, qui se recouvrent mutuellement'. It should be remembered that in the Wernerian terminology prevalent while Hegel was lecturing at Jena, ‚wachsen' had various technical meanings associated with the 'aggregation' of crystals, i.e. their natural occur-rence; see T. Weaver op. cit. p. 268.

115, 11

See the account by Johannes Scheuchzer (d. 1733) of the huge rock-crystals found in a quartz vein in the Grimsel pass in 1720: 'Phil. Trans. Roy. Soc.' 1727 p. 260. Many of the rock-crystals found on that occasion weighed a hundredweight, and some as much as eight hundredweight. 'In other mountains in the Alps, cavities have been opened, containing rock-crystals weighing upwards of fourteen hundred weight, and measuring in diameter three and a half feet, in length two and a half, and each lateral plane one and a half feet broad . . . Large and beautiful crystals . . . are found in Madagascar.' Robert Jameson (1774–1854) 'A System of Mineralogy' (3 vols. Edinburgh, 1820) vol. I pp. 182–196.

The large Madagascan crystals mentioned by Hegel certainly originated in the Archaean crystalline and eruptive rocks forming the eastern massifs of the central plateau of the island. In the central and northern parts of this mountainous region, quartz is still mined commercially. See Alexis-Marie Rochon (1741–1817) 'Voyage à Madagascar et aux Indes orientales' (Paris, 1791), tr. Joseph Trapp 'A Voyage to Madagascar and the East Indies' (London, 1793) p. 277, 'Those who prefer mineralogy to botany, will find in the high mountains of *Ambotismena*, plenty of objects worthy their attention. They will find stupendous masses of rock-crystal; some are perfectly crystallized, others seem to have no regular form, many of them contain sherls and other strange bodies.'

Cf. H. Steffens 'Vollständiges Handbuch der Oryktognosie' (4 pts. Halle 1811–1824) pt. I pp. 105–110: G. K. C. Storr (1749–1821) 'Alpenreise' (2 pts. Leipzig, 1784–1786) II pp. 40–130: F. J. M. A. Billiard (1788–c. 1860) 'Voyage aux colonies orientales' (Paris, 1822).

115, 20

See the note II. 328. For further details concerning Werner see the note III. 218.

115, 28

See M. H. Klaproth (1743–1817) and F. B. Wolff (1766–1845) 'Chemisches Wörterbuch' (9 vols. Berlin, 1807–1819) vol. I pp. 652–660, 'Sein Gefüge ist blättrig, und der Durchgang der Blätter richtet sich stets und einzig nach den acht Seiten des oktaedrischen Grundkrystalls; daher sich auch der Diamant bloß nach diesen Richtungen spalten oder kloven läßt'.

There were some excellent works on this subject available to Hegel: see David Jeffries 'Treatise on Diamonds and Pearls' (London, 1751, ed. Holmes, 1871, Germ. tr. Danzig, 1756): John Mawe (1764–1829) 'Treatise on Diamonds and Precious stones. To which is added some account of the best methods of cutting and polishing them' (London, 1813, ed. Grodzinski, London, 1950): R.-J. Hauy (1743–1826) 'Traité des caractères physiques des pierres précieuses' (Paris, 1817): Moritz Pinder (1807–1871), who worked in the Royal Library at

Berlin from 1829, 'De adamante commentatio antiquaria' (Berlin, 1829): John Murray (1786?–1851) 'Memoir on the Nature of the Diamond' (London, 1831), see especially John Mawe op. cit. (2nd ed., London, 1823) p. 30.

115, 30

René-Just Hauy (1743–1822) was born at Saint-Just in the department of Oise. His parents were too poor to pay for his further education, but friends of the family recognized his brilliance, and helped him to finish his studies at the college of Navarre and the college of Cardinal Lemoine and finally to take holy orders. It was at the latter institution that he became a teacher and met Charles François Lhomond (1727–1794), who introduced him to the study of natural sciences, especially botany, and became his lifelong friend.

It was a series of lectures on mineralogy by L. J. M. Daubenton (1716–1800), author of the 'Tableau méthodique des minéraux' Paris, 1784), which gave him his grounding in crystallography. On February 12, 1783 he was elected member of the French Academy for his discovery of the *law of rational indices* or *intercepts*. In his 'Essai d'une Théorie sur la Structure des Crystaux' (Paris, 1784) he expounded this theory at some length. He postulated a 'cleavage nucleus' (see the note II. 328) as being basic to all crystalline form, and then showed how the various secondary faces on a crystal are related to it by a law of whole numbers, and how the angles between them can be arrived at by mathematical calculation. He took this 'secondary form' of the crystal to be built up from regular or irregular layers of the 'nucleus', each of which is so small that it is not separately visible. See the excellent article by A. Q. Buée (1748–1826) 'Outlines of the Mineralogical Systems of Romé de Lisle and Abbé Hauy; with observations' ('Nicholson's Journal' IX pp. 26–39, 78–88, 1804). Cf. W. H. Wollaston (1766–1828) 'On the elementary Particles of certain crystals' ('Phil. Trans. Roy. Soc.' 1813 pp. 51–63).

For those who, in Hauy's lifetime, added to his work, see C. M. Marx (1794–1864) 'Geschichte der Crystallkunde' (Carlsruhe and Baden, 1825) pp. 132–213. J. F. C. Hessel (1796–1872) showed that as a consequence of Hauy's law of rational indices, thirty two types of symmetry are possible in crystals; see his article 'Krystallometrie' in 'Gehler's Physikalisches Wörterbuch' vol. V, 1830: published separately (Leipzig, 1831).

During the revolution Hauy was imprisoned for a while. In 1793 he was appointed member of the commission for weights and measures however, see his 'Instruction sur les measures déduites de la grandeur de la terre' (Paris, 1794). In 1802 Napoleon appointed him professor of mineralogy at the museum of natural history, and in 1803 canon of Notre Dame. His 'Traité de minéralogie' (4 vols. Paris, 1801) was translated into German (Karsten, 3 vols. Leipzig, 1803), as was his 'Traité élémentaire de physique' (Paris, 1803, tr. Blumhof, Weimar, 1804). When Napoleon visited the National Museum during the hundred days he told the canon, 'Monsieur Hauy, j'ai emporté votre physique à l'île d'Elbe, et je l'ai relue avec le plus grand intérêt'.

Hauy gave the completest account of his work on crystals in his 'Traité de crystallographie' (3 vols. Paris, 1822). He died at Paris on June 3, 1822. George Cuvier (1769–1832) said of him, in the funeral oration, 'Comme on a dit avec raison qu'il n'y aura plus un autre Newton, parce qu'il n'y a pas un second système du monde, on peut aussi dans une sphère plus restreinte, dire qu'il n'y aura point un autre Hauy, parce qu'l n'y aura pas une deuxième structure des cristaux'. This observation may well have incited Hegel into observing that Hauy concentrated mainly upon *describing* the forms of crystals.

115, 40

At that time, the word 'fossil' was used to refer to any rock, mineral, or mineral substance dug out of the earth.

116, 3

Hoffmeister's version of this sentence has been translated here ('Jenenser Realphilosophie' II p. 55). Hegel actually wrote ‚Er nimmt den Kern an, läßt auf diesen sich die Molecules nach einer Art von Reihung, worin durch . . .' Michelet emends this, and has clearly checked on Hegel's source.

116, 6

Hauy gives his fullest account of this doctrine in his 'Traité de crystallographie' (3 vols. Paris, 1822) see I p. 52 etc. Cf. Henry James Brooke (1771–1857) 'A Familiar Introduction to Crystallography' (London, 1823) p. 43, 'The whole theory of molecules and decrements is to be regarded as little else than a series of symbolic characters, by whose assistance we are enabled to investigate and to demonstrate with greater facility the relations between the primary and secondary forms of crystals'.

As this passage dates from Hegel's Jena period however, it is almost certainly based upon pp. 21–22 of Hauy's 'Essai d'une Théorie sur la Structure des Crystaux' (Paris, 1784).

116, 8

See J. J. Bernhardi (1774–1850) 'Ueber das Kristallisationssystem der chemischen Elemente' ('Schweigger's Journal' 1817 vol. XXI i p. 7). See also the articles by Armand Lévy (1794–1841) in Thomson's 'Annals of Philosophy' 1823–1825 and the 'Edinburgh Philosophical Journal' 1822–1826.

It was in fact research in this field which led Eilhard Mitscherlich (1794–1863) to the discovery of *isomorphism*, and so to the disproving of Hauy's theory. As Mitscherlich made his discovery at Berlin in 1818, and was professor of chemistry there from 1822 onwards, it is rather curious that Hegel should not have made more of his work. Hegel may have felt that too full a treatment of the *chemical* factors in crystallization would have involved his abandoning the valuable standpoint that the essence of crystalline structure is its *figuration*, and that this is closely related to *magnetic* 'lines of force' (note II. 327). See Mitscherlich's 'Ueber die Krystallisation der Salze' ('Abhandlungen der Königlich Preussischen Akademie der Wissenschaften, physikalische-mathematische Klasse' 1818–1819 pp. 427–327): 'Ueber die Körper, welche in zwei verschiedenen Formen Krystallisiren' (op. cit. 1822–1823 pp. 43–48): 'Om Förhållandet imellan Chemiska Sammansättningen och Krystallformen' ('Kungliga Svenska Vetenskaps-Akademiens Handlingar' 1822 pp. 4–79).

Several facts which were in disagreement with Hauy's theory were known before Mitscherlich published these papers. In 1787 for example, N. Leblanc (1742–1806) discovered that alum crystals, which he obtained both as cubes and as octahedra, could contain considerable amounts of iron: see 'Journal de Physique' 1788, vol. 28, p. 341. In 1816 L. J. Gay-Lussac (1778–1850) grew crystals of ammonia alum over those of potash alum, and suggested that 'the molecules of the two alums have the same form and are acted upon by the same forces': see 'Annales de Chimie' 1816 vol. ii p. 176.

116, 12

Giovanni Girolamo Zannichelli (1662–1729), in his 'De ferro ejusque nivis praeparatione in qua varia de ipso metallo explicantur' (Venice, 1713, 2nd ed. Venice, 1719) notices that blocks of iron, when they are broken, will sometimes display crystalline formations. J. B. L. Romé de l'Isle (1736–1790), in his 'Cristallographie ou Déscription de Formes propres à tous les corps du règne mineral' (3 vols. Paris, 1783) vol. III p. 2 observed of metals that, 'tous sont susceptibles de prendre en cristallisant, soit par la voie humide, soit par la voie sèche, la forme cubique ou son inverse qui est l'octaèdre'.

In 1808 Aloys Beck von Widmannstätten (1753–1849) noticed the crystalline figurations in metal caused by the corrosion brought about by nitric acid. Carl Franz Anton von Schreibers (1775–1852), in his 'Beyträge zur Geschichte und Kenntniss meteorischer Stein- und Metal- Massen' (Vienna, 1820), drew attention to the observations of von Widmannstätten (pp. 70–80) and laid the foundation of modern metallography through his examination of the crystalline structure of meteoric iron. See especially tables VIII and IX of this book, 'Der Zweck der bildlichen Darstellungen dieser Tafeln ist die Versinnlichung des merkwürdigen krystallinischen Gefüges der vorzüglichsten Gediegeneisen-Massen'. Cf. H. C. Sorby (1826–1908) 'On the microscopical structure of iron and steel' (British Association, 1864).

The crystalline structure of metals was fairly well confirmed in Hegel's day therefore. On the crystalline structure of bismuth see M. H. Klaproth (1743–1817) and F. Wolff (1766–1845) 'Chemisches Wörterbuch' (9 vols. Berlin,

1807–1819) 4th supplementary volume pp. 403–408: John Murray (d. 1820) 'System of Chemistry' (4 vols. Edinburgh, 1819) vol. III pp. 400–406.

116, 14

'Moiré metallique'. It was evidently L. J. Proust (1754–1826) who first discovered that when tin-plate is dipped in a weak acid, the surface layer of tin is dissolved, and that various crystallizations, often exhibiting striking patterns, are formed in the lower layers: 'Sur l'étamage' ('Annales de Chimie' 1804 pp. 44–74, 'Tilloch's Philosophical Magazine' 1805 pp. 313–319). In 1815 a certain M. Allard of Paris patented a technique for treating the surfaces of metal goods. L. W. Gilbert (1769–1824) gave an account of the process in 'Moirirtes Metall und Malerei darin, oder das Moiré metallique' ('Gilbert's Annalen der Physik' vol. 64 pp. 279–302): John Frederic Daniell (1790–1845) 'On some phenomena attending the process of solution, and on their application to the laws of crystallization' ('Quarterly Journal of Science' I pp. 24–49, 1816): Samuel Parkes (1761–1825) on tin-plate in 'Quarterly Journal of the Manchester Physical Society' (Oct. 1819).

The concisest contemporary English account of the phenomenon mentioned here by Hegel is to be found in 'The Journal of Science and the Arts. Edited at the Royal Institution of Great Britain' (London, 1818) vol. V p. 368: Miscellaneous Intelligence 11. On the Moiré Metallique, or Fer blanc moiré. 'This is an article of Parisian manufacture, much employed to cover ornamental cabinet work, dressing boxes, telescopes, opera glasses, etc. etc. and is prepared in the following manner.

Sulphuric acid is to be diluted with seven or nine parts water, then dip a sponge or rag into it, and wash with it the surface of a sheet of tin, which speedily will exhibit an appearance of crystallizations, which is the Moiré.

This effect however cannot be easily produced upon every sort of sheet tin, for if the sheet has been much hardened by hammering or rolling, then the moiré cannot be effected until the sheet of tin has been heated so as to produce an incipient fusion on the surface, after which the acid will act upon it and produce the moiré. Almost any acid will do as well as the sulphuric, and it is said that the citric acid dissolved in a sufficient quantity of water, answers better than any other.

The moiré has of late been much improved by employing the blow pipe, to form small and beautiful specks on the surface of the tin, previous to the application of acid.

When the moiré has been formed, the plate is to be varnished and polished, the varnish being tinted with any glazing colour, and thus the red, blue, green, yellow, and pearl coloured moirés are manufactured.'

Cf. John Badcock 'Domestic Amusements or Philosophical Recreations' (London, 1823) p. 140; 'The New Monthly Magazine and Literary Journal' (London, 1823) vol. IX pp. 551–552; Andrew Ure (1778–1857) 'A Dictionary of

Arts, Manufactures, and Mines' (London, 1839), Germ. tr. 'Technisches Wörter-buch oder Handbuch der Gewerbskunde' (tr. K. Karmarsch and F. Heeren, 3 vols. Prague, 1843–1844).

117, 4

Theophrastus Bombast von Hohenheim (Paracelsus) (c. 1490–1541), the famous German physician. Hegel is referring here to his 'De tribus primis Essentiis', which is to be found in his 'Opera Omnia Medico-Chemico Chirur-gica' (ed. De Tournes, 3 vols. Geneva, 1658) vol. I p. 354. Cf. 'Theophrastus von Hohenheim gen. Paracelsus: Sämtliche Werke' 1. Abteilung 'Medizi-nische, naturwissenschaftliche und philosophische Schriften' (ed. Karl Sudhoff, Munich and Berlin, 1922–1933) vol. III pp. 1–11; J. R. Partington 'A History of Chemistry' (London, 1961) vol. II p. 142. Hegel may have known of the doctrine of Paracelsus and his followers from T. A. Rixner and T. Siber 'Leben und Lehr-meinungen beruehmter Physiker am Ende des XVI und am Anfange des XVII. Jahrhunderts' (7 vols. Sulzbach, 1819–1826: 2nd ed. Sulzbach, 1829) or from Kurt Sprengel (1766–1833) 'Versuch einer pragmatischen Geschichte der Arzneikunde' (5 vols. Halle, 1792–1828).

The remark attributed here to Boehme was anticipated by Joseph Du Chesne (1544–1609), the physician-in-ordinary to Henry IV of France, who also taught that all bodies are composed of three substances as God is of three principles. He took these substances to be the solid contained in saltpetre, the volatile salt of sulphur and the volatile mercurial salt.

117, 5

Jacob Boehme (1575–1624): see 'The Works of Jacob Behmen' (ed. William Law, 4 vols. London, 1764–1781). Boehme mentions this doctrine on several occasions: see 'The Three Principles of the Divine Essence' (1619) chs. I and II (op. cit. vol. I), 'Behold, there are especially three Things in the Originality, out of which all Things are, both Spirit and Life, Motion and Comprehensibility, viz. *Sulphur, Mercurius,* and *Sal* . . . Now to speak in a creaturely way, *Sulphur, Mercurius,* and *Sal*, are understood to be thus. *Sul* is the Soul or the Spirit that is risen up, or in a Similitude [it is] God: Phur is the *Prima Materia*, or first Matter out of which the Spirit is generated, but especially the Harshness: *Mercurius* has a fourfold from in it, *viz.* Harshness, Bitterness, Fire, Water: Sal is the Child that is generated from these four, and is harsh, eager, and a Cause of the Com-prehensibility.

Understand right now what I declare to you: Harshness, Bitterness, and Fire, are in the Originality, in the first Principle: The Water-source is generated therein: And God is not called God according to the first Principle; but accord-ing to that, he is called Wrathfulness, Anger, the earnest [severe or tart] Source, from which Evil, and also the woeful tormenting Trembling, and Burning, have their Original'. Cf. 'The Threefold Life of Man' (1619–1620) op. cit. vol. II pp. 12–13: 'The Mysterium Magnum' (1623) op. cit. vol. III p. 17: 'Signatura Rerum' (1621) op. cit. vol. IV pp. 18–19.

117, 11

‚der Gedanke, der noch nicht frei war'. Nicolin and Pöggeler, in their edition of the 'Enzyklopädia' (Hamburg, 1959) have removed the last five words without explaining why.

117, 24

‚immer noch etwas Besonderes ausgegangen zu haben'. In *standard* German the verb ‚ausgehen' has several meanings (to go out, emanate, come off, be extinguished, terminate etc.), but not that given to it here by Hegel, who is merely saying that these new facts or 'particularities' are brought under *observation* or into the sphere of *experience*. This is an example of his native Swabian, although even in this dialect, this use of the word is not common: see Hermann Fischer and Wilhelm Pfleiderer 'Schwäbisches Wörterbuch' (Tübingen, 1904–1936) vol. 1 col. 472.

One of the earliest instances of its being used in this way in Swabian is to be found in the account by Hans Jakob Breuning (1552?–1616) of a journey he made to London in the summer of 1595, in order to enquire into the possibility of the Garter's being conferred upon duke Frederick I of Württemberg: see 'Relation über seine Sendung nach England' (ed. Schlossberger, Stuttgart, 1865) p. 48, ‚Monsieur Robert Sydenay, guberneur de Flüssingen, aber hatt mir zugesagt, wölle E.F.G. ein Paar (Bluthunde) ußgheen . . . Solche sollen E.F.G. von ihmme bey nechster gelegenheytt . . . zu empfangen haben.'

119, 37

‚Dieß Seelenhafte'. See the notes II. 282 and III. 318.

120, 5

For Hegel's treatment of the senses see the note on III. 327.

121, 19

In the second edition of the 'Encyclopaedia' (1827), Hegel added, 'And within it, light and darkness are mere possibilities', but he removed these words from the 1830 edition.

122, 5

‚ist das Aufgehen der Lichtseite in der Gestalt selbst.'

122, 22

‚So sind sie andererseits auch nur außer der Individualität der Körper schwebend'.

122, 31

Christoph Friedrich Luwig Schultz (1781–1834) signed himself C. L. F. Schultz and is entered in the baptismal register as L. C. F., but his Christian names are usually given in the above order. He was born at Marienwerder in West Prussia, where his father was a civil servant employed in administering the crown lands and organizing defence.

Until 1795 he was educated privately by his grandfather. In that year he entered the Joachimsthal Grammar School in Berlin, and in 1799 the University of Halle, where he studied law and cameralistics (the management of state property). He entered the Prussian civil service in 1804, and in 1805 was appointed director of the Royal Porcelain Factory at Bruckberg near Ansbach. It was at this time, through the attempts to improve the colouring (especially white) of porcelain, that he began to interest himself in the theory of colours.

In 1814 C. F. Zelter (1758–1832), knowing that Schultz's studies in the field of optics were likely to be of interest to Goethe, brought the two men into contact. An extensive correspondence ensued and a close friendship developed, which lasted until Goethe's death; see H. Düntzer 'Briefwechsel zwischen Goethe und Staatsrath Schultz' (Leipzig, 1853). On November 18, 1819 K. F. S. Altenstein (1770–1840), the Prussian Minister of Culture, appointed Schultz 'curator' of Berlin University, in accordance with the Carlsbad decrees (see the note III. 319). By this time Schultz was known for his wide interests, which ranged from musical composition to philology, archaeology, and physics, and Altenstein evidently hoped that he would interpret his censorial duties in a liberal manner and interfere as little as possible with the life of the university. In fact Schultz took his new position very seriously, and soon alienated all but the most reactionary members of the academic body. He was eventually forced to relinquish the post in 1825, frustrated, embittered and friendless. His health declined, he had a disease of the lungs, he lost his eldest son, and it was only the friendship of Goethe which lightened his last years.

During the winter of 1821–1822 Hegel, Leopold von Henning (1791–1866) and Karl Ernst Schubarth (1796–1861) met one evening a week at Schultz's house in Berlin to study Goethe's 'Theory of Colours'; see Schultz's letter to Goethe August 16, 1822 (Düntzer op. cit. p. 250). One outcome of these meetings was a paper by Hegel, dated November 21, 1821, criticizing § 32 of Schultz's article in Schweigger's Journal; see K. Rosenkranz 'Leben Hegel's' (Berlin, 1844) p. 340, cf. the note III. 326.

Hegel is here referring to Schultz's paper, 'Über physiologe Farbenerscheinungen, insbesondere das phosphorische Augenlicht, als Quelle derselben, betreffend' which was finished on July 27, 1821, a few weeks after Schultz had visited Goethe at Weimar (Düntzer op. cit. letters 67, 72–74, 78, 86). Goethe reprinted the paper in his 'Zur Naturwissenschaft Überhaupt' pt. II (ed. Kuhn, Weimar, 1962 pp. 296–304).

Schultz was evidently influenced by Plato's theory of vision, according to which our visual perceptions are caused by a light issuing from our eyes and mingling with that originating from the sun (see the note II. 396). In a paper printed by Düntzer (op. cit. pp. 391–398) he mentions Plato's theory (§ 23). In the paper referred to by Hegel however, his main point is that the light of the *phosphorus* in the eyes is essential to sight. He attempts to explain all the pathological and physiological phenomena of sight and colours by referring Goethe's theory of optics and colour back to this physiological 'fact'. There is a criticism of his theory by Carl Asmund Rudolphi (1771–1832) in 'Grundriss der Physiologie' (Berlin, 1823) § 316 obs. I.

Rudolphi points out that the hypothesis of light 'issuing from our eyes' is extremely doubtful, as no amount of subjective activity will enable us to see in the dark. He takes the lights which appear when we close our eyes and rub them to be the same as the ringing we hear when our ears are struck, and not to indicate the actual *presence* of light. He also notices a certain similarity between Schultz's theory and that put forward by Andrew Horn in his 'The seat of vision determined' (London, 1813).

123, 37

Michelet took this passage from a section of the 'Jenenser Realphilosophie II' (p. 73) in which Hegel was attempting to formulate a transition from what at that time he called 'shaping and chemism' (gravity, elasticity, heat, process), to what he then took to constitute 'physics' (colours, chemical substances, chemical process).

Crystals as such had already been dealt with at this juncture (see pp. 54–55), and if this passage is considered in its context, it becomes apparent that it refers not simply to the diamond as such, as Michelet evidently thought, but to the *Earth* (cf. the note III. 215). After the passage quoted, Hegel continues as follows, 'This pure crystal is to the same extent pure movement within itself however; it is dissolution which dissolves itself, and which resembles heat in that it holds all shape within an undivided and restless unity. It is the living sun, true reality, that which has power, all-animating light: it is the universal soul, the universal life itself . . . One might say that in this absolute process *the sun acts* in opposition to the firmness of the crystal, sunders the absolutely rigid singularity of its dead carbon and draws it into movement'. In the margin at this point Hegel then added, 'Diamond, interior of the Earth'.

124, 20

See 'Goethe, die Schriften zur Naturwissenschaft' pt. I vol. 4 'Zur Farbenlehre . . . Didaktischer Teil' (ed. Matthaei, Weimar, 1955) §§ 495–6 (p. 157). Hegel is here referring to that part of Goethe's work which deals with *chemical colours* in their most basic forms. After dealing with the 'opposition' of acid and alkali, Goethe goes on to treat of the 'derivation' of white and black, the 'stimulation' of colour itself etc. At the end of this section he deals with the more complex colours of *organisms*.

124, 33

In support of this statement, Hegel quotes a passage from J. B. Biot's 'Traité de physique expérimentale et mathématique' (4 vols. Paris, 1816) vol. III p. 199 which he translates, 'On a un autre exemple de cette propriété, en jetant dans de l'huile d'olive des morceaux irréguliers de borax; car ces morceaux, à cause de leurs inégalités et du défaut de poli de leur surface, ne transmettent pas régulièrement la lumière lorqu'ils sont plongés dans l'air; mais ils deviennent parfaitement limpides quand ils sont plongés dans l'huile d'olive, parce qu'elle compense toutes leurs inegalités; et il se fait si peu de réflexion à la surface commune de ces deux substances, qu'on à peine à distinguer les limites de leur séparation'.

On hydrophane cf. Gren's 'Journal der Physik' VII p. 143 (Leipzig, 1793). Cf. Robert Smith (1689–1768) 'A Compleat System of Opticks' (2 vols. Cambridge, 1738) vol. i p. 96.

124, 39

For *Newton's* views on transparency, see his 'Opticks' bk. II pt. iii. His main proposition (no. 2) is that, 'The least parts of almost all natural bodies are in some measure transparent: And the opacity of those bodies ariseth from the multitude of reflexions caused in their internal parts'. Huyghen's deals with the matter in ch. 3 of his 'Traité de la Lumière' (Leyden, 1690), 'The waves of light are carried on in the ethereal matter, which continuously occupies the interstices or pores of transparent bodies. For since it passes through them continuously and freely, it follows that they are always full of it. And one may even show that these interstices occupy much more space than the coherent particles which constitute the bodies.' Leonhard Euler (1707–1783), in his 'Nova theoria lucis' (Berlin, 1746) § 102 assumed that the particles of transparent bodies undergo compression, and transmit the vibrations communicated to them by the oscillations of the ether.

Although Johann Heinrich Lambert (1723–1777), Pierre Bouguer (1698–1758) and Count Rumford (1753–1814) subsequently investigated *degrees* of transparency, it was not until Maxwell discovered that the equations governing the behaviour of *electric waves* are equally applicable to light, that any real advance was made in this branch of physics.

Hegel was clearly justified in regarding an explanation of transparency as being a necessary preliminary to any fully intelligible consideration of refraction and colours however.

130, 33

Although Hegel does not acknowledge the fact, this explanation clearly owes something to *Newton's* observation that the refraction of light is not caused solely by the rays falling on the *actual surfaces* of bodies, but that it is effected, without any contact, by the action of a *power* belonging to bodies and extending a certain distance beyond their surfaces. See Newton's 'Opticks' Bk. III pt. i qu. 20, 'Doth not this aethereal medium in passing out of water, glass, crystal, and other compact and dense bodies into empty spaces, grow denser and denser by degrees, and by that means refract the rays of light not in a point, but by bending them gradually in curved lines? And doth not the gradual condensation of this medium extend to some distance from the bodies, and thereby cause the inflexions of the rays of light, which pass by the edges of dense bodies, at some distance from the bodies?'

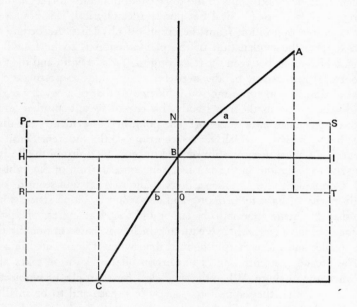

'The manner in which Refraction is performed by mere attraction, without contact, may be thus accounted for: Suppose HI the boundary of two mediums, N and O; the first the rarer, ex. gr. air; the second the denser, ex. gr. glass; the attraction of the mediums here will be as their densities. Suppose pS to be the distance to which the attracting force of the denser medium exerts itself within the rarer. Now let a ray of light Aa fall obliquely on the surface which separates the mediums, or rather on the surface pS, where the action of the second and more resisting medium commences: as the ray arrives at a, it will begin to be turned out of its rectilinear course by a superior force, with which it is attracted by the medium O, more than by the medium N; hence the ray is bent out of its right line in every point of its passage between pS and RT, within which distance the attraction acts; and therefore between these lines it describes a curve aBb; but beyond R T, being out of the sphere of attraction of the medium

N, it will proceed uniformly in a right line, according to the direction of the curve in the point b.' Charles Hutton (1737–1823) 'A Mathematical and Philosophical Dictionary' (2 vols. London, 1795) II p. 344. On the significance of density here see the note on II. 355.

130, 35

Michelet commented upon this as follows: 'Hegel's explanation of the phenomenon of elevation seems to me to be predominantly correct and appropriate, but since it is not physical but purely metaphysical, it is bound to encounter extensive opposition from the empirical physicists. According to the emission theory, the explanation of the phenomenon is to be found in the attraction which exists between the refracting matter and light, and the undulation theory is then driven by the need for consistency to postulate another variation of this, in which the motion is likened to that of a cavalry regiment. Where do these various theories stand with regard to one another and with regard to the Hegelian interpretation? The point here is evidently the displacement of the light image, which varies according to the different densities and rigidities of substances, for variations in the material intensity of the body must also give rise to variations in the expansion or concentration of the light-image (p. 126). Consequently, the denser a body is the more it will seem to obscure the virgin purity of light by breaking and dispersing it within its crass materiality, so that the image appears to be larger and therefore closer. The principle is the same in embroidery, where a pattern which is executed in fine silk threads is much smaller and more sharply defined than when it is executed in a coarse wool. The greater concentration or expansion of this elevation takes place in one and the same medium. When the air is clear for example, I see objects with clear outlines, so that they appear to occupy less space and to be smaller and further away than they do in dull weather, although perhaps not to be situated at a different angle. The sun and moon have to shine through a greater amount of vapour when they first rise than when they are standing high in the clearer regions of the heavens, and this gives rise to their apparently greater size. Similarly, the things seen under the water by a diver will certainly appear larger than when they are viewed in the atmosphere. In order that what is called refraction should occur with elevation however, the light-image has to traverse two media, in one of which there is a concentration and in the other of which there is an expansion of light, so that there are two distinct displacements. The angle of refraction will then be caused by the line of vision being different in the two media. It is true that the light-image will be displaced by the specific determinateness of a single medium, but as this takes place uniformly throughout the whole distance between the object and the eye, the direction of the light does not diverge from a straight line, so that the displacement takes place without refraction. Even when there are two media between the eye and the object, no refraction will take place if their powers of displacement are equal. Finally, it is also impossible for refraction to occur if there are two media of differing density and the eye is located on the perpendicular above the object, as in the following diagram, in which E is the eye and O is the object.

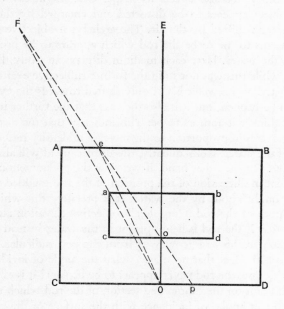

In this case the visual water-space abcd, which is more concentrated in the air, merely lifts the object O towards the eye as far as o, without fixing the relation between this place and the place in the more expanded visual water-space A B C D at an angle, for the line of vision EO appears to coincide with Eo. If the eye is located at point F, and so stands at an angle to the object, it is impossible for the light-image to follow the same line in the air as it did through the water (Oe) in reaching the eye. It is diverted into the eF direction, so that to the eye located at point F, the object at O no longer appears to be lifted to o, but as it must always be assumed to lie on the bottom, it will appear to be shifted further to point p. It is here therefore that refraction first occurs. When it is realized that the effects of both media have to combine, in order for example that the gold coin at the bottom of a vase may be simultaneously lifted and shifted and so appear longer and distorted, it becomes apparent how complicated this is. The coin's apparent increase in size is the result of the expansion of the light by the water, and this enlargement alone can cause the object to seem closer to the eye, for if one places one's eye so close to the water that there is no longer any air in between, the elevation still takes place. However, by reason of its lower density, the air also contributes to this phenomenon by its further concentration of the whole visual water-space of the gold coin. Consequently, it is only natural that in order to reach the eye, the light-image of the coin should assume a different direction when it emerges from the water into the air. That is to say that the air is merely determinative of the place of the light-image, while the water also effects its shape. One might say therefore that whereas the object appears to be distorted and enlarged by the water, it is brought nearer and shifted by the air. The archetypal objective phenomenon of refraction seems to me to be the rod which appears to be broken where it emerges from the water. Here each medium displays an easily distinguishable kind of effect, while this was not so in the former subjective example. The part of the rod situated in the water is not only shifted towards the eye, so that the rod appears to be broken, but it is also the case that the further it extends into the water, the thicker it appears to be. This indicates that the distortion of the light-image increases in proportion to the increase in density resulting from the greater mass of the water. Consequently, this displacement will also be apparent under the water. On the other hand, if we view the phenomenon through air, the air's apparent modification of the position of the rod is added to the change in its shape brought about by the water. It is precisely this which causes the apparent obliquity of the rod. Completely objective elevation also takes place without refraction if the rod is held upright in the water instead of obliquely; it is not necessary in this case to view it from the perpendicular. How do the physicists explain the fact that no matter what the angle of incidence assumed by the eye in this case, the rod never appears to be broken? It is evident that the rays from each point on the submerged section of the rod which reach the eye, must form different angles of incidence with the surface of the water. Taking elevation and not refraction as our point of departure, our solution is quite simply that as long as the rod is in a perpendicular position, the elevation of that part of it which is submerged, and which merely appears to be thickened by the water, simply joins up with the perpendicular part that is above the water. As soon as the rod is placed obliquely in the water however, the perpendicular elevation of the oblique part under the water has to connect up at a certain angle with the oblique part above the water. Consequently, as the one part of the rod appears to assume a greater obliquity, both parts can no longer form one straight line. This concentration of a formerly more expanded light-image is expressed by Hegel in a somewhat more subtle metaphysical form, when he says that the greater density of the water concentrates the visual air-space into the density of water in an ideal manner.'

131, 15

This passage calls to mind the famous remark in the 'Philosophy of History' (tr. Sibree, Dover Publications 1956) p. 32, 'No man is a hero to his valet-de-chambre', is a well-known proverb; I have added—and Goethe repeated it ten years later—'but not because the former is no hero, but because the latter is a valet'.

131, 25

Willebrord Snell (1580–1626), commonly known as Snellius, was born at Leyden in 1580, not 1590 or 1591 as is so often stated. There is record of his attending school in the town in 1590. In 1613 he succeeded his father Rudolph Snell (1546–1613) as professor of mathematics at Leyden university.

He was author of a great many learned mathematical works, but is mainly remembered for his 'Eratosthenes Batavus' (Lugd. Bat. 1617), in which he describes a new method of finding the dimensions of the earth by determining the distance of one point on its surface from the parallel of another, by means of triangulation. Hegel is referring here to his equally famous discovery of the law governing the refraction of light. He never published his work in this field, and there is good reason to believe that Descartes, when he formulated the law of refraction in a slightly different manner in his 'Discours de la méthode' (Dioptrics) (Leyden, 1637), was drawing upon his knowledge of Snell's manuscripts, although he failed to acknowledge this. See Christian Huyghens (1629–1695) 'Dioptrica' pp. 2–3, published in his 'Opera posthuma' (Leyden, 1703): Isaac Vossius (1618–1688) 'Responsio ad objecta Johannis De Bruyn' (Hagae Com. 1663) p. 32: Joseph Priestley 'The History and present state of discoveries relating to vision, light and colours' (2 vols. London, 1772, Germ. tr. Leipzig, 1776) vol. I pp. 102–106: Emil Wilde 'Geschichte der Optik' (2 vols. Berlin, 1838) I pp. 215–271: P. Kramer in 'Abhandlungen zur Geschichte der Mathematik' IV (Leipzig, 1882): Korteweg 'Descartes et les manuscrits de Snellius' ('Revue de metaphysique et de morale' IV, 1896): Milhaud 'Descartes et la loi des sinus' ('Revue générale des sciences' XVIII, March, 1907): Vollgraf 'Optica cum annotationibus Willebrordi Snelli' pars I, lib. i (Ghent, 1918).

132, 3

Michelet commented upon this as follows, 'Here one might well ask the physicists why an incident ray which falls perpendicularly should not be refracted. The refractive power of the medium cannot be weakened by perpendicularity, and the ray itself is not aware that it is perpendicular. The only satisfactory explanation of this is to be found in the perpendicularity of elevation.'

132, 9

The 'perpendicularity of elevation' as Michelet calls it, was explained in most text-books of the time by the ordinary laws of refraction. See for example

Charles Hutton (1737–1823) 'A Mathematical and Philosophical Dictionary' (2 vols. London, 1795) vol. II p. 347.

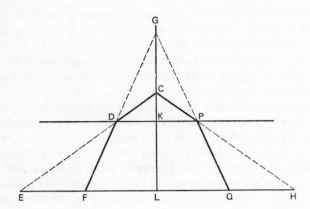

'If two rays CD and CP, proceeding from the same radient C, and falling on a plane surface of a different density, so that the points of Refraction D and P be equally distant from the perpendicular of incidence GK, the refracted rays DF and PQ have the same virtual focus, or the same point of dispersion G.— Hence, when refracted rays, falling on the eye placed out of the perpendicular of incidence, are either equally distant from the perpendicular, or very near each other, they will flow upon the eye as if they came to it from the point G; consequently the point C will be seen by the refracted rays as in G. And hence also: if the eye be placed in a dense medium, objects in a rarer will appear more remote than they are; and the place of the image, in any case, may be determined from the ratio of Refraction: Thus, to fishes swimming under water, objects out of the water must appear farther distant than in reality they are. But, on the contrary, if the eye at E be placed in a rarer medium, then an object G placed in a denser, appears, at C, nearer than it is; and the place of the image may be determined in any given case by the ratio of Refraction: and thus the bottom of a vessel full of water is raised by Refraction a third part of its depth, with respect to an eye placed perpendicularly over the refracting surface; and thus also fishes and other bodies, under water, appear nearer than they really are.'

If the matter was treated in a way which took *both eyes* into consideration, the explanations became more complicated, but the principles remained the same; see 'Gehler's Physikalisches Wörterbuch' vol. I pp. 1148–1149 and fig. 260 (Leipzig, 1825).

132, 36

This should evidently be regarded as a criticism of Newton's 'Opticks' bk. III pt. i qu. 20 (see the note II. 340).

Hegel is referring here to F. A. C. Gren (1760–1798) 'Grundriss der Naturlehre zum Gebrauch akademischer Vorlesungen' (4th ed. Halle, 1801); see the note II. 267. In §700 Gren gives P. van Musschenbroek (1692–1761), 'Introductio ad philosophiam naturalem' (2 vols. Lugd. Bat. 1762) §§1720–1724 as an authority, and writes, ‚Beŋ der Brechung des Lichts in seinem Uebergange aus einem durchsichtigen Mittel in ein anderes hängt also der Brechungswinkel theils von der Natur des brechenden Mittels, theils von der Neigung des eingefallenen Strahles ab. Gemeinhin sind zwar die brechenden Kräfte der durchsichtigen Mittel im Verhältnisse mit ihrer Dichtigkeit; man kann indessen nicht sagen, daß diese Regel ganz genau und daß sie allgemein zutreffe; denn einige durchsichtige Mittel brechen stärker, andere schwächer, als es nach Verhältniß ihres eigenthümlichen Gewichts geschehen sollte. So kann daher manchmal das Licht beym Uebergange aus einem Mittel in ein anderes merklich gebrochen werden, obgleich die specifischen Gewichte dieser Mittel nicht merklich verschieden sind, z.b. Alaun und grüner Vitriol; so kann es ferner aus einem Mittel in ein anderes ohne Brechung übergehen, obgleich die Dichtigkeiten derselben verschieden sind, wie z.B. beŋ Baumöhl und Borax; ja es kann endlich sogar beym Uebergange aus dem dichtern ins dünnere Mittel dem Perpendikel zu gebrochen werden, wie beŋ Wasser und Terpentinöhl'.

133, 8

J. B. Biot 'Traité de physique expérimentale et mathématique' (4 vols. Paris, 1816). Biot bases these remarks, as he acknowledges, upon the observation, made by Newton; see the 'Opticks' bk. II pt. 3 prop. 10. Hegel seems to have been incapable of acknowledging that Newton had any virtues.

133, 17

When judging the exposition of refraction given here by Hegel it should be remembered that he is attempting not merely to *state* the facts of the case, but to *explain* them. It was generally realized at that time that the mechanical explanations of refraction put forward by Descartes, Pierre Fermat (1601–1665), C. F. M. Dechales (1601–1678), Jean Bernoulli (1667–1748), Daniel Bernoulli (1700–1782), J. J. Mairan (1678–1771), P. L. M. Maupertius (1698–1759) etc. were inadequate. See Robert Smith (1689–1768) 'A compleat system of Opticks' (2 vols. Cambridge, 1738, Germ. tr. Kästner, Altenburg, 1755) Remarks p. 70: Charles Hutton (1737–1823) 'A Mathematical and Philosophical Dictionary' (2 vols. London, 1795) II pp. 343–344: 'Gehler's Physikalisches Wörterbuch' vol. I pp. 1127–1164.

F. A. C. Gren (1760–1798), in § 698 of his 'Grundriss der Naturlehre' (4th ed. Halle, 1801), the work quoted by Hegel on p. 132 notes that, ‚So viele

Erklärungen auch über die wirkende Urſache des Phänomens der Brechung gegeben worden ſind, ſo iſt doch keine befriedigender, als die, welche uns Newton ſelbſt davon gegeben hat. Sie reducirt ſich auf die Kraft der Cohärenz, oder, wenn man lieber will, der Anziehung der durchſichtigen Materie mit dem Stoffe des Lichts, ſo wie die Reflexion im Gegentheile den Mangel dieſer Cohärenz oder Anziehung anzeigt'.

Although Hegel cannot bring himself to acknowledge the fact, he utilizes *Newton's* explanation of the phenomenon in his exposition of it (see the note II. 340). By insisting upon what he calls 'the advanced spirituality' of refraction, and by refusing to accept the purely mechanical 'explanations' of it proffered in the text-books of the time, he may not have added anything to scientific knowledge, but he did at least contribute towards keeping the way open for the demonstration, on the basis of the undulatory theory, that refraction may be explained from the fact that the *velocity of light is inversely proportional to the refractive index of the medium through which it passes.*

133, 24

Hegel adds the following footnote here, 'By formal equality I mean the general shape of the cube. The following passage from Biot's 'Traité de physique' (vol. III ch. 4 p. 325) will suffice to indicate the internal figuration of crystals giving rise to the so-called double refraction of light. "This phenomenon occurs in all transparent crystals the primitive form of which is neither a cube nor a regular octahedron." '

133, 37

Cf. the note II. 340. As the result of the *mechanical* interpretations of the refraction of light prevalent in the eighteenth century, the category of *power* or force was often used in explanations of this phenomenon; see the note above. Hegel realized that this category had been overused in this context. In the case of *double refraction* however, which he took to involve the internal mirroring and reflecting structure of crystals, he regarded it as being relevant to explanation, probably on account of its being involved in the study of *surface forces*.

This assessment would have been more intelligible to the German physicists of Hegel's day than to their French or English counterparts, since the study of surface forces was an accepted and clearly defined part of their work; see the note II. 280.

134, 11

The first volume of Goethe's 'Zur Farbenlehre' (Tübingen, 1808, ed. Matthaei, Weimar, 1955) contains definitions of *four* kinds of colour.

'§ 143. Those colours which arise when light and darkness have an effect upon the eye or upon confronting surfaces after passing through an achromatic medium are said to be *dioptric*. In this case it is necessary that the medium should be transparent or at least have a certain degree of translucency.

§ 366. When we speak of *catoptric* colours, we are indicating those colours known to us through their appearing by means of a reflection. We take as given that the light, as well as the surface from which it reflects, is in a completely achromatic condition.

§ 391. The *paroptic* colours have been so named on account of its being necessary for light to fall upon an edge in order that they may be elicited. They do not appear *whenever* light falls upon an edge however; other quite particular secondary circumstances are also necessary.

§ 430. *Epoptic* colours occur for various reasons on the surface of an achromatic body originally devoid of communication or colour'.

In 1809 É. L. Malus (1775–1812), J. B. Biot (1774–1862) and D. F. J. Arago (1786–1853) began to investigate the polarization of light, particularly with regard to double refraction in Iceland spar (see the notes to §§ 276–278), and this gave rise to the discovery of what Thomas Johann Seebeck (1770–1831) called *entoptic* colours; see his 'Von den entoptischen Farbenfiguren und den Bedingungen ihrer Bildung in Gläsern' ('Schweiggers Journal' 1813, 1814) Goethe took the matter up, and in his 'Zur Naturwissenschaft Überhaupt' vol. I (Stuttgart and Tübingen, 1817–1822; ed. Kuhn, Weimar, 1962 pp. 94–138) gave an account of these colours in the light of his own theory. He took them to be closely related to epoptic colours and added that, 'they were called *entoptic* because they are to be seen within certain bodies'.

For a contempory British account of them see David Brewster (1781–1868) 'On the laws which regulate the absorption of polarized light by doubly refractory crystals' ('Phil. Trans. Roy. Soc.' 1819 pp. 11–28).

134, 16
'Goethe, die Schriften zur Naturwissenschaft' pt. I vol. 8 'Naturwissenschaft-liche Hefte' (ed. D. Kuhn, Weimar, 1962) pp. 108–109. In the section referred to Goethe says that it is, 'the variegated passage of the folia and the resultant interplay of mirrorings' which gives rise to double refraction in rhomboidal Iceland spar, and that the same effect might be produced artificially, by means of mirrors. He has in fact just dealt with the nature of mirroring (sects. XVII–XXI).

Then follows the passage quoted by Hegel, ,. . . . nun gehen wir zu den natürlichen, durchsichtigen, kristallisierten Körpern über, und sprechen also von ihnen aus: daß die Natur, in das Innerste solcher Körper, einen gleichen Spiegelapparat aufgebaut habe, wie wir es mit äußerlichen, physisch-mecha-nischen Mitteln getan'.

Hegel adds, in a footnote here, 'What I have said about this exposition was so favourably received by Goethe that it may be found in part 4 (p. 294) of "On the Science of Nature".' See Kuhn's ed. (op. cit. pp. 212–214).

Hegel's communication is dated from Berlin, February 20, 1821, and is therefore almost certainly the outcome of his weekly meetings with Schultz, von Henning and Schubarth (see the note II. 338). In it Hegel says that despite the many experiments performed since Malus published his first papers in 1808 (see the note II. 241), the *understanding* of entoptic colours had not been furthered until Goethe's work on them appeared, 'at least so far as I am concerned, understanding is of prime importance, and the bare phenomenon has interest for me only in so far as it awakens my desire to understand it'. He goes on to point out the importance of Goethe's archetypal phenomenon to a philosophic interpretation of colour.

134, 17

‚eine innere Damaſtweberei der Natur'. Nicolin and Pöggeler, in their edition of the 'Enzyklopädie' (Hamburg, 1959) p. 262 delete this phrase, without noting the fact or explaining why. This is unfortunate. Hegel is evidently referring to an advanced form of entoptic colour mentioned by Goethe in sect. XXXIV of the work just referred to (ed. Kuhn, Weimar, 1962 pp. 128–129).

134, 26

Hegel changes this quotation somewhat, although not significantly.

134, 28

op. cit. (ed. Kuhn, Weimar, 1962 pp. 16–20) 'Doppelbilder des Rhombischen Kalkspats'. The essay is dated Weimar, January 12, 1813.

135, 3

See the preceding note. Hegel evidently has in mind the following passage, ‚Die zarten epoptiſchen Farben ſpielen wie ein Hauch durch die ganze Maſſe und zeugen von der feinſten Trennung der Lamellen. Durch ein Prisma von einem ſo gearteten Exemplar würde man die bewundernswürdigſte Fata Morgana vorſtellen können'.

Rasmus Bartholin (1625–1698), professor at Copenhagen, was the first to discover the double refraction of light in Iceland spar; see his 'Experimenta Crystalli Islandici Disdiaclastici, quibus mira refractio detegitur' (Copenhagen, 1669): 'Phil. Trans. Roy. Soc.' no. 67. Christian Huyghens (1629–1695) investigated the phenomenon very thoroughly and published the results of his work in his 'Traité de la Lumière' (Leyden, 1690) ch. V, but he did not feel able to offer an explanation of it.

Newton 'Opticks' Bk. III i qu. 25 concluded from Huyghens' experiments that, 'There is an original difference in the rays of light, by means of which some rays are in this experiment constantly refracted after the usual manner, and others constantly after the unusual manner; for if the difference be not original, but arises from new modifications impressed on the rays at their first refraction, it would be altered by new modifications in the three following refractions; whereas it suffers no alteration, but is constant, and has the same effect upon the rays in all the refractions. The unusual refraction is, therefore, performed by an original property of rays.'

Here the matter rested until the beginning of the last century, when Thomas Young's revival of the wave-theory (see the note II. 229), and É. L. Malus's discovery of the polarization of light (see the note II. 241) showed that Newton's conclusion had been correct, and opened the way for the work of A. J. Fresnel (see the note II. 229).

By attributing the phenomenon of double refraction *exclusively* to the lamellae or interior shape of the crystal, Goethe and Hegel were turning their backs upon some of the most valuable research being done in this field at that time. Their fault lay in regarding the work of Young, Malus, Brewster, Fresnel etc. as *merely* a continuation or degeneration of Newtonianism. It was in fact laying the foundations of Maxwell's dynamical theory of light. On the other hand, although it was outdating Newton, it was not *disproving* him, and it was certainly not opening the way for any 'refutation' of Newton on Goethean lines.

135, 9

The explanation of the fata morgana by J. B. Biot (1774–1862) in his 'Traité de Physique' (4 vols. Paris, 1816) vol. III pp. 320–324 is substantially correct, and Hegel was right in regarding it as a phenomenon of refraction. When he says that it 'finds its place here' however, this is only partly correct, for the double refraction dealt with elsewhere in this paragraph also involves the *polarisation* of light.

The refractive index of the atmosphere is continuously varying, and the meteorological optical phenomena which this gives rise to are caused either by the *normal* variation experienced as one ascends, or by the sporadic variations brought about by irregular heating. In accordance with the ordinary laws of refraction, the rays of light deviate from their rectilinear path as they pass from one homogeneous medium to another, assuming of course that the refractive indices of these media are different. Consequently, the path of the rays through continuously varying atmospheric media becomes *curvilinear*, i.e. compounded of a large number of these small rectilinear deviations.

Biot informs us that it was Gaspard Monge (1746–1818) who drew his attention to phenomena of this kind. Monge had accompanied Napoleon on his expedition to Egypt and Syria, and had therefore had occasion to study mirages in the desert. See C. Dupin (1784–1873) 'Essai historique sur les services et les travaux scientifiques de Gaspard Monge' (Paris, 1819).

For contemporary accounts of the fata morgana, see: Antonio Minasi (1736–1806) 'Disertazione sopra un fenomeno volgarmente delto Fata Morgana cet' (Rome, 1773), cf. 'Gilberts Annalen der Physik' XII p. 520: Patrick Brydone (1736–1818) 'A Tour through Sicily and Malta' (London, 1773, Germ. tr. Leipzig, 1774): A. P. Buchan (1764–1824) 'Account of an appearance of Brighton Cliff seen in the air by reflection' ('Nicholson's Journal' 1806 XIV p. 340): H. H. Blackadder 'On Unusual Atmospherical Refraction' ('Edinburgh Philosophical Journal' XIII pp. 66–72, 1825). On the famous 'Brockengespenst' see J. E. Silberschlag (1721–1791) 'Geogonie' (3 pts. Berlin, 1780–83) pt. I p. 139. See also the 'Asiatic Journal and Monthly Register' (Sept. 1829): J. M. Pernter 'Meteorologische Optik' (Vienna and Leipzig, 1906): R. W. Wood Physical Optics' (New York, 1905).

135, 30

‚So gibt dann ein auch für sich existierendes Finsteres und für sich vorhandenes Helles'.

136, 13

The best known English work on this subject was done by Edward Hussey Delaval (1729–1814): see his 'On the agreement between the specific gravities of the several metals and their colours when united to glass' ('Phil. Trans. Roy. Soc.' 1765 p. 10): 'An experimental Inquiry into the Cause of Changes in Opake and coloured Bodies' (London, 1777). There is a valuable and concise survey of the subject as it was understood at the turn of the century in the 'Dictionary of Chemistry and Mineralogy' (2 vols. London, 1807) vol. I pp. 506–513, by Arthur Aikin (1773–1854) and Charles Rochemont Aikin (1775–1847).

The Aikins observe that, 'The metallic oxyds when mixed with any of the glasses, dissolve in them with ease at a melting heat, and always change the colour more or less, sometimes producing very beautiful compounds, which when well prepared, have a lustre and richness of colour strongly resembling that of the natural gems, though in an inferior degree'. They note for example that *gold* gives rise to purple, *silver* to yellow, *iron* to yellow, green, brown, black and red, *copper* to green, red and black, *lead* to yellow, *antimony* to yellow, *manganese* to purplish-red and black, *cobalt* to blue and green, *nickel* to violet-blue, *tungsten* to blue, and *chrome* to red and green. They also give references to certain continental writers on the subject.

Cf. Edward Nathaniel Bancroft (1772–1842) 'Experimental Researches concerning the Philosophy of Permanent Colours' (London, 1794: 2nd. ed. enlarged, 2 vols. London, 1813). Bancroft introduced the important distinction between *substantive* dyes which, 'do not depend upon any basis or mordant, either for their permanency or their lustre', and '*adjective* dyes', capable of being enlivened and fixed only by being adjected or applied upon a suitable basis'.

136, 19

,Jn ber gemadjten Aufzeigung bes Ganges ber Verbunkelung'. 'Course', 'progress', 'manner' would perhaps be more *accurate* equivalents for ,ber Gang'.

136, 24

Cf. II. 190, 16 and the note II. 407.

137, 5

Newton's basic proposition concerning colour is to be found in bk. I pt. 2 (prop. 5 theorem 4) of his 'Opticks', 'Whiteness, and all grey colours between white and black, may be compounded of colours, and the whiteness of the Sun's light is compounded of all the primary colours mixed in a due proportion'. He then describes six experiments involving prisms, combs, soap suds and powders, which he takes to indicate that this is so. Goethe discusses the merits of these experiments in 'Zur Farbenlehre. Polemischer Teil' (ed. Matthaei, Weimar, 1958) pp. 149–170.

His criticism of Newton is based upon his conception of the 'archetypal phenomenon' of colour mentioned here by Hegel. According to Goethe colour arises not from light alone, but from *light* and *darkness*. Instead of taking the colours of the spectrum to be the constituents of white light, he takes light and darkness to be the constituents of colours. In § 739 of his 'Zur Farbenlehre. Didaktischer Teil' (ed. Matthaei, Weimar, 1955) pp. 216–217 he gives his main reason for this, 'Everything which appears and which we encounter as a phenomenon must either indicate an original division capable of union or an original unity capable of division, and must display itself as such'. It is not difficult to see why such an archetypal phenomenon should have appealed to Hegel. See C. H. Pfaff (1773–1852) 'Ueber Newton's Farbentheorie, . . . Goethe's Farbenlehre und den chemische Gegensatz der Farben' (Leipzig, 1813) pp. 21–27: Emil Wilde 'Geschichte der Optik' (2 vols. Berlin, 1838–1843) vol. 2 pp. 197–217.

The invention of the diffraction grating by Joseph Fraunhofer (1787–1826), by making it possible to separate wave lengths which are very close together, gave a great impetus to *spectroscropy*, and since Goethe's day gratings have largely replaced prisms for the study of complicated spectra.

The advances made in this branch of physics as the result of Fraunhofer's invention now enable us to assess Newton's theory of white light more sensitively than was possible when Hegel published this defence of Goethe's archetypal phenomenon in 1830. It is now realized that one would be justified in saying that the spectroscope *creates* coloured light, although this statement may be harmonized with the classical Newtonian theory by adding that the pulse of light can be analysed mathematically into an integral composed of lights of all wave lengths. In this sense it is correct to say that white light *contains* all the

M

colours, even though it is unnatural to attribute any periodic *quality* to a single pulse.

There is no basic difference between the *resolution* of light by a grating and the forming of the spectrum of white light by a prism. The prism merely converts a single pulse into successions of pulses differently spaced for the different directions. The analysis of light into wave lengths is mainly a matter of mathematical *convenience* therefore. It should be added however, that these wave lengths are important in practical spectroscopic analysis on account of the very nearly pure monochromatic lines which occur in the spectra emitted by *gases*.

Consequently, it is to be presumed that any *modern* attempt to harmonize the differences between Newton's conception of white light as compound and Goethe's archetypal phenomenon would concern itself with the nature of the *pulse* and the part played by it in the appearance of colour. See the interesting and valuable attempt by Erwin Heintz to present Goethe's theory *mathematically*: 'Licht und Finsternis, Ein Beitrag zu Goethes Farbenlehre', in G. Wachsmuth 'Goethe in unserer Zeit' (Basel, 1949) pp. 185–208. Cf. E. H. Land 'Colour in the Natural Image' ('Proc. Roy. Inst. of Great Britain' 39 pt. I no. 176 1962 pp. 1–15). George Magyar 'On the dual nature of light' ('British Journal for the Philosophy of Science' vol. xvi pp. 44–49, 1966).

137, 32

In the second edition of Goethe's 'Zur Farbenlehre' (Tübingen, 1810) the passage referred to here occurs on p. 181. Hegel may be referring to the first edition (Tübingen, 1808). See 'Zur Farbenlehre, Didaktischer Teil' (ed. Matthaei, Weimar 1955) § 471 (p. 151), 'Sechste Bedingung. Wenn Metalle erhitzt werden, so entstehen auf ihrer Oberfläche flüchtig auf einander folgende Farben, welche jedoch nach Belieben fest gehalten werden können'.

137, 35

This is evidently a reference to the eighteenth century doctrine that, 'phlogiston is nothing but the pure matter of light fixed immediately in bodies.': see P. J. Macquer (1718–1784) 'Dictionnaire de Chymie' (2nd ed. 4 vols. Paris, 1778) vol. iii p. 144. Christophe Opoix (1745–1840), building on Macquer's work, showed from many facts that light is the material principle of colours, and that from its fixation as phlogiston in bodies it produces every species of colour according to its mode of combination: see his 'Observations physico-chimiques sur les Couleurs' (Paris, 1784), and 'Théorie des Couleurs et des Corps Inflammables' (Paris, 1808).

138, 9

Nicolin and Pöggeler, in their edition of the 'Enzyklopädie' (Hamburg, 1959) omit, ,Aber auch äußerliche Trübung ist nicht Schwächung des Lichts überhaupt, z.B. durch Entfernung: sondern . . .'

138, 23

‚die Eigenschaft des Prisma, trübend zu wirken'. The verb ‚trüben' and the noun ‚die Trübe' are central to Goethe's theory of colour. In this paragraph Hegel uses the words consistently, evidently with Goethe's theory in mind. They have usually been translated as 'to dim' and 'dimness'.

In his 'Zur Naturwissenschaft überhaupt' vol. I pt. 4 pp. 226–228 (ed. Kuhn, Weimar, 1962) Goethe discusses 'der Ausdruck Trüb'. He notes that it always involves *transparency*, which is a necessary factor in both light and darkness, and adds, 'Just as the individual colours relate themselves to the light and darkness out of which they arise, so dimness, which is their corporeality or medium, relates itself to that which is transparent. The former give rise to the spirit of colour, the latter gives rise to its body'.

He takes dimness to be, 'The primary mitigation of transparency, the first faintest filling of space, which is as it were the initiation of an opaque corporeal being . . . the first lamellae of corporeality.' This dimming body disturbs the clarity of light and so gives rise to colour.

Goethe then goes on to discuss the meaning of the Latin word 'turbidus' and its cognate forms in the Romance languages.

138, 31

‚der Tag vertreibt die Finsternis' Cf. the note II. 365.

139, 9

'Zur Farbenlehre, Didaktischer Teil' (ed. Matthaei, Weimar, 1955) p. 77 et. seq. (§ 197 et. seq.).

139, 20

‚das Farben-Viereck'. This is evidently a reference to a series of experiments described by one of the first critics of Goethe's 'Farbenlehre', Christoph Heinrich Pfaff (1773–1852), professor of physics and chemistry at the university of Kiel. See 'Ueber die farbigen Säume der Nebenbilder des Doppelspaths' ('Schweiggers Journal fur Chemie und Physik' 1812 pp. 177–210); 'Ueber Newton's Farbentheorie, Herrn von Goethe's Farbenlehre und den chemischen Gegensatz der Farben' (Leipzig, 1813) pp. 125–148; cf. Pfaff's 'Lebenserinnerungen' (Kiel, 1854) pp. 108 and 296–298.

Goethe, in 'Zur Farbenlehre. Didaktischer Teil' § 558 et passim had put forward his theory of the archetypal phenomenon of colour, and on the basis of it denied Newton's proposition that, 'Whiteness, and all grey colours between white and black, may be compounded of colours, and the whiteness of the Sun's light is compounded of all the primary colours mixed in a due proportion' ('Opticks' bk. I pt. 2 prop. 5). In order to show that Goethe's criticism was not justified, Pfaff placed a white square against a black background and viewed it through Iceland spar. As the result of the double refraction, the secondary image appeared against the background of the white square and the black, so that three rectangles of white or grey were apparent, as well as three edging colours, blue, yellow and red. Pfaff showed that this superpositing of a 'dimmed' black or white did not give rise to the colours which should have appeared had Goethe's theory been correct, and that the colours that did appear could be explained by means of the known laws of refraction.

In this 'account' of Pfaff's experiment Hegel evidently has in mind Goethe's theory of the relationships between colours (see p. 152), but the mere *statement* that the colours which have appeared are primary and therefore an expression of 'the same difference' as that found in the opposition between light and darkness within the archetypal phenomenon itself, can hardly be regarded as an *explanation* of what Pfaff had demonstrated. Although it might be conceded that Pfaff's black background and white square had 'distinct existences' and could not therefore be expected to change the intensity of the brightness or darkness of the 'dim medium', it is difficult to see why the secondary image should also be regarded as a distinct existence with regard to the first, especially as it is this image which gives rise to the colours.

Pfaff's book is supplied with some admirable diagrams.

139, 26

See the note II. 353. Cf. Newton 'Opticks' bk. II pt. i obs. 14, 'And hence I seem to collect that the thicknesses of the air between the glasses there, where the ring is successively made by the limits of the five principal colours (red, yellow, green blue, violet) in order . . . are to one another very nearly as the sixth lengths of a chord which sounds the notes in a sixth major, sol, la, mi, fa, sol, la. But it agrees somewhat better with the Observation to say that the thickness of the air between the glasses there, where the rings are successively made by the limits of the seven colours (red, orange, yellow, green, blue, indigo, violet in order) are to one another as the cube roots of the squares of the eight lengths of a chord, which sound the notes in an eighth . . .'

139, 35

In a footnote Hegel quotes Goethe's comment on Bk. I pt. 2 prop. 10 prob. 5 exper. 17 of Newton's 'Opticks', which is to be found in 'Zur Farbenlehre. Polemischer Teil' (ed. Matthaei, Weimar, 1958) § 645 (p. 183), 'But I can see well enough that lies are needed, and plenty of them'.

It is only fair to note that Goethe is quoting Reynard the fox, and says as much. See 'Reinke de Vos' (Lübeck, 1498), Hartmann Schopper (1542–c. 1600) 'Opus Poeticum de admirabili fallacia et astutia Vulpeculae Reinikes' (Frankfurt, 1567), and Goethe's version of this book (Berlin, 1794). Cf. Carlyle's 'On German Literature of the Fourteenth and Fifteenth Centuries' ('Foreign Quarterly Review' 1831): T. J. Arnold 'Reynard the Fox: after the German version of Goethe' (London, 1860).

139, 40

Hegel is here referring to Newton's proposition that 'Homogeneal light is refracted regularly without any dilatation splitting or shattering of the rays, and the confused vision of objects seen through refracting bodies by hetero-geneal light arises from the different refrangibility of several sorts of rays'.

The three experiments described by Newton surely prove his point. Hegel evidently has in mind Newton's concluding remark, 'And in these three experiments it is further very remarkable that the colour of homogeneal light was never changed by the refraction'.

It is perhaps worth quoting Goethe's comment on this sentence ('Zur Far-benlehre. Polemischer Teil' § 288), 'It is, to be sure, highly worthy of note, that only at this point does Newton become aware of the very ABC of prismatic observations, namely that a coloured surface is no more susceptible to change by means of refraction that is a black, white or grey surface, and it is merely the edges of the images which exhibit colouration'.

140, 5

The English version of the passage referred to is as follow, 'Among all the Observations there is none accompanied with so odd circumstances as the twenty-fourth. Of those the principal are, that in thin plates which to the naked eye seem of an even and uniform transparent whiteness, without any terminations of shadows, the refraction of a prism should make rings of colours appear, whereas it usually makes objects appear coloured only there where they are terminated with shadows, or have parts unequally luminous; and that it should make these rings exceedingly distinct and white, although it usually renders objects confused and coloured.'

This reference is interesting in that it indicates which edition of the 'Opticks' Hegel used. The work first appeared in English in 1704, and was translated by Samuel Clarke (1675–1729), the first edition of the Latin version appearing in 1706. Goethe often indicates that he had compared the English and Latin versions of Newton's text (e.g. 'Zur Farbenlehre. Polemischer Teil' §§ 37, 133 etc.).

140, 7

In the second edition of the 'Encyclopaedia' (1827), Hegel inserted the following sentence here, 'According to his kind of reasoning, all the sculptor does with his hammer and chisel is to discover the statue within the block of marble, for like the kernel in the nut, its form is encased there from the start'.

140, 12

See Newton 'Opticks' Bk. I pt. 2 prop. 8 prob. 3, 'By the discovered proper-ties of light, to explain the colours made by prisms'. Hegel probably has in mind the following passage, 'And if one look through a prism upon a white object encompassed with blackness or darkness, the reason of the colours arising on the edges is much the same, as will appear to one that shall a little consider it. If a black object be encompassed with a white one, the colours which appear through the prism are to be derived from the light of the white one, spreading into the regions of the black, and therefore they appear in a contrary order to that, when a white object is surrounded with black. And the same is to be understood when an object is viewed, whose parts are some of them less luminous than others. For, in the borders of the more luminous parts, colours ought always by the same principles to arise from the excess of the light of the more luminous, and to be of the same kind as if the darker parts were black, but yet to be more faint and dilute.'

Hegel's criticism of this passage is, in effect, that Newton did not attach the same significance to this phenomenon as Goethe. Even if one consults the corresponding paragraphs in 'Zur Farbenlehre. Polemischer Teil', (§§ 597–607) however, it is still difficult to see where, in this particular instance, the superiority of Goethe's interpretation was supposed to lie.

140, 19

See Goethe's account of his first experiments with the prisms he borrowed from Christian Wilhelm Büttner (1716–1801) in 'Zur Farbenlehre. Historischer Teil' (ed. Kuhn, Weimar, 1957) pp. 418–422. Cf. G. H. Lewes 'The Life and Works of Goethe' (Everyman ed. 1949) Bk. V ch. ix pp. 341–2. Lewes is right when he says that Goethe had misunderstood Newton on this point; see the Opticks' Bk. I pt. 2 prop. 8 prob. 3.

Cf. 'Gehler's Physikalisches Wörterbuch' vol. VII pp. 927–947 (Leipzig' 1834); E. Wilde 'Geschichte der Optik (2 vols. Berlin, 1838–1843) vol. II pp. 208–217.

140, 22

In the first edition of the 'Encyclopaedia' (1817), the following was added here, 'not forgetting the indiscriminate *peddling* of it which has been going on now for almost a century and a half, and the *ignorance* of those who have defended its crassitude'.

140, 27

David Gregory (1661–1708), in his 'Catoptricae et Dioptricae Sphaericae Elementa' (Oxford, 1695) was the first to suggest that an achromatic telescope might be built if attempts were made to reproduce the *lens of the human eye*, 'Perhaps it would be of service to make the object lens of a different medium, as we see done in the fabric of the eye; where the crystalline humour (whose power of refracting the rays of light differs very little from that of glass) is by nature, who never does any thing in vain, joined with the aqueous and vitreous humours (not differing from water as to their power of refraction) in order that the image may be painted as distinct as possible upon the bottom of the eye'.

Newton concluded, from some rough experiments, that all refracting substances disperse the prismatic colours in a constant proportion to their mean refraction. From this he drew the natural conclusion that refraction could not be produced without colour, and therefore that no improvement could be expected from the refracting telescope ('Opticks' bk. I pt. i prop. 7 theorem 6: bk. I pt. ii prop. 3). Cf. Goethe 'Zur Farbenlehre. Polemischer Teil' (ed, Matthaei, Weimar, 1958) §§ 303–315.

C. M. Hall (1703–1771), after arguing like Gregory from the mistaken premise of the achromaticism of the lens of the human eye, attempted to correct the effect of the unequal refrangibility of light by combining lenses formed of different kinds of glass, and in 1733 finally succeeded in constructing telescopes which exhibited objects free from colour. See 'Gentleman's Magazine' 1766 p. 102, 1771 p. 143, 1790 pt. ii p. 890: 'Encyclopaedia Metropolitana' (London, 1817–1845) vol. iii p. 408, vol. iv p. 411. Hall, who was a gentleman of private means, did not publicize his invention however, and when Leonhard Euler (1707–1783) published his papers on the possibility of an achromatic telescope in 'Mémoires de l'Academie de Berlin' (1747, 1753, 1754), the existence of such instruments was unknown to him; see H. Servus 'Geschichte des Fernrohr' (Berlin, 1886) p. 77 et seq. It was also unknown to Hall's countryman John Dollond (1706–1761), who questioned the soundness of Euler's suggestions in a letter sent to the Royal Society ('Phil. Tran. Roy. Soc.' 1753 pp. 289–291), the main arguments of which were based upon Newton's work and authority. The Swedish physicist Samuel Klingenstjerna (1698–1765) then pointed out that Newton's law of the dispersion of refracted light did not harmonize with certain observed facts; see his main work on the subject 'Tentamen de definiendis et corrigendis ab errationibus radiorum luminis' (St. Petersburg, 1762): cf. B. Hildebrand in 'Kungliga Svenska Vetenskapsakademiens Handlingar' 1939. This led Dollond to reinvestigate the matter, and to confirm Klingenstjerna's theories by discovering, 'a difference far beyond my hopes, in the refractive qualities of different kinds of glass, with respect to their divergency of colours', and finally to construct his own achromatic telescope. See his 'Account of some Experiments concerning the different Refrangibility of Light' ('Phil. Trans. Roy. Soc.' 1758 pp. 733–743). See John Kelly (1750–1809) 'The Life of John Dollond' (London, 1808): 'Astronomical Register' XIX p. 194 and 'Observatory' for May 1886.

Dollond discovered that different refractions may be produced by different mediums, while at the same time, the dispersion caused by one refraction may be exactly countered by that caused by another, so that an object may be seen through mediums which, together, cause the rays to converge, without appearing of different colours. He discovered that *crown glass* causes the least dispersion, and *white flint* the most, when they are wrought into forms that produce equal refractions.

Goethe, in his 'Zur Farbenlehre. Historischer Teil' (ed. Kuhn, Weimar, 1957) pp. 361–365 took this discovery of achromatism to be the initiation of anti-Newtonianism. Newton's view that all refracting substances disperse the prismatic colours in a constant proportion to their mean refraction had certainly been disproved, but this did not imply, as Goethe asserted, that the distinction between refraction and dispersion ('divergency' as it was then called, i.e. „Zerſtreuung') should be abandoned, and was in any case irrelevant to an understanding of colour.

Hegel clearly has Goethe's interpretation of Hall's discovery in mind here.

Cf. W. Whewell 'History of the inductive sciences' (3 vols. London, 1837) vol. II pp. 349–361: David Brewster (1781-1868) 'Remarks on Achromatic Eye-pieces' ('Nicholson's Journal' XIV, 1806, pp. 388–389): Robert Blair (d. 1828) 'The Principles and Application of a new Method of considering Achromatic Telescopes' ('Nicholson's Journal of Natural Philosophy' 1794, 'Gilberts Annalen' 1800, vi p. 129); Goethe (Diary) studied this article between March 28th and April 6th 1810.

141, 2

In the first edition of the 'Encyclopaedia', the following passage was inserted here, 'Absurdities such as this justify themselves by claiming the physicists' privilege of employing so-called *hypotheses*. Even jokes are not improved by inanities however, and as hypotheses are not formulated in the interests of hilarity, they should most certainly be denied these embellishments.'

141, 3

See the note II. 241.

141, 4

Cf. the note II. 241. Hegel indicates in a footnote that he is referring here to the work of Johann Tobias Mayer (1752–1830) on the *refraction* and *polarisation* of light. He expresses his understanding and assessment of this work as follows, 'One takes two mirrors, one of which is weak and made merely of transparent glass, and places them together at any angle less than 90°. Then one moves the lower one round so that a light-image is obtained which disappears once they stand at a right-angle to one another. If one then continues to move the lower mirror round, the light will be visible on two sides, but not on the other two. With a power of intellect common at Göttingen, Prof. Mayer has deduced the four-sidedness of sunbeams from this experiment.' See the two papers by Mayer 'Commentatio de apparentiis objectorum terrestrium a refractione lucis in atmosphaera nostra pendentibus' and 'Commentatio de Polaritate Luminis' published in 'Commentationes Societatis Regiae Scientarum Gottingensis' vols. I and II (Göttingen 1811, 1813).

Mayer's father, also Johann Tobias (1723–1762), was eminent as a mathematician, physicist and astronomer. The younger Mayer had the same interests as his father and a very similar career. He studied at Göttingen and took his doctorate and qualified as a university teacher there. After teaching at Altdorf and Erlangen he returned to Göttingen as professor. Most of his writings were concerned with mathematics and physics, and appeared in Gren's Journals and various Göttingen periodicals. He published several excellent text-books however, which held their own in German university teaching for many years. His 'Lehrbegriff der höheren Analysis' (2 pts. Göttingen, 1818) is his main work, his 'Gründlicher und ausführlicher Unterricht zur praktischen Geometrie' had run to a fourth edition by 1818, and his 'Gründliche Anweisung zur Verzeichnung der Land-See-und-Himmelskarten' (Erlangen, 1794) remained the standard work on the subject until the appearance of H. F. Gretschel's 'Lehrbuch der Karten-Projektion' (Weimar, 1873).

Light is thrown upon Hegel's opinion of the powers of intellect common at Göttingen (‚Göttinger Verstand') by Goethe's 'Zur Farbenlehre. Historischer Teil' (ed. Kuhn, Weimar, 1957) pp. 351–352. Goethe implies that it was Göttingen's connection with England, through the House of Hanover, which made it such a hot-bed of Newtonianism.

Cf. Newton's 'Opticks' bk. III pt. i query 26, 'Have not the rays of light several sides, endued with several original properties?'

141, 6

See J. B. Biot (1774–1862) 'Traité de Physique' (4 vols. Paris, 1816) vol. IV pp. 499–542, 'Expériences sur les plaques de cristal de roche taillées perpendiculairement à l'axe de cristallisation'. *Michelet*, in a note, calls particular attention to the following passage (op. cit. p. 521), 'D'après ce rapprochement, on doit sentir que le sens de la rotation des molécules, et la marche des teintes dans l'ordre des anneaux, sont deux choses liées entre elles, et telles, que la première est le principe de la seconde. On peut donc juger de l'une par l'autre; et en conséquence, si l'on avait des plaques de cristal de roche pour lesquelles les couleurs montassent dans l'ordre des anneaux, lorsqu'on tourne le rhomboïde de gauche à droite, on devrait en conclure que ces plaques font également tourner la lumière de gauche à droite, c'est-à-dire en sens contraire des précédentes: c'est en effet ce qui m'est arrivé'.

He then adds, 'Another remarkable phenomenon is supposed to occur as the result of this. When the oscillatory movement is from right to left, it is the violet and blue rays which move in front, while when the movement is from left to right, it is the red rays. It often happens that only the blue and violet rays are given out in this rotatory activity, but in general it is the blue rays which appear when the rotation is faster, and the red rays when it is slower (pp. 514–517). It appears to be difficult to reconcile this last fact with the supposed alternation of the moving in front and staying behind of these opposing colours.'

141, 8

See Newton 'Opticks' bk. II pt. 3 prop. 13, 'Definition. The returns of the disposition of any ray to be reflected I will call its fits of easy reflexion, and those of its disposition to be transmitted its fits of easy transmission, and the space it passes between every return and the next return, the interval of its fits'. Cf. J. B. Biot (op. cit. IV pp. 88–122) 'Sur les Accès de facile transmission et de facile réflexion'. For the broader context of Biot's researches in this field see the notes II. 239:241.

141, 13

Differential calculus or the theory of finite differences, the branch of mathematics which deals with the successive differences of the terms of a series, was first used by Henry Briggs (1556–1630), who laid down the rules of it in his 'Arithmetica Logarithmica' (London, 1624) chs. XII and XIII, and his 'Trignometrica Britannica' (Goudae, 1633).

Newton, in his 'Mathematical Principles of Natural Philosophy' Bk. iii lemma 5, used the theory as a method of describing a curve of the parabolic kind, through any given number of points. This gave rise to its use in the field of *mechanics*, which is praised here by Hegel: see however the note I. 349. Its use in the field of *chromatics* (diffraction, dispersion etc.) was justified by Newtonianism but not by the Göthean hypothesis, hence Hegel's objection.

142, 7

See the brilliantly lucid and concise exposition of the 'Wissenschaftslehre' given by Robert Adamson (1852–1902) in his 'Fichte' (Edinburgh and London, 1881) pp. 144–188. Cf. C. C. Everett 'Fichte's Science of Knowledge. A Critical Exposition' (Chicago, 1884).

142, 17

The full text of the passage from which Michelet selected the following sentences is to be found in 'Jenenser Realphilosophie II' (ed. Hoffmeister, Leipzig, 1931) pp. 80–81. Very little would be gained from a detailed indication of the many changes he has made, the omissions, the words emphasized by Hegel, the marginal notes to be found in the original etc.

142, 36

'Opticks' bk. I pt. i def. VII, 'The light whose rays are all alike refrangible I call Simple, Homogeneal and Similar; and that whose rays are some more refrangible than others I call compound, heterogeneal and dissimilar'.

Def. VIII, 'The colours of homogeneal lights I call primary, homogeneal and simple; and those of heterogeneal lights, heterogeneal and compound'.

143, 7

This remark almost certainly dates from the *second* series of lectures on the philosophy of nature given by Hegel at Berlin. These lectures were delivered during the winter of 1821–2 and concluded on March 23, 1822. It was during this period that the weekly meetings devoted to Goethe's theory of colours were held at Schultz's house (see the note II. 338).

Hegel is referring here to the public lectures on Goethe's theory of colours given at Berlin by Leopold Dorotheus von Henning (1791–1866) between 1822 and 1835.

Henning came of a military family. He was born at Gotha and studied jurisprudence, history and philosophy at Heidelberg. He joined the Saxon army during the War of Liberation and after the first peace of Paris visited London and Vienna, where he studied political economy. He practised as a referendary at Königsberg and Erfurt for a while, and in 1818 arrived at Berlin. He soon became acquainted with Hegel, who in July 1820 got him a university appointment.

Henning's first publication was a translation of Thomas Jefferson's 'A Manual of Parliamentary Practice' (Washington, 1801, 2nd ed. 1812), which appeared as 'Handbuch des Parlamentarrechts' (Berlin, 1819). His habilitation thesis 'De systematis feudalis natione' (Berlin, 1821) was also concerned with constitutional and legal matters, but at about the same time, probably under the influence of Hegel, he began to concern himself with the natural sciences see 'Das Verhältniss der Philosophie zu den exacten Wissenschaften' ('Neue Berliner Monatsschrift' 1821).

On August 2, 1821 Hegel wrote to Goethe concerning Henning's proposal to lecture on 'Zur Farbenlehre' at Berlin. On October 18th Henning met Goethe at Jena to discuss the matter, and on the following day Goethe wrote to Zelter, ,es wäre wunderlich genug, wenn ich auch noch in dieser Provinz triumphierte'. During the following winter, as we have noticed, Henning worked on the subject with Hegel, Schultz and Schubarth, a laboratory was put at his disposal by the university, and as the result of this activity he was able to publish an introduction to the forthcoming lectures, 'Einleitung zu öffentlichen Vorlesungen über Goethes Farbenlehre, gehalten an der Königlichen Universität zu Berlin' (Berlin, 1822).

Goethe was pleased. On September 6, 1822 he wrote to Boisserie, ,Eigentlich darf ich sagen, daß ich wohl verdiene, nach dreißigjährigem Schweigen zu der niederträchtigen Behandlung, die ich von meinen Zeitgenossen erduldete, endlich durch eine frische, hochgebildete Jugend zu Ehren zu gelangen'. He supplied Henning with apparatus and advice and kept up a regular correspondence with him on the subject. On August 9, 1830 Henning reported to Goethe that he had just lectured for the tenth time on 'Zur Farbenlehre', to a considerable audience of students from all faculties. As usual, there were also young artists, officers and others interested in the natural sciences among them. A year later he estimated that about four hundred persons ,der verschiedensten Lebensverhältnisse fast aus allen Gegenden Deutschlands' had heard the lectures. It is clear therefore that the lectures were not attended only by physicists!

Henning was appointed assistant professor in 1825 and professor in 1835. From 1827 until 1847 he edited the 'Berlin Yearbooks', the official literary organ of orthodox Hegelianism. He also prepared the definitive edition of Hegel's 'Wissenschaft der Logik' (Berlin, 1834). Despite his excursion into the theory of colours, his main publications were concerned with sociological and constitutional matters; see 'Principien der Ethik in historischer Entwicklung' (Berlin, 1824), 'Zur Verständigung über die preussische Verfassungsfrage' (Berlin, 1845).

F. T. Bratranek 'Goethes naturwissenschaftliche Correspondenz' (2 vols. Leipzig, 1874): Erna Arnhold 'Goethes Berliner Beziehungen' (Gotha, 1925).

144, 4

This treatment of shadows is based to a great extent upon Goethe's 'Zur Farbenlehre'. Didaktischer Teil' (ed. Matthaei, Weimar, 1955) §§ 62-88.

Between the revival of the *wave* theory of light by Thomas Young (1773–1829) at the turn of the century (note II. 229), and the brilliant exposition of the *mathematical* theory of light by A. J. Fresnel (1788–1827) in the 1820's, there was much uncertainty in theories concerning shadows. Coloured shadows attracted a great deal of attention. Benjamin Thompson, count Rumford (1753–1814) regarded them as an *illusion* ('Phil. Trans. Roy. Soc.' 1794 pp. 1, 107: 'Gren's Neues Journal der Physik' vol. II p. 58). C. Opoix (1745–1840) attributed them to diffraction ('Journal de Physique' vol. XXIII p. 402). The very variable quality of the observations and experiments described by J. H. Hassenfrate (1755–1827) in 'Journal de l'École Polytechnique' XI p. 272 provides a good example of the *uncertain* state of knowledge in this field prevalent at the time.

Pietro Petrini (1785–1822) emphasized the importance of *physiological* factors in the appearance of coloured shadows ('Memorie di matematica e fisica della Societa Italiana' vol. XIII p. 11). It may well have been J. H. D. Zschokke (1771–1848), 'Die farbigen Schatten' (Aarau, 1826), who confirmed Hegel in the view that truly colourless shadows are a *rare phenomenon*.

Cf. the articles by Kaspar Pohlmann (c. 1800–1836) and G. T. Fechner (1801–1887) in J. C. Poggendorff's 'Annalen der Physik' vol. XXXVII p. 319 and vol. XLIV p. 137.

144, 9

See Newton 'Opticks' bk. I pt. 2 prop. 5 theorem 4 exp. 10, 'When the motion was slow there appeared a perpetual succession of the colours upon the paper; but if I so much accelerated the motion that the colours by reason of their quick succession could not be distinguished from one another, the appearance of the single colours ceased. There was no red, no yellow, no green, no blue, nor purple to be seen any longer, but from a confusion of them all there arose one uniform white colour.'

144, 14

Newton himself mentions this analogy in connection with the experiment described in the preceding note. 'If a burning coal be nimbly moved round in a circle with gyrations continually repeated, the whole circle will appear like fire; the reason of which is that the sensation of the coal in the several places of that circle remains impressed on the sensorium until the coal return again to the same place'.

144, 20

The ultimate German origin of the song referred to here is 'Ein New Gesengbuchlen' (Jungbunzlau, 1531) by Michael Weisse (d. 1534). This is the most famous of the early collections of songs by the Bohemian Brethren. On the mediaeval origins of Weisse's collection see Walter Blankenburg 'Zur Frage nach der Herkunft der Weisen des Gesangbüchleins der Böhmischen Brüder von 1531 'Musik und Kirche' 21 Jahrgang, 1951 Hft.2): B. Stäblein 'Die mittelalterlichen liturgischen Weisen im Gesangbuch der Böhmischen Brüder von 1531' ('Musikforschung' V, 1952). Cf. G. D. Schöber 'Die wahre Gestalt der sämtlichen Herrnhutischen Gesangbücher' (Leipzig, 1760). Michael Praetorius (1571–1621) reprinted the song in his 'Musae Sioniae' (pts, 2,3,4, Jena, Helmstedt, Wolfenbüttel, 1607), and from then on its popularity was widespread.

By the end of the eighteenth century it was common as a nightwatchman's song:

> ‚Ihr lieben Christen, seid munter und wacht!
> Der Tag vertreibt die finstre Nacht,
> Ja, ja, finstre Nacht,
> Daß ihr vom Schlaff erwacht.
> Wacht auf in Gottes Namen, Durch Jesum Christum, Amen!

G.U.A. Vieth (1763–1836), of Dessau mentions it in connection with a certain acoustical peculiarity ('Gilberts Annalen der Physik' vol. XXI p. 269, 1805), 'I have usually noticed this peculiarity early on winter mornings at about four o'clock, when although it has still been pitch-dark, the nightwatchman has loudly broadcast the untruth that the day is driving away the black night, and when it has been pretty certain that among the dear Christians of Kavalierstrasse, only he and I have been up and astir'.

The song was sung by the nightwatchman at Würges near Limburg in the lower Taunus as recently as 1877. See Johann Lewalter 'Deutsche Volkslieder. In Niederhessen aus dem Munde des Volkes gesammelt' (3 pts. Hamburg, 1890–1892): Ludwig Erk and F. M. Böhme 'Deutscher Liederhort' (3 vols. Leipzig, 1893–4): J. Wichner 'Stundenrufer und Lieder der deutschen Nachtwächter' (Regensburg, 1897).

Cf. St. Luke I v. 79, and the hymn 'Werde licht, du Stadt der Heiden' by Johann Rist (1607–1667) verse 5:

> 'Jesu, reines Licht der Seele, du vertreibst die Finsternis.'

144, 27

See Thomas Pownall (1722–1805) 'Inquiries into Coloured Light, by a Collation of the Experiments and Observations made by Sir Isaac Newton on that Subject', an article published in 'The Philosophical Magazine' (ed. A. Tilloch vol. XII pp. 42–49 and 107–112, London, 1802). Pownall had met Benjamin Franklin as early as 1754, and a life-long friendship between the two had developed. It was probably Franklin who inspired him with an interest in physics. He is of course mainly known for his activities as a colonial stateman and soldier. He was commissary-general of the British troops in Germany at the end of the Seven Years' War. See C. A. W. Pownall 'Thomas Pownall, M.P., F.R.S.' (London, 1908).

In this article, which probably interested Hegel for a while on account of its providing a possible link between the theories of Newton and Goethe, Pownall suggests that, 'There is but one *primary colour* in our solar system, and . . . all the rest in the prismatic image are, on one side of the scale, only gradations of that colour towards pure light; and, on the other side of the scale, merely degradations from light towards the actual absence of it . . . There are not seven, nor three, not two, but *only one primary colour*—a compound basis of all the tints of red, orange, and yellow: . . . green, as an actual and uncompounded primary colour, has no existence: and . . . the blues are only hues arising from a partial deprivation of light as it goes off into darkness'.

Cf. the curious physiological phenomenon described by Huddart in 'Phil. Trans. Roy. Soc.' 1777 p. 260.

144, 29

Michelet has the following footnote at this point, 'The editor has thought it advisable not to suppress this polemic of Hegel's against Newtonian theory of colours, for the theory of waves and interference which is finding favour at present, and which is threatening to supplant Newton's theory, is merely another hypothesis, and although it has been regarded as replacing its predecessor, it has retained the whole of Newton's way of reasoning and method of drawing conclusions.' (see 'Halle Yearbooks' December 1838 nos. 305–307). See the note II. 229.

The article referred to is Michelet's 'Zugeständnisse der neuesten Physik in Bezug auf Göthe's Farbenlehre' which was published in the 'Hallische Jahrbücher für deutsche Wissenschaft und Kunst' (ed. A. Ruge and T. Echtermeyer) nos. 305–307 Dec. 21st–24th 1838. In it, he presents many of the views expounded by Hegel in these 'additions', emphasizes the physiological aspect of colour, claims that Young's hypotheses of 1802 were built into Goethe's theory, compares Aristotle's idea of the aether with that current in the late 1830's, and makes the general point presented in this note.

The article was a review of an attack on Goethe's theory made by H. W.

Dove (1803–1879) in 'Die neuere Farbenlehre mit andern chromatischen Theorieen verglichen' (Berlin, 1838).

145, 2

Newton 'Opticks' bk. I pt. 2 prop. 2 theor. 2, 'The light of the Sun consists of rays differently refrangible'. et seq.

145, 8

See William Kirby (1759–1850) and William Spence (1783–1860) 'An Introduction to Entomology' (5th ed. 4 vols. London, 1828) vol. iii pp. 644–652, 'The Order, the clothing of whose organs of flight excites the admiration of the most incurious beholder, is that to which the excursive butterfly belongs, the *Lepidoptera*. The gorgeous wings of these universal favourites, as well as those of the hawkmoths and moths, owe all their beauty, not to the *substance* of which they are composed, but to an infinite number of little *plumes* or *scales* so thickly planted in their upper and under surface, as in the great majority entirely to conceal that substance.'

There was some doubt at the time as to the precise nature of these 'scales', cf. the accounts of microscopic investigations of them in R.A.F. Réaumur (1683–1757) 'Mémoires pour servir à l'histoire des insectes' (6 vols. Paris, 1734–1742) vol. I p. 200. Charles de Geer (1720–1778) 'Mémoires pour servir à l'histoire des insectes' (7 vols. Stockholm 1752–1778). Vol. I p. 63. J. U. Vallot 'Concordance systematique . . . à Mémoires pour servir à l'histoire des insectes' (Paris, 1802). Bernard Deschamps 'Recherches microscopiques sur l'organisation des ailes des Lépidoptères' ('Annales des sciences naturelles' 2nd series vol. III p. iii, 1835): H. Fischer 'Mikroskopische Untersuchungen über die Käferschuppen' ('Isis' 1846 p. 401): Goethe 'Zur Farbenlehre. Didaktischer Teil' (ed. Matthaei, Weimar, 1955) §§ 649–651.

145, 20

This type of horn music was devised by Johann Anton Maresch (1719–1794), and was popular in Russia until about a century ago.

Maresch was born at Chotěšov in Bohemia, and had his first musical training in the monastery there. He then studied at Dresden under Anton Joseph Hampel (d. 1768), a specialist in horn music, and at Berlin under Joseph Zyka, the famous violin cellist. In 1746 he began to teach music at Berlin. One of his pupils was the son of the Russian chancellor Count Bestuscheff, and it was through this connection that he went to St. Petersburg in 1748, where he was employed in the Bestuscheff chapel, and soon built up a horn band. This band gave its first public performance in 1751. The Empress Elizabeth (1709–1762) was so impressed by it while visiting Bestuscheff that she took Maresch into her service, and from 1756 until 1769 he had the full resources of the imperial chapel at his disposal for the development of the type of music mentioned here by Hegel.

He took completely untrained huntsman's boys and equipped them with instruments closely resembling ordinary hunting horns. Each horn had its particular note however, and the full range of the band consisted of 54 whole- and semitones, covering three complete octaves. By the turn of the century most of the higher Russian noble families were maintaining similar bands. See the account of a visit to St. Petersburg in 1802 by Ludwig Spohr (1784–1859), 'It is hardly to be believed that they performed the most rapid passages (of a Gluck overture) with the greatest precision, and I could not have believed it possible, had I not heard it with my own ears'. 'Autobiography' (1860–1, Eng. tr. 2 pts. London, 1865) I p. 46. Cf. the account of a visit of a similar Russian band to Scotland in 1833: J. G. Dalyell (1776–1851) 'Musical Memoirs of Scotland' (Edinburgh and London, 1849), pp. 170–172.

See J. C. Hinrichs 'Entstehung, Fortgang und Beschaffenheit der russischen Jagdmusik' (St. Petersburg, 1796): G. J. Dlabacz 'Allgemeines historisches Künstler-Lexikon für Böhmen' (Prague, 1815) vol. II col. 258: G. Seaman 'The Russian Horn Band' ('Monthly Musical Record' 89, 1959 pp. 93–99). These Russian horns were usually manufactured in Germany: there is an interesting collection of them in room IX of the Berlin 'Musikinstrumentensammlung' (Berlin 15, Wilmersdorf, Bundesallee 1–12).

146, 19

See the note II. 353.

146, 29

Werner Heisenberg (b. 1901), in a stimulating lecture given to the Society for Cultural Co-operation in Budapest on May 5, 1941, pointed out that Newton's and Goethe's theories of colour deal with, 'two completely different levels of reality', that whereas Newton's theory is concerned mainly with the *objective nature* of colour, Goethe's is concerned more with its *subjective significance*, and that, 'It is not enough to be aware of the laws in accordance with which all the events in the objective world are governed, it is also necessary that we should constantly hold before us all the consequences which these laws have for the world of our senses'. He quotes with approval Helmholtz's observation that Goethe's theory should be regarded as an attempt to do justice to the immediate truth of *sensuous* impression in the face of a simply *physical* interpretation of colour, and expresses the view that *both* Newton's and Goethe's approaches are relevant to any full understanding of the phenomenon. See 'Wandlungen in den Grundlagen der Naturwissenschaft' (4th ed. Leipzig, 1943) pp. 58–76 'Die Goethesche und die Newtonsche Farbenlehre im Lichte der modernen Physik'.

If Heisenberg's line of argument does enable one to work out a truly balanced assessment of Goethe's attack upon Newton, it has to be admitted that Goethe was wrong in thinking that his theory constituted a *refutation* of Newtonianism, and that Hegel was wrong in treating colour from a Goethean standpoint *at this juncture*. The value of Goethe's theory, according to Heisenberg, only becomes apparent once the relationship between colour and consciousness is our main concern, the nature of colour *as such* being explained much more accurately by means of Newton's purely physical hypotheses. In his 'Philosophy of Nature' Hegel should therefore have attempted to assess *Newton's* theory, and Goethe's theory should have been presented in the very early stages of his 'Philosophy of Subjective Spirit' ('System der Philosophie' pt. iii ed. Boumann, Stuttgart, 1958).

Heisenberg's attitude towards this controversy throws light upon Hegel's observation that no *artist* is stooge enough to be a Newtonian. It is in fact among psychologists, artists and philosophers that Goethe's theory of colour has found its most enthusiastic supporters. Wilhelm Wundt (1832–1920), in his 'Grundzüge der physiologischen Psychologie' (5th ed., 2 vols. Leipzig, 1912), praises Goethe as the 'founder of the impression method', i.e. as the first systematic investigator of the influence colours have upon *feelings*. Sir Charles Lock Eastlake (1793–1865) provides the best example of Goethe's influence upon British artists; see his translation of the didactic part of 'Zur Farbenlehre', 'Goethe's Theory of Colours' (London, 1840); cf. Brewster's review of the book in 'The Edinburgh Review' Jan. 1841.

Many German artists have defended Goethe's theory; see Mathias Klotz (1748–1821) 'Gründliche Farbenlehre' (Munich, 1816): J. W. C. Roux (1777–1831) 'Die Farben' (Heidelberg, 1829): P. O. Runge (1777–1810) 'Farbenkugel, oder Construction des Verhältnisses aller Mischungen der Farben zueinander und ihrer vollständigen Affinität' (Hamburg, 1840): J. K. Bähr (1801–1869) 'Vorträge über Newton's und Göthe's Farbenlehre gehalten im Künstler-Verein zu Dresden' (Dresden, 1863): Ernst Bücken 'Die Grundlagen der Goetheschen Tonlehre' ('Technische Mitteilungen für Malerei' 21ste Jahrgang Munich 1915–16): Johannes Hoppe 'Goethes Farbenlehre' (op. cit. 1916–17) etc.—many articles on the subject appeared in this periodical between 1914 and 1917. Cf. the interesting assessment of 'Zur Farbenlehre' given by the *mathematician,* (not physicist) Andreas Speiser (b. 1885) in 'Goethe und die Wissenschaft' (Frankfurt-on-Main, 1951) pp. 82–91, 'hier Kunst und Wissenschaft eine Einheit bilden, wie in wenigen Werken der Weltliteratur'.

Of the philosophers who have been sympathetic towards Goethe's theory mention should perhaps be made of Schopenhauer's 'Ueber das Sehen und die Farben' (Leipzig, 1816) and F. T. Vischer (1807–1887) 'Aesthetik oder Wissenschaft des Schönen' (3 vols. Reutlingen and Leipzig, 1847) pt. II pp. 37–55.

146, 34

This word-play is also to be found in Schelling's 'Zeitschrift für speculative Philosophie' ii, p. 60, 'Let us thank the gods that they have emancipated us from the Newtonian spectrum (*spectrum* truly!) of composed light. We owe this to the genius to whom our debt is already so large'. Cf. G. H. Lewes 'The Life and Works of Goethe' (Everyman ed. 1949) p. 344.

147, 4

See Newton's 'Opticks' bk. pt. 2 exp. 11.

147, 27

Hegel quotes here from Samuel Clarke's Latin translation of Newton's 'Opticks' (London, 1719) pp. 120–121 (bk. I pt. 2 exp 7), 'amicus, qui interfuit et cujus oculi coloribus discernendis acriores quam mei essent, notavit lineis rectis imagini in transversum ductis confinia colorum'. He then adds, 'Newton has become such a good friend to all physicists; no one has seen this himself, and if he has seen it he has spoken and thought like Newton'.

147, 29

See the note II. 253.

148, 10

See Newton 'Opticks' bk. II pts 1 and 2, Cf. the note II. 239.

148, 17

See Goethe 'Zur Farbenlehre, Historischer Teil' (ed. Kuhn, Weimar, 1957). The book gives a very thorough and comprehensive survey of all the main theories of colour formulated since the time of *Pythagoras*. Goethe concludes it with an analysis of the lectures of Robert Blair (d. 1828), and a 'confession' concerning the origins of his own interest in the subject. Historical knowledge is no substitute for successful scientific research however, and as Goethe revived many pre-Newtonian 'errors' in his own theory, these historical labours may not have had an entirely beneficial effect upon his experimental and 'didactic' work in this field.

149, 16

This curious remark may be connected in some way with the investigation of the *inflection* of light through cloth, made by David Rittenhouse (1732–1796) on the instigation of Francis Hopkinson (1737–1791); see 'An optical problem proposed by Mr. Hopkinson' in 'Transactions of the American Philosophical Society' vol. II pp. 201–205, (Philadelphia, 1786): cf. 'Nicholson's Journal' vol. I p. 13 Hopkinson had viewed a street lamp through a silk handkerchief.

149, 31

Goethe's 'Zur Farbenlehre. Didaktischer Teil' (ed. Matthaei, Weimar, 1955) §§ 155–169 provides all the examples of the 'archetypal phenomenon' given here by Hegel, including the instance of the smoke (§ 160).

The infusion mentioned (§ 162) is that of *nephritic wood*, i.e. the nephritic tincture formerly used as a remedy for diseases of the kidney: see Johann Wittich (1537–1598) 'Vinariensis . . . de Ligno Nephritico' (Leipzig, 1589, 1592): Rudolph Jakob Camerarius (1665–1721) 'Disputatio Schematismi colorum infuso ligni nephritici propriorum' (2 vol. Tübingen, 1689, 1690): Johann Friedrich Carthenser (1704–1796) 'Dissertatio de Ligno Nephritico' (Frankfurt-on-Oder, 1749). Goethe refers to it as 'Guilandia Linnaei', but it is usually known as the *Horse-radish* or *Ben-nut tree* (Moringa pterygosperma), and is a native of Ceylon and of some places on the Malabar coast. Robert Boyle (1627–1691) mentions experiments made with its tincture in 'A continuation of new experiments physico-mechanical' (London, 1682) II p. 140, and 'Short memoirs for the natural experimental history of mineral waters' (London, 1685). Robert Smith (1689–1768), in his 'A Compleat System of Opticks' (2 vols. Cambridge, 1738) vol. I. p. 86 cf. pp. 98–99, explains its coloured properties as follows, 'And much after the same manner that leaf gold is yellow by reflected and blue by transmitted light, there are some sorts of liquours, as the tincture *lignum nephriticum*, and some sorts of glass, which transmit one sort of light most copiously and reflect another sort, and thereby look of several colours according to the position of the eye to the light'.

The opal mentioned (§ 166) is called by Goethe 'Opalglass (vitrum astroides, girasole)'. He evidently treated it with a 'metallic calx' (i.e. metal oxide) in order to heighten its dimming property. William Nicholson (1753–1815), in his 'A Dictionary of Chemistry' (2 vols. London, 1795) I pp. 349–350 notes, '*Girasole*, a name given by the Italians to the opal, which is of the flint kind, and remarkable for the mutability of its colours, according to the various directions of the light which falls on it, and the position of the eye of the observer'. The exact kind of opal used by Goethe is not easy to determine with any certainty however: see H. Steffens (1773–1845) 'Vollständiges Handbuch der Oryktognosie' (4 pts. Halle, 1811–1824) pt. i pp. 135–145; there was evidently some doubt as to the true classification of the 'girasole'

Goethe subsequently (1820–1826) corresponded with the extraordinary adventurer Eduard Romeo von Vargas-Bedemar (1768–1847) on the nature of opals: see F. T. Bratranek 'Goethes Naturwissenschaftliche Correspondenz' (2 vols. Leipzig, 1874) I pp. 30–31: Weimarer Ausgabe (1887–1919) IV 33 no 118, 34 no. 46, 40 nos. 46 and 107. At that time Vargas-Bedemar had recently. made himself known in Germany as an expert on the geology of Scandinavia: see his 'Om Vulcaniske producter fra Island' (Copenhagen, 1817): 'Die Insel Bornholm' (Frankfurt-on-Main, 1819), 'Reise nach dem hohen Norden' (2 vols. Frankfurt-on-Main, 1819), and he sent Goethe some of the *common opals* found on the Faeroe Islands and Iceland. Cf. his 'Der Opal auf den Faröern' ('Leonhard, Taschenbuch' 1822 XVI pp. 11–30): 'Analyser af Faerøiske Mineralier' ('Tidsskrift for Naturvidenskaberne' ed. Ørsted, Copenhagen, 1823 vol. II pp. 134–135). See also Otto Deneke 'Der Malteser-Ritter von Göttingen' (Göttingen, 1937) pp. 11–12.

149, 36

Hegel's house in Berlin was destroyed during the last war and has been replaced by a children's playground. He lived at Am Kupfergraben 4, directly opposite the present entrance to the Pergamon Museum. His window would have faced NE, and from it he would have seen a branch of the river Spree and the island on which the museums are now situated. The Berlin weather reports for January 5, 1824 confirm that for the greater part of the day at least, the sky was overcast. Although they conflict with regard to the exact direction of the wind and give no indication of its strength, they agree with regard to its having blown from *behind* Hegel's house.

See 'Allgemeine Preussische Staats-Zeitung' no. 5 p. 20, no. 6 p. 24 Berlin, 5th and 6th January, 1824): 'Meteorological Observations: January 5th':

	Barometer	Thermometer	Hygrometer	Wind	Weather
Early	28°7′	$+1\frac{1}{2}$°R	81°	Southerly	Snatches of Sunshine
Midday	28°7′	$+2\frac{1}{2}$°R	72°	Southerly	Dull
Evening	28°7′	-1°R	83°	Southerly	Star-bright

Cf. the 'Wetterbeobachtungen vom Jahr 1824' made by Carl Ludwig Gronau (1742–1826) rector of the Parochialkirche in Berlin, and now in the possession of the 'Deutschen Akademie der Wissenschaften zu Berlin', 22–23 Otto Nuschke Strasse.

	Barometer	Thermometer	Wind	Weather
Early	28°7′	34°F	Westerly	Dull, brilliant sunrise
Midday	28°7′	38°F	Westerly	Dull
Evening	28°7′	32°F	Westerly	Starry, frost

149, 39

Goethe sent Hegel a similar tumbler from Karlsbad. It carried the following inscription, ,Dem Abſoluten empfiehlt ſich ſchönſtens zu freundlicher Aufnahme das Urphänomen' i.e. 'The archetypal phenomenon, in anticipation of a cordial acceptance, humbly recommends itself to the Absolute'. Hegel thanked Goethe for the gift in a witty and humorous letter written on August 2, 1821: 'Briefe von und an Hegel' (ed. Hoffmeister, 2 vols. Hamburg, 1953) vol. II pp. 275–278. On July 8, 1821 K. F. Zelter (1758–1832) wrote to Goethe informing him that, 'The day before yesterday we drank the health of all archetypal souls from the magnificent archetypal tumbler you have sent Hegel'. See K. Rosenkranz (1805–1879) 'Hegel's Leben' pp. 339–40. (Berlin, 1844): Erna Arnhold 'Goethes Berliner Beziehungen' (Gotha, 1925) pp. 177–178.

The tumbler Hegel received was almost certainly manufactured at the *Fikentscher* glass-works in Marktredwitz. At that time this part of Bavaria belonged to Bohemia. Wolfgang Kaspar Fikentscher (1770–1837) established the first German chemical firm in July 1788; his son Friedrich Christian (1799–1864) founded the glass-works, and corresponded with Goethe regarding the production of dimming and entoptic glasses. See F. Strehlke 'Goethe's Briefe'. 'Verzeichniss unter Angabe von Quelle Ort, Datum und Anfangsorten' pt. I p. 183 (Berlin, 1882): W. Biedermann 'Goethe und die Fikentscher' ('Goethe Forschungen' Frankfurt-on-Main, 1879 pp. 295–312): Hans Zedinek 'Zwei Briefe an Goethe aus dem Fikentscherhaus in Marktredwitz' ('Der Siebenstern. Vereinszeitschrift des Fichtelgebirgsvereins' 4 Jahrgang July 1930 no. 7 pp. 98–101): 'Goethe im chemischen Laboratorium zu Marktredwitz' (ed. R. Matthaei, Marktredwitz, 1938).

149, 40

See the note II. 353.

150, 17

See Newton 'Opticks' Bk. II pt. i obs 24. Hegel is quoting from Newton's remarks on this observation (op. cit. bk. II pt. 2), 'the refraction of a prism should make rings of colours appear, whereas it usually makes objects appear coloured only there where they are terminated with shadows, or have parts unequally luminous'.

Michelet comments upon this as follows, 'The words of Newton which are quoted here indicate that the sole condition for colours is either a mere inequality of lighting, or a meeting of light and shade. Do they not contradict his whole theory?'

Hegel and Michelet could not accept the explanation which Newton gives of this phenomenon because they denied the connection between colour and degrees of refrangibility.

150, 18

In the light of Goethe's hypothesis of course. See 'The Logic of Hegel' (tr. Wallace, Oxford, 1963) § 92, 'If we take a closer look at what a limit implies, we see it involving a contradiction in itself, and thus evincing its dialectical nature. On the one side the limit makes the reality of a thing; on the other it is its negation.'

Michelet comments as follows upon this, 'It is not only the empirical physicists who have objected to Goethe's theory because of this, and Hegel deals with it in the course of his argument. It is only necessary to call attention to what has already been said (p. 144), i.e. that as the prism has a different thickness at each point of its breadth, each point of the light image and its base must also be drawn apart, and raised and displaced to a different extent. Consequently, as different and very closely contiguous displacements are received simultaneously by the eye, all their limits are necessarily drawn into one another. This happens to a greater extent of course when the distance is increased and the displacements are therefore greater.'

150, 26

This is a translation of Hegel's original sentence ('Jenenser Realphilosophie' II p. 83). Michelet altered it somewhat.

151, 14

The inflection or diffraction of light was first discovered by F. M. Grimaldi (1613–1663), see his 'Physico-mathesis de lumine, coloribus et iride' (Bologna, 1665). Cf. Robert Hooke (1635–1702) in 'Phil. Trans. Roy. Soc.' 1672.

Grimaldi noticed that when light proceeding from a very small aperture falls upon an opaque object, a shadow is cast upon a screen situated behind the obstacle, and that this shadow is bordered by the alternations of brightness and darkness which are now known as *diffraction bands*. *Newton* took the matter up and describes the experiments he performed in his 'Opticks' bk. III pt. i. He did not feel however that his work enabled him to offer a satisfactory explanation of the phenomenon, and he merely concluded his consideration of the matter with a series of queries.

Very little important work was done in this field during the eighteenth century, although Huyghen's wave theory could have provided the basis for constructive experimentation: see J. N. Delisle (1688–1768) 'Mémoires de l'academie ... de Paris' 1715 p. 147: G. F. Maraldi (1665–1729) 'Mémoires de l'academie ... de Paris' 1723 p. 111: W. J. S'Gravesande (1688–1742) 'Physices elementa mathematica' (Leyden, 1721) p. 725: Henry Peter Brougham (1778–1868) 'Phil. Trans. Roy. Soc.' 1796 p. 227–277: 1797 pp. 352–385.

The revival of the wave theory of light by Thomas Young (1773–1829), see the notes II. 229: 234 did not lead to immediate advances in the explanation of diffraction, since Young assumed that the waves are *longitudinal*. Consequently, when the Academy of Nîmes offered a prize for the best thesis on this subject in 1811, it was awarded to Honore Flaugergues (1755–1835) for his, 'Sur la diffraction de la lumière' (Nîmes, 1812) cf. 'Journal de Physique' vol. 75 p. 16, vol. 76 pp. 142, 278, in which no real advance was made upon Newton, and in which postulates such as attractive and repulsive forces were utilized.

It was not until about 1815 that D. F. J. Arago (1786–1853) and A. J. Fresnel (1788–1827) began to follow up Young's suggestions. After they had adopted the hypothesis of *transverse* waves, Fresnel was able to formulate the first truly modern theory of diffraction (see the notes II. 229:233) Cf. Josef Fraunhofer(1787–1826) and the invention of the diffraction grating (note II. 353); G. Merz 'Das Leben und Wirken Fraunhofers' (Landshut, 1865).

The plausible but completely amateurish explanation which Hegel gave of diffraction in 1805–6, would have been of interest until Young's, Arago's and Fresnel's publication became generally known. By 1830 however, most textbooks of physics contained competent expositions of their work, so that there is no excuse for his having ignored it: see 'Gehlers Physikalisches Wörterbuch' vol. V pt. ii (Leipzig, 1830) pp. 681–742.

151, 27

'Jenenser Realphilosophie' II p. 83, ‚es ist das Heraustreten des an die Gestalt als das Ding gebunden erscheinenden Ideellen'.

Michelet altered this somewhat, ‚Es ist das Heraustreten des in die Gestalt, als das Ding, gebunden erscheinenden Ideellen'. 'This is the emergence of that which is of an ideal nature and which, as thing, appears to be bound within shape.'

151, 32

‚wodurch Schatten-Linien neben einander entstehen'. The manuscript text is clearly incomplete: Hoffmeister's suggested reading is ‚so daß sich Schatten-linien nebeneinander bilden' ('Jenenser Realphilosophie' II p. 83).

151, 37

‚Die Farbe ist nun eine bestimmte' (Jenenser Realphilosophie' II p. 82).

152, 5

‚Die Farbe als das wahrhaft Negative, als das Wirkliche' ('Jenenser Real-philosophie' II p. 82). Michelet omitted the emphasized words.

152, 14

Christoph Friedrich Ludwig Schultz (1781–1834): see the note on II. 338 Hegel is referring to Schultz's 'Ueber Physiologe Farberscheinungen', which Goethe published in his 'Zur Naturwissenschaft Überhaupt' vol. II sect. i (ed. Kuhn, Weimar, 1962) pp. 296–304.

In § 38 of this work Schultz summarizes Goethe's theory of colours in the following way, ‚Um dieses deutlicher zu machen, wollen wir uns die Hauptfarben, nach Goethes Lehre von deren Enstehung, durch trübe Mittel, in ihren Elementen, als gewissen Graden des Trüben, in Bezug auf einen durchwirkenden hellen oder dunkeln Grund, oder, wie wir es auch nennen können, in Bezug auf Durchleuchtung oder Durchschattung, vorstellen. — Solches würde (indem wir zur Vereinfachung des Beispiels der mitwirkenden Beleuchtung und Beschattung nicht erwähnen) wohl am zweckmäßigsten in der Art geschehen können, daß wir 3 Grade der Trübung annehmen, welche, vermöge Durchleuchtung oder Durchschattung, die sechs Hauptfarben des Goetheschen Farbenkreises folgendermaßen ergeben:

Durchleuchtetes Trübes — Gelb
Durchschattetes Trübes — Violett
Durchleuchtetes Trüberes — Orange
Durchschattetes Trüberes — Blau
Durchleuchtetes Trübstes — Rot
Durchschattetes Trübstes — Grün.'

Hegel evidently has his reservations with regard to accepting this exposition. He probably realized that the three grades of dimness constituted an *arbitrary* enumeration.

152, 18

Leonardo da Vinci was evidently the first to suggest that the sky appeared to be blue on account of our viewing the dark *space* beyond the regions of the atmosphere through the *air* illuminated by the sun, i.e. that this blue was a mixture of black and white: see his 'Trattato della pittura' (Paris, 1551 tr. Rigaud, London, 1877) sect. 328. Cf. the treatment of light and shadows in his diaries, 'Tagebücher und Aufzeichnungen' (ed. Lücke, Leipzig, 1952) ch. XXXII.

Goethe, in his 'Zur Farbenlehre. Historischer Teil' (ed. Kuhn, Weimar, 1957) pp. 162, 176, 307 notices that the same view was put forward by Antonius de Dominis (d. 1624) in his 'De radiis visus et lucis' (Venice, 1611), by Athanasius Kircher (1601–1680) in his 'Ars magna lucis et umbrae' (Rome, 1646), and by Philip de la Hire (1640–1718) in his 'Accidents de la vue' ('Anc. Mém. Par.' vol. IX, 1678). Hegel probably has in mind Goethe's exposition of this theory in 'Zur Farbenlehre. Didaktischer Teil' (ed. Matthaei, Weimar, 1955) §§ 74, 155, 156.

By accepting this explanation of the blue of the sky, Hegel and Goethe were rejecting the predominant theory of the time, which was that put forward by Newton ('Opticks' bk. II pt. 3 prop. 7), according to which the vapours in a blue sky had attained consistence enough to reflect the most reflexible (azure) rays, but not enought to reflect any of the less reflexible ones. Newton's theory was propagated most notably by Thomas Melvill (1726–1753) in his 'Observations on Light and Colours' (1752) and 'Edinburgh Physical, and Literary Essays' II p. 75, Pierre Bouguer (1698–1758) in his 'Traité d'Optique' (Paris, 1729) p. 368, and J. A. Nollet (1700–1770) in his 'Leçons de physique expérimentale' (6 vols. Paris, 1743–1750, Germ. tr. Erfurt, 1749–1764) vol. VI p. 17. H. B. de Saussure (1740–1799) accepted it as basic to his work with the *cyanometer*: see 'Journal de Physique' 1791 p. 199: Gren's 'Journal der Physik' VI p. 93.

In the early part of the last century it was by no means unchallenged however. Many responsible physicists such as J. J. Berzelius (1779–1848) in his 'Lehrbuch der Chemie' (2nd ed. 3 vols. Reutlingen, 1821–1828) vol. I p. 257 and Benjamin Scholz (1786–1833) in his 'Anfangsgründe der Physik' (Vienna, 1816) p.

408, accepted the theory put forward by Leonhard Euler (1707–1783), and widely known on account of his 'Briefe über verschiedene Gegenstände aus der Naturlehre' (tr. Kries, Leipzig, 1792) I p. 177, according to which *air itself* is somewhat bluish. G. W. Muncke (1772–1847), in his 'Anfangsgründe der Naturlehre' (2 vols. Heidelberg, 1819–1820) vol. I p. 210 and in an article published in 'Schweiggers Journal' vol. 30 p. 83, even argued that the blue of the atmosphere must be a purely subjective phenomenon: see Goethe's 'Zur Naturwissenschaft Überhaupt' vol. I pt. iv (ed. Kuhn, 1962) pp. 192–195.

152, 23
See the note II. 358.

153, 13
This passage is clearly influenced by Goethe's 'Zur Farbenlehre. Didaktischer Teil' (ed. Matthaie, Weimar, 1955) sect. VI 'Sinnlich-sittliche Wirkung der Farbe' and §§ 915–920. Hegel treats the subject in a more extended manner in his 'Philosophy of Subjective Spirit' (ed. Boumann, Stuttgart, 1958) §401. Wilhelm Wundt (1832–1920), in his 'Grundzüge der physiologischen Psychologie' (5th ed. 2 vols. Leipzig, 1912) praises Goethe as the 'founder of the impression method', i.e. as the first systematic investigator of the influence colours have upon *feelings*.

153, 30
'Zur Farbenlehre. Didaktischer Teil' §§ 809–810 et seq. 'Zur Naturwissenschaft Überhaupt' (ed. Kuhn, Weimar, 1962) p. 190 (vol. I sect. iv.).

153, 37
'Zur Farbenlehre. Didaktischer Teil' §§ 62–68.

154, 19
Christoph Friedrich Ludwig Schultz (1781–1834), see the note II. 338. The work referred to is 'Ueber Physiologe Farbenerscheinungen insbesondere das phosphorische Augenlicht, als Quelle derselben, betreffend' which Schultz completed on July 27, 1821 and which appeared in the first part of Goethe's 'Zur Naturwissenschaft Überhaupt' vol. II (1822) (ed. Kuhn, Weimar, 1962) pp. 296–304.

In Michelet's text Hegel refers to 'interesting experiments with these psychological colours', but this is clearly a mistake.

154, 26
This could be a reference to 'Zur Farbenlehre. Historischer Teil' (ed. Kuhn, Weimar, 1957): see the note II. 362, but Hegel probably has in mind the collection of references to the theory of colours published by Goethe in his 'Zur

Naturwissenschaft Überhaupt' vol. I sect. iv (ed. Kuhn, Weimar, 1962) pp. 202–220. For an exhaustive bibliography of *subsequent* literature relating to this subject see Günther Schmid's 'Goethe und die Naturwissenschaften' (Halle, 1940).

154, 40

Michelet inserts the following footnote at this point, 'In the lectures based upon the first edition of the Encyclopaedia, this first part of the theory of colours followed on immediately after the doctrine of the reflection of light (see above § 278 Add.), in which place this paragraph was also inserted. At this juncture however, the exposition of the entoptic colours came straight after the doctrine of double refraction.'

See 'Enzyklopädie . . . und andere Schriften aus der Heidelberger Zeit' (ed. Glockner, Stuttgart, 1956) pp. 175–176 and 192–194.

155, 8

See 'Zur Naturwissenschaft Überhaupt' I sect. iii (ed. Kuhn, Weimar, 1962) pp. 94–138. Cf. the note II. 348: 'Gehler's Physikalisches Wörterbuch' vol. IV p. 99 (Leipzig, 1827).

156, 9

Michelet adds a footnote at this point. 'This accounts for the black undulating lines which occur when one causes these colours to pale by subjecting them to intense light.'

Newton's 'Opticks' bk. II pts. i and ii, i.e. the 'Observations concerning the relexions, refractions, and colours of thin transparent bodies', initiated the research into what Goethe called 'epoptic' colours: see the notes II. 240: 348. The colours of thin plates and Newton's rings are now regarded as an *interference* phenomenon. For the ordinary explanation of them given by the physicists of Hegel's day, see the article 'Anwandelungen' in 'Gehler's Physikalisches Wörterbuch' vol. I pp. 301–321 (Leipzig, 1825). It was based mainly on the work of Newton and Biot.

15, 614

See J. F. Meckel (1781–1833) 'Über die Federbildung' ('Reil's Archiv für die Physiologie' vol. XII pp. 37–96, Halle, 1815), 'For the brightest colours always appear at the ends of the feathers, as the result of the influence of the sunlight' (p. 70). J. M. Bechstein (1757–1822) discusses the markings of pigeons in some detail in his 'Gemeinnützige Naturgeschichte Deutschlands' (4 vols. Leipzig, 1801–1807) vol. III pp. 985–988, but gives no explanation of this iridescence. Cf. Goethe 'Zur Farbenlehre. Didaktischer Teil' §§ 389–428, 653–661.

158, 15

See 'Die vier edlen Metalle' (1802), reprinted in 'Schellings Werke' 1st supplementary volume (ed. Schröter, Munich, 1962) pp. 565–574. Hegel evidently has § XVII of this work in mind, ‚Süd und Ost sind die beiden erfreulichsten Weltgegenden, so ist auch das Gold das heiterste Metall, welches ein glücklicher Instinkt früher schon als das geronnene Licht mit dem Zeichen der Sonne bezeichnet hat'.

158, 29

On contemporary ways of separating lead and silver see J. P. F. Duhamel (1730–1816), 'A memoir on the refining of Lead in the large way' ('Nicholson's Journal' 1805 vol. xi pp. 206–215). See also John Murray (d. 1820) 'System of Chemistry' (4 vols. Edinburgh, 1819) vol. III pp. 200–207. Murray refers to 'der Silberblick' as the 'brightening', 'The appearance of a vivid incandescence or brightening, denotes when the silver has become pure'. Newton Ivory Lucas however, in his 'A Dictionary of the English and German and German and English Languages' (4 vols. London and Bremen, 1854–1868) vol. 4 p. 1799 gives the 'lightening of silver' as the correct technical term.

Cf. the early discoveries relating to *photochemistry* surveyed in J. R. Partington's 'A History of Chemistry' vol. 4 pp. 713–718 (London, 1964).

159, 7

Goethe 'Zur Farbenlehre. Didaktischer Teil' (ed. Matthaei, Weimar, 1955) §§ 472–477. This quotation is by no means word perfect.

159, 27

See 'Zur Farbenlehre. Historischer Teil' (ed. Kuhn, Weimar, 1957). Goethe is here *translating* from the second part of 'Traité de la nature des couleurs' (Paris, 1688) by Edme Mariotte (d. 1684).

159, 30

'Zur Farbenlehre. Didaktischer Teil' § 533.

160, 16

‚Die Natur, welche zuerst sich als ihren Sinn des Gefühls entwickelte' ('Jenenser Realphilosophie' II p. 81). Michelet omitted the emphasized words.

160, 34

See Schiller's 'Das Lied von der Glocke':

,Wohltätig ist des Feuers Macht,
Wenn sie der Mensch bezähmt, bewacht . . .
Wehe, wenn sie losgelassen,
Wachsend ohne Widerstand
Durch die volkbelebten Gassen
Wälzt den ungeheuren Brand!
Denn die Elemente hassen
Das Gebild der Menschenhand.'

The German text and an English prose translation of this poem are to be found in 'The Penguin Book of German Verse' (ed. L. Forster, 1957) pp. 260–278.

160, 37

There is no detailed criticism of Hegel's treatment of Goethe's theory of colours, and even Goethe's criticism of Newton has yet to be subjected to a balanced full-scale analysis. *English* readers have to rest content with the exposition of the matter given by G. H. Lewes in his 'The Life and Works of Goethe' (Everyman ed. 1949) pp. 340–353, with the articles mentioned at the end of this note, and with Burton Chance's 'Goethe and his theory of colours' ('Annals of Medical History' New Series, New York, vol. V 1933 pp. 360–375), none of which is very constructive.

The most worthwhile approach to this subject is undoubtedly that of the *physicist* unblinkered by the presuppositions of his particular field: see Hermann von Helmholtz 'Vorträge und Reden' (4th ed. 2 vols. Braunschweig, 1896) I pp. 23–47: Werner Heisenberg 'Wandlungen in den Grundlagen der Naturwissenschaft' (4th ed. Leipzig, 1943) pp. 58–76. For the extensive literature relating to the subject see Günther Schmid 'Goethe und die Naturwissenschaften' (Halle, 1940): 'Goethes Werke. Hamburger Ausgabe' vol. XIII pp. 638–642 (3rd ed. Wegner Verlag, Hamburg, 1960).

From the physicist's point of view, Goethe's basic fault in 'Zur Farbenlehre' ('Polemischer Teil' ed. Matthaei, Weimar, 1958 §§ 610–677) is his rejection of Newton's proposition ('Opticks' bk I pt. 2 prop. 10) that the various colours of bodies arise from their reflecting most copiously this or that kind of light ray. This rejection forced him to deal with the various appearances of colour as involving physiological, physical, chemical and even organic factors, which were not only inessential to the treatment of colour *as such*, but which were not to be satisfactorily explained by the physiology, physics, chemistry and organics of his day, and which were *certainly* not to be explained simply in terms of the 'archetypal phenomenon', i.e. the opposition between light and darkness.

The great merit of his work in this field is that it consistently exhibits colour as an experience involving *concrete appearances*, although his attempt to refute Newton would seem to imply either that he regarded a purely physical interpretation of colour as being indefensible and unwarranted, or that he considered the

'archetypal phenomenon' to be justified on purely physical grounds. Schopenhauer was evidently aware of the potential and weakness of Goethe's approach
when he advised him to examine more carefully the relationship between physical
and psychic factors in the perception of colour: 'Goethes Werke—Hamburger
Ausgabe' (3rd ed. 1960) vol. XIII pp. 612–613.

As a *purely physical* explanation of colour, Newton's theory would appear to
be immensely superior to Goethe's for it still constitutes the broad basis of all
modern physical research in the fields of light and optics. It has of course
been modified (notes II 229: 233 : 358 : 364), and some important modifications were made during Goethe's lifetime, but subsequent developments such
as the postulation of 'phases' in wave theory and of 'photons' in quantum
mechanics have only tended to confirm the accuracy of Newton's experimentation and the soundness of the conclusions he drew from it. When Goethe
published 'Zur Farbenlehre', Young's revival of the wave theory had yet to be
justified, and Malus' 'polarization' constituted the very latest discovery in this
field. During the next fifteen years the work done by Biot, Brewster, Arago,
Fraunhofer and Fresnel etc. brought about the virtual completion of the *geometrical* part of the wave theory, and prepared the field for Maxwell's *dynamical*
interpretation of light. Goethe chose either to ignore these developments or to
attempt a refutation of them in the light of his 'archetypal phenomenon'!

How are we to assess Goethe's influence upon Hegel's treatment of light and
colours? In some respects (notes: II. 242, III. 148:214:255) Hegel's views on
light accord well with modern research, but in his rejection of Newton and
the 'Newtonian' physics of his own day, he was clearly influenced by Goethe
and very largely in the wrong.

Goethe's theory appealed to him because it made it comparatively easy to
work out a hierarchical exposition of colour (see his letter to Goethe Feb. 20,
1821, printed in 'Zur Naturwissenschaft Überhaupt' vol. I sect. iv pp. 212–214,
1962 ed.), in which justice could be done to both its physical and *spiritual* significance. For Hegel of course, this 'spiritual' significance involved not only the
'psychic' factor mentioned by Schopenhauer, but also the 'intelligible' factor of
a *dialectical* interpretation, employing the fundamental antithesis exhibited by
the 'archetypal phenomenon'. Had he accepted Newton's theory that white
light is a compound of the colours of the spectrum, his treatment of colour
would have been much more closely juxtaposed to his treatment of light, and
what is more, much more difficult to interpret dialectically. According to
Goethe's theory however, it is the various *circumstances* in which light and darkness are combined which give rise to colour. These circumstances involve a
complexity of physical factors, and consequently, as Hegel took light to constitute the *simplest* level of physics, he did not treat colour till he had worked out the
dialectical exposition of those *further* physical stages which he considered to be
involved in its production. For the *development* of his views on this from *1801*
onwards see 'Jenenser Logik' etc. (ed. Lasson, Leipzig 1923) pp. 307–309:

'Jenenser Realphilosophie' I (ed. Hoffmeister, Leipzig, 1932) pp. 54–56: 'Jenenser Realphilosophie' II (ed. Hoffmeister, Leipzig, 1931) pp. 33–34, 79–85: Heidelberg 'Encyklopädie' (ed. Glockner, Stuttgart, 1956) §§ 220–221.

Although this approach is rather more sophisticated than Goethe's, it reproduces many of Goethe's errors. It fails for example to treat colour *as such*, and while honestly purporting to be an essentially physical doctrine, actually misinterprets physical phenomena by bringing psychic and metaphysical considerations into an assessment of them. However, Hegel was undoubtedly convinced that Goethe had refuted Newton on *purely physical grounds*, and was therefore not aware that at this juncture the coincidence of the dialectical method and the archetypal phenomenon was bogus. It has to be admitted therefore, that in the light of his system and knowledge of the facts, he was justified in *placing* and *treating* colour as he did. Consequently, although these paragraphs are not *intrinsically* erroneous, they are unsatisfactory, not only because Hegel erred in his assessment of the physics of his day, but because he violated (though inadvertently) an important principle of his own system, by introducing *psychic* factors at a level which should have been devoted solely to the treatment of physical phenomena.

Goethe's theory of colour is certainly not without its merits (note II. 368), and Hegel oftens shows that he was aware of its true importance. If he had also been aware of Goethe's shortcomings as a *physicist*, he might very easily have anticipated Heisenberg (loc. cit) by converting the apparent contradiction between the Newtonian and Goethean theories into an exposition of their *complementarity*. His system was well adapted to help him do this; in accordance with its principles, Newton's theory should have been assessed in the 'Philosophy of Nature' and Goethe's presented in the initial stages of the 'Philosophy of Spirit'.

There are very few English works relating to this subject: see however Brewster's review of Eastlake's translation of the didactic part of 'Zur Farbenlehre' in 'The Edinburgh Review' vol. 72 pp. 99–131. (Edinburgh, 1841): John Tyndall 'Goethe's Farbenlehre' in 'The Fortnightly Review' vol. 27 pp. 471–490 new series (London, 1880): A Schuster 'Goethe's Farbenlehre' in 'Publications of the English Goethe Society' no. 5 pp. 141–151 (London, 1890).

161, 12

See the note on II. 259.

161, 22

A fifteenth century 'Vocabularius' (Augsburg, 1473) contains the following entry, ‚Smecklich -odoriferus . . . omne illud quod potest odorari', and in a pre-Lutheran south German translation of the Bible, it is said of Lazarus' body that it ‚smeckt iezunt' (John XI 39) Hegel may also have known the Swabian rhyme

,Ein Hirte ohne Stecken
Ist wie ein Hund ohne Schmecken'.

See H. Fischer and W. Pfleiderer 'Schwäbisches Wörterbuch' (6 vols. Tübingen, 1904–1936) vol. 5 cols. 986–989, vol. 6 pt. ii col. 3002.

161, 29

‚als Kalk'. See A, and C. R. Aikin 'A Dictionary of Chemistry and Mineralogy' (2 vols. London, 1807) I p. 177, 'The term calcination is derived from the Latin calx, which signifies quick-lime, and is applied by the old chemists to the conversion of a comparatively dense substance into a light and porous one, by the action of fire . . . Most metals when exposed to the joint action of heat and air are converted to a loose powdery substance which was denominated by the old chemists the calx of the metal, but which in the modern nomenclature is called an oxyd.'

162, 30

On this transition from colour to odorous matter see A. F. Fourcroy (1755–1809) 'Elements of Naural History and Chemistry' (tr. W. Nicholson, 3 vols. London, 1790) vol. III p. 96, where the opinion is expressed that the colour of a dye is perhaps, 'a very subtle body, perhaps not less so than the principle of smells' etc. Working on the analogy of the propagation of *light* and sound, Johann Georg Steinbuch, in his 'Beitrag zur Physiologie der Sinne' (Nuremberg, 1811) p. 304, considered the possibility of there being 'odorous rays' (Riechstrahlen).

P. J. Macquer (1718–1784), in 'Elements of the Theory and Practice of Chymistry' (tr. Reid, 2 vols. London, 1758) and 'Dictionnaire de Chymie' (2nd ed. 4 vols. Paris, 1778) vol. ii p. 451 says that the smell of essential oils is due to a *spiritus rector*, a kind of gas which escapes from them. Fourcroy, in his 'Elemens d'histoire naturelle et de chimie' (5th ed. 5 cols. Paris, 1793) vol. I ch. iv pp. 139–146, and in two articles ('Bull. Soc. Philomath'. 1797 no. 7, 52, and Ann. Chim. 1798, xxvii, 232) also defended the hypothesis of a spiritus rector, although in his 'Systèmes de Connaissances Chimiques' (11 vols. Paris, 1801–2 tr. Nicholson, London, 1804) vol. VII p. 361, he says that the odour of each essential oil is its *specific property*. Cf. F. A. Gren (1760–1798) 'Systematisches Handbuch der gesammten Chemie' (3 vols. Halle, 1806–7) vol. II § 1307.

The colours of metallic salts, especially oxides, were probably considered by Hegel to be further evidence of the validity of this transition (note II. 352). John Murray (d. 1820), in his 'A System of Chemistry' (4 vols. Edinburgh, 1819) vol. IV pp. 319–336 considers colours, aroma and taste in the same sequence as Hegel. Unlike Hegel however, he does not distinguish between 'odour' and 'fragrancy'.

162, 36

See the note II. 256.

163, 6

Hegel added a note here, 'Chemistry distinguishes between solution and resolution; resolution is a separation into component parts, solution simply takes place in water'.

163, 14

On water of crystallization, see the distinction drawn by G. F. Rouelle (1703–1770), 'J'appelle cette eau qui entre ainsi dans la formation des crystaux, l'eau de la crystallisation, afin de la distinguer de l'eau qui se dissipe par l'évaporation, à laquelle je donne le nom d'eau surabondante à la crystallisation, ou d'eau de la dissolution'.

There was much uncertainty as to the nature of water of crystallisation. A. L. Lavoisier (1743–1794) in 'Mémoires de Chimie' (2 vols. Paris, 1803) vol. II p. 765 took it to be in the form of ice ('dans l'état de glace'), but J. B. Richter (1762–1807) was convinced that this could not be the case: see his 'Ueber die neuern Gegenstände der Chymie' (11 pts. Breslau etc., 1791–1802) pt. X p. 250. Berzelius discovered that in compounds of different bases with water, the oxygen in the water is in simple ratio to that in the anhydrous base, and that the oxygen in water of crystallisation in acids and salts is in a simple ratio to that in the basic water or basic oxide ('Gilberts Annalen' 1812, 50 p. 287). Cf. his 'Lärbok i Kemien' pt. III p. 84 (Stockholm, 1818). For later views on the subject see John Dalton (1766–1844) 'On the Quantities of Acids, Bases and Water in the different Varieties of Salts' (Manchester, 1842).

Considering the basic uncertainty of this knowledge, Hegel's assessment of the matter is by no means unreasonable.

163, 34

In the textbooks of the time, taste was taken to involve the two basic factors of sweetness and bitterness: see J. F. Pierer 'Medizinisches Realwörterbuch' (8 vols. Leipzig, 1816–1829) vol. III p. 660. Most chemical descriptions involved giving the taste of the material being described, but the exact nature of this characteristic was not closely investigated, and in the British textbooks of the time taste was only treated in detail as an attribute of vegetable substances. See Thomas Thomson (1773–1852) 'A System of Chemistry' (5 vols. Edinburgh, 1810) vol. V pp. 31–37: John Murray 'A System of Chemistry' (4 vols. Edinburgh, 1819) vol. IV pp. 333–335. Murray distinguishes between the acrid, narcotic and bitter principles, but admits that the whole subject has not been satisfactorily investigated.

165, 38

'The Logic of Hegel' (tr. Wallace, Oxford, 1963) pp. 180–181.

167, 28

The distinction between vitreous and resinous electricity was first made by C. F. Dufay (1698–1739), who announced his discovery in the 'Mémoires de l'Academie Royale des Sciences' 1733 cf. 1734 pp. 303, 341: 1737 pp. 86, 307: 'Phil. Trans. Roy. Soc.' vol. 38 p. 258. He writes, 'There are two kinds of electricity, very different from one another, one of which I call *vitreous* (positive) and the other *resinous* (negative) electricity. The first is that of glass, rock crystal, precious stones, hairs of animals, wool, and many other bodies. The second is that of amber, copal, gum-lac, silk, thread, paper and a vast number of other substances. The characteristics of these two electricities are that they repel themselves and attract each other.'

168, 19

Claude Louis Berthollet (1748–1822). The main importance of his book on chemical statics, 'Essai de Statique Chimique' (2 vols. Paris, 1803), which was based on investigations into chemical reaction made between 1799 and 1803, is the influence it had upon the development of the theory of *chemical affinity*. In this work he attacked the *law of constant proportions* which formed the basis of the quantitative analytical method employed among others by Richard Kirwan (1733–1812): see for example Kirwan's 'Experiments and Observations on the Specific Gravities and Attractive Powers of various Saline Substances' ('Phil. Trans. Roy. Soc.' 1781 p. 7, 1782 p. 179, 1783 p. 15 tr. Crell 'Versuche und Beobachtungen' etc. 2 pts. Berlin and Stettin, 1783–1785).

According to Berthollet, chemical reactions are usually incomplete, and when substances of definite composition *are* formed, they are either the result of a *mutual saturation* of an acid by a base, in which the powers of each are simply neutralized in a certain proportion, or they are due to changes in *physical* factors such as cohesion or elasticity.

The chapter of the book referred to by Hegel is headed 'De l'action de la lumière et du fluide électrique'. In the passage referred to Berthollet admits the *analogy* existing between 'caloric' and 'electric fluid', and attempts to show why their effects are often similar. He believes that when metals are oxidized, the electric fluid merely causes a 'dilatation' of bodies, and suggests that both oxidation and fusion are facilitated by the molecules of the metal being *dispersed* by the electricity. He notices for example that if heavy electrical charges are passed through platinum wire, the motion imparted will cause the latter to acquire a *temperature* about equal to that of boiling water, which is by no means high enough to fuse it. Consequently, he attributes the fusion and oxidation which occur to the *vibrations* set up by the electricity, and suggests that the electric *shock* (note II. 226), is the root cause of all these electro-chemical changes.

169, 14

See the note II. 306.

169, 25

This passage is evidently meant to be a *recapitulation* of the progression from colour to smell and taste worked out in §§ 321–322.

On the *colour* of electric light see J. Priestley (1733–1804) 'Experiments and Observations on Different Kinds of Air' (3 vols. Birmingham, 1790) vol. I pp. 115, 232 etc. Priestley notices that in 'fixed air' (CO_2), the electric spark is 'exceedingly white', and that in 'inflammable air' (H_2) it is red or purple, which he considers to be its characteristic colour. See also his 'The History and Present State of Electricity' (London, 1769) pt. VIII, sect. xvi exp. 12, 'The electric spark, taken in the middle of a phial filled with inflammable air, is always of a red or purple colour, and cannot be made to look white; but the larger the explosion is, the nearer it approaches to white'. G. C. Morgan (1754-1798) regarded light as a body subject to gravity but heterogeneous, the same attractive power operating differently on its different parts. Like Priestley, he noticed that electric light assumes different colours according to the *medium* in which it is taken. He noticed for example that a spark conveyed through an imperfect vacuum displays its indigo rays, while in the vapour of ether it displays its green rays, and in ammoniacal gas, its red rays ('Phil. Trans. Roy. Soc.' 1785 vol. 75 p. 190).

On the smell of electricity, see 'Gehler's Physikalisches Wörterbuch' vol. III p. 385 (Leipzig, 1827). It is clear from this account that the attribution of this property to the phenomenon was extremely hypotheitcal. See also L. V. Brugnatelli (1761–1818) in 'Gilberts Annalen der Physik' 1803, vol. viii pp. 284–299. Brugnatelli regarded the 'galvanic fluid' as an electric *acid*, with the *smell* of *phosphorus*, from which he claimed to have prepared, a series of salts. Cf. 'Nicholson's Journal' vol. IV p. 261: P. F. Mottelay 'Bibliographical History of Electricity and Magnetism' (London, 1922) pp. 361–363.

Johann Georg Sulzer (1720–1779) seems to have been the first to notice the *taste* of electricity: see his 'Theorie der angenehmen und unangenehmen Empfindungen' (Berlin, 1762), 'When two pieces of metal, one of lead and the other of silver, are so joined together that their edges make one surface, a certain sensation will be produced on applying it to the tongue, which comes near to the taste of vitriol of iron; whereas each piece by itself betrays not the slightest trace of that taste'. See F. C. Bakewell 'Manual of Electricity' (London, 1857) ch. III p. 28. Cf. the note II. 412.

169, 28

This is a reference to the 'figures' discovered by Georg Christoph Lichtenberg (1744–1799) in 1777. His accounts of them have recently been edited as no. 246 of Ostwald's 'Klassiker der Exacten Wissenschaften': see 'Über eine neue Methode die Natur und die Bewegung der elektrischen Materie zu erforschen' (ed. Pupke und Zaunick, Leipzig, 1956). Cf. Tiberius Cavallo (1749–1809) 'An account of some new experiments in electricity' ('Phil. Trans. Roy. Soc.' 70 i pp. 15–29, 1780): Thomas Young (1773–1829) 'A course of lectures on natural philosophy' (2 vols. London, 1807) vol. II pp. 119, 419, 426.

These figures are produced by tracing any desired lines upon a cake of resin with a needle in contact with a Leyden jar, and by dusting upon the cake a well-triturated mixture of sulphur and of red lead. These substances having been brought by friction into opposite electrical conditions, the sulphur collects upon the positive and the lead upon the negative portions of the cake: positive electricity producing an appearance resembling feathers, and negative electricity an arrangement more like stars.

Lichtenberg gives a list of the substances and powders he used (op. cit. pp. 32–33), but does not mention colophony. Hegel may have in mind a paper published by Adolph Traugott von Gersdorff (1744–1807), in which many experiments similar to Lichtenberg's are described: see 'Über einige elektrische Versuche' ('Neue Schriften der Berlinischen Gesellschaft naturforschender Freunde' vol. II 1799).

Historically, the main importance of Lichtenberg's work on electricity was that it provided support for the *two fluid theory* of electricity, championed among others, by Robert Symmer (d. 1763) in his 'New Experiments and Observations concerning electricity' ('Phil. Trans. Roy. Soc.' 51 i pp. 371–389, 1760), as opposed to the *one fluid theory* championed by Franklin: see C. van Doren 'Benjamin Franklin' (New York, 1938). Lichtenberg's work inspired Chladni to look for his figures' (note II. 286).

Cf. K. Przibram 'Lichtenberg als Physiker' ('Naturwissenschaft' vol. 15 pp. 423–425, 1927): G. Knoerzer and W. Kossel 'Zweipolige Lichtenberg-Figuren' ('Naturwissenschaft' vol. 37 p. 357, 1950): J. A. Deluc (1727–1817) 'Idées sur la Météorologie' (2 vols. London, 1786–1787). I p. 490.

F. H. Mautner and F. Miller 'Remarks on G. C. Lichtenberg' ('Isis' 1952 pp. 223–231).

169, 34

Various theories based upon the assumption of electrical *matters* were current at the end of the eighteenth century. W. J. G. Karsten (1732–1787), in his 'Anleitung zur gemeinnützigen Kenntniss der Natur' (Halle, 1783) § 497 assumed positive electricity to be pure *air* saturated with elemental fire, and negative electricity to be *phlogiston* combined with a weak acid. To some extent he based his work on the theory of heat put forward by Adair Crawford (1749–1795) in his 'Experiments and Observations on Animal Heat' (London, 1779). J. R. Forster (1729–1798) formulated a similar theory in 'Über die Natur des Feuers und der Elektricität' ('Crell's neueste Entdeckungen' vol. 12 p. 154, 1784).

Hegel probably has in mind J. A. Deluc's theory of an electric *fluid*: see his 'Neue Ideen über die Meteorologie' (Berlin und Stettin, 1787) 'Traité élémentaire sur le fluide électro-galvanique' (2 vols. Paris, 1804). Cf. J. G. F. Schrader (1763–c. 1825) 'Versuch einer neuen Theorie der Elektricität' (Altona, 1797):

W. A. Lampadius (1772–1842) 'Versuche und Beobachtungen über die Elektricität' (Berlin and Stettin, 1793).

170, 7

The best known German writer on occult agents is Agrippa von Nettesheim (1487–1537): see his 'De occulta philosophia' (Cologne, 1533). John French (1616–1657) published an English translation of this work (London, 1651), which has since been edited by W. F. Whitehead (Chicago, 1898). John Ferguson, professor of chemistry at Glasgow, has published bibliographical notes on it (Edinburgh, 1924).

The work of Karl Kiesewetter, thorough though it is, is curiously weak on *mediaeval* theories of occultism: see 'Der Occultismus des Altertums' (Leipzig, 1896) and 'Geschichte des neueren Occultismus' (ed. Blum, Leipzig, 1909). Cf. A. E. Waite 'The Occult Sciences' (London, 1891): G. B. Alfano 'Piccola enciclopedia di scienze occulte' (Naples, 1949).

If Hegel is not referring to occultism as such, he probably has in mind such use of the concept as that mentioned by Edward Stillingfleet (1635–1699) in his analysis of Epicurus, 'But for one to say that atoms move, because it is their nature to move, and give no other account of it, is so precarious, that it will never give the least satisfaction to an inquisitive mind: and it will be the least of all pardonable in the exploders of substantial forms and occult qualities, when the origin of the whole world is resolved into an occult quality which gives motion to atoms.': see 'Origines Sacrae' (1662, III ii § 14, new ed. 2 vols. Oxford, 1797) II p. 40. Newton, in his 'Opticks' (4th ed. London, 1730) bk. III pt. i query 31 comments as follows upon the concept, 'And the Aristotelians gave the Name of occult Qualities, not to manifest Qualities, but to such Qualities only as they supposed to lie hid in Bodies, and to be the unknown causes of manifest Effects: Such as would be the causes of Gravity, and of magnetick and electrick Attractions, and of Fermentations, if we should suppose that these Forces or Actions arose from Qualities unknown to us, and uncapable of being discovered and made manifest. Such occult Qualities put a stop to the improvement of natural Philosophy, and therefore of late Years have been rejected.' Despite this Leibniz accused Newton of reviving the occult qualities of the schools: see his letter to Abbé Conti (Nov.–Dec. 1715) published in J. Raphson 'The History of Fluxions' (London, 1715) p. 97: cf. D. Brewster 'Memoirs ... of Sir Isaac Newton' (2 vols. Edinburgh, 1855) vol. II p. 60.

Voltaire, in his 'Philosophical Dictionary' (Eng. tr. London, 1765), defends the postulation of *occult* qualities. See also Alexandre Koyré 'Newtonian Studies' (London, 1965) appendix B.

170, 10

Jöns Jacob Berzelius (1779–1848) had his sandbath and furnace in his *kitchen*; see Friedrich Wöhler (1800–1882) 'Jugend Erinnerungen eines Chemikers' (Berlin, 1875) viii 841. Wöhler spent a year with Berzelius in Stockholm

(1823–4), and in 1825 became a teacher at the newly-founded technical school in *Berlin*. Berzelius certainly regarded atmospheric and 'laboratory' electricity as being identical, see his 'Lärbok i Kemien' pt. III (Stockholm, 1818) p. 62.

Cf. Jean Antoine Nollet (1700–1770) 'Leçons de Physique' (6 vols. Paris, 1743–1750) vol. IV p. 314, and the note II. 266.

170, 11

Jacques Rohault (1620–1675), in his 'Traité de Physique' (2 vols. Paris, 1673), accounted for *thunder* by supposing that clouds *collide*. L. U. de Tessan (1804–1879) in 'Observation d'un coup de tonnerre accompagné de sifflement' ('Comptes Rendus' 1841 vol. XII pp. 791–794) put forward the curious view that thunder was caused by the *elasticity* of the clouds being removed by the dissipation of electricity in the lightning flash. Cf. 'Proceedings of the London Electrical Society' ed. Walker 1843 pp. 180–184. C. H. Pfaff (1773–1852) in 'Von den Gewitterwolken' ('Gehler's Phys. Wört.' vol. I p. 989, Leipzig, 1825) makes the point that the *friction* of air particles cannot play a very large part in the generation of atmospheric electricity because lightning often occurs when the air is comparatively still.

170, 33

See §§ 275 and 315.

171, 13

See the note II. 265.

171, 19

The gold-leaf electrometer devised by Abraham Bennet (1750–1799) and described by him in an article published in 'Phil. Trans. Roy Soc.' 1787 pp. 26–32, was the most sensitive instrument of its kind available to physicists at this time: cf. Bennet's 'New Experiments of Electricity' (Derby, 1789).

Georg John Singer (1786–1817) improved upon Bennet's instrument by reducing the amount of moisture precipitated upon the surface of insulators (1810). Robert Hare (1781–1858) devised (1821) a single gold-leaf electrometer of such delicacy that it enabled him to detect the electricity produced by one contact between a zinc and copper disc, each six inches in diameter: see Silliman's 'American Journal of Science and Arts' vol. 35 p. 329.

171, 23

J. B. Biot (1774–1862) 'Traité de Physique' (4 vols. Paris, 1816) vol. II p. 217, 'Nous voyons donc que lorsqu'un corps a été préalablement électrisé et isolé, comme notre petit pendule, les autres corps électrisés qui en approchent n'agissent pas tous sur lui de la même manière, puisque les uns le repoussent et les autres l'attirent: cela nous oblige désormais à distinguer deux sortes d'électricités, l'une analogue à celle que développe le verre frotté par une étoffe de laine; nous la nommerons l'*électricité vitrée*; l'autre, semblable à celle qu'exerce la resine, pareillement frottée avec une étoffe de laine; nous la nommerons l'*électricité resineuse*. Cette belle decouverte est due a Dufay'. See the note II. 385.

171, 28

René-Just Hauy (1743–1822): see the note II. 332. His 'Traité de mineralogie' (4 vols. Paris, 1801) was translated into German (Karsten, 3 vols. Leipzig, 1803), but Hegel is here making his own translation of the original (vol. I p. 237), 'L'électricité partage tout le règne minéral en trois grandes divisions, qui suivent à peu pres l'ordre méthodique generalement adopté pour la classification des êtres de ce règne. Presque toutes les substances connues les unes sous le nom de *pierres*, les autres sous celui de *sels*, acquièrent, à l'aide du frottement, l'électricité vitreé, pourvu qu'elles jouissent d'un certain degré de pureté. Les substances inflammables proprement dites, à l'exception du diamant, étant de même frottées, reçoivent au contraire l'électricité résineuse. Les substances métalliques possèdent en général eminemment la propriété conductrice de l'électricité.'

Hegel's apparent mistranslation of Hauy's statement concerning the diamond is almost certainly due to David Brewster's subsequent discovery of the *pyroelectrical condition of this stone*: see P. F. Mottelay 'Bibliographical History of Electricity and Magnetism' (London, 1922) p. 465: Brewster's articles in 'Annals of Philosophy' Dec. 1824 p. 469: 'Edinburgh Journal of Science' Oct. 1825 nr. 2 p. 208: J. S. C. Schweigger's 'Jahrbuch der Chemie und Physik' vol. XIII pp. 87–106 (Halle, 1825).

For an interesting *recent* survey of the background to this subject see Robert Siegfried 'Sir Humphry Davy on the Nature of the Diamond' ('Isis' vol. 57, pt. 3 no. 189 pp. 325–335, Autumn, 1966).

172, 15

Benjamin Franklin (1706–1790), in one of his first experiments, insulated two men from the ground by standing them on *cakes of wax*. In this experiment one of them rubbed a *glass tube*. The other then passed his hand along it, and so received a charge of 'vitreous' electricity. Franklin discovered that both men were then about equally electrified, for the sparks obtained when either touched an uninsulated conductor were of equal intensity. If the men touched *each other* before touching the insulated conductor however, he found that they were completely discharged. He used this experiment to explain the nature of positive and negative electricity.

172, 20

Johann Karl Wilcke (1732–1796), in his 'Disputatio inauguralis physica'

(Rostock, 1757) notices that the electricity of melted sulphur does not appear until it commences to cool and to contract, its maximum being reached at its point of greatest contraction. He regarded electricity produced by the liquefaction of electrics as being 'spontaneous'.

172, 21

As Hegel is here making his *own* selective translation of Biot's text, it may be of interest to give the original: see 'Traité de Physique' (4 vols. Paris, 1816) vol. II pp. 356–359, 'Lorsque les surfaces de deux corps sont frottées ensemble, celle dont les particules intégrantes s'écartent le moins les unes des autres, et font des excursions moindres autour de leurs positions naturelles d'equilibre, paraît, par cela même, plus disposée à prendre l'électricité vitrée; cette tendance augmente si la surface éprouve une compression passagère.

Réciproquement celle des deux surfaces dont les particules se trouvent plus écartées par la rudesse de l'autre ou par toute autre cause quelconque, est, par cela même, plus disposée à prendre l'électricité résineuse. Cette tendance augmente si la surface éprouve une véritable dilatation. . . .

Ainsi, lorsqu'une substance animale ou végétale solide et sèche est frottée contre une surface métallique qui a de la rudesse, elle donne des signes d'électricité résineuse; c'est le cas où ses molécules sont écartées. Lorsqu'elle est frottée contre un métal très-poli qui altère peu sa surface, ou dont l'effet se borne à la comprimer par parties, sans écarter individuellement les particules qui la composent, elle ne donne aucun signe d'électricité, ou elle donne des signes d'électricité vitrée. . . .

Lorsqu'on frotte les poils d'une peau de chat contre une surface métallique polie ou dépolie, ils ne peuvent que céder à son choc, et se refouler les uns sur les autres; mais ils se compriment ainsi, tout d'une pièce, sans aucune vibration de leurs particules. Ils sont donc disposés d'une manière éminemment favorable pour prendre l'électricité vitrée. . . .

. . . il est de fait qu'une étoffe de soie noire *neuve* de forte teinte, étant frottée contre un ruban de soie blanche, prend toujours cette espèce d'électricité. Mais lorsque l'étoffe noire est *usée* et sa couleur affaiblie, si l'on dilate les pores du ruban blanc par la chaleur, il acquiert à son tour, pour l'électricité résineuse, une plus grande tendance que l'étoffe noire, et par consequent il la rend vitrée. . . . Un ruban blanc sec frotté contre une étoffe de laine blanche, donne toujours des signes d'électricité résineuse; mais contre une étoffe de laine teinte en noir, il donne des signes d'électricité vitrée'.

Robert Symmer (d. 1763), in an article published in 'Phil. Trans. Roy. Soc.' 1759 vol. 51 pt. i was the first to show that quite small differences determine the sign of the electrification generated by the friction of two bodies one against the other. When wearing black and white silk stockings one over the other, he had found that they were electrified oppositely when rubbed and drawn off.

172, 32

‚fich barauf befchränkt, fie zu brücken, unb einzeln bie Teilchen zu entfernen'. Biot wrote, 'ou dont l'effet se borne à la comprimer par parties, sans écarter individuellement les particules qui le composent'.

173, 14

The article Hegel is quoting here appeared in the 'Jahrbücher für wissenschaftliche Kritik' (Stuttgart and Tübingen, 1829), the official publication of the Hegelian school, which was edited by Leopold von Henning (1791–1866): see the note II. 362. It was a review by Georg Friedrich Pohl (1788–1849) of the *third volume* of 'Gehler's Physikalisches Wörterbuch' (Leipzig, 1827), not of the first three volumes as stated by Hegel, and appeared as a series of continuous articles published between July (op. cit. p. 18) and September 1829 (op. cit. p. 451). The passages quoted by Hegel are taken from Pohl's analysis of the article on 'Electricity' by C. H. Pfaff (1773–1852), which occupies pp. 233–406 of this volume of the dictionary.

The original 'Physikalisches Wörterbuch' by Johann Samuel Traugott Gehler (1751–1795) appeared in four volumes with a supplement (Leipzig, 1787–1795). The edition of it mentioned here by Hegel was edited, among others, by Georg Wilhelm Muncke (1772–1847), professor of physics at Heidelberg, and appeared in eleven volumes between 1825 and 1845. The dictionary is distinguished by its thoroughness, comprehensiveness and accuracy, by the excellence of its historical surveys and bibliographies, and by its being completely free from Schellingianism (see vol. VII pp. 547–548).

Pohl, writing from an Hegelian standpoint, criticises the general arrangement of the work in that it is merely *alphabetical*, and takes Pfaff's article as typifying the failures of a merely empirical approach to the subject matter of physics, in that its contents are *selected arbitrarily* and *treated* fussily and *pedantically*. He concludes however by wishing the authors well in their gigantic undertaking.

174, 10

Hans Christian Ørsted (1777–1851), professor of natural philosophy in Copenhagen. R. C. Stauffer, in 'Speculation and Experiment in the Background of Oersted's Discovery of Electromagnetism' ('Isis, Official Quarterly Journal of the History of Science Society' vol. 48 pp. 33–50, Cambridge Mass, 1957) has traced the influence of Schellingianism upon Ørsted.

In 1819 Ørsted discovered that when a wire joining the end plates of a voltaic pile is held near a pivoted magnet or compass needle, the latter is deflected and places itself more or less transversely to the wire, the direction depending upon whether the wire is above or below the needle, and on the manner in which the copper or zinc ends of the pile are connected to it. See his 'Experimenta circa effectum conflictus electrici in acum magneticam' (Copenhagen, 1820), and the

English translation of this work in 'Thomson's Annals of Philosophy' vol. XVI pp. 273–6 (1820): Gilbert's 'Annalen der Physik' LXVI, 1820–304.

A. A. De la Rive (1801–1873) repeated Ørsted's experiments before the French Academy of Sciences on September 11, 1820, and seven days later A. M. Ampère (1775–1836), in a paper read before this society, made known the law governing electro-magnetism: cf. his 'Recueil d'Observations' (Paris, 1822).

B. Dibner 'Oersted and the discovery of Electromagnetism' (Norwalk, 1961).

174, 30

'Electric rain' is described in 'Gehler's Physikalisches Wörterbuch' vol. III p. 307 (Leipzig, 1827), 'It is this principle of attraction and repulsion . . . which explains the experiments with . . . small particles of cork or elderberry pith, which hop up and down on a table under an electrified bell. When there are enough of these particles and they are sufficiently small, or even better, when tiny strips of gold paper are used, they give rise, by their rustling and moving about, to what is called *electric rain*'. Tiberius Cavallo (1749–1809), in his 'A complete treatise on electricity' (London, 1777 Swedish tr. 3 vols. Lund, 1795–1796) vol. II ch. xi exp. 17 describes a similar experiment.

Joseph Priestley (1733–1804), in 'The History and Present State of Electricity' (London, 1769) pt. VII sect. i pp. 522–523, after presenting certain, 'practical maxims for the use of young electricians', describes a number of amusing electrical playthings, including *electric chimes*, '*Suspend* one plate of metal to the conductor, and place a metal stand, of the same size, at the distance of a few inches exactly under it, and upon the stand put the figures of men, animals, or whatever else shall be imagined, cut in paper or leaf gold, and pretty sharply pointed at both extremities; and then, upon electrifying the upper plate, they will perform a dance, with amazing rapidity of motion, and to the great diversion of the spectators. . . . To the dancing figures above-mentioned it is very amusing to add a set of *electrical bells*. These consist of three small bells, the two outermost of which are suspended from the conductor by chains, and that in the middle by a silken string, while a chain connects it with the floor; and two small knobs of brass, to serve instead of clappers, hung by silken strings, one between each two bells. In consequence of this disposition, when the two outermost bells, communicating with the conductor, are electrified they will attract the clappers, and be struck by them. The clappers, being thus loaded with electricity, will be repelled, and fly to discharge themselves upon the middle bell. After this, they will be again attracted by the outermost bells; and thus, by striking the bells alternately, a continual ringing may be kept up as long as the operator pleases. . . . When these two experiments of the bells and the figures are exhibited at the same time, they have the appearance of men or animals dancing to the music of the bells; which, if well conducted, may be very diverting.' Cf. Cavallo op. cit. vol. II ch. xi exp. 14.

175, 5

See Schelling's 'Zeitschrift für spekulative Physik' vol. I (Jena and Leipzig, 1800). In the long article 'Allgemeine Deduction des dynamischen Processes oder der Categorieen der Physik', Schelling discusses the relatedness of electricity and magnetism at great length, and sums up his argument as follows, , So wäre also ... die wahre Stuffenfolge der dynamischen Naturprocesse diese:

1. Magnetismus — sein Schema die Linie.
2. Electricität — ihr Schema der Winkel.
3. Galvanismus — sein Schema der Triangel.

Jene drei sind also gleichsam die Primzahlen der Natur, diese ihre allgemeinen Hieroglyphen'.

175, 6

Michelet comments upon this as follows, 'It could be said that it is because magnetism is the infinite activity of form as undisclosed identity, that the magnetic insulators of existing magnetism exhibit the oppositions of form in their context, while the conductors of sublated magnetism divide them between themselves; conversely, that as electricity exhibits the infinite activity of form as disclosed differentiation, the insulators divide the existing oppositions between themselves while the conductors connect those which are sublated. One is also able to see why the undifferentiated bodies are magnetic insulators, while the bodies of differentiation are electric insulators, for as insulation is displayed within existence, the undifferentiation of magnetism exhibits itself in metal, while the differentiation of electricity exhibits itself in the opposition between combustibility and neutrality. Chemistry on the contrary is the totality of the process which exhibits itself at every stage of corporeality.'

175, 21

John Canton (1718–1772) was the first to establish the fact of electrification by *induction*, or, as he terms it, 'relating to bodies immerged in electric atmospheres'. The principle he enunciates is that, 'the electric fluid, when there is a redundancy of it in any body, repels the electric fluid in any other body when they are brought within the sphere of each other's influence and drives it into remote parts of the body; or quite out of it, if there be any outlet for that purpose. In other words, bodies immerged in electric atmospheres always become possessed of the electricity contrary to that of the body in whose atmosphere they are immerged.' ('Phil. Trans. Roy. Soc.' Dec. 1753).

176, 16

,so ist die Intensität an der Stelle der Berührung =0, stärker an den entfernten Punkten der Kugeln'.

176, 21

These experiments are taken from the well-known articles by Charles Augustin de Coulomb (1736–1806), which appeared in the 'Mémoires de l'Academie Royale des Sciences' between 1784 (p. 266) and 1789 (p. 455). From them, Coulomb concluded that the attractive force of two small globes, one electrified positively and the other negatively, is in the inverse ratio of the squares of the distances of their centres, and that the repulsive force of the two globes, charged either with positive or negative electricity, is inversely as the squares of the distances of the centres of the globes. This hypothesis brought electrical phenomenon within the domain of *mathematical analysis*. See S. D. Poisson (1781–1840) 'Traité de Mécanique' (Paris, 1811), in which theorems are deduced for determining the distribution of the 'electric fluid' on the surfaces of two conducting spheres, when they are placed in contact or at any given distance.

176, 26

René-Just Hauy (1743–1822) 'Traite de minéralogie' (4 vols. Paris, 1801): see the note II 332.

In 'Curiöse Speculationen bei schlaflosen Nächten' (Chemnitz and Leipzig, 1707), a certain J. G. S. gave the first account of the development of electricity in tourmaline by means of *heat*, and stated that it was the Dutch who had first brought this stone from Ceylon in 1703. Cf. J. Beckmann (1739–1811) 'Beiträge zur Geschichte der Erfindungen' (Leipzig, 1782) pt. I sect. 2 no. 5 p. 241.

This discovery initiated research into the subject of *pyro-electricity*, or the power possessed by some minerals of becoming electrified when merely heated, and of exhibiting positive and negative electricity. For eighteenth century developments in this field see: Louis Lémery (1667–1743) in 'Histoire de l'Academie' (1717 p. 7): Linnaeus 'Flora Ceilonica' (Copenhagen, 1747) p. 8, who gives the stone the name of 'Lapis electricus': F. M. U. T. Aepinus (1724–1802) in 'Mémoires de l'Academie de Berlin' (1756 p. 110) and 'Receuil de différens mémoires sur la Tourmaline' (St. Petersburg, 1762): Benjamin Wilson (1721–1788) in 'Phil. Trans. Roy. Soc.' vol. 51 pt. i p. 308 (1760): John Canton (1718–1772) in 'Phil. Trans. Roy. Soc.' vol. 52 pt. ii p. 443. By 1820 electricity had also been discovered in topaz, oxinite, boracite, prehnite, sphene, diamond, garnet, amethyst, borate of magnesia and tartrate of potash etc.: see P. F. Mottelay 'Bibliographical History of Electricity and Magnetism' (London, 1922) p. 153.

Hauy was however the first to throw clear light on this curious branch of physics by tracing the relationship between the secondary forms of crystals and their electrical polarity. For later views on the subject see David Brewster's articles in 'Trans. Roy. Soc. Edin.' (1845) and 'Philosophical Magazine' (Dec. 1847). There is also a full discussion of the subject in the 'Treatise on Electricity' by A. de la Rive (tr. Walker, London, 1856) vol. II pt. 5 ch. i. Cf. 'Gehler's Physikalisches Wörterbuch' vol. IX pp. 1088–1104 (Leipzig, 1839).

177, 4

Cf. the note on C. F. L. Schultz (1781–1834) II. 338. Plato develops this theory in the 'Timaeus' ($45b^2$–$46a^2$), 'And first of the organs they (the gods) wrought light-giving eyes, which they fixed there on the plan I shall explain. Such sort of fire as had the property of yielding a gentle light but not of burning, they contrived to form into a substance akin to the light of every day. The fire within us, which is akin to the daylight, they made to flow pure smooth and dense through the eyes, having made close the whole fabric of the eyes and especially the pupils, so that they kept back all that was coarser and suffered this to filter through unmixed and pure. Whenever then there is daylight surrounding the current of vision, then this issues forth as like into like, and coalescing with the light is formed into one uniform substance in the direct line of vision, wherever the stream issuing from within strikes upon some external object that falls in its way.' 'The Timaeus of Plato' (ed. R. D. Archer-Hind, London, 1888).

A. E. Taylor, in his 'Commentary on Plato's Timaeus' (Oxford, 1928) pp. 276–290 notices the similarity between Plato's thinking here and the famous parallel between vision and knowledge, the sun and the form of good, in the sixth book of the Republic. Cf. Goethe's adaptation of Plotinus:

> ,Wäre nicht dein Auge sonnenhaft,
> Wie könnt' es je die Sonn' erblicken?
> We'ste nicht in uns die eigne Gotteskraft,
> Wie könnt' uns Göttliches entzücken?'

'Naturwissenschaftliche Hefte' ed. Kuhn (Weimar, 1962) p. 296. See also F. M. Cornford 'Plato's Cosmology (London, 1937) pp. 151–159.

177, 11

The *destructive* powers of lightning attracted much attention about the middle of the eighteenth century. In 1764 St. Bride's Church, London, was struck by lightning, which 'bent and broke asunder an iron bar two and a half inches broad and half an inch thick'. ('Phil. Trans. Roy. Soc.' 1762, 1764). In 1769 St. Paul's Cathedral was first provided with lightning *conductors*.

Benjamin Franklin recommended the use of *pointed* conductors. After the outbreak of the American Revolution he was of course regarded as an enemy of England, and patriotism demanded that a new form of conductor should be introduced. *Knobs* were proposed, and enthusiastically prescribed by the King, who requested that Sir John Pringle (1707–1782), the President of the Royal Society, should advocate their introduction. Sir John hinted that the laws and operations of nature could not be reversed at royal pleasure, whereupon it was intimated to him that a President of the Royal Society entertaining such an opinion ought to resign, and he accordingly did so. In a letter written to J. Ingenhousz (1730–1799) on Oct. 14, 1777 Franklin comments that, 'The King's changing his *pointed* conductors for *blunt* ones is therefore a matter of small importance to me. If I had a wish about it, it would be that he had rejected them altogether as ineffectual.'

On the volatilization of gold see John Murray (d. 1820) 'A System of Chemistry' (4 vols. Edinburgh, 1819) vol. III p. 171. Martin van Marum (1750–1837) and John Cuthbertson (d.c. 1845), working the great frictional machine in the Teyler Institute at Haarlem, caused gold to burn by powerful electric sparks, and found that when, 'electric discharges are transmitted over a gold wire enclosed in a glass tube with atmospheric air, they convert it into a powder of a brownish purple colour, while the air is diminished in volume, and rendered incapable of supporting combustion' ('Nicholson's Journal' vol. V p. 146). J. B. Trommsdorff (1770–1836) found that electricity caused gold to burn with a bright white light: see P. F. Mottelay op. cit. p. 352.

177, 14

Alessandro Volta (1745–1827), in letters written early in January 1777, described an 'electric pistol' in which a cork was blown out of a closed tube by the explosion, by an electric spark, of a mixture of hydrogen and oxygen. See 'Collezione dell' opere del. . . . Volta' (Florence, 1816) vol. III pp. 133, 176 etc.: cf. 'Briefe über die entzündbare Luft . . . von Herrn Alex. Volta' (tr. C. H. Köstlin, Stuttgart, 1778). Similar experiments are described by J. C. Schäfer (1718–1790) in his 'Abbildung und Beschreibung der elektrischen Pistole' (Regensburg, 1779): Joseph Weber (1753–1831) in his 'Abhandlung vom Luftelektrophor' (2nd ed. Ulm, 1779), and Jan Ingenhousz (1730–1799) in his 'Nouvelles Expériences et Observations sur divers Objets de Physique' (2 vols. Paris, 1785–1789) vol. I p. 150.

The main importance of Volta's invention was that it prepared the way for Cavendish's well known paper on the synthesis of water: see 'Experiments on Air' ('Phil. Trans. Roy. Soc.' 1784 pp. 119–153): cf J. R. Partington. 'A History of Chemistry' vol. III pp. 325–338 (London, 1962).

177, 24

See the notes II. 269–271. *Hegel's* fault evidently lies in his having failed to distinguish between the states of solidity, liquidity and gaseousness as dependent upon *temperature* and *pressure*, and the same states as the outcome *chemical* structure or composition.

177, 35

Michelet notes that the following was added here in the Heidelberg 'Encyclopaedia' (1818), 'or individualization. The individuality of the body is the negative unity of the Notion, and is clearly neither an immediacy nor an unmoved universal, but is merely a determination which posits itself through the mediation of the process. Consequently, the body is a product, and its shape is a presupposition, of which it is rather the end into which it passes which is presupposed'.

178, 6

,Die Eltern sind so das Unmittelbare, von dem man anfängt; sie selbst bestimmen sich dann aber auch als Gesetztes, der Existenz nach'. Cf. Hegel's 'Philosophische Propädeutik' ed. Glockner (Stuttgart 1949) p. 89 ,Diese Gesinnung besteht näher darin, daß jedes Glied der Familie seine Wesen nicht in seiner eigenen Person hat, sondern daß nur das Ganze der Familie ihre Persönlichkeit ausmacht'.

179, 33

See the definition of 'saturation' given by A. and C. R. Aikin in 'A Dictionary of Chemistry and Mineralogy' (2 vols. London, 1807), 'A substance is said to be saturated with another, either (in the case of simple solution) when the solvent will take up no more of the substance dissolved, or (in the case of mutual chemical action) where the compound produced is perfectly neutralized'.

Hegel probably has in mind Berthollet's definition of saturation as *dependent upon* individual circumstances, relationships and forces, rather than as a distinct and *definite state*: see M. H. Klaproth (1743–1817) and Friedrich Wolff (1766–1845) 'Chemisches Wörterbuch' (9 vols. Berlin, 1807–1819) vol. IV pp. 294–299.

180, 4

,der die ganze Gestalt entamirt'. ,Entamiren' is an unusual word. Heyse and Wittich 'Fremdwörterbuch' (14th ed. Hanover, 1870) give the following account of it, 'initiate, open up, set going, a transaction for example'. It originates from the French word *entamer*, which occurs in English as 'entame' (to open) or 'attame' (to broach, attack, initiate).

None of these definitions seems to cover the meaning attached to it here by Hegel.

180, 24

See the note II. 321.

180, 26

See the note II. 275. Hegel is evidently criticizing the hypothesis put forward by J. W. Ritter (1776–1810) that the northern lights have a ten year periodicity and are in some way connected with the regular appearance of meteorites: see his 'Einiges über Nordlichter und deren Perioden, und über den Zusammenhang des Nordlichts mit dem Magnetismus' ('Gilberts Annalen' vol. XV pp. 206–226): 'Physische-Chemische Abhandlungen' (3 vols. Leipzig, 1806) vol. III pp. 164–186. Ritter's *theory* was not confirmed by the *events* of 1806–1816.

On Sept. 25, 1827, the northern lights were seen in Switzerland, Holland and Paris, ('Quarterly Journal of Science' N.S. IV 385). J. J. D. de Mairan (1678–1771) was of the opinion that these lights appear only in the *winter* and usually at *night*, but the brilliant display of the southern light at *Cuzco* on Aug. 20, 1744, which took place during the day, attracted a great deal of attention and brought his view into discredit: see 'Mémoires de l'Academie' 1745: A. J. Sertorius 'Dissertatio de aurora borealis' (Heidelberg, 1760) p. 7.

180, 35
See the note II. 392.

182, 7
See Christopher Hansteen (1784–1873) 'Untersuchungen über den Magnetismus der Erde' (Christiania, 1819): P. F. Mottelay 'Bibliographical History of Electricity and Magnetism' (London, 1922) pp. 444–446: 'Gehler's Physikalisches Wörterbuch' vol. VI pp. 1023–1071 (Leipzig, 1836).

182, 9
J. W. Ritter (1776–1810) 'Galvanische Beobachtungen während der Sonnenfinsterniss vom 11. Februar 1804' ('Voigt's Magazin für den neuesten Zustand der Naturkunde' vol. VII pp. 175–179): Ritter's 'Physische-Chemische Abhandlungen' (3 vols. Leipzig, 1806) vol. III pp. 308–319.

The eclipse began at 11.18 a.m., and about half an hour later Ritter noticed a decrease in the activity of his voltaic battery. It was at its maximum at 12.33 p.m., and half an hour later the battery was only working at $\frac{3}{4}$ of its normal rate. It was over by 1.53 p.m., and by 5.30–6.30 the battery was functioning at only $\frac{9}{13}$ of its normal rate.

Ritter suggested that the voltaic battery might be used for gauging the effects of *unobserved* eclipses.

182, 37
In the second edition of the 'Encyclopaedia' (1827), Hegel added, 'It is this process which has been called *synsomation*'.

183, 6
Addition in the second edition (1827), 'The only change is in the determinateness of their specific weight, hardness, cohesion, fusibility and colour, etc.'

183, 10
Jacob Joseph Winterl (1732–1809), Hegel, in a footnote, gave the following account of him, 'He was professor at Pest, and at the beginning of this century had an urge towards a deeper insight into chemistry. He claimed to have dis-

covered a particular substance *andronia*, but the discovery has not been confirmed.'

Winterl was born at Eisenerz in Steiermark and originally intended to study theology. He finally decided to read botany at Vienna however, and it was there that he met H. J. N. von Cranz (1722–1799), who evidently awoke his interest in chemistry: see J. R. Partington 'A History of Chemistry' vol. III, pp. 148–189, 599–600 (London, 1962). He eventually took his degree in philosophy and medicine, and then worked for several years as a general practitioner in the hill villages of Hungary.

In 1771 he was appointed professor of botany and chemistry at *Tyrnau*, and in the following year published his 'Systema artis pharmaceuticae' (Tyrnaviae, 1772). He improved the botanical garden at Ofen despite the limited finances he had at his disposal, and in 1785 published the first catalogue of its contents; he also helped to improve the efficiency of Hungarian fruit growing. His attempt to found a Hungarian learned society came to nothing however, on account of his Austrian origins and Hungarian nationalism. When Tyrnau university removed to Buda in 1777, and transferred to Pest in 1783, Winterl moved with it. He was a member of many learned societies, including those at Göttingen, Heidelberg and Jena.

Until the turn of the century his publications were concerned mainly with *specialized* chemical and medical topics: see 'Methodus analyseos aquarum mineralium' (Budae et Viennae, 1781): 'Die Kunst, Blutlauge und mehrere zur Blutfarbe dienliche Materien im Grossen zu bereiten und solche zur Blaufärberei anzuwenden' (Vienna, 1790), interesting as a possible source of Hegel's 'blood acid' (note II. 438) 'Ueber das Brown'sche System' (Ofen, 1798), cf. notes III. 378:379.

At the beginning of the new century however, he published two books in which an attempt was made to *generalize* chemical phenomena into a new system: see 'Prolusiones ad chemiam saeculi decimi noni '(Budae, 1800), 'Accessiones novae ad prolusionem suam primam et secundam' (Budae, 1803). This work was known to German chemists mainly through the publications of *Johan Schuster* (1777–1839), who was Winterl's assistant and successor at the university, and who made it the basis of his 'Darstellung der vier Bestandtheile der anorganischen Natur' (Jena, 1804), and 'System der dualistischen Chemie des Prof. Jakob Joseph Winterl' (2 vols. Berlin, 1807), the second of which is quoted by Hegel on two occasions (note II. 426). Winterl's views enjoyed a considerable vogue when they first became known: see H. C. Ørsted (1770–1851) 'Die Reihe der Säuren und Basen' ('Gehlens Journal für die Chemie und Physik' 1806 ii pp. 509–547): R. C. Stauffer 'Speculation and Experiment in the background of Oersted's Discovery of Electromagnetism' ('Isis' vol. 48 pp. 33–50, Cambridge Mass., 1957).

Winterl's basic propositions were that *matter* is in itself *inactive*, that it only becomes active by means of two *alien* and mutually opposite *principles*, and that these principles are *combined* with matter by means of a *mediating substance*

(Schuster's 'Darstellung' etc. p. xii). The *acidic* and *basic* principles (principium aciditatis et principium basicitatis) were supposed to adhere to the substratum of material atoms, and so impart acidic and basic *properties* to them. The *various* properties of these atoms were taken to be due to their more or less complete saturation. *Water* was regarded as an *element* forming hydrogen when *'animated'* by the 'principium animans' of the basic principle or *negative electricity*, and oxygen when animated by the acid principle or positive *electricity*.

Some of Winterl's observations were valuable and accurate; he recognized for example that acids need not contain oxygen, that silica has acidic properties, and that many metallic calces are acidic. He also put forward worthlessly fantastic views on the chemical elements however; he attempted for example to show that copper is a *compound* of nickel, molybdenum, silica, and a volatile substance ('Crell's Annalen' 1787 ii. p. 519, 1788 i p. 493).

The putative discovery of *'andronia'* mentioned by Hegel ruined Winterl's reputation. Winterl regarded it as the main constituent of milk, albumin etc. when combined with hydrogen, and as forming ammonia and an acid analogous to putrefying organic matter when negatively electrolyzed. He obtained it by heating nitre and charcoal and careful neutralization with acid, and regarded it as forming a link between inorganic and organic chemistry. Richard Chenevix (1774–1830) and Christian Friedrich Bucholz (1770–1818) found that Winterl's method for the preparation of andronia gave only *silica*: see 'Neues allgemeines Journal der Chemie' ed. Gehlen 1804 iii, pp. 105–108: 1805 iv, pp. 583: 1806 vi, p. 605: 'Journal für die Chemie und Physik' ed. Gehlen 1806 i p. 313; 1807 iii p. 336. L. B. Guyton de Morveau (1737–1816) reviewed Winterl's book very sceptically: see 'Annales de Chimie' 1802 (An. XI) vol. 47 p. 312. Winterl therefore sent specimens of andronia to the Paris Institute, together with a Latin letter. The substance was examined by A. F. Fourcroy (1755–1809), L. N. Vauquelin (1763–1829) and C. L. Berthollet (1748–1822), who discovered that it consisted mainly of *silica*, contaminated with lime, alumina, potash and iron. In their report they said that, 'M. Vinterl n'a ni notions exactes sur les caractères qui distinguent des corps, ni ces exercices si nécessaires aux chimistes pour reconnoître les substances diverses qu'ils trouvent dans leurs analyses' ('Annales de Chimie' 1809, vol. 71 pp. 225–253).

183, 14

,Synſomatien' (Greek συν with + σωμα body), as Hegel refers here to a *process*, the slight inaccuracy involved in anglicizing this term would appear to be justified. If we are to judge from the definition of synsomation given by Winterl's assistant Johan Schuster (1777–1839) in his 'System der dualistischen Chemie des Prof. Jakob Joseph Winterl' (2 vols. Berlin, 1807) I pp. 447–450, Hegel alters the meaning of the term somewhat, 'Synsomates (Synsomazien) are combinations of homogeneously animated matters. Consequently, their reaction is either acidic or basic. They are to be distinguished from neutral matter in that (1) they are not demulceated, and have lost neither their taste nor their power to alter pigments, and (2) in that the relationship of their constituents depends upon external influences such as temperature, water and the atmosphere, and is therefore variable. Each is grounded in the bond which tends to augment the material part of the substratum.'

184, 2

Hegel is here referring to the famous account of Archimedes' calculations given by Marcus Vitruvius Pollio (fl. 1st cent. B.C.) in his 'De Architectura', a work which was translated into German by A. Rode (2 vols. Leipzig, 1796): see M. H. Morgan's edition (Cambridge Mass. 1914) IX introd. 9–12. Hegel seems to have misinterpreted the story somewhat however, for the king did not supply the contractor with silver, 'Hiero, after gaining the royal power in Syracuse, resolved, as a consequence of his successful exploits, to place in a certain temple a golden crown which he had vowed to the immortal gods. He contracted for its making at a fixed price and weighed out a precise amount of gold to the contractor. At the appointed time the latter delivered to the king's satisfaction an exquisitely finished piece of handiwork, and it appeared that in weight the crown corresponded precisely to what the gold had weighed.

But afterwards a charge was made that gold had been abstracted and an equivalent weight of silver had been added in the manufacture of the crown. Hiero . . . requested . . . Archimedes to consider the matter. He made two masses of the same weight as the crown, one of gold and the other of silver. After making them, he filled a large vessel with water to the very brim and dropped the mass of silver into it. As much water ran out as was equal in bulk to that of the silver sunk in the vessel. Then, taking out the mass, he poured back the lost quantity of water, using a pint measure, until it was level with the brim as it had been before. Thus he found the weight of the silver corresponding to a definite quantity of water.

After this experiment, he likewise dropped the mass of gold into the full vessel and, on taking it out and measuring as before, found that not so much water was lost, but a smaller quantity: namely, as much less as a mass of gold lacks in bulk compared to a mass of silver of the same weight. Finally, filling the vessel again and dropping the crown itself into the same quantity of water, he found that more water ran over for the crown than for the mass of gold of the same weight. Hence, reasoning from the fact that more water was lost in the case of the crown than in that of the gold and made the theft of the contractor perfectly clear.'

It was impossible therefore that Archimedes should have been unjust to the goldsmith. The crown should not have contained *any* alloy.

To anyone familiar with the principle of Archimedes, the mere fact that the crown displaced a volume of water greater than that displaced by an equal weight of gold, would indicate the impurity of its content. Consequently, Hegel is probably right in assuming that Archimedes determined the *proportion* of gold and silver in the crown. Vitruvius' account may not give an accurate description of the way in which he did this however. In his 'On floating bodies' ('Works' ed. Heath pp. 252–300), Archimedes deals with the principles of hydrostatics, and in the first book of this work formulates the following proposition (no. 7), 'A solid heavier than a fluid will, if placed in it, descend to the bottom of the fluid, and the solid will, when weighed in the fluid, be lighter than its true weight by the weight of the fluid displaced'. It seems likely therefore that he found the proportion of gold and silver in the crown, not by measuring the displacement of the water, but by weighing the three bodies in water and noting the apparent loss of *weight* in each case.

'Archimedes von Syrakus vorhandene Werke' (ed. E. Nizze, Stralsund, 1824): 'Archimedis opera omnia' (ed. J. L. Heiberg, 3 vols. Leipzig, 1881–1913): 'The Works of Archimedes' (ed. T. L. Heath, 2 vols. Cambridge, 1897–1912: Dover Publications, New York): J. T. Hjelmslev 'Über Archimedes Grössenlehre' ('Det Kgl. Danske Videnskabernes Selskab. Matematiske-fysiske meddelelser' vol. 25 no. 15, 1950).

184, 9

In Hegel's day '*amalgam*' was taken to refer more exclusively to the mercurial alloys than is now the case. See the method of extracting *silver* described by A. and C. R. Aikin in 'A Dictionary of Chemistry and Mineralogy' (2 vols. London, 1897) II pp. 309–310, '*Reduction by Amalgamation*. This most ingenious method of working silver ores, was first practised by the Spaniards in South America, and has since been adopted with numerous and essential improvements, in Saxony, Bohemia, Hungary, and some other parts of Europe. . . . A sufficient quantity of roasted ore and mercury, in nearly equal proportions, is added, to bring the whole to the consistence of thin mud. The machinery is now put in motion, and is continued incessantly for from thirty to forty-eight hours, according to the richness of the ore, at which period the amalgamation is completed.' Cf. Thomas Thomson (1773–1852) 'A System of Chemistry' (5 vols. Edinburgh, 1810) vol. I pp. 182–185.

184, 20

Jean d'Arcet (1725–1801) was the son of a lawyer, and was disinherited by his father for deciding to study the natural sciences instead of law. In 1762 the faculty of medicine at Paris awarded him a doctorate for his thesis 'Ergo omnes humores corporis tum excremento tum recremento ex fermentatione producuntur' (Paris, 1762). Despite his having qualified as a doctor he never practised as such. His interest turned to chemistry, and he studied for a while under G. F. Rouelle (1703–1770), who numbered many famous French chemists among his pupils, including Lavoisier.

D'Arcet fought in Germany during the Seven Years' War, and spent his leave exploring the Harz. He subsequently became lecturer in chemistry at the Collège de France. His 'Mémoire sur le diamant et quelques autres pierres précieuses' (Paris, 1771) is notable in that it established that the stone may be destroyed by fire. His son Jean-Pierre-Joseph d'Arcet (1777–1844) also became prominent as a chemist.

The solder mentioned here by Hegel is described by d'Arcet in 'Expériences sur quelques alliages métalliques qui ont la propriété de se ramollir, et même de fondre et de couler dans l'eau bouillante', which was first published in the 'Journal de Médecine, Chirurgie, Pharmacie etc.' vol. XLIII pp. 552–561 (June, 1775), and republished unaltered in 'Observations sur la Physique' Jan. 1777 pp. 217–221. D'Arcet informs us that it was the researches of *Newton* which led him to investigate the properties of various combinations of bismuth, tin and lead. He describes fourteen different combinations of these metals, and notes the temperatures at which they melt. The combination mentioned by Hegel is number *ten*, 'Huit parties de bismuth, cinq parties de plomb, et trois parties, d'étain, forment un alliage qui fond avant que l'eau soit bouillant; étant place sur un support, il font l'instant d'après que l'eau a commencé à bouillir. J'ai fait deux livres à-là-fois de cet alliage; et, lorsqu'il est en grande masse, il coule aussi facilement qu'en petite'.

M. J. J. Dizé 'Précis historique sur la vie et les travaux de Jean d'Arcet' (Paris, 1802).

184, 30

Hegel refers to this acid by its older name of ‚Königsäure', although it was usually known either as ‚Königswasser' or ‚salpetrichte Salzsäure'. In the English terminology of the time it was known either as 'aqua regia' or as 'nitro-muriatic' acid. It was first mentioned by Isaac Hollandus (Dutch, late 16th), and was called *Regia* on account of its being the solvent for gold, the *king* of metals.

See C. L. Berthollet (1748–1822) 'Observations sur l'eau régale et sur quelques affinités de l'acide marin' ('Histoire de l'Academie Royale des Sciences' 1785 (1788) pp. 296–307): John Murray (d. 1820) 'A System of Chemistry' (4 vols. Edinburgh, 1819) vol. II pp. 477–478.

186, 27

Johann Bartholomäus Trommsdorff (1770–1837) came of a famous Erfurt family of chemists and apothecaries. He had an extensive *practical* training as an apothecary, which probably accounts for the comprehensively *empirical* nature of the numerous text-books he wrote.

His main contribution to the scientific life of Germany was his introduction of the scientific method into the practice of pharmacy and his diffusion of chemical and pharmaceutical knowledge. In 1796 he founded a Chemico-Physical-Pharmaceutical Institute at Erfurt, which functioned for thirty years and trained over 300 students, many of whom became prominent as apothecaries, doctors, professors and manufacturers. He was professor of physics and chemistry at the university of Erfurt from 1795 until its dissolution in 1816, and after 1823 director of the Erfurt Academy of Sciences. He was offered Klaproth's chair at Berlin, but refused it as he could not bring himself to leave his home town. He also founded one of the earliest chemical *factories*, later developed by his son C. W. H. Trommsdorff (1811–1884), which concentrated upon the production of rare alkaloids such as morphine.

In 1794 he started his famous 'Journal der Pharmacie für Aertzte, Pharmaceuten und Chemiker' which he continued to edit until 1834, and which was then continued by J. Liebig (1803–1873). Hegel is here quoting his 'Systematisches Handbuch der gesammten Chemie zur Erleichterung des Selbststudiums dieser Wissenschaft' (2nd ed. Erfurt, 1805–1820) vol. IV p. 235 § 2812 (Erfurt, 1812). The first volumes of the *first* edition of this book appeared only a few years earlier (Gotha and Efurt, 1800–1807).

Cf. J. R. Partington 'A History of Chemistry' vol. III pp. 587–589 (London, 1962).

186, 35

Louis Bernard Guyton de Morveau (1737–1816), the French chemist. He studied law at university, and first made his mark with a satirical poem on the Jesuits entitled 'Le Rat iconoclaste, ou le Jésuite croqué' (1763). He began to interest himself in chemistry about 1764. An essay on chemical nomenclature which he published in the 'Journal de physique' (vol. 19 p. 370 May, 1782), was ultimately developed, with the aid of Lavoisier, Berthollet and Fourcroy, into the 'Méthode d'une nomenclature chimique' published in 1787. The principles of this work were speedily adopted by chemists throughout Europe.

He adopted revolutionary principles after 1789, and in 1791 was a member of the National Assembly in Paris. In 1794 he became professor of chemistry at the institution which was later to become the Paris Polytechnic. See J. R. Partington 'A History of Chemistry' vol. III pp. 516–534 (London, 1962).

Hegel is referring here to the article which Guyton wrote in conjunction with C. B. Desormes (1777–1862): see 'Essai sur l'analyse et la recomposition des deux alcalis fixes, et de quelques unes des terres reputées simples'. ('Mémoires de l'Institut National' 1802 vol. III pp. 321–336). They claimed that natron (soda) consists of *magnesia* and hydrogen however, not *talc* and hydrogen. Valentin Rose (1762–1807) and C. J. B. Karsten (1782–1853) were unable to examine the validity of their statements concerning the composition of lime and soda on account of their not possessing a platinum crucible: see H. E. Roscoe and C. Schorlemmer 'Treatise on Chemistry' (6th ed. London, 1923) vol. ii p. 1453. Darracq, in 'Expériences concernant l'analyse et la synthèse des alcalis et des terres' ('Annales de Chimie' XL pp. 171–195, 1801), cf. Tilloch's 'Philosophical Magazine' vol. XI, 1801 pp. 344–355, showed however that their conclusions regarding the composition of these substances were erroneous on account of their not having taken impurities into account, and on account of their having drawn wrong inferences from mistaken resemblances: see Thomas Thomson (1773–1852) 'A System of Chemistry' (5 vols. Edinburgh, 1810) vol. II pp. 32–33, 41, 58.

In his second Bakerian Lecture of November 19, 1807, Sir Humphry Davy (1778–1829) suggested that the alkaline earths might be metallic oxides, and that potash and soda were 'evidently' compounds: see 'On some new phenomena of chemical changes produced by electricity, particularly the decomposition of the fixed alkalies, and the exhibition of the new substances which constitute their bases' ('Phil. Trans. Roy. Soc.' 1808 vol. 98 pp. 1–44).

186, 37
Steffens 'Grundzüge der philosophischen Naturwissenschaft' (Berlin, 1806) pp. 113–114, ‚Die Pflanzen zeigen im ſtarren Gegenſatze hervortretenden Kohlenſtoff und zurückgedrängten Stickſtoff, im beweglichen Gegenſatze hervortretende Hydrogeniſation und zurückgedrängte Oxydation . . . Die Thiere zeigen im ſtarren Gegenſatze hervortretenden Stickſtoff und zurückgedrängten Kohlenſtoff, im beweglichen Gegenſatze hervortretende Oxydation und zurückgedrängte Hydrogeniſation'. See also his 'Beyträge zur innern Naturgeschichte der Erde' (pt. i Freiberg, 1801) p. 60 etc.

187, 17
G. E. Stahl (1660–1734), the founder of the 'phlogiston' theory, thought that phlogiston is expelled from a metal during 'calcination', and that the remaining 'calx' is the base with which this phlogiston was formerly combined. An obvious objection to this theory was that it failed to account for the necessity of the presence of *air* to metallic calcination. The fact that the metal *increased* in weight as the result of calcination also told against Stahl's hypothesis.

Antoine Laurent Lavoisier (1743–1749), in his 'Sur la Calcination des Métaux dans les vaisseaux fermés, et sur la cause de l'augmentation de poids qu'ils acquirent pendant cette opération' ('Observations sur la Physique' 1774 vol. IV pp. 448–452) showed that Stahl's theory was untenable and prepared the way for the discovery of *oxygen* and of *oxidation*. See John Murray (d. 1820) 'A System of Chemistry' (4 vols. Edinburgh, 1819) vol. III p. 133 ff.

187, 40
This claim, that nitrogen, oxygen, hydrogen and carbon are to be regarded as constituting the three moments of basic to all the chemical elements, obviously has to be interpreted in the same way as the claim made by Hegel in § 281.

Hegel would have been better advised, if at this juncture he had attempted a critical reconstruction of the *chemical atomic theory* put forward by John Dalton (1766–1844). This theory evidently grew out of Dalton's consideration of the *specific gravities* of gases: see 'Manchester Memoirs' 1805 i p. 244: 'A New System of Chemical Philosophy' (3 vols. Manchester, 1808, 1810, 1827).

190, 26

Hegel shows here that he was aware of the need for a new system of chemical classification. It is curious that he should not have given more consideration to Dalton's *atomic theory*: see F. Wolff's translation of Dalton's work 'Ein neues System des chemischen Theiles der Naturwissenschaften' (2 vols. Berlin, 1812–1813). In 1826 J. J. Berzelius (1779–1848) revised his theory of *chemical proportions* and published it separately: see 'Über die Bestimmung der relativen Anzahl von einfacher Atomen in chemischen Verbindungen' ('Gilberts Annalen der Physik' 1826 vii pp. 397–416: 1826 viii pp. 177–190).

J. L. G. Meinecke (1781–1823), 'Erläuterung zur chemischen Messkunst' pt. ii (Halle, 1817) pointed out that the numbers representing the chemical proportions of the elements are whole multiples of that of hydrogen. Hegel probably anticipated difficulties in showing the relationship between this theory and chemical *process*.

192, 17

Michelet notes, that 'In the first edition, galvanism forms the conclusion of electricity, 'Galvanism is the developed permanence of the electrical process. It has this permanence through the contact of two differentiated and unrigid bodies, which *on account of their fluid nature*, or the so-called conducting power of metals, immediately give determinate being to the *whole* of their differentiation, and because of their *solidity* and the superficiality of this relation, preserve a state of *tension* between themselves. It is merely through this particular peculiarity of bodies that the galvanic process assumes more concrete and corporeal nature, and so makes the transition to the chemical process'. In the Jean lectures on the contrary, it forms the transition from the chemical process to the organism, for Hegel placed it at the end of the chemical process, and called it 'the image of the organic process'.

See 'Jenenser Realphilosophie' II (ed. Hoffmeister, Leipzig, 1931) pp. 100–103: 'Enzyklopädie ... und andere Schriften aus der Heidelberger Zeit' (ed. Glockner, Stuttgart, 1956) § 249 pp. 193–194.

192, 25

In the first edition of the 'Encyclopaedia' (1817) Hegel added the following observation here, 'It is only an oxide which, on account of the inner undifferentiation of its compact nature, approximates to the stage of metallicism as calx. The impotence of nature in holding fast to the determinate Notion also allows certain metals to pass so far into the opposition however, that their oxides even take the place of acids. As is well known, chemistry is now able to demonstrate the existence of a metallic base, not only in an alkali and natron and even ammonium, but also in strontian, barytes, and even in earths, at least in their amalgams, and so to recognize these bodies as oxides. What is more, the chemical elements are abstract bodies which are so constituted, that if they exhibit their distinctness in a gaseous form, they interpenetrate like light, for despite their ponderability, their material impenetrability shows itself as elevated into immateriality. Oxygen and hydrogen have such a minimal determination dependent upon corporeal individuality however, that oxygen unites itself with bases in order to form oxides and alkalies as well as the opposing acids; in hydrothionic acid on the contrary, the acid determination shows itself as hydrogenation.'

'Enzyklopädie . . . und andere Schriften aus der Heidelberger Zeit' (ed. Glockner, Stuttgart, 1956) § 253 pp. 195–196.

193, 29

Georg Friedrich Pohl (1788–1849) was born at Stettin, and studied theology, philosophy, mathematics and the natural sciences at Halle and Frankfurt-on-Oder. He regarded the first two subjects as essential to any sound view of existence as a whole, and the last two as being basic to all forms of precise knowledge. It is not surprising therefore that Heinrich Steffens (1773–1845) should have interested him in Schellingianism, and that he should have found Hegelianism congenial.

He taught in a Stettin Grammar School from 1810 until 1813, and after the War of Liberation took up a similar post in Berlin. In 1820 he was appointed professor of mathematics and physics at the Frederick William Grammar School in Berlin and began to attend Hegel's lectures at the University.

His first published work was concerned with improving the teaching of geometry and trigonometry: see 'Die Kugelfläche als mathematisches Constructionsfeld' (Berlin, 1819). Hegel's lectures probably inspired his 'Andeutungen über die Einheit der Natur und Geschichte' (Berlin, 1822) but, as Hegel notes, it was in the fields of magnetism, electricity and galvanism that he first made his mark as a thoughtful research worker. He was in many ways a model Hegelian, for although his experimentation was carried out in a thoroughly 'empirical' manner, its results were referred back to an *overall* assessment of the field being investigated.

Between 1821 and 1848 Pohl published thirty three articles, most of them being concerned with magnetism, electricity and galvanism. The book mentioned here by Hegel is 'Der Process der galvanischen Kette' (Leipzig, 1826). In Hegel's lifetime Pohl also published 'Der Elektromagnetismus theoretisch und practisch dargestellt' (Berlin, 1830), and two articles relating to this subject: see 'Über den Zusammenhang des Magnetismus mit der Elektricität und dem Chemismus' ('Gilberts Annalen' vol. 74, 1823): and 'Über das polare Verhalten der Flüssigkeit in der galvanischen Kette' ('Poggendorfs Annalen' XVI, 1829).

In 1826 the University of Erlangen awarded him a doctorate for this work, and in 1829 he became a professor at Berlin. In 1832 he was appointed professor of physics at Breslau, and remained there for the rest of his life. In his later years his interest turned to *astronomy*: see 'Grundlegung der drei Keppler'schen Gesetze' (Breslau, 1845); 'Der Elektromagnetismus und die Bewegung der Himmelskörper' (Breslau, 1846): 'Ueber das Wesen der Elektricität und Schwere' (Breslau, 1848).

194, 15

‚wo auch ganz äußerlicherweise jenes für sich grundlose, heimliche Durch= marschieren der Gase oder Molecules nach ihrer gleichnamigen Seite unmöglich ist;'

194, 22

‚in diesem sensibeln Medium'. This could mean 'in this visible medium', i.e. Hegel might be referring to the change of colour in the litmus.

194, 32

J. B. Biot (1774–1862) 'Traité de Physique' (4 vols. Paris, 1816). Hegel is quoting here from bk. III ch. xvi of this work, which is concerned with 'Effets chimiques de l'Appareil électromoteur' (vol. II pp. 505–514).

Biot, who informs us that he is basing his remarks upon the researches of J. L. Gay-Lussac (1778–1850) and L. J. Thenard (1777–1857), attributes the discovery of the decomposition of water by electricity to Carlisle and Nicholson. He then describes an experiment in which water is decomposed into two parts hydrogen to one part oxygen, and then converted into water again by an electric spark. He notices however that the *quantities* of gas given off in a given time vary in accordance with the chemical content of the water, and that concentrated saline solutions and mixtures of acid and water give off the gases most copiously and rapidly, whereas boiled and perfectly pure water hardly give off any gas at all. From this fact he draws the conclusion quoted here by Hegel.

Hegel's objection to Biot's reasoning is that it is based on the assumption that Galvanic activity of this kind is not a distinct *chemical process*, but merely involves the *transmission of electricity*.

See William Nicholson (1753–1815) 'Account of the new electrical or galvanic apparatus of Sig. Alex Volta' ('Nicholson's Journal' 1808 iv pp. 179–187) and the other articles on this subject published in this volume: J. J. Berzelius (1779–1848) and W. Hisinger (1766–1852) 'Versuche über die Wirkung der elektrischen Säule auf Salze und auf einige von ihren Basen' ('Gehlen's Neues allgemeines Journal der Chemie' 1803 vol. I p. 115): Theod. von Grotthuss (1785–1822) 'Mémoire sur la décomposition de l'eau et des corps, qu'elle tient en dissolution, à l'aide de l'électricité galvanique' (Rome, 1805) cf. 'Philosophical Magazine' 1806 XXV pp. 330–339: Ostwald's Klassiker, 1906 no. 152. Grotthuss put forward the theory, dominant throughout the nineteenth century, that the volataic pile is an electric *magnet*, each pair of plates having a positive pole.

Sir Humphry Davy (1778–1829) reproduced Grotthuss's theory without mentioning him ('Phil. Trans. Roy. Soc.' 1807 vol. 97 pp. 1–56) and Biot treated the matter in a fuller manner in his 'Précis Élémentaire de Physique Expérimentale' (3rd ed. Paris, 1824) vol. I p. 641.

195, 22

Jöns Jacob Berzelius (1779–1848), see the note II. 432. Hegel is quoting his 'Essai sur la théorie des proportions chimiques et sur l'influence chimique de l'électricité, par J. J. Berzelius, . . . traduit du suédois sous les yeaux de l'auteur, et publie par lui-même' (Paris, 1819). This essay first appeared in Berzelius's 'Lärbok i Kemien' pt. III (Stockholm, 1818) pp. 1–132 as 'Forsök till en theoretisk åsigt af läran om de kemiska proportionerna, samt af elektricitetens inflytelse såsom kemiskt agens': see esp. p. 62 f. K. A. Blöde (1773–1820) published a German translation of it, based on the Swedish and French texts: 'Versuch über die Theorie der chemischen Proportionen' (Dresden, 1820): see pp. 79–81.

The following is the full text of the passage referred to by Hegel (op. cit. pp. 72–74), 'Dans l'état actuel de nos connaissances, l'explication la plus probable de la combustion et de l'ignition qui en est l'effet, est donc: *que dans toute combinaison chimique, il y a neutralisation des électricités opposées, et que cette neutralisation produit le feu de la même manière qu'elle le produit dans les décharges de la bouteille électrique, de la pile électrique et du tonnerre, sans être accompagnée dans ces derniers phénomènes, d'une combinaison chimique.*

Il s'élève cependant ici une question qui ne peut être résolue par aucun phénomène analogue de la décharge électrique ordinaire. Après que les corps se sont combinés par l'effet d'une décharge électrochimique, et en produisant le phénomène du feu, ils restent dans cette combinaison avec une force qui, comme nous l'avons dit, est supérieure à toutes celles qui peuvent produire une séparation mécanique. Les phénomènes électriques ordinaires expliquent bien l'action des corps à plus ou moins de distance, leur attraction avant l'union, et le feu que cette union produit; mais ils ne nous éclairent pas sur la cause de l'union permanente des corps avec une si grande force, après que l'état d'opposition électrique est détruit. Est-ce l'effet d'une force particulière inhérente aux atomes comme la polarisation électrique, ou est-ce une propriété de l'électricite qui n'est pas sensible dans les phénomènes ordinaires? Si l'on tente de décider cette question l'on trouve que, dans le premier cas, la permanence de la combinaison ne devrait pas être soumise à l'influence de l'électricité, et que, dans le second, le rétablissement de la polarité électrique devrait détruire même la plus forte combinaison chimique. Aussi savons-nous que la décharge de la batterie électrique surmonte l'affinité chimique et sépare les corps combinés, c'est-à-dire qu'elle vainc ou annule la force par laquelle les atomes, après la décharge électrochimique, continuent à être unis. On peut, par exemple, au moyen d'une petite batterie électrique de 8 ou 10 paires de disques d'argent et de zinc, grands comme une pièce de 5 francs, décomposer la potasse, avec l'intermède du mercure; ce qui fait voir que ce que nous appelons affinité de combinaison, affinité chimique, a une relation nécessaire et inaltérable avec les phénomènes électro-chimiques, quoique nous ne puissons pas l'expliquer par les phénomènes connus jusqu'à présent des décharges de l'électricité produite par le frottement.'

195, 38

Cf. Schelling's 'Benehmen des Obscurantismus gegen die Naturphilosophie' ('Neue Zeitschrift fur speculative Physik' vol. I pt. i Tübingen, 1802 pp. 161–185).

196, 1

See Schelling's 'Zeitschrift fur speculative Physik' vol. I (Jena and Leipzig, 1800). Hegel may have in mind §§ 60–62 of Schelling's 'Allgemeine Deduction des dynamischen Processes' (op. cit. II pp. 80–83).

198, 18

,der Edelkeit'. See A. and C. R. Aikin 'A Dictionary of Chemistry and Mineralogy' (2 vols. London, 1807) vol. II p. 94, 'Much about the same time arose the chemical distinction of metals unalterable by exposure to the air at a fusing heat, and those which in the same circumstances were liable to be calcined. The former of these were called *perfect* or *noble* metals, and the latter *imperfect* or base metals.'

199, 4

J. B. Trommsdorff (1770–1837) discusses the subject mentioned here by Hegel in §§ 2668, 2669 of his 'Systematisches Handbuch der gesammten Chemie' (1st ed. vol. IV pp. 117–119, Erfurt, 1803: 2nd ed. vol. IV pp. 119–121, Erfurt, 1812). He could be referring to Goethe's acquaintance Christian Wilhelm Büttner (1716–1801): see the note II. 358.

199, 9

Schelling 'Neue Zeitschrift für speculative Physik' Ersten Bandes drittes Stück (Tübingen, 1802). Hegel is referring to Schelling's Article 'Die vier edlen Metalle' § VIII, ,Da das Wesen oder die Substanz an sich und absolut edel ist, so kann ein Besonderes, z.B. Metall nur in dem Maaße edel heißen, als es von dem Wesen in sein Besonderes (als die Form) aufnimmt'.

199, 17

See the note II. 309. In 1803 Smithson Tennant (1761–1815) began to work on the residue remaining when crude platinum is dissolved in aqua regia. This led to his discovery of *osmium* and *iridium*: see 'On two metals found in the black powder remaining after the solution of platina' ('Phil. Trans. Roy. Soc.' 1804 vol. 94 pp. 411–418). Iridium was discovered independently by A. F.

Fourcroy (1755–1809), L. N. Vauquelin (1763–1829) and H. V. Collet-Descotils (1773–1815) at almost the same time: see 'Annales de Chimie' 1803 vol. 48 pp. 153, 177; 1804 vol. 49 pp. 188, 219; 1804 vol. 50 p. 5. The French chemists at first confounded the two elements however and took them to be a single metal, which they called *ptene*.

W. H. Wollaston's discovery of *palladium* was announced early in 1803: see R. W. T. Gunther 'Early Science in Cambridge' (Oxford, 1937) p. 234. In an article published in the 'Phil. Trans. Roy. Soc.' (1804 vol. 94 p. 419), Wollaston described the preparation of this metal from native platinum and also announced the discovery of *rhodium*. In 'Mémoire sur l'iridium et sur l'osmium' ('Annales de Chemie' 1814 vol. 89 pp. 150, 225), Vauquelin described a method of separating platinum, osmium, iridium, palladium and rhodium. For an excellent survey of contemporary knowledge of these metals see John Murray (d. 1820) 'A System of Chemistry' (4 vols. Edinburgh, 1819) vol. III pp. 218–265. Murray does not regard these discoveries as evidence that platinum has 'metallic moments', 'All these metals form but a small *proportion* of *crude platina*; and their discovery exhibits, in a striking point of view, the delicacy and accuracy of chemical analysis'.

199, 21

See the note II. 280. Steffens first attempted to range metals into an order in his 'Ueber Mineralogie und das mineralogische Studium' (Altona, 1797) pp. 135–143. Hegel evidently has in mind his extended treatment of the matter in his 'Beiträge zur innern Naturgeschichte der Erde' (pt. i, Freiberg, 1801) pp. 101–176 (sect. iv). The doctrine of their density standing in inverse ratio to their cohesion is formulated more succinctly in Steffens' 'Grundzüge der philosophischen Naturwissenschaft' (Berlin, 1806) pp. 88–95.

199, 28

Hegel probably has in mind the thesis 'Memoria sull Ellettricita animale' (Brugnatelli's 'Giornale di Fisica, Chimica, e Storia Naturale' vol. I Pavia, 1792) by Allessandro Volta (1745–1827): cf. 'Volta's Schriften über die thierische Elektricität' (ed. Mayer, Prague, 1793): Volta's letters (Autumn 1792) to Tiberius Cavallo (1749–1809) in 'Phil. Trans. Roy. Soc.' 1793 vol. 83 pp. 10–44. In these publications Volta questioned Galvani's hypothesis of there being a distinct *animal electricity*. He showed that the effects observed by Galvani are due to 'the actions of a very weak artificial electricity which was excited in a way which would not be suspected, viz. *simply by bringing together two coatings of different metals*'. Cf. the experiments made with his *electrical doubler* by Abraham Benner (1750–1799), described in his 'New Experiments on Electricity' (Derby, 1789) p. 75 ff.

199, 39

L. Galvani (1737–1798), in 'De Viribus Electricitatis in Motu Musculari Commentarius' ('Comment. Bonon.' VII 1791), see R. M. Green's translation 'Commentary on the Effects of Electricity on Muscular Motion' (Cambridge, Mass., 1953), supposes that the convulsion of the frog's legs when the muscles and nerves are simultaneously touched with an arc composed of two metals, is due to a peculiar kind of electricity possessed by the bodies of animals. He thinks that the motion is communicated through both nerve and muscle, positive electricity going to the nerve, while negative electricity goes to the muscle, and that the muscles represent the exterior and the nerves the interior of the *Leyden jar*, the discharge being similarly produced by the metal which communicates with both.

Alessandro Volta (1745–1827) in 'Sopra l'elletricita animale' (1792, 'Opere' 1918 vol. i pp. 13, 40, and addition p. 75), and J. C. I. A. Creve (1769–1863) in his 'Beiträge zu Galvanis Versuchen' (Frankfurt and Leipzig, 1793) and an article in Gren's 'Journal der Physik' (1793 vol. vii pp. 323–331) disproved the Leyden jar theory by using two metals in producing the effects, proving that the action is only on the nerves, and showing that the same result follows if the bands are of two different metals brought into contact by a third metal.

Volta freed the study of galvanism from biological factors. In his latter publications he reiterates his theory that the effects of the pile are due to contact of the *metals* ('Nicholson's Journal' 1802 i pp. 135–142), and it is probably correct that the seat of the electromotive force in the pile is ultimately at the contact of the two metals. Volta was wrong however in supposing that this contact is also the source of the *current* (Gren's 'Neues Journal der Physik' 1796 iii p. 479 f). Sir Humphry Davy (1778–1829) showed that the current is provided by the *chemical action* in the pile: see 'On the Relations of Electrical and Chemical Changes' ('Phil. Trans. Roy. Soc.' 1826), 'there is no instance of continued electro-motion, except in cases where *chemical changes* can take place.' If Hegel's statement here is not actually based on Davy's researches, it is at least compatible with them.

200, 3

J. W. Ritter (1776–1810) 'Das Elektrische System der Körper' (Leipzig, 1805), ‚Zu allem diesem verstand sich von selbst, daß das Metall, die Kohle u.s.w., ein solcher Körper war, der von der Flüßigkeit angegriffen werden konnte', (p. 48 cf. the list on p. 109).

Hegel probably heard Ritter lecture on galvanism at Jena in the winter 1803–1804, but he does not seem to have remembered his remarks with *complete* accuracy. See 'Dictate aus Vorlesungen über den Galvanismus', published in Ritter's 'Physisch-Chemische Abhandlungen' (3 vols. Leipzig, 1806), vol. III p. 269, ‚Zugleich schließen sich an sie noch mehrere andere Körper an, die man nicht geradezu Metalle nennt, die aber doch eben so gute Leiter, wie sie, sind; als Kohle, Reißbley, eine Menge Verbindungen oder Vererzungen der Metalle.'

200, 9

Alessandro Volta (1745–1827) wrote to F. A. C. Gren (1760–1798) describing this and similar experiments: see Gren's 'Neues Journal der Physik' 1796 vol. iii p. 479, 1797 vol. iv pp. 107, 473: cf. 'Philosophical Magazine' 1799 vol. iv pp. 59, 163, 309. See also Giovanni Aldini (1762–1834) 'Dissertation on Animal Electricity' (tr. R. B. Green, Cambridge, Mass. 1953) XXI, XXII.

200, 10

Alexander von Humboldt (1769–1859): see his 'Versuche über die gereizte Muskel-und Nervenfaser' (2 vols. Posen and Berlin, 1797) vol. I pp. 471–478. Humboldt corresponded with Dr. John Ash (1723–1798) of Trinity College Oxford on the subject.

200, 11

Johann Salomo Christoph Schweigger (1779–1857) was the son of a professor of theology at Erlangen. He took his doctorate at Erlangen in 1800 with a thesis on a philosophical subject 'De Diomede Homeri'. His interests shifted to mathematics and the natural sciences however, and when he began to teach at his university, he lectured on these subjects.

In 1803 he left Erlangen to teach mathematics and physics at a grammar school in Bayreuth. From 1811 until 1816 he taught these subjects in a school at Nuremburg, so he must have known Hegel personally. In 1810 he began to edit his 'Journal für Chemie und Physik' which was a continuation of A. F. Gehlen's 'Journal für die Chemie Physik und Mineralogie'. This work broadened and deepened his knowledge of the natural sciences, and made him realize that reforms were needed in the way in which they were being taught.

In 1816 he was appointed member of the Munich Academy. He then spent two years as professor of physics and chemistry at Erlangen before taking up a similar appointment at Halle in 1819, where he worked for the rest of his life.

Most of Schweigger's writings are concerned with galvanism and electromagnetism. Hegel is referring here to his 'Galvanische Combinationen' which appeared in vol. VII pp. 537–578, vol. IX pp. 316–331 and pp. 701–706 of the 'Journal für die Chemie, Physik und Mineralogie' edited by Adolph Ferdinand Gehlen (1775–1815). These researches are mentioned by P. F. Mottelay in his 'Bibliographical History of Electricity and Magnetism' (London, 1922) pp. 412–414. Schweigger's object in performing the particular experiment mentioned by Hegel was to show that a mere difference in temperature can initiate electrical differentiation (op. cit. pp. 704–706).

200, 28

William Hyde Wollaston (1766–1828) was educated at Charterhouse and Caius College, Cambridge. He took the degrees of M.B. (1787) and M.D. (1793), and practised medicine at Bury St. Edmunds and later at London. When he failed to obtain a vacant physicianship at St. George's hospital however, he abandoned medicine and took to original research.

He was elected a fellow of the Royal Society in 1793, and interim president on the death of Sir Joseph Banks in 1820. In 1812 he also became a member of the Geological Society of London.

Most of his original work deals more or less directly with chemical subjects, but he also concerned himself with astronomy, acoustics, optics, mineralogy, botany, physiology and even art and fairy-rings. See George Wilson 'Religio Chemici' (London and Cambridge, 1862) p. 253: 'Nature' 1928 vol. 122 p. 970.

Hegel is referring here to his 'Experiments on the chemical production and agency of electricity' ('Phil. Trans. Roy. Soc.' 1801 pp. 427–434) in which Wollaston shows that the oxidation of the metal is the primary cause of the electrical phenomena obtained in the voltaic pile. Cf. 'Gilberts Annalen der Physik' 1802 pp. 104–113.

200, 30

See the note II. 391.

200, 39

'The Logic of Hegel' (tr. Wallace, Oxford, 1963) §§183–189.

201, 11

J. B. Trommsdorff (1770–1837), in his 'Systematisches Handbuch der gesammten Chemie zur Erleichterung des Selbststudiums dieser Wissenschaft' (8 vols. Erfurt, 1805–1820), gives a 'Geschichte des Galvanismus . . . besonders in chemischer Hinsicht' in volume five (Erfurt, 1808), and it is to this part of his book that Hegel is referring (vol. V p. 68).

Trommsdorff is evidently summarizing the six papers published by Sir Humphry Davy (1778–1829) in 'Nicholson's Journal' in 1801–1802. In these papers, which constitute the earliest of Davy's published work on galvanism, the action of the pile is shown to be dependent upon the presence of oxygen. It is also stated that with solutions, the power of action, 'appears to be, in a great measure, proportional to the power of the conducting fluid substance between the double plates to oxydate the zinc'. The exact nature of this process was not clear to Davy however, 'the oxydation of the zinc in the pile, and the chemical changes connected with it are *somehow* the cause of the electrical effects it produces'. See 'The Collected Works of Sir Humphry Davy' (ed. J. Davy, 9 vols. London, 1839–40) vol. II pp. 139–181.

Davy subsequently noticed however that electrification actually arises by contact and is sometimes more pronounced the greater the precautions taken to prevent chemical changes, and that very vigorous chemical changes can occur without the slightest development of electrification, and this led him to abandon the chemical theory of galvanism in favour of Volta's contact theory (note II. 413): see 'Phil. Trans. Roy. Soc.' 1807 vol. 97 p. 1: 'Collected Works' vol. V pp. 32, 44, 49 f.

J. B. Biot (1774–1862) describes the experiment mentioned by Hegel in his 'Traité de Physique' (4 vols, Paris, 1816) vol. II pp. 528–529, and concludes from it that, 'Cette expérience montre que l'appareil électromoteur a une action propre indépendante de la présence de l'oxigène; résultat conforme à ce qu'établissaient les expériences fondamentales de Volta sur le contact des métaux isolés'.

201, 25

Jan Swammerdam (1637–1685) noticed the muscular contraction of frog's legs by contact with copper and silver wires as early as 1678: see his 'Biblia naturae sive historia insectorum' (2 vols. ed. Boerhaave, Leyden 1737–1738, Germ. tr. Leipzig, 1752, Eng. tr. London, 1758). In the second volume of this work Swammerdam alludes to one of the many experiments he made before the Grand Duke of Tuscany in 1678, 'Let there be a cylindrical glass tube in the interior of which is placed a muscle, whence proceeds a nerve that has been enveloped in its course with a small silver wire, so as to give us the power of raising it without pressing it too much or wounding it. This wire is made to pass through a ring bored in the extremity of a small copper support and soldered to a sort of piston or partition; but the little silver wire is so arranged that on passing between the glass and the piston the nerve may be drawn by the hand and so touch the copper. The muscle is immediately seen to contract.'

Luigi Galvani (1737–1798), professor of anatomy in Bologna, noticed that a frog's legs are convulsed when its thigh nerve is touched with an iron rod while at the same time a spark is drawn from an adjacent electrical machine, and that the same movement occurs when lightning strikes or thunder-clouds pass near a wire connected with the frog's legs, or when the muscles and nerves are simultaneously touched with an arc composed of two metals. See his 'De Viribus Electricitatis in Motu Musculari Commentarius' (Comment. Bonon. VII, 1791) R. M. Green has recently published an English translation of this work 'Commentary on the Effects of Electricity on Muscular Motion' (Cambridge, Mass. 1951). Galvani supposed the phenomenon to be due to *animal electricity* identical with the 'vital spirits' coming the brain, but Alessandro Volta (1745–1827) proved that all the effects are due to *common electricity* (note II. 413).

201, 29

Giovanni Aldini (1762–1834) was born at Bologna, and was a founder member and one of the guiding spirits of the National Institute of Italy, a scientific society whose declared object it was to combat the doctrines of Volta and defend those of *Galvani*. As Felice Fontana (1730–1805), Bassano Carminati (1750–1830) and Gioachino Carradori (1758–1818) had already founded a society at *Pavia* with the object of furthering the doctrines of *Volta* and disproving those of Galvani, a lively but somewhat futile debate ensued. During the early 1790's similar societies espousing the cause of Volta were formed throughout Europe, Tiberius Cavallo (1749–1809) leading the English one. See Cavallo's 'Compleat Treatise on Electricity. Supplementary volume' (London, 1795): Richard Fowler (1765–1863) 'Experiments and observations relative to the Influence lately discovered by Mr. Galvani' (London, 1793, Germ. tr. Leipzig, 1796).

Aldini was not only Galvani's nephew, but also his assistant for a period of fourteen years. He had considered taking holy orders, but finally decided upon an academic career as a scientist. He took his doctorate in 1782, and in 1788 was appointed honorary professor at the university of Bologna. In 1803 he was appointed professor of experimental physics there in succession to Sebastiano Canterzani (1734–1819) under whom he had worked. He held this position until 1807, and subsequently found employment as a town councillor in Milan.

Aldini was an indefatigable investigator, and in that he was also a good linguist and had the knack of devising striking and memorable experiments, was highly successful as a *popularizer* of scientific matters. He visited Paris in 1802 and London and Oxford in 1803, and performed various macabre experiments demonstrating the effects of 'animal electricity'.

Hegel is referring here to his 'Essai Théorique et Expérimental sur le Galvanisme' (2 vols. Paris, 1804). See vol. I pp. 53–55 of this work, 'Proposition XIII. Le galvanisme parcout une chaîne, soit métallique, soit animale, avec une rapidité analogue à celle du fluide électrique. XXXVIII Exp. Je disposai dans mon cabinet un fil de fer de 250 pieds de long, de manière qu'il ne se touchât nulle part. Les deux extrémités de ce fil venaient aboutir à la table préparée pour l'expérience. J'en fis communiquer une à la base d'une pile de 50 plaques de cuivre et de zinc; et, prenant l'autre dans ma main gauche, je touchai de la droite le sommet de la pile. J'éprouvai le même effet que si j'eusse touché la base de la pile avec la main qui tenait le fil de fer. Aucun de ceux qui répétèrent publiquement l'expérience n'y sut distinguer de différence. Les 250 pieds de ce fil étaient donc parcourus par le galvanisme dans un espace de temps inappréciable.'

The experiment with the mercury is described in vol. II p. 143, 'Deux vases de verre sont placés l'un au-dessus de l'autre; le supérieur, qui est remply de mercure, reçoit la moelle épinière d'une grenouille préparée à cet effet; le fond en est percé d'un trou, que l'on ouvre à volonté, et qui laisse couler le mercur, de manière à toucher dans quelque point les muscles placés au dessous. Quand on établit cette communication, les muscles se contractent: cependent l'arc est de mercure, l'armature en est aussi; l'électricité est la même dans tous les deux; donc on ne devrait attendre aucune de l'électricité extérieure. Ainsi vous observez une contraction dont on ne peut en chercher la cause dans l'électricité des métaux.'

Many of Aldini's works appeared in English: see for example 'An account of the galvanic experiments performed by Prof. J. Aldini on the body of a male-factor lately executed at Newgate' (London 1803), 'General views on the application of galvanism to medical purposes' (London, 1819). For a full account of them see W. Fulton and H. Cushing 'A bibliography of the Galvanic and Aldini writings on animal electricity' ('Annals of Science' 1936 I pp. 357–372).

201, 32

See the letter written by Luigi Galvani (1737–1798) to Bassano Carminati (1750–1830) on May 8, 1792, 'In fact his (Volta's) experiments will clearly demonstrate that the electric fluid can have muscular motions directly not only from the muscle to the nerve but starting from the nerve to the muscle, or be it from the brain to the muscle, and can occur not only through the means of the discharge, but again by means of a forced and impetuous overcharge of the supposed muscular phial: this being admitted, who does not see how happily successful is the explanation of voluntary muscular motions?

To excite these, the mind needs only, from the brain where it resides, with its marvellous and incomprehensible power and command to determine a greater quantity of animal electric fluid, collected in the brain, through the nerve-conductor to the muscle, or else perhaps to give a greater impulse to that which naturally exists in that muscle; the contractions then will occur no otherwise than they did with the most illustrious Signor Volta, when he added to the animal electricity of the nerve a little bit of artificial electricity and in consequence increased the impulse and the action of that which was static on the internal surface of the muscular fibre, in a sort of inertia and of idle equilibrium.' See R. M. Green 'A Translation of Luigi Galvani's Commentary' etc. (Cambridge, Mass, 1953) p. 92.

201, 33

Alexander von Humboldt (1769–1859): see his 'Versuche über die Gereizte Muskel-und Nervenfaser' (2 vols. Posen and Berlin, 1797) vol. I pp. 78–79 'Of all the physical experiments I have hitherto had the pleasure of performing in the presence of other natural scientists, I have found none which, on account of its extreme delicacy, can cause so much astonishment as this *coating by means* of breathing. The circuit of dry metals, gold, zinc and gold, gives rise to no stimulation. One breathes upon *either* the lower or upper surface of Z, and allows the gaseous water we exhale with carbonized nitrogen to cover this surface. The muscle will then be convulsively disturbed to the same extent as it would if the stimulator of the muscle were in contact with the damp or dry side of Z.'

202, 6

See the note II. 324. Cf. the first of the three letters which Volta wrote to F. A. C. Gren (1760–1798) during 1796: 'Lettera I, II, e III al Prof. Gren d'Hala sul galvanismo' (Gren's 'Neues Journal der Physik' 1796 iii p. 479), 'We see now wherein the whole secret, the whole magic of galvanism lies. It is nothing but artificial electricity set in motion by the contact of heterogeneous conductors'. (§ 54).

202, 19

C. H. Pfaff (1773–1852) and Martin van Marum (1750–1837) 'Account of some comparative experiments made with the Teylerian electrical apparatus' ('Tilloch's Philosophical Magazine' XII 1802 pp. 161–164): John George Children (1777–1852) 'An account of some experiments performed with a view to ascertain the most advantageous method of constructing Voltaic apparatus' ('Phil. Trans. Roy. Soc.' 1809 pp. 32–38): Sir Humphrey Davy (1778–1829) 'Elements of Chemical Philosophy' (London, 1812) p. 152.

202, 35

J. B. Biot (1774–1862) 'Traité de Physique' (4 vols. Paris, 1816) vol. II pp. 436–437. Hegel has adapted this quotation somewhat, and made one unwarranted alteration. Biot wrote 'par des fils très-fins' not 'par des fils tresseés' (twisted). Biot quotes Wollaston in translation but does not mention his source here. He is evidently referring to Wollaston's 'Experiments on the chemical production and agency of electricity' ('Phil. Trans. Roy. Soc.' 1810 pp. 427–434: 'Gilberts Annalen der Physik' 1802 vol. XI pp. 104–113).

202, 36

Johann Wilhelm Ritter (1776–1810): see the note II. 270. In February 1802 Ritter constructed the first 'dry pile' in which instead of wet cardboard, sheep's leather, waxed cloth and thin glass plates were placed between the pairs of zinc and copper plates. When he removed all humidity from this apparatus however, it ceased to function. Ritter published his first account of these experiments in 'Der Reichsanzeiger' 1802, no. 66 p. 813: cf. the review of them in the 'Intelligenzblatt der Allgemeinen Lit. Zeitung' Nov. 1803: Ritter's 'Physische-Chemische Abhandlungen' (3 vols. Leipzig, 1806) vol. II p. 270.

The usual form of the so-called 'dry pile' was evolved by J. A. Deluc (1727–1817), see 'Nicholson's Journal' 1810 vol. 26 p. 69 and Guiseppe Zamboni (1776–1846), see his 'Della pila elletrica a secco' (Verona, 1812), 'Annales de Physique' 1815 vol. 49 p. 35. George John Singer (1786–1817) constructed a dry pile of 20,000 zinc and silver pairs separated by paper; it charged Leyden jars but could not decompose salt solutions: see 'Nicholson's Journal' 1813 vol. 35 p. 84: P. F. Mottelay 'Bibliographical History of Electricity and Magnetism'

(London. 1922) pp. 430–432: 'Gehler's Physikalisches Wörterbuch' vol. VIII pp. 115–161 (Leipzig, 1836).

203, 20

Cf. the notes II. 386 and 413.

203, 25

Richard Fowler (1765–1863) describes an experiment of this kind in his 'Experiments and observations relative to the Influence lately discovered by Mr. Galvani and commonly called animal Electricity' (Edinburgh and London, 1793, Germ. tr. Leipzig, 1796). See also the experiments made by John Robinson (1739–1805) described at the end of Fowler's book, and Alexander Monro (1733–1817), 'Experiments on the nervous System' (Edinburgh, 1793 Germ. tr. Leipzig, 1796).

204, 24

J. W. Ritter (1776–1810), 'Versuche zum Erweise, dass auch bey der gewöhnlichen Electricität, in chemischer Hinsicht, die positive die oxygenee, die negative die hydrogenee sey'. This paper was first printed in 'Gilberts Annalen der Physik' vol. IX pp. 1–17, and subsequently republished in Ritter's 'Physische-Chemische Abhandlungen' (3 vols. Leipzig, 1806) vol. II pp. 126–141.

Hegel evidently has the following passage in mind, ‚Was auf der negativen Seite vorgehen wird, wird immer zuletzt sich reduciren auf Desoxygenation der Hydrogen, oder kürzer Hydrogenation; — und so ist es, ohne einen fremden Begriff damit zu verbinden, wohl erlaubt, in chemischer Hinsicht die positive Electricität die oxygenee, die negative Electricität hingegen die hydrogenee, zu nennen in der Hoffnung, daß niemand daran denken werde jene Electricität für Oxygen selbst, diese hingegen für Hydrogen selbst ausgegeben wissen zu wollen, was in der Bedeutung, die diese Stoffe bisher gehabt haben und noch haben, wohl nie geschehen darf und kann'.

204, 35

Cf. the note II. 403. Thomson discusses mercuric amalgams of gold, platinum and silver (op. cit. I pp. 182–185). There is a much fuller discussion of the matter in A. and C. R. Aikin 'A Dictionary of Chemistry and Mineralogy' (2 vols. London, 1807) vol. II pp. 90–92. Cf. M. H. Klaproth and F. Wolff 'Chemisches Wörterbuch' vol. IV. pp. 191–196 (Berlin, 1809).

204, 38

This mineral was known as 'Wolform' by the miners of the Erzgebirge as early as the sixteenth century. The name was Latinized as 'spuma lupi'. It was known as such because it hindered the smelting of the tin ores with which it commonly occurs in Cornwall, Saxony and Bohemia, 'drawing the tin forth and devouring it, as the wolf does the sheep'. See A. Götze 'Zeitschrift für deutsche Philologie' 1929 vol. 54 p. 24 ff.: 'New English Dictionary on Historical Principles' (ed. Murray, Bradley, Craigie, Onions, Oxford 1888–1933).

Wolfram was first shown to be a tungstate of iron and manganese by the Spanish chemists Fausto (1755–1832) and Juan Josef De Elhuyar, in 1783: see 'Extractos de las Juntas generales de la Sociedad Vascongada' 1783 pp. 46–88; 'A Chemical Analysis of Wolfram; and Examination of a New Metal, which enters into its Composition. By Don Juan Joseph and Don Fausto de Luyart. Translated from the Spanish by Charles Cullen, Esq. To which is prefixed A Translation of Mr. Scheele's Analysis of the Tungsten, or Heavy Stone; With Mr. Bergmann's Supplemental Remarks' (London, 1785). Cf. 'Journal of Chemical Education' 1934 vol. xi p. 413: 'Isis' 1935 vol. 23 p. 526: 'Lychnos' 1959 p. 161.

204, 40

Carl Wilhelm Scheele (1742–1786) in his 'Chemische Abhandlung von der Luft und dem Feuer' (Upsala and Leipzig, 1777, Eng. tr. Kirwan, London, 1780) vol. I p. 196, II p. 75 § 82 first showed that ammonia consists of nitrogen and *hydrogen*. C L. Berthollet (1748–1822) and his son confirmed Scheele's analysis, and found that ammonia contained 18·87 hydrogen and 81·13 nitrogen 'Analyse de l'acali volatil' ('Mémoires de l'Academie Royale des Sciences' 11 June *1785* p. 316), 'Mémoires de Physique et de Chimie de la Société d'Arcueil' 1809 vol. ii p. 268. William Austin (1754–1793) calculated that the ratio of the weights of nitrogen and hydrogen in ammonia is 121:32 ('Phil. Trans. Roy. Soc.' 1788 vol. 78 p. 379).

As the true nature and composition of ammonia were well known by the close of the eighteenth century, Hegel's characterization of it might appear to be inexcusable. It is almost certainly based upon the paper 'On the Decomposition and Composition of the Fixed Alkalies', by Sir Humphry Davy (1778–1829), which appeared in the 'Phil. Trans. Roy. Soc.' in 1808. At that time ammonia, potash and soda were taken to be the three alkalies. Davy's discovery that the last two were 'metallic oxides' led him to postulate a *metallic* base to ammonia, and to suspect that the gas might also contain *oxygen*. See the sympathetic exposition of Davy's views by Thomas Thomson (1773–1852) in his 'A System of Chemistry' (5 vols. Edinburgh, 1810) vol. II pp. 4–21: cf. W. Henry (1774–1836) 'Experiments on Ammonia' ('Phil. Trans. Roy. Soc.' 1809 p. 130): M. H. Klaproth and F. Wolff 'Supplemente zu dem chemischen Wörterbuche' vol. I pp. 73–112 (Berlin, 1816).

205, 20

Michelet notes that in the first edition of the 'Encyclopaedia' (1817), this paragraph read as follows, 'The *compact* undifferentiation of particularized corporeality stands opposed to physical brittleness, which is particularity held together in the unity of a selfhood. *Ore* exhibits this totality as the combination of sulphur and metal. This brittleness is the *real nature of the possibility* of being kindled; fire, as the actuality of self-consuming being-for-self is still external to it. It is by means of the air, the physical element of abstract negativity, that it mediates the *inner differentiation* of the combustible body with *posited being* or reality, and activates this body into *acid*. The air is however dirempted by this into oxygen, its negative principle, and into the defunct positive residue of nitrogen.'

206, 28

In the manuscript ('Jenenser Realphilosophie' II p. 93), Hegel mentions ‚Schwefelbaryt', i.e. heavy spar (barium sulphate) as an example of this. See L. B. Guyton de Morveau (1737–1816) 'Observations minéralogiques et chymiques sur le spat pesant et sur la manière d'en retirer le barote ou terre barotique' ('Nouveaux Mémoires de l'Academie des Sciences, Arts et Belles Lettres de Dijon' 1782 vol. i pp. 159–175): J. A. C. Chaptal (1756–1832) 'Elements of Chemistry' (3 vols. tr. Nicholson, London, 1791) vol. II pp. 45, 203.

206, 29

‚Das erste Verbrennliche'. Hegel wrote ‚Das eigentlich Brennliche', i.e. '*That* which actually *burns*'. 'Jenenser Realphilosophie' II p. 93.

206, 38

Jacob Joseph Winterl (1732–1809): see the note II. 399. Hegel is referring here to the 'System der dualistischen Chemie des Prof. Jacob Joseph Winterl' (2 vols. Berlin, 1807) by Johan Schuster (1777–1839). ‚Schwefel. Er ist eine Säure, da er die salzigen und erdigen Basen, und die Metalle, selbst ohne die für die übrigen Säuren bedingte Wassersäure zu gebrauchen, neutralisiert; da er verschiedener Grade der Säuerung fähig ist. Der einfache Schwefel ist eine in Hinsicht der salzigen Basen schwache, in Hinsicht der Metalle starke Base, da er sie den meisten Säuren entreißt'.

207, 5

The validity of Hegel's remarks at this juncture is difficult to assess. Lime, barytes and potash are certainly not 'nothing but oxides', for apart from their metallic bases, barytes and potash also contain sulphur and hydrogen. The terms 'alkali' and 'earth' were always somewhat vague, and although they still were in general professional use at the beginning of the last century, chemists were not able to use them with any precision. For a very useful survey of the background to these remarks see Thomas Thomson (1773–1852) 'A System of Chemistry' (5 vols. Edinburgh, 1810) vol. II pp. 1–111.

207, 6

A. L. Lavoisier (1743–1794), in his 'Traité Élémentaire de Chimie' (2 vols. Paris, 1789) pp. 176, 179 thought that, 'Oxygen is the bond of union between metals and acids, and this . . . may lead us to suppose that all substances which have a great affinity for acids contain oxygen. It is thus quite probable that the four alkaline earths . . . contain oxygen, and that this is the bond which unites them with acids . . . These substances may be nothing by oxidised metals, with which oxygen has more affinity than for carbon, and by this circumstance are irreducible. This is only a conjecture which later experiments alone can confirm or destroy.'

Robert Kerr (1755–1813), in his translation of Lavoisier's work, 'Elements of Chemistry' (Edinburgh, 1796) p. 213, suggested that potash might be, 'a metallic substance in some hitherto unknown state of combination'. William Nicholson (1753–1815), in his 'Dictionary of Chemistry' (2 vols. London, 1795) vol. I p. 105 suggested that, 'the alkalis may consist of certain substances combined with vital (oxygen) or perhaps with phlogisticated (nitrogen) air'.

These books led Sir Humphry Davy (1778–1829) to his discovery of the alkali metals *potassium* and *sodium* in the October of 1807: see 'The Collected Works of Sir Humphry Davy' (ed. J. Davy, 9 vols. London, 1839–1840) vol. V p. 60, 'Although potash, perfectly dried by ignition, is a non-conductor, yet it is rendered a conductor, by a very slight addition of moisture, which does not perceptibly destroy its aggregation; and in this state it is readily fused and decomposed by strong electrical powers.

A small piece of pure potash, which had been exposed for a few seconds to the atmosphere, so as to give conducting power to the surface, was placed upon an insulated disc of platina, connected with the negative side of a battery of the power of 250 of 6 and 4, in a state of intense activity; and a platina wire, communicating with the positive side, was brought in contact with the upper surface of the alkali. The whole apparatus was in the open atmosphere. Under these curcumstances a vivid action was soon observed to take place. The potash began to fuse at both its points of negative electrization. There was a violent effervescence at the upper surface; at the lower or negative surface, there was no liberation of elastic fluid; but small globules having a high metallic lustre, and being precisely similar in visible characters to quicksilver, appeared, some of which burnt with explosion and bright flame, as soon as they were formed, and others remained, and were merely tarnished, and finally covered with a white film which formed on their surfaces. These globules, numerous experiments soon showed to be the substance I was in search of, and a peculiar inflammable principle the basis of potash.'

207, 7

See for example John Murray (d. 1820) 'A System of Chemistry' (4 vols. Edinburgh, 1819) vol. II p. 602, 'Besides existing in vegetables, (potash) is a principle in several of the animal fluids. It has also been discovered in the mineral kingdom as a constituent part of several fossils. Klaproth discovered it first in the leucite. Vauquelin found it in the lava in which that fossil is imbedded; Dr Kennedy detected it in pumice, and it has since been discovered in stones which cannot be suspected of volcanic origin, as in zeolite, feldspar, lepidolite, and others. Some of these contain 16 or 18 of potash in 100 parts.'

207, 21

N. Lémery (1645–1715) describes the making of sulphuric acid in 'A Course of Chymistry' (tr. Harris, London, 1680) p. 214. The sulphur was burnt under a glass bell, and he notes that it was essential that the air should be allowed to enter. Joshua Ward (1685–1761) used the much same process as Lémery, but kept it a secret, and it was not until John Page published an account of it that it became generally known: see 'Receipts . . . made use of by the late Mr. Ward . . . by John Page, Esq., to whom Mr Ward left his Book of Secrets' (London, 1763). Ward made sulphuric acid using large glass globes of 40–50 gallons capacity containing a little water. A stoneware pot was put inside the globe, and on it rested a red-hot iron saucer, into which was put a mixture of sulphur and saltpetre, the neck of the globe being closed by a wooden stopper. The charge was repeated.

During the early decades of the nineteenth century Tennant and Co., St. Rollox, Glasgow, were the largest manufacturers of sulphuric acid, making 200,000 lb. of it a week. The chamber acid was concentrated by boiling in large cylindrical platinum stills.

See A. and C. R. Aikin 'A Dictionary of Chemistry and Mineralogy' (2 vols. London, 1807) vol. II pp. 368–371: J. R. Partington 'A History of Chemistry' vol. III pp. 560–562 (London, 1962): L. F. Haber 'The Chemical Industry during the Nineteenth Century' (Oxford, 1958).

207, 35

A. F. Fourcroy (1755–1809) found that the white oxide of arsenic has certain peculiar properties. He noticed that it has an acrid taste and is corrosive; that it is soluble in water, and that when it is dissolved in boiling water and this solution is then cooled, tetrahedral or octahedral crystals are deposited; and that it reddens litmus and combines with the alkalies. From this evidence he proposed that it should be considered as an *acid* rather than an *oxide*, and named it 'Arsenious Acid'. See John Murray (d. 1820) 'A System of Chemistry' (4 vols. Edinburgh, 1820) vol. III p. 425: M. H. Klaproth and F. Wolff 'Chemisches Wörterbuch' vol. I p. 158 (Berlin, 1807): J. B. Trommsdorff 'Systematisches Handbuch der gesammten Chemie' vol. IV p. 477 (Erfurt, 1812), ‚Daß das weiße Oryd des Arſeniks eine wirkliche Säure iſt, und als eine unvollkommene Säure betrachtet werden muß, haben wir . . . geſehen'.

208, 19

'Carbonic acid is not acted upon by oxygen, nor is it altered by any of the simple combustibles, incombustibles, or metals. Charcoal indeed absorbs it, but it gives it out again unchanged'—Thomas Thomson (1773–1852) 'A System of Chemistry' (5 vols. Edinburgh, 1810) vol. II p. 211.

208, 31

Hegel is using outdated terminology here, 'The term caustic prefixed to the alkalies and earths to distinguish the pure or decarbonated state, is omitted on the modern nomenclature, being rendered unnecessary by the use of the term *carbonate*; thus to the terms *caustic potash* and *mild potash* are substituted those of *potash* and *carbonate of potash* respectively'—A. and C. R. Aikin 'A Dictionary of Chemistry and Mineralogy' (2 vols. London, 1807) vol. I p. 273.

Hegel probably has in mind the paper by W. H. Wollaston (1766–1828) 'On superacid and subacid Salts' ('Phil. Trans. Roy. Soc.' 1808). Wollaston discovered that when crystallized carbonate of potash, or of soda, is exposed for a short time to a red heat, it passes into a subcarbonate, which yields, when decomposed by an acid, exactly half the quantity of carbon dioxide which the crystallized carbonate does. Wollaston applied the terms *carbonate* and *bi-carbonate* to these compounds. For the controversies surrounding this subject see C. L. Berthollet (1748–1822) 'Troisième suite des recherches sur les lois de l'affinité' ('Journal de Physique' 1807 vol. 64 pp. 168–187, 193–219).

209, 12

‚Schwefelleber', i.e. Hepar sulphuris or Liver of Sulphur, was formed by heating two parts of potash and one of sulphur in a crucible until they melted and combined to form a brown substance, not unlike the liver of animals.

'When sulphuret of potash is exposed to the air, or when it is moistened with water, its properties very soon change. It acquires a green colour, and exhales the odour of sulphuretted hydrogen gas. This change is due to the formation of a quantity of sulphured hydrogen, in consequence of the decomposition of the water. This new-formed substance combines with the sulphuret, and converts it into *hydrogureted sulphuret of potash*, which is soluble in water, and has a brownish-green colour ... Hydrogureted sulphuret is capable of oxidizing and dissolving almost all the metals.'—Thomas Thomson op. cit II p. 30. Cf. A. F. Fourcroy (1755–1809) 'Système des Connaissances Chimiques' (11 vols. Paris, 1801–1802) vol. II p. 203: C. L. Berthollet (1748–1822) 'Observations sur l'hydrogène sulfuré' ('Annales de Chimie' 1798 vol. 25 pp. 233–271): L. J. Proust (1754–1826) 'Sur les sulfures métalliques' ('Tilloch's Phil. Mag.' vol. 21, 1805 pp. 208–213 'Journal de Physique' vol. 59 pp. 260–265).

209, 21

Steffens 'Grundzüge der philosophischen Naturwissenschaft' (Berlin, 1806)

p. 117, ‚Die gallertartige Zähigkeit zeigt den Uebergang aus dem in sich Verschlossenen der relativen Kohärenz des oxydirtesten Kohlenstoffs zur Allgemeinheit der Hydrogenisation. Daher die Entstehung einer Gallert durch Verbindung des Kiesels und Thons mit Kali — daher das Verschwinden des gallertartigen Zusammenhangs, je ätherischer die Oele werden'.

209, 22

Johann Constantin Schuster (1777–1839) was born at Fünfkirchen in Hungary and educated at the Grammar School there. In 1796 he went to the University of Pesth to study medicine, and took his degree in 1800 and his doctorate in 1802. He then worked at the University as Winterl's assistant for two years. In 1804 he visited a number of German universities and stayed for some time at Berlin.

He returned to Pesth in 1806 and taught pharmacy, chemistry, mineralogy and metallurgy at the university until Winterl's death in 1809. He then taught botany and chemistry, being appointed professor in these subjects in 1811. After a separate chair for botany had been endowed in 1817, he concentrated upon his original disciplines of pharmacology and pathology. He also held various administrative posts at the university during these years.

In 1829 he supervised the first thesis on pharmacy published in Hungarian, and for this service he was elected member of the Hungarian Academy in 1831. He first became widely known on account of his exposition of Winterl's works on chemistry (note II. 399). He holds an important position in the history of Hungarian *botany*: see his 'Terminologia botanica' (Budae, 1808), A. Kanitz 'Versuch einer Geschichte der ungarischen Botanik' (Halle, 1865) p. 135: but it is mainly as a doctor and writer on *pharmacy* that he will be remembered: see his translation of P. Orfilas' 'Rettungsverfahren bei Vergiftung und dem Scheintode' (Pesthe, 1819): 'Taxa medicamentorum pro Regno Hungariae' (Ofen, 1824): 'De opio', 'De iodo', 'De ferro' (Pesth, 1819, 1827, 1829): 'Kleiner chemischer Apparat' (Pesth 1830).

He also showed an interest in local history and topography: see his 'Geschichte der Stadt Pesth' (Pesth, 1829), his edition of the 'Hydrographia Hungariae' (Pesth, 1829) by Paul Kitaibel (1757–1818), and his work on organizing and drawing up a catalogue for the Hungarian National Museum.

Hegel is referring here to his 'System der dualistischen Chemie des Prof. Jakob Joseph Winterl' (2 vols. Berlin, 1807): see vol. I pp. 129–130 ‚Die Alaunerde kommt mit den abgehandelten Körpern darin überein, daß sie die Säuren abstumpft und dieselben neutralisirt, denn auch sie hebt die Eigenschaften, die Reaktion der Säuren auf; über sie abgezogene Salzsäure geht in einem minder reagirenden (entsäuerten) Zustande hervor; sie bildet mit den Säuren Neutralen, meist durch stärkere Basen gefällt. Sie verbindet sich mit der (sauer reagirenden) Kieselerde (Alaunerde und Kieselauflösung fällen sich vereint Darracq Ann. d. Ch. T.40) die sie oft so fest hält, daß sie ihr kaum entrissen werden kann. Sie ist also eine Base.

Allein sie ist auch in Alkalien auflöslich, und wird daraus durch Säuren gefället, (s. Alaunerde zu Ende der Säuren); sie reagirt also auch wie eine Säure.'

Cf. op. cit. pp. 415–417, where Schuster refers to C. L. Berthollet's 'Statique Chimique' (2 vols. Paris, 1803) vol. II p. 309 and T. Thomson's 'System der Chemie' (tr. Wolff, 5 vols. Berlin, 1805–1811) vol. I p. 668 in support of his views on this subject.

The origin of the 'dualism' on which Winterl and Schuster based their theorizing is to be found in A. L. Lavoisier (1743–1794) 'Traité Élémentaire de Chimie' (2 vols. Paris, 1789: Eng. tr. R. Kerr 5th ed. Edinburgh, 1801: Germ. tr. S. F. Hermbstädt, 2 vols. Berlin and Stettin, 1803). In this work an *acid* was taken to be a combination of a radical and oxygen, a *base* to be a combination of a metal and oxygen, and a *salt* to be a combination of a base and an acid. The theory had a great influence upon *Berzelius*: see J. R. Partington 'A History of Chemistry' vol. IV pp. 166–168 (London, 1964)

209, 25

'Alumina has the property of combining, in the humid way, with the fixed alkalis. When any of its salts is decomposed by potash or soda, if an excess of alkali be added, the precipitate first formed is re-dissolved; a solution of the pure earth is also effected, when it is boiled in an alkaline solution . . . This combination of alumina with an alkali is subverted, by the addition of an acid which saturates the alkali, and precipitates the earth'. John Murray (d. 1820) 'A System of Chemistry' (4 vols. Edinburgh, 1820) vol. III p. 79.

209, 32

See Schuster's 'System der dualistischen Chemie des Prof. Jakob Joseph Winterl' (2 vol. Berlin, 1807) vol. I pp. 412–413, ,Kieselerde. Sie ist eine Säure, obgleich eine schwache: 1. denn sie neutralisirt die Basen: sie verbindet sich mit Kali oder Natron zum Glase oder zur Kieselfeuchtigkeit; Kieselerde und Kalk schmelzen in gleicher Menge durch heftiges Feuer zum Emaille'.

Cf. Richard Kirwan (1733–1812) 'Elements of Mineralogy' (2 vols. London, 1794–1796) vol. I pp. 56–73. Schuster had read this source. See also Thomas Thomson (1773–1852) 'A System of Chemistry' (5 vols. Edinburgh, 1810) vol. II p. 100, 'There is a strong affinity between silica and fixed alkalies . . . When the potash exceeds the silica considerably, the compound is soluble in water, and constitutes what was formerly called *liquor silicum* and now sometimes *silicated potash* or *soda*. When the silica exceeds, the compound is transparent and colourless like rock crystal, and is neither acted on by water, air, nor (excepting one) by acids. This is the substance so well known under the name of *glass*.'

209, 33

C. L. Berthollet (1748–1822) 'Essai de Statique Chimique' 2 vols. Paris,
1803): see the note II. 385.

210, 7

Until Berthollet suggested ('Statique Chimique' vol. I p. 69) that acids should
be regarded as bodies capable of combining with alkalies and of neutralizing
them, while at the same time they lose their acidity, there was no very satisfactory definition of an acid. Oxygen was often regarded as the acidifying principle, but merely because it was known to exist as a component part in the
greater number of acids.

Henry Cavendish (1731–1810), in his 'Three Papers containing experiments on
factitious airs' ('Phil. Trans. Roy. Soc.' 1766) took a metal to consist of its calx
and 'phlogiston' and thought that when an acid is added to it, the calx and the
acid form the salt while the 'phlogiston' is given off as inflammable air (hydrogen).

A. L. Lavoisier (1743–1794), in his 'Mémoire dans lequel on a pour objet de
prouver que l'Eau n'est point une substance simple' ('Mémoires de l'Academie'
1784 p. 468), taking the case of zinc dissolved in dilute sulphuric acid, was able
to say that the metal takes oxygen from the water to form oxide of zinc, which
dissolves in the acid to form a salt, the hydrogen *of the water* being set free.

Hegel was evidently not satisfied with the criticism of this theory put forward
by F. A. C. Gren (1760–1798) in his 'Journal der Physik' 1798 vol. viii p.14.

210, 23

Jeremias Benjamin Richter (1762–1807) was born at Hirschberg in Silesia and
served in the army as an engineer from 1778 until 1785. He then studied mathematics at Königsberg, and took his doctorate there in 1789 with a dissertation 'De
usu matheseos in chymia', in which he already shows his interest in the idea *that
chemistry is a branch of applied mathematics*. Kant had probably set him thinking
along these lines.

He failed to gain an academic position, and became a mining official at Breslau in 1794. In 1798 he was appointed chemist to the royal porcelain factory at
Berlin, and died in Berlin on April 4, 1807.

Richter was one of the first chemists to determine the weight of the quantities
in which acids saturate bases and bases acids, and to entertain the idea that those
amounts of different bases which can saturate the same quantity of a particular
acid are equivalent to each other. On the basis of these researches and ideas he
attempted to trace a law according to which the quantities of different bases
required to saturate a given acid form an arithmetical progression, and the
quantities of acids saturating a given base form a geometrical progression. See
'Anfangsgründe der Stöchyometrie' (op. cit.) pt. I sect. ii p. vii.

The law mentioned here by Hegel is usually known as *'the law of neutrality'*, and is formulated as follows by Richter, 'When two neutral solutions are mixed, and decomposition follows, the new resulting products are almost without exception also neutral; the elements must, therefore have among themselves a certain fixed ratio of mass'. See 'Anfangsgründe der Stöchiometrie oder Messkunst chymischer Elemente' (3 vols. Breslau and Hirschberg, 1792–1794) pt. i pp, xx, xxii. In his 'Ueber die neuern Gegenstände der Chymie' (11 pts. Breslau and Hirschberg, 1791–1802) pt. 8 p. 82 f; pt. 9 pp. 10, 145; pt. 11 p. 84. Richter also points out that when two metallic salts exchange acids and bases by double decomposition, the metal of one finds in the other exactly the quantity of oxygen necessary to keep it dissolved in the acid; i.e. that the quantitites of different metals necessary for the formation of neutral salts combine with identical weights of oxygen.

Richter's work was generally known through *Berzelius's* 'Essai sur la Théorie des Proportions Chimiques' (Paris, 1819) and 'Lehrbuch der Chemie' (Dresden, 1827) III, i, 17 f. Berzelius made the mistake of attributing it to C. F. Wenzel (1740–1793), and it was not until *1841* that G. H. Hess (1802–1850), professor of chemistry at St. Petersburg, corrected the error and so brought Richter to the notice of the non-specialist. Cf. J. R. Partington 'A History of Chemistry' vol. III pp. 674–688 (London, 1962).

210, 27

L. B. Guyton de Morveau (1737–1816): see the note II. 405. Hegel is here referring to the article on 'Affinité' which Guyton wrote for the 'Encyclopédie Methodique' vol. I pt. i pp. 535–613 (1786). S. F. Hermbstädt (1760–1833) translated it into German and added notes: 'Allgemeine theoretische und praktische Grundsätze der chemischen Affinität oder Wahlanziehung' (Berlin, 1794). Cf. 'Nicholson's Journal' 1799 ii p. 340. Sir Humphry Davy (1778–1829) in a paper read to the Royal Society in November 1810 ('Phil. Trans. Roy. Soc.' 1811 vol. 101 pt. i p. 17) speaks of Richter and Guyton as the discoverers of the 'mutual decomposition of the neutral salts'. Cf. 'Gilberts Annalen der Physik' 1811 vol. 39 p. 394: 'Chemiker Zeitung, Cöthen' 1930 vol. 54 p. 1005.

Guyton's initial consideration of the subject took the form of a criticism of the figures for the combining properties of acids and bases given by Richard Kirwan (1733–1812) in his 'Elements of Mineralogy' (London, 1784) pp. 181–207, 406. He finally arrived at the following generalizations (op. cit. pp. 598 f., 600), '1. A weak base takes more of the same acid than a strong base. 2. The quantities of bases necessary for the saturation of an acid in the direct ratio of their affinities with this acid, or (what is the same) an acid takes more of a base for saturation the greater the affinity it has for it. 3. The quantities of acids taken by the same base are in the ratio of the powers of the acids in the order of affinities or a base takes more of an acid according as it is stronger.'

211, 20

C. L. Berthollet (1748–1822) 'Essai de Statique Chimique' (2 vols. Paris, 1803): see the German tr. by G. W. Bartoldy (ed. E. G. Fischer, 2 vols. Berlin, 1811). In the introduction to this work (I p. 9), Berthollet observes that, 'Dès que l'on a reconnu les propriétés générales auxquelles doivent aboutir tous les effets de l'action chimique, on s'est hâté d'établir, comme lois constantes et déterminées, les conditions de l'affinité qui ont paru satisfaire à toutes les explications, et c'est dans la superficie que la science acquiest par là, que l'on fait principalement consister ses progrès'. Cf. the German edition p. 11.

212, 23

W. H. Wollaston (1766–1826), in his paper on equivalents, read to the Royal Society on November 4, 1813 ('Phil. Trans. Roy. Soc.' vol. 104 p. 1) refers to Richter. In this paper he makes use of *Dalton*'s (not, as he states Higgins's) theory of the atomic nature of chemical combination, but his exposition of the theoretical foundations for his 'equivalents' is not at all clear. Hegel may have known the account of Wollaston's work given by M. H. Klaproth and F. Wolff in 'Supplemente zu dem chemischen Wörterbuche' vol. IV pp. 192–200 (Berlin, 1819). Wollaston was not quite the first to introduce Richter's theories into England however, for Thomas Thomson (1773–1852) made mention of them in his 'A System of Chemistry' (5 vols. Edinburgh, 1807) vol. III pp. 624–624.

212, 24

C. L. Berthollet (1748–1822), in his 'Essai de Statique Chimique' (2 vols. Paris, 1803) vol. I p. 116 f. gives an abstract of Richter's views taken from 'C. L. Berthollet über die Gesetze der Verwandtschaft' (Berlin, 1802), by E. G. Fischer (1754–1831), who taught physics and mathematics at a Berlin grammar school. He says that Richter's experiments on mixing solutions of neutral salts which form precipitates seemed, 'to lead necessarily to the consequence which I did not indicate in my researches, viz. that the different acids follow corresponding proportions with different alkaline bases to arrive at a neutral state of combination'.

The obscurity of Richter's style probably accounts in no small measure for the tardiness of his fellow chemists and countrymen in appreciating his views: see L. W. Gilbert's complaints in his 'Annalen der Physik' 1811 vol. 39 pp. 361, 394.

212, 30

Phrenology, the empirical system of psychology formulated by Franz Joseph Gall (1758–1828), was based upon five main principles: (i) the brain is the organ of the mind; (ii) the mental powers of man can be analysed into a definite number of independent faculties; (iii) these faculties are innate, and each has its seat in a definite region of the surface of the brain: (iv) the size of each such region is the measure of the degree to which the faculty seated in it forms a constituent element in the character of the individual; (v) the correspondence between the outer surface of the skull and the contour of the brain-surface beneath is sufficiently close to enable the observer to recognize the relative sizes of these several organs by the examination of the outer surface of the head. See Gall's 'Anatomie et physiologie du système nerveux en général et du cerveaux en particulier' (4 vols. Paris, 1810–1818).

Gall's theories were based upon research he did in Vienna, where he took his doctorate in 1785, and where he lectured privately for some years. On December 24, 1801 he was forbidden to continue his lectures on the ground that they were detrimental to religion, and in March 1805 he left Vienna with his disciple J. C. Spurzheim (1776–1832) and toured Germany, lecturing on his doctrines: see 'Meine Reise durch Deutschland' (Erfurt, 1806). In January 1808 he settled in Paris as a Doctor. In 1821, when E. Geoffrey Saint-Hilaire (1772–1844) proposed him as a member of the Academy, he was unable to find a seconder.

Gall's teachings enjoyed a tremendous vogue in Great Britain, and in 1832 there were no less than twenty-nine British phrenological societies. The clergy were affected by the doctrines, and even Richard Whately (1787–1863), archbishop of Dublin, took them seriously. See George Combe (1788–1858) 'Essays on Phrenology' (Edinburgh, 1819), 'Elements of Phrenology' (Edinburgh, 1824), 'Systems of Phrenology' (Edinburgh, 1825), 'Phrenological Journal' (20 vols. Edinburgh, 1823–1847).

August von Kotzebue (1761–1819) satirized phrenology in his comedy 'Die Organe des Gehirns' (Vienna, 1807): Eng. tr. by Capadose 'The Organs of the Brain' (London, 1838), and the teaching was also very cleverly parodied in 'The Craniad', a poem by Francis Jeffrey (1773–1850) and J. Gordon (Edinburgh, 1817). Rather more serious refutations of it are to be found in J. F. Ackermann (1765–1815) 'Die Gall'sche Gehirnlehre widerlegt' (Heidelberg, 1806) and J. F. W. Himly 'Erörterung der Gall'schen Lehre' (Rudolstadt, 1807). For an attempt at a balanced assessment, see the lecture delivered to the Royal College of Surgeons in June 1821 by John Abernethy (1764–1831) 'Reflections on Gall and Spurzheim's 'System of Physiognomy and Phrenology' (London, 1821).

212, 32

Jeremias Benjamin Richter (1762–1807): see the note II. 428. Hegel evidently has in mind his 'Anfangsgründe der Stöchyometrie oder Messkunst chymischer Elemente' (3 vols. Breslau and Hirschberg, 1792–1794). In the preface to this work he says that he had often pondered on the extent to which chemistry was a branch of applied mathematics, especially on account of the common experience that two neutral salts when they mutually decompose each other, give rise to further neutral compounds. From his subsequent investigations he concluded that, 'there must be definite ratios of magnitude between the constituents of the neutral salts'.

This led him to define *stoichiometry*, 'Since the mathematical part of chemistry is mostly concerned with bodies which are undecomposable bodies or elements, and teaches how to determine the mass ratios between them, I have been able to find no shorter and more suitable name for this scientific discipline than *Stöchyometry* from στοιχεῖον, which in the Greek language means something which cannot be divided further, and μετρεῖν which means to find out relative magnitudes'.

213, 4

Hegel is here referring to the *Prussian* currency of his day. In 1750 this currency had been reformed under the direction of Johann Philipp Graumann (c. 1690–1762), and it remained substantially the same until the Austro-Prussian currency agreement of 1857.

The *Friedrichsdor*, which was minted until about 1850, was the Prussian equivalent of the Spanish pistole. In 1740, when it first appeared, it had a gold content of 6·055 gr., which in 1770 was reduced to 6·032 gr. After 1786 it was known officially as a 'Friedrich-Wilhelmsdor', but it kept its original name in everyday speech.

The *taler* was the approximate equivalent of the English crown piece. It first appeared at the end of the fifteenth century, and got its name from the Joachimstal silver mines, in Bohemia. The Prussian taler of 1750 has a silver content of 16·704 gr. and was officially valued at five to a Friedrichsdor. This proved to be an overvaluation however, and in order to check the subsequent disappearance of the gold currency, it was revalued at $5\frac{1}{3}$ to a Friedrichsdor after the Seven Years' War. It was during the Napoleonic wars that the further adjustment of $5\frac{2}{3}$ talers to the Friedrichsdor was made. There were twenty four *groschen* in a taler.

See J. P. Graumann 'Gesammelte Briefe von dem Gelde' (Berlin, 1762), F. Schrötter 'Wörterbuch der Münzkunde' (Berlin and Leipzig, 1930).

213, 10

Jöns Jacob Berzelius (1779–1848) the famous Swedish chemist. He was born in East Gothland and brought up by his stepfather. In 1793 he entered the grammar school at Linköping where the excellent teaching of C. F. Hornstedt awoke his interest in botany and entomology. He had originally planned to follow the family tradition and train for the church, but in 1796 he went up to Uppsala to read medicine. His means were so limited however that he was soon forced to leave the university. He found work as an apothecary at Vadstena, and it was there that he first became interested in chemistry through meeting an Italian who taught him how to blow glass and use various instruments. In 1798 he won a small scholarship and in 1802 graduated M.D. with a thesis on the medical applications of galvanism.

In Stockholm he worked with Wilhelm Hisinger (1766–1852) on the effect of an electric current on salt solutions and published his lectures on animal chemistry: 'Föreläsningar i Djurkemien' (2 vols. Stockholm, 1806, 1808: Eng.

tr. Brunnmark, London, 1813, Germ. tr. Sigwart, Nuremberg, 1815). He was successively reader in chemistry at the Carlberg Military Academy (1806), professor of medicine and pharmacy at the Stockholm School of Surgery (1807), and professor at the Caroline Medico-Chirurgical Institute (1810–1832). In 1808 he was elected member of the Swedish Academy of Sciences, of which he became permanent secretary in 1818.

He made several journeys abroad and corresponded with many of the scientists he met: see 'Jac. Berzelius Bref' (ed. H. G. Söderbaum, 7 vols. Stockholm and Uppsala, 1912–1935). He visited Copenhagen in 1807 and met H. C. Ørsted (1777–1851). In 1812 he visited London and was greatly impressed by the experimental lectures given at Guy's Hospital by A. J. G. Marcet (1770–1820). On this occasion he also became personally acquainted with Davy, Smithson Tennant (1761–1815), Wollaston and Thomas Young. He renewed many of these acquaintances when he visited London again in 1818, but on this occasion his main objective was Paris, where he was well received by Berthollet, Gay-Lussac, Thénard, Chaptal, Vauquelin, Chevreul and other French chemists. See 'Kungliga Svenska Vetenskapsakademiens Årsbok för år 1953' pp. 325–362. He met Goethe at Karlsbad in 1822, took part in scientific meetings at Berlin in 1827 and 1828, and in 1830 met J. von Liebig (1803–1873) in Hamburg. See J. Carrière 'Berzelius und Liebig, ihre Briefe von 1831–1845' (Munich and Leipzig, 1892). Once the pan-Scandinavian scientific meetings had been organized, Berzelius supported them, and attended those held at Copenhagen in 1840 and 1847, Stockholm in 1842 and Kristiania in 1844.

After 1819 he did not enjoy good health, he tended to do less experimental work, and spent more time in backing up the ideas he had already put forward. Within Sweden his most prominent critic was Israel Hwasser (1790–1860), a Schellingian who had practised medicine in Germany during the 1813–1814 campaign, and subsequently (1830) became professor of medicine at Uppsala: see 'Valda skrifter' (4 vols. ed. P. Hedenius, Stockholm, 1868–1870): U. Quesnel's article in 'Uppsala läkareförbundets förhandlingar' 1932.

Berzelius's main works are his 'Lärbok i Kemien' (3 vols. Stockholm, 1808–1818) and 'Lärbok i Organiska Kemien' (3 vols. Stockholm, 1827–1830), Numerous German translations and editions of them were published and they also appeared in French, Dutch, Italian and Spanish, but they were never translated into English. Some of his minor works were however: see 'An attempt to establish a pure scientific system of mineralogy' (tr. Black, London, 1814): 'The use of the blowpipe in chemical analysis' (tr. Children, London, 1822). Much of his work appeared in periodicals.

Berzelius is important in the history of chemistry mainly for the following reasons: 1. He was one of the first chemists to make use of *chemical symbols*. 2. He developed Dalton's atomic theory into the *corpuscular theory*, which is based on the assumption that bodies are aggregates of spherical atoms which in chemical combination neutralize those of their kind with opposite electric charges.

Berzelius notes that the weights found from *volumes* are the same as Dalton's atomic weights, but have the advantage of being based on facts and not on an hypothesis. 3. He formulated the *electrochemical theory* criticized by Hegel in § 330 (note II. 410). He noticed that *heat* is given off in every chemical combination, and that bodies may be classed and graded as *electropositive* and *electronegative*, according to the charges they take up in contact with each other. He regarded *electrolysis* as being the exact reverse of chemical combination, and suggested that the electric charges lost on combination are restored to the two parts of the compound, which appear in the free state. For his final account of this theory see: 'Traité de Chimie' (tr. Esslinger and Hoefer, 6 vols. Paris, 1845–1850) vol. i p. 105 f.

Hegel is referring here to Berzelius's work on *combining proportions*, an English translation of which appeared as, 'An Attempt to determine the definite and simple proportions, in which the constituent Parts of Unorganic Substances are united with each other' ('Philosophical Magazine' vols. 41–43 1813–1814): cf. 'Versuch die bestimmten und einfachen Verhältnisse aufzufinden nach welchen die Bestandtheile der Unorganischen Natur mit einander verbunden sind' (Ostwald's Klassiker, 1892, no. 35). On the three oxides of tin see M. H. Klaproth and F. Wolff 'Supplemente zu dem chemischen Wörterbuche' vol. IV pp. 427–433 (Berlin, 1819). It was evidently Richter's 'Über die neuern Gegenstände der Chemie' pt. VIII p. 82 f. (Breslau and Hirschberg, 1797) and to a lesser extent Dalton's 'A New System of Chemical Philosophy' (2 pts. Manchester, 1808–1810) which encouraged Berzelius to make the attempt at working his researches out into a 'universal law'.

See Arne Holmberg 'Bibliografi över J. J. Berzelius' (Stockholm and Uppsala, 1933).

213, 17

John Dalton (1766–1844): see his 'A New System of Chemical Philosophy' (3 pts. Manchester, 1808, 1810, 1827). On the whole, the book was well received in Germany; F. Wolff (1765–1845) published a translation of the first two parts 'Ein neues System des chemischen Theils der Naturwissenschaften' (2 vols. Berlin, 1812–1813).

Hegel evidently has in mind the following passages in this work (pt. i pp. 141-4, 211-20), 'All bodies of sensible magnitude, whether liquid or solid, are constituted of a vast number of extremely small particles, or atoms of matter bound together by a force of attraction, which is more or less powerful according to the circumstances, and which as it endeavours to prevent their separation, is very properly called in that view, *attraction of cohesion*; but as it collects them from a dispersed state (as from steam into water) it is called, *attraction of aggregation*, or more simply, affinity . . . we may conclude that *the ultimate particles of all homogeneous bodies are perfectly alike in weight, figure*, etc. . . . every particle of water is like every other particle of water; every particle of hydrogen is like every other particle of hydrogen etc. . . .

'Repulsion . . . is now generally, and I think properly, ascribed to the agency of heat. An atmosphere of this subtile fluid constantly surrounds the atoms of all bodies, and prevents them from being drawn into actual contact. . . .

It is the one great object of this work, to show the importance and advantage of ascertaining *the relative weights of the ultimate particles, both of simple and compound bodies, the number of simple elementary particles which constitute one compound particle, and the number of less compounds particles which enter into the formation of one more compound particle'*.

213, 18

See the note II. 410.

213, 19

Johann Salomo Christoph Schweigger (1779–1857): see the note II. 414. Schweigger assumed the permanent polarization of atoms *before* Berzelius, but his views received little attention: see his 'Journal fur Chemie und Physik' 1812, v. 49; 1814, xiv, 497; 1823, ix, 231.

213, 24

Sir Humphry Davy (1778–1829): see his Bakerian Lecture of November 20, 1806 'On some chemical agencies of electricity' ('Phil. Trans. Roy. Soc.' 1807 pp. 1–56). Despite the war, Napoleon awarded Davy a prize of 3000 francs for this lecture.

213, 34

In the first edition of the 'Encylopaedia' (1817), Hegel added 'of oxides and acids, this also returns.'

214, 1

In the second edition of the 'Encylopaedia' (1827), Hegel added, 'The production of these processes presupposes a conditioning by the abstract agency of an acid, not a neutrality, working upon a neutral substance. This presupposition is rooted in the finite nature of the chemical process, the bodies of which are differentiated, and have at the same time an independent subsistence.'

215, 25

See notes, II, 256: 258: 264: 406. If Hegel had been content merely with distinguishing between the two meanings of the word 'element' he could have avoided making a controversy out of this issue. In that it is *gaseous* oxygen is of course to be distinguished from gold, silver and sulphur in that they are *solids*. However, in that both oxygen and gold etc. are *simple bodies* which had hitherto resisted analysis, the chemists of his day were perfectly justified in regarding them as 'elements'.

215, 40

Cf. Lavoisier's definition of an element as, 'the last point which analysis is capable of reaching' ('Traité Élémentaire de Chimie' 2 vols. Paris, 1789 pref. xvii, 192), 'Nous attachons au nom d'élémens ou de principes des corps l'idée du dernier terme auquel parvient l'analyse, toutes les substances que nous n'avons encore pu décomposer par aucun moyen, sont pour nous des élémens; ... puisque nous n'avons aucun moyen de les séparer, ils agissent à notre égard à la manière des corps simples, et nous ne devons les supposer composés qu'au moment où l'expérience et l'observation nous en auront fourni la preuve.'

M. H. Klaproth and Friedrich Wolff in their 'Chemisches Wörterbuch' vol. I pp. 321–325 (Berlin, 1807) avoid the use of the word 'Elemente' (see op. cit. II p. 58), and refer only to 'Bestandtheile' (constituent parts). Cf. the excellent summary of the subject by Thomas Thomson (1773–1852) in his 'A System of Chemistry' (5 vols. Edinburgh, 1810) vol. I pp. 626–631, 'As the term *simple substance* in chemistry means nothing more than a body whose component parts are unknown, it cannot be doubted that, as the science advances towards perfection, many of those bodies which we consider at present as simple will be decomposed; and most probably a new set of simple bodies will come into view, of which we are at present ignorant. These may be decomposed in their turn, and new simple bodies discovered; till at last, when the science reaches the highest point of perfection, those really simple and elementary bodies will come into view, of which all substances are ultimately composed.'

216, 3

In the second edition of the 'Encyclopaedia' (1827), Hegel added, 'such as the positing of phosphorous in oxygen.'

216, 11

In the second edition of the 'Encyclopaedia' (1827), Hegel added, 'Consequently, although these particular processes belong to the total process, they are traditionally called the *wet* and *dry* way, to which one has had to add the galvanic way. Their relationship has to be grasped more determinately however. The superficial distinction between wet and dry contains nothing which might determine the nature of bodies, and as these processes are related to one another as a determinative progression and a return into the indeterminate, a multitude of these products is furnished in an external way by their relationship.'

217, 13

Lavoisier first demonstrated the composition of carbon dioxide: see 'Mémoires de l'Academie des Sciences de Paris' 1781 p. 448: cf. Smithson Tennant

(1761–1815) in 'Phil. Trans. Roy. Soc.' vol. 81, 1791 p. 182: G. Pearson (1751–1828) in 'Phil. Trans. Roy. Soc.' 1792 p. 289.

217, 24

This identification of fire with time is evidently inspired by Heraclitus: see Hegel's 'History of Philosophy' (tr. Haldane 3 vols. London, 1963) vol. I p. 287, 'To Heraclitus the truth is to have grasped the essential being of nature, i.e. to have represented it as implicitly infinite, as process in itself; and consequently it is evident to us that Heraclitus could not say that the primary principle is air, water, or any such thing. They are not themselves process, but fire is process; and thus he maintains fire to be the elementary principle and this is the real form of the Heraclitean principle, the soul and substance of the nature-process. Fire is physical time, absolute unrest, absolute disintegration of existence, the passing away of the 'other', but also of itself.' Cf. W. Pagel 'John Baptist van Helmont: *De Tempore* and the history of the biological concept of time' ('Isis' 1941–1942 pp. 621–623).

217, 25

Hegel is referring here not to ‚Bergnaphta', i.e. the mineral oil obtained at that time from Monte Ciaro, near Piacenza, in Italy, and from Baku on the north-west shore of the Caspian, but to what British chemists knew as '*sulphuric ether*', i.e. a mixture of alcohol and sulphuric acid. For a discussion of it as the base of organic 'oils' see Fourcroy and Vauquelin 'De l'action de l'acide sulfurique sur les substances végétales et animales' ('Annales de Chimie' 1797 vol. xxiii pp. 186–215, 'Nicholson's Journal' 1797 vol. i pp. 385–394): T. Thomson (1773–1852) 'A System of Chemistry' (5 vols. Edinburgh, 1810) vol. II pp. 440–455.

For contemporary German views on the matter see Johann Friedrich August Göttling (1755–1809) 'Almanach oder Taschenbuch fur Scheidekünstler und Apotheker' (Weimar, 1797) 66: cf. H. Kopp 'Geschichte der Chemie' (4 vols. Brunswick, 1843–7) vol. IV p. 284. Also S. F. Hermbstädt (1760–1833) 'Physikalisch-chemische Versuche und Beobachtungen' (2 vols. Berlin, 1786–9) vol. I p. 162.

217, 28

‚Wasserstoffsäure,—die Salzsäure'. The true nature of hydrochloric acid (HCl) had not at that time been completely settled. The issue was complicated by Lavoisier's theory that *oxygen* is essential to an acid: see 'Mémoires de l'Academie Royale' 1784 p. 468, 1786 p. 530. Christoph Girtanner (1760–1800) in his popular text-book 'Anfangsgründe der antiphlogistischen Chemie' (2nd ed. Berlin, 1795) p. 154 takes 'muriatic' acid to be a compound of hydrogen and oxygen. J. B. Van Mons (1765–1842) in 'Examen des faits . . . sur la nature du radical de l'acide muriatique' ('Mémoires de l'Institut National' 1798 vol. i pp. 36–44) refuted this view, and attributed the production of hydrogen from muriatic acid to the decomposition of water.

Sir Humphry Davy's discovery of *chlorine* in 1810 clarified the field: see 'Researches on the Oxymuriatic Acid, its nature and combinations' ('Phil. Trans. Roy. Soc.' 1810 pp. 231–57) cf. 'Phil. Trans. Roy. Soc.' 1818 pp. 169–171. A. Avogadro (1776–1856) gives the correct formula for hydrochloric acid in his 'Essai d'une manière de déterminer les masses relatives des molécules élémentaires des corps' ('Journal de Physique' 1811 vol. 73 pp. 58–76: Ostwald's Klassiker no. 8), but as late as 1828 John Murray (1798–1873) considered the matter to be controversial: see his edition of his father's 'A System of Chemistry' (6th ed. Edinburgh, 1828) vol. II pp. 665–70 (appendix).

217, 35

‚Blutſäure', i.e. Acidum sanguinis. This acid, which was evidently a thiocyanate, is only mentioned in a few of the text-books of the time. Hegel probably knew of it from the writings of J. J. Winterl (1732–1809) who refers to it in his 'Die Kunst, Blutlauge und mehrere zur Blutfarbe dienliche Materien im Grossen zu bereiten und solche zur Blaufärberei anzuwenden' (Vienna, 1790): see also J. C. Schuster (1777–1839) 'System der dualistischen Chemie des Prof. Jakob Joseph Winterl' (2 vols. Berlin, 1807) vol. I pp. 398–399, who says that it is to be obtained by slowly heating blood and potash in a sealed container without bringing them to a red heat. According to Winterl alcohol forms a salt with the residue out of which muriatic acid precipitates blood acid in the form of a curdled cheese.

Rink repeated Winterl's experiments and confirmed his conclusions 'Beitrag zu den Verhandlungen über Blausäure' ('Neues allgemeines Journal der Chemie' 1804 II pp. 460–466), as also did C. F. Bucholz (1770–1818): see his edition of Gren's 'Grundriss der Chemie' (2 pts. Halle, 1796–7) vol. I p. 504; cf. the English translation of this work by Gruber, a pastor of the Austrian colony in London 'Principles of Modern Chemistry' (2 vols. London, 1800).

M. H. Klaproth and Friedrich Wolff in their 'Supplemente zu dem chemischen Wörterbuche' vol. I pp. 275–277 suggested that Winterl's acid mght be the same as the 'sulphuretted chyazic acid' discovered by Robert Porrett (1783–1868): see Nicholson's Journal 1810 vol. 25 p. 344, 'Phil. Trans. Roy. Soc.' 1814 vol. 104 pp. 527–556. Berzelius took the matter up in 'Om sammansättningar af svafelhaltigen blåsyra salter' ('Kungliga Svenska Vetenskaps Academiens Handlingar' 1820 pp. 82–99: 'Schweigger's Journal' 1820 vol. 30 pp. 1–67), and referred to Winterl's book (1790) and to Bucholz's 'Beiträge zur Erweiterung und Berichtigung der Chemie' (Erfurt, 1799) in the course of his argument. He rightly diagnosed the quantitative composition (HCNS) of Porrett's discovery.

Raymund de Vieussens (1641–1716) in his 'Deux dissertations . . . La première touchant l'extraction du sel acide du sang' (Montpellier, 1698) cf. 'Epistola de

Sanguinis Humani, cum sale fixo, spiritum acidum suggerente' (Leipzig, 1698) claimed to have discovered an acid in the four ounces of residue left from the evaporation of fifty pounds of blood, but in Hegel's day this was regarded as a putative discovery: see J. F. John (1782–1847) 'Handwörterbuch der allgemeinen Chemie' (4 vols. Leipzig and Altenburg, 1817–1819) vol. I pp. 115–116; J. F. Pierer (1767–1832) 'Anatomisch-physiologisches Realwörterbuch' vol. I p. 887 (Leipzig and Altenburg, 1816).

218, 19

In a marginal note on this sentence Hegel writes ('Jenenser Realphilosophie' II p. 94): 'Clay (a) aspect of the process *with sulphur*, combustibility, (b) of the crystal, *hardness* uncrystallized, corundum, sapphire, very hard. *Water* does not become *water* of *crystallization. Acid* is not (produced), but (remains) *for itself*, intro-reflected.—Sapphire as clay—. *The earths*, processless, because abstract subjects, need an other, consequently they exhibit this determinate being of the process, but the result of each only has the form of something sublated, like metallicism; burning which does not become acetose.—(It is) rather inner dry discrete hardness, as the hardness of the crystal, like *natural glass*, absolute *singular* being-for-self. *Processless damp heat* with *water* does not give rise to chemical differentiation, but to greater external hardness.'

Hegel seems to have in mind the fact that *alum crystals* are formed through the action of sulphuric acid upon alumina and *potash*. Sulphuric acid and *pure alumina* will not form alum: see T. Thomson (1773–1852) 'A System of Chemistry' (5 vols. Edinburgh, 1810) vol. II pp. 670–676.

Six kinds of jasper were distinguished at that time:—Egyptian, striped, porcelain, common, agatine and marbled. Blue porcelain jasper from Töplitz was analysed by W. A. Lampadius (1772–1842), who found that it contained 33·5% silica, 58% alumina, 4% talc and 3% iron oxide see his 'Sammlung praktisch-chemischer Abhandlungen und vermischter Bemerkungen' (3 vols. Dresden, 1795–1800) vol. II p. 223, vol. III p. 246.

It is probable that Hegel is merely saying that both alum and jasper contain a large percentage of alumina. He is certainly mistaken if he is attributing the *formation* of procelain jasper to the action of sulphuric acid upon alumina. He may have had in mind the *glazing* of procelain, done by dipping the biscuit ware in a mixture of 60 parts litharge, 10 of clay, and 20 of ground flint, diffused in water to a creamy consistence, and then fusing it in a kiln at a moderate *heat*: see A. and C. R. Aikin 'A Dictionary of Chemistry and Mineralogy' (2 vols. London, 1807) vol. II pp. 243–247.

218, 19

‚Härte (Kriſtalliſation) verdankt ſie dem Feuer'. ('Jenenser Realphilosophie, II p. 94). Michelet altered the sentence somewhat.

218, 23

Michelet's version of this sentence has been revised in the light of the original which is as follows: ,(3) Talk-oder Bittererde als Subjekt des Salzes; Bitterkeit des Meeres-Salz als Subjekt, Mittel, Geschmack, der zum Feuerprinzip geworden, Seifenartig, eben der Rückgang des Neutralen ins Feuerprinzip.' Hegel has two marginal notes relating to the sentence: see 'Jenenser Realphilosophie' II p. 94.

219, 4

This assessment of the 'concrete elements' as a 'system of determinately differentiated corporeality' should be compared with Hegel's exposition of the 'elements' in §§ 281–285.

219, 8

In the first edition of the 'Encyclopaedia' (1817) Hegel added, 'It merely makes its appearance however, it does not become *objective*'.

219, 11

In the first edition of the 'Encyclopaedia' (1817) Hegel added, 'immediate and contingent' before 'conditions'.

219, 23

,eines anfänglichen Selbstbestimmens.' The 1827 edition of the 'Encyclopaedia' had ,einer anfänglichen Selbstbestimmung', and the 1830 edition, probably on account of an oversight due to the alteration of the text, ,einem anfänglichen Selbstbestimmen.'

220, 5

,das Ganze des chemischen Processes enthält einerseits die feste Bestimmtheit, in der Weise der Indifferenz zu seyn, und auf der andern Seite den Trieb, als Entgegensetzung seiner in sich zu seyn, worin dann die Bestimmtheit wegfällt.'

220, 22

In the first edition of the 'Encyclopaedia' (1817) Hegel wrote, 'concrete universality'.

220, 34

,in diesem Wechsel der Accidenzien'. See, 'The Logic of Hegel' (tr. Wallace, Oxford, 1963) 150 (pp. 273–274): cf. Aristotle's 'Metaphysics' IV 1025 a 14.

221, 9

In a marginal note ('Jenenser Realphilosophie' II p. 93) Hegel comments upon this as follows, 'Instability in the relationships of the constituent parts, and further fixed points, as in the thermometric scale, character.'

221, 16

On the oxides of copper see Richard Chenevix (1774–1830) 'An analysis of the red octahedral Copper Ore of Cornwall' ('Phil. Trans. Roy. Soc.' 1801 pp. 193–240), L. J. Proust (1754–1826) 'Recherches sur le cuivre' ('Annales de Chimie' 1799 vol. 32 pp. 26–54) and J. J. Berzelius (1779–1848) 'An attempt to determine Proportions ('Philosophical Magazine' 1813 vol. 41. p. 200). Cf Thomas Thomson (1773–1852) 'A System of Chemistry' (5 vols. Edinburgh, 1810) vol. I pp. 206–7, 'There are two oxides of copper at present known; and it does not appear that the metal is capable of being exhibited in combination with more than two doses of oxygen. The *protoxide* is found native of a red colour, but when formed artificially it is a fine *orange*; but the *peroxide* is *black*, though in combination it assumes various shades of blue, green, and brown.'

222, 24

See the note II. 306.

222, 28

'Αὔη ψυχὴ σοφωτάτη καὶ ἀρίστη' (The dry soul is wisest and best). See I. Bywater 'Heracliti Ephesii Reliquiae' (Oxford, 1877) no. 74. For the various corruptions of this text see J. Burnet 'Early Greek Philosophy' (London, 1908) p. 152. For a recent discussion of Heraclitus's view of the soul see P. Wheelwright 'Heraclitus' (Princetown, 1959) ch. IV. Cf. the notes II. 226: 437.

INDEX TO TEXT VOL 2.

absorption, 208, 218

accident, 220

accretion, 86

achromaticism, 140, 142, 153

acid, 124, 163, 177, 179, 190, 191, 208; activity, 104, 110; and alkali, 189, 190, 194, 205, 211, colour, 221, litmus, 159, neutrality, 218, oxidation, 210, 219, 221; atmosphere, 151; causticity, 39; classification of, 217; concentrated, 186; fluidity, 200; neutralized, 216; sulphur, 206; water, 118, 186; weak, 198

acidity, 19, 182; affinity of, 212; property of, 192

activation, 185, 188, 207, 209, 219; activated bodies, 182, 191

activity, 85; acidic, 104, 110; and materialities, 190; aqueous, 193; artistic, 97; chemical, 188, 202, 203, 216, 219; electrical, 202; galvanic, 169, 199, 200, 203; igneous, 205, 221; linear, 111; magnetic, 107, 111; mechanical, 174; mechanizing, 168; Notional, 111; physical, 168; spiritual, 28, 222

acumination (crystalline), 114

adhesion, 63

aerolite, 50, 52, 53

affinity, 210

agent, 214, 221

aggregation, 17, 116, 213

Aigle, 53

air: and acid, 208, metal, 186, 204, metalloid, 193, odour, 162, quicksilver, 198, sound, 70, 72, 73; as conductor, 172, gas, 217, mediator, 207; atmospheric, 187, 201, 202; destructiveness of, 161; dry, 46, 172, 186; element of, 35, 44, 117, 123, 185, 207, 215; humid, 186, 208; negativity of, 39; neutrality of, 204; pressure, 49; pump, 201

alcohol, 183

Aldini, G., 201

Alix, J. A. F., 16, 47

alkali, 218; and absorption, 208, acid, 182, 189, 194, 195, 207, 208, 209, 210, 211, causticity, 205, 207, 208, colour, 159, earths, 209, metal, 190, 208, oxidation, 207, 209; as whole body, 179; classification, 217; grading, 210–11

alloy, 183

alum, 132; earth, 209

alumina, 124, 209, 218

amalgam, 53, 183, 184, 197, 204, 209

amber, 171

America, 51, 83

ammonia, 204

analogy, 15, 16, 42, 75, 145, 209

Ancients (the), 26, 35, 45, 76

angle, 65, 97, 98; of refraction, 132

anhydrous, 209

animal, 29, 51, 177, 186; acids, 217; colours, 83; constituents, 34; electricity, 201; forms, 37; fluids, 35; life, 187; oils, 217; reproduction, 195; substances, 172, 214

animation, 29, 33, 51, 52, 108, 179, 219

antimony, 219

antinomy, 67

antithesis, 26, 50, 61, 87, 109, 157, 198, 205, 218

aquafortis, 217

aqua regia, 184

archetypal: crystal, 123; phenomenon, 148, 149, 154, 155, 193

Archimedes, 183, 184

architecture, 75

Aristotle, 32, 45

arithmetic, 77, 209; arithmetical progression, 78

armature, 201

arsenic, 219; acid, 207; oxide, 207

art, 97; artist, 146

Asia, 51

astral powers, 31

astronomy, 18, 26, 30

atmosphere: air of, 187, 201, 202; and barometer, 60, blue of sky, 152, comet, 28, 28, heat, 91, magnetism, 104, refraction, 20; caloric, 213; Earth's, 49, 91; electric,

151; formation of, 151, 162; gas of, 187; inter-stellar, 20; lunar, 26; planetary, 27; pressure of, 98; stimulation of, 104

atom, 66, 67, 213; metaphysical, 213

attraction, 61, 108, 111, 113, 168; force of, 49

aurora borealis, 52

axis, 48, 103, 105, 180; rotation of, 16, 30

azurite, 221

Baffin's Bay, 53

balance, 58

balances, 19

balloon ascent, 16

barometer, 49, 51, 59, 60

barytes, 204, 207, 209

base, 124, 161, 186, 197, 204, 209, 210, 212, 216, 217

battery; electric, 197; galvanic, 210, 203

Bayreuth, 104

beauty (line of), 98

bell, 71, 88

Berlin: Academy, 45, University, 143, Yearbooks, 173

Berthollet, C. L., 168, 209, 211, 212

Berzelius, J. J., 195, 196, 197, 213

Biot, J. B., 37, 73, 80, 132, 135, 141, 147, 171, 194, 201, 202

bird, 51; shape, 98: song, 83, 84

bismuth, 116, 184

bitterness, 218

bitumen, 206

black, 173; composition, 144; of sky, 149

bleach, 118

blood acid, 217

blue: copper sulphate, 221; of sky, 143, 152, 153

Bode, J. E., 29

Boehme, J., 32, 117

bones, 73

borax, 124

Boston, 59

brass, 184

Brazil, 53, 83

brightness, 139

brittleness, 27, 63, 65, 221; and combustibility, 206, shape, 99, 100, 123, 141; of bitumen, 206, glass, 65, 105, 135, 155, iron and steel, 65, 104, metals, 198, naphtha. 206. resin, 198, silica, 218,

sulphur, 198, 206; mechanical, 161; resonance of, 82

bronze, 73

Brugmans, A. (not Brugmann); 105

bubble, 41, 177

burning, 202; glass, 85

butterfly, 145

Caesar, 20

calcareous substance, 218

calculus (differential), 141

caloric, 86, 89, 213, 216

calx, 161, 193, 198; calcined iron, 104, quicksilver, 199

candlelight, 143, 144

cannon, 85; cannonade, 73

capillary tube, 63

carbon, 185, 187, 190, 215

carbonic acid, 124, 207, 208, 216, 217; gas, 217

carboniferous seam, 52

cardboard, 201

Carlsruhe, 60

Cassel, 16

category, 17, 23, 43, 58, 84, 85, 88, 133, 136, 154, 215

Catherine the Great, 90

catskin, 172, 200

caustic, 39, 193, 210; alkali, 205, 207 208; condition, 207; potash, 189

centre, 16, 25, 28, 40, 55, 60, 68, 103; centrality, 42, 59, 100, 142,

centrifugal force, 106

centripetal force, 106

chaos, 142

charcoal, 198, 199

chemical: action, 202; activity, 188, 202, 203, 216, 219; analysis, 35; change, 198; combustion, 161; compounds, 197; elements, 185, 186, 187, 196, 207, 215, 217–219; form, 213; kitchens, 170; moments, 185; opposition, 205, 210, 213; process, 16, 31, 88, 95, 121, 162, 163, 164, 173, 174, 177, 178, 188, 189, 205, 216, 219, 222; relationship, 169; substances, 116, 215

chemism, 106, 109, 175, 180, 181, 194

chemistry, 34, 136

Chinese, 102

Chladni, E. F., 73, 74

chromatic difference, 159

circle, 144

circuit (galvanic) 109, *193*, 199; Erman's rotation, 110
cirrus (clouds), 52
citric acid, 217
classification, 188, 190, 214
climate, 47, 83, 84
cloud, 47, 49, 50, 51, *52*, 53, 170
coagulation, 156, 158
cobalt, 103, 184
cobweb, 169
coffee, 90
coherence, 64, 82, 85
cohesion, 57, 61, *62*, 69, 74, 81, 84, 85, 87, 88, 89, 92, 114, 118, 130, 137, 156, 166, 169, 183, 184, 199, 211, 220
coincidence, 23
cold, 48, 85, 88, 89, 152
collision, 68, 170
Cologne pipes, 73
colour, 22, 23, 51, 118, 119, *135-160*, 163, 220; and chemical process, 179, electricity, 168, 173, heat, 83, light, 122, magnetism, 174, metal, 184, 218, 221; matter of, 136; of animals and birds, 83; rings, 155; shadows, 143; square, 139; subjectivity of, 122
column (of air), 73
combination, 183, 184, 190, *191*, 196, 200, 212, 214, 216, 218, 219
combustion, 15, 90, 117, 118, 162, 189, 202; combustibility, 27, 130, 161, 163, 171, 187, 205, 207, 217
comet, 26, 27, 28, 31, 48, 123; Halley's, 28
comma (musical), 78
commonsense, 32, 43
compactness, 157, 158, 187, 192, 198, 218
compass, 102, 104
complementary colours, 153
composition, 139, 142, 187, 215
compound, 190
compressibility, 41, 68
concentration: of light, 25; of acid, 186
conduction: and galvanism, 210; of electricity, 170, *171*, 175, 194; of heat, 84, 86; wet and dry, 192, 202
consistence, 63
constructive force, 97
contact, 171, 176, 186, 199, 200, 204
contiguity, 185, 198
continuity, 67, 71, 85, 104, 218
contraction, 68, 125
convergence, 108

copper, 31, 64, 65, 73, 184, 199; bowls, 200; salts, 221
corolla, 173
corpuscle, 20, 141
corrosion, 36, 98, 207
cosmic: causes 60; forces, 33
courtier, 29
crystal, *112-116*; and light, 123, *171*; densities, 133; dissolution, 90; form, 97, 117, 170; indifference of, 164; mechanical composition of, 96; of the Earth, 27, 103, 113; of the Moon, 28; reticulation, 96; transparency, 121, 123, *133*, 135, 156, 170; water, 43, 46, 47, 163
crystalline: connectedness, 218; lens, 152
crystallization, 27, 28, 34, 103, 135, 211; of alumina, 218; form, 97; heat, 88
crystallography, 115, 116
crucible, 213
cube, 103, 134
culmination points, 105, 169
cumulus cloud, 52
currency (Prussian), 212-213
current: electric 173; magnetic, 103
curve, 97, 108
customs officer, 44
cylinder, 175

Dalton, J., 213
D'Arcet, J., 184
darkening, *135*, 155
darkness, 14, 21, 22, 25, 117, 137, 139, 142, 148, 156
Davy, H., 210, 213
daylight, 143
deal, 73
death, 159, 214
declination (of magnetic needle), 103
decoction, 149, 159
decomposition, 36, 160, 163, 193, 198, 200, 202, 216
dehydration, 46
Deluc, J. A. 45, 50
demagnetization, 105
density, 57, 59, 61, 68, 69, 125, 126, 132, 133, 135, 159, 184
Descartes, R., 131
deuteroxide (of tin), 213
deviation, 109, 151, 172
dew, 49
dialectic, 66, 67, 222

diamond, 115, 123, 133
dicotyledon, 32
diffusion: of heat; 84; of things, 170
dimension, 63, 65
dimming, 138, 143, 148, 150
discharge (electric), 168, 196, 202, 211
disharmony, 74
disoxidation, 173
displacement, 172
disposition (magnetic), 180
dissolution, 40, 43, 50, 82, 90, 91, 92, 120, 165, 166, 197, 200
divergence, 108, 144
diverse refrangibility, 145
double image, 126, 150, 151
double refraction, 133, 141
dry conductor, 192, 202
ductility, 63, 65, 198
dynamic physics, 58

ear, 73, 76, 77, 78, 79, 80
earth (element), 41, 123, 218; cf. 'earthy'
Earth (planet), 27, 29, 30, 33, 42, 48, 51, 53, 54, 59, 60, 122, 179, 180, 181; crystal of, 27, 103, 113; magnetic axis, 103; magnetism, 99; rotation, 106
earthenware, 73
earthquake, 50
earths, 104, 124, 184, 193, 204, 205, 208, 209, 214, 127, 218
earthy: acids, 217; bases, 206, 217; element, 218; fire, 218; fracture, 104; metal, 104; principle, 218
eating utensil, 162
eclipse (solar), 182
ecliptic (inclination to), 105
ego, 13, 31, 119
elasticity, 46, 66, 67, 68, 83; elastic fluids, 89
elective affinity, 210–213
electric: atmosphere, 151; battery, 197; chimes, 174; currents, 173; discharge, 168, 196, 202, 211; field, 175; fluid, 173; force, 166, 176, 196; light, 165, 166, 167, 169, 170, 171; matter, 169; opposition, 173; rain, 174; shock, 167, 168; tension, 165, 166, 167, 168, 170, 175
electrical: activity, 202; differentiation, 171; figuration, 169; opposition, 173; machine, 171; process, 109, 168, 186, 189
electricity, 44, 95, 106, 107, 120, 164–177, 178, 192, 193, 195, 197, 200, 203, 206, 212

electro-galvanic activity, 109; electrochemism, 107, 174; electro-chemistry, 200–213; electrometer, 171, 174; électromoteur, 194, 197
element (chemical), 185–187, 196, 207, 215, 217–219
element (universal, physical), 32, 33, 43, 50, 54, 95, 116, 117, 123, 160, 163, 180, 181, 182, 185, 186, (217–219)
elephant, 131
elevation (perpendicularity of), 131
elision, 19
ellipse, 28, 97, 154
Empedocles, 34
empiricism, 16, 17, 18, 20, 37, 43, 87, 88, 107, 117, 131, 136, 141, 142, 158, 167, 174, 181, 190, 191, 193, 214, 215
England, 180; the English, 144, 212
entoptic colour, 23, 135, 137, 155
epoptic colour, 155, 158
equator, (52), 106
equilibrium, 39, 58, 61, 87, 104, 105, 114
equinox, 48
Erman, P., 110
eruption, 50
essence, 9, 11
ether, 20
Euler, L., 20
euphony, 75
Europe, 51, 52
evaporation, 46, 89
expansion, 18, 83, 89, 172
experiment, 137, 143
explosion, 16
eye, 18, 22, 124, 129, 131, 149, 151, 153

face (lines of), 98
fading (of colour), 160
fall, 106
fata morgana, 135
feather, 98
feeling, 71, 75, 119
fermentation, 88, 90
fertility, 53
fibrousness, 65
Fichtean idealism, 142
figuration: electrical, 169; spatial, 92
fire (element), 15, 16, 32, 38–41, 51, 85, 162, 171, 183, 186, 198, 207, 208, 216, 217, 219, 222; connection with air, 38; earthy, 218; free, 198, 222; imperishable,

222; process of (15), 27, 50, 52, 187, 190, 191, *205–208*, 221
fireball, 26, 53
fire-rose, 202
fish (shape of), 98
fits (Newtonian), 141
fixation, 87
flame, 91, 123, 153, 162, 166, 169, 205, 206
flax, 90
flint, 91;—glass, 150
flower, 83, 162
fluid, 89, 94, 98, 199; fluidity, 53, 68, 71, 82, 92, 93, 98, 117, 192, 198, 200
flute, 145
focus, 19, 154
folia, (passage of), 113, 115, 134
force, 42; and acid, alkali, 196, cohesion, 83, dissolution, 82, elements, 187, form, 96, friction, 185, refraction, 133, 134, transparency, 135, 136; attractive, 49; category, 133; chemical, 34; constructive, 97; cosmic, 33; electric, 166, 176, 196; mechanical, 38; motive, 106; sonic, 92; surface, 64
forest, 73, 83
forging (of iron), 65, 104
formic acid, 217
fossil (shape of), 115
fracture: crystal, 114, 115; earthy, 104, 124 granular, 65, 104
fragrancy, 162
France, 53; the French, 32, 135, 212
free: colour, 143; element, 198, 222
French horn, 146
friability, 218
friction, 16, 72, 85, 86, 88, 90, 91, 166, 169, 171, 185, 196
frigate, 90
frog, 201
fulcrum, 58
furnance, 198
fusion, 16, 177, 186, 202, 218

Gall, F. J., 212
Galvani, L., 201; galvanism, *191–205*
galvanic: action, 210, 203, 209; activity, 109, 199, 200, 203; battery, 110, 207; circuit, 109, *193*, 199; form, 180; pile, 46, 210; process, 177, 181, 182, 190, 192, 200, 204, 206, 213; product, 204; theory, 174

gas, 38, 46, 136, 172, 189, 194, 203, 205, 214, 216, 217
Gehler, J. S. T., 173
generation: of electricity, 197; of heat, 90
Geneva, 85
geognosy, 26
geology, 27, 51
geometry, 63, 98, 114, 115, 131
Germany, 50; the Germans, 212
glass, 44, 64, 65, 70, 71, 73, 82, 84, 134, 155, 171, 172, 175, 176, 177, 218; brittleness, 135, 141; coloured, 147; composition, 150; dark, 149; milky, 141; plate, 63, 171, 176; porcelain, 149; powdered, 124; prism, 144; transparent, 143; tubes, 172
globularity, 98, 100
Goethe, J. W., von: on meteorology, 51, 52, 59, 60; on colour, 23, 124, 134, 139, 140, 142, 146, 148, 149, 153, 154, 159, 212
gold, 31, 59, 61, 64, 65, 104, 156, 183, 184, 190, 198, 199, 202, 204, 215; coins, 198; colour, 156; Schelling on, 158; volatilization of, 177
good (the), 17
'Göttingen Literary Advertiser,' 90
granular fracture, 65, 104
graph, 59
gravity, 19, 53, 54, 55, 62, 122, 151, 206; and crystal, 96, form, 114, heat, 160, individuality, 92, light, 218, magnetism, 108, pendulum, 106, specific gravity, 89, touch, 160; determination of, 86; direction of, 64, 65; liberation from, 56; possibility of, 156; sphere of, 59; terrestriality of, 120, cf. specific gravity.
Greeks, 19
Gren, F.A.C., 45, 63, 132
grey, 138, 114, 148, 149; shadow, 139
guitar, 80
guttate fluidity, 198
Guyton de Morveau, L. B., 186, 210

hail, 49
hair, 172
half-shadow, 151
Halley's comet, 28
hammering, 65, 104
hardness, 68, 218
harmonic: limit, 77; ratio, 78; triad, 76, 77; harmony, 30, 74, 75, 76, 79, 81
harp, 78

Hauy, R.-J., 115, 171, 176
head, 73, 98
health, 29
hearing, 72, 119
heat, 44, 47, 48, 57, 81, *82–93*, 119, 152, 160, 166, 168, 192, 196, 208
heavenly body, 11, 15, 16, *25–31*, 105, 170, 181
hedgehog, 18
height (of mountain), 60
Heim, J. L., 26, 27
hemisphere, 18, 105
hemp, 90, 201
Heraclitus, 45, 222
hero, 131
Herschel, F. W., 20, 21
Hiero, 183
hindering (of illumination), 137
history (of philosophy), 34
hoar-frost, 49
horizon, 127
horn (instrument), 145, 146
horse, 53
hue (variety of), 142
Humboldt A. von, 47, 104, 200, 201
humidity, 44, 46, 49, 170
hydracid, 217
hydrate, 192
hydrochloric acid, 210
hydrogen; and acid, 206, Volta's pistol, 177, water, 35, 46, 192, 193, 206; Alix's theory, 16, 47; as principle of combustion, 185, 187, 217; classification of, 190, 214; hydrogenation, 192, 204, 209, of metals, 204, of sulphur, 209
hydrophane, 124
hygrometer, 46
hyperoxide (of tin), 213
hypothesis, 21, 173

ice, 40, 41, 124, 156, 172; spicula, 112
Iceland-spar, 115, 134, 135, 150
idealism, 142
igneous: principle, 117; process, 15; ignition, 168; cf. fire
image, 134
immutability (of substances), 215
impact, 11, 62, 64, 70
inactive materialities, 190
incidence (angle of), 22, 23, 132
inclination, 105

incoherence, 84
India, 52; the Indians, 13, 19
indifference (points of), 104, 105
induction (electrical), 168, 175
inertia, 167, 177
infection, 111
infinitude, 31, 64
inflection (of light), *151*
infusion (plant), 159
inorganic: being, 222; confusion, 217; shape, 97
insect (shape of), 98
instinct, 32
instrument (musical), 70, 72, 75, 78, 79
insulation, 172, 175, 176, 194, 201, 202
integrality, 12; integration, 208; integrant molecules, 116, 134
intelligence, 114, 193
intensity, 58
interfusion, 183
interval (musical), 77
intuition, 17, 82, 193
iridescence, 156
iridium, 199
iris (or eye), 154
iron, 31, 53, 64, 65, 102, 103, 104, 116, 184, 186, 199; cast, 65; forged, 65; ore, 104; stone (magnetic), 104; sulphate, 203
irrelativity, 24

Jena, 59
Jupiter, 31; satellites, 20
jurist, 154
Jussieu, A. L. de, 32

Kent I., 58
Kepler, J., 30, 32
key (musical), 78, 145
key-note, 75, 76, 79

lamella, 115, 134, 135
language, 71
Laplace, P. S. 28, 30
lark, 83
latency, 43, 47, 86, 87, 89, 105, 163
Lavoisier, A. L. 187
law, 20, 42, 111, 115, 132, 141, 210, 212
lead, 31, 64, 159, 184, 186, 198, 202
leaf shape, 98

lens, 19, 137, 148, 152, 154, 155
level (metaphysical), 109, 119, 143, 190, 214, 215; cf. stage
lever, 71, 105
levity, 17, 206
Lichtenberg, G. C., 45, 50
life, 9, 29, 94, 96, 182, 205, 219, 220, 221, 222
ligation, 43
light, *12–25*, 117, 174; activity, 33; and colour, *135–160*, 162, crystal, 123, 171, dimming, 141, flame, 91, gravity, 218, heat, 91, illumination, 135, prism, 150; as element, 160; corpuscles, 19, 141; differentiated, 165; electric, 165, 166, 167, 169, 170, 171; galvanic, 203; Goethe's theory, *148*; Newton's theory, *20, 139*, oscillation, 19; particles, 17; passive, 36; pervasion by, 156; primary, 9; propagation, 18, 20, 130; rays, 17, 23, 144; reflection, *22–25*, 135, 155, 167; refraction, 13, 20, *125–135*, 155; selfhood, 54, 55, 121; self-substantiating, 93; stimulation, 104; subjective, 203; waves, 19; weight of, 19
lightening (of silver), 158
lighter (pneumatic tinder-box), 38
lightning, 44, 52, 170, 180
lime, 124, 186, 204, 207, 209, 216, 218
line, 74, 92, 97–98, 100, 115; of crystal, 114; lineality, 89; linear activity, 111; linearity, 63, 100, 107, 110, 112, 113
Linnaeus, C. von, 32
lips, 203
liquid, 171
litmus, 159
living: being, 189, 219; creature, 160; existence, 108; process, 181
Livy, T., 53
loadstone, 103
logic, 11, 27, 116, 165, 200; logical progression, 178
London, 59
luminescence, 52
luminosity, 20
lunar matter, 52
lunatic, 29
lustre, 159, 197, 220
lye (alkaline), 203

Madagascar, 115
magensia, 124, 209, 218

magnet, 101, 109, 166, 211, 212
magnetic: disposition, 180; matter, 102; needle, 99, 105, 174, 180; pole, 102, 109
magnetism, 58, 62, *99–111*, 113, 165, 170, 174, 175, 179, 182, 195
magneto–electro–chemism, 107
malleability, 63, 104
materiality, 190; materiature, 92, 93, 222
matter: and animation, 108, fire, 91, form, 55, 71, 94, 108, gravity, 54, 55, heat, 82, 85; calorific, 86; category, 85; combustible, 163; dark, 22, 156; electrical, 169, 170; immediacy of, 91; individuality of, 9, 108; modal condition of, 85; negative 67; notion of, 54; of light, 17; penetrability, 92; primary, 12; qualified, 21; subjective, 43, 94, 100; weighted, 55, 87, 92, 117, 199
mechanical: activity, 174; being, 174; cohesion, 165; compounding, 96; contact, 166, 169; determination, 40, 45, 65, 81; disturbance, 88; effect, 167; force, 38; friction, 90, 91; impression, 156; independence, 166; individuality, 119; inertia, 167; interruption, 74; light, 71; manner, 68; mass, 114; materiality, 119; neutrality, 122; penetration, 123; physics, 37; point of view, 43; pressure, 40, 177; property, 126; relation, 166; relationship, 164; response, 62; self-preservation, 165; sphere, 70, 72, 75, 95; tension, 168; totality, 119, 157, 165, 171; treatment, 118; unity, 123
mechanics, 42, 55, 95, 141, 168
mechanism, 96, 106, 116
mechanizing: activity, 168; geometry, 63
mediation, 16, 83, 152, 200, 203, 211
mediatory colour, 152
medium (physical), 125, 183
medius terminus, 200
melody, 75, 83
melting, 88, 184; point, 88
memory, 18
mercury, 32, 117; calxes, 199; oxide, 199; cf. quicksilver
Mercury (planet), 27, 31
meridian, 103, 105
metabasis, 44
metal, 158, 208; and acid, 186, 210, atmosphere, 52, chemical attack, 200, chemical process, 162, colour, 120, 122, 136, 137.

221, combination, 200, electricity, 179, galvanism, 192, 193, 197, 199, 205, heat, 86, 137, specific gravity, 32, 90, 124, 187, 192, 197, 199, transmission of sound, 70, water, 163, 214; classification, 218–219; cohesion, 199; conductor of heat, 84; conductor of electricity, 171, 175, 193; crystallization, 116; density, 199; ductility, 65; implicit, 221; internal shape, 97; magnetization, 103; neutrality, 200, 221; opacity, 123; ore, 163; oxidation, 187, 189, 200, 210, 221; precious, 162, 198, 199; pure, 216; ring of, 71, 73; salt, 221; smell, 161, 162, 221; specific gravity, 136

metal oxide, 189, 204, 205, 209

metallic: amalgam, 183; atmosphere, 151; base, 204; calx, 207; element, 204; principle, 136; salt, 124; series, 31, 64; surface, 172

metallicism, (32), 157, 159, 191, 199, 204, 205, 218

metalloid, 193, 198, 204, 214

metallurgy, 158, 184

metaphysics, 67, 86, 87, 103, 141, 154, 213, 214

meteor, 26, 27, 53

meteorology, 11, 42–54, 59, 169, 180, 181, 187

mica, 124

midday, 180

mineral kingdom, 171

mirage, 135

mirror, 22, 24, 85, 134

mist, 45

mixture, 183; mixing (of colours), 146

mode, 42, 62, 64, 71, 107, 191; condition, 85; of activity, 207, alteration, 183, existence, 221, iron, 221, production, 136, sensation, 119

moisture, 44, 49, 163

molecule, 66, 116, 134, 194

Möller, J. N., 98

monochord, 75

monochromatic (part of spectrum), 139

monocotyledon, 32

monotone, 76

Moon, 26–27, 28, 29, 31, 48, 123; –light, 143

motion, 12, 66, 67, 71, 107, 108, 109, 114, 164, 173, 174

mountain, 52, 73, 91; air, 47; blue, 221; chain, 51

mouth, 203

Muncke, G. W., 173

Munich, 46; Academy, 202

muriatic: acid, 184, 217; copper oxide, 221

muscle, 72, 200, 201

music, 75, 78; theory of, 81

muslin, 149

naphtha, 89, 206, 217

natron, 204

natural science, 43

nature, 10, 12, 14, 19, 32, 33, 40, 97, 104, 169, 173, 181, 185, 195, 220; activity of, 113; purposiveness of, 114; system of, 109

navigation, 109

nebulae, 21

negative, 169, 171, 209

neptunism, 51

nerve, 20, 201

neutral, 206; body, 216, 219; colour, 152; point, 102

neutrality, 34, 39, 118, 163, 210; neutralization, 185, 221

Newton, I., 18, 30, 139, 142, 143, 144, 146, 147, 153, 154

nickel, 53, 103

night, 48, 142, 149; —watchman's song, 144

nightingale, 83

nisus, 92, 93

nitric acid, 184, 217

nitrogen, 35, 185, 187, 190, 204, 217

node (of vibration), 74

noise, 68, 166

non-magnetism, 105

north pole, 99–105, 110, 170, 174, 180, 211, 212

northern lights, 52, 180

nose, 169

note (musical), 75, 145

nuclear shape, 113, 115

number, 75

numerical: ratio, 79; relationship, 74

occludence, 90

occult qualities, 170

odour, 37, 40, 118, 119, 151, 161–162, 163, 169, 174, 179

Oersted, H. C., 174, 180

oil, 41, 117, 124, 130, 133, 161

opacity, 21, 24, 36, 121, 122, 123, 124, 159, 220

opal, 149
optics, 18
ore, 163
organ (musical), 77, 80, 145
organic: being, 31, 37, 97, 118, 122, 162, 164, 170; factors, 210; nature, 220; process, 188; shape, 97; sphere, 159
organism, 83, 220, 222
oriental intuition, 17
oscillation, 13, 68, 73, 74, 164
osmium, 199
oval line, 98
oven (iron), 105
oxidation, 118, 173, 200; and acid, 39, 161, colour, 221, galvanism, 192, 204, 205; degrees of, 213; of iron, 104, metals, 198, 218, 221, nitrogen, 187
oxidized metal, 159, 198, 204, 218, 221
oxygen: and air, 35, 46, 47, 187, galvanism, 192, metal, 161, 202, 204, Volta's pistol, 177, water, 35, 187, 193–194; atmospheric, 210; classification, 190, 214, 217; element, 185, 187
oxygenation, 209

palladium, 199
parabola, 28
Paracelsus, 32, 117
parents, 9
paroptic colour, 156, 158
Parry, W. E., 48, 52, 105, 180
particle, 68, 83, 172
passion, 75
passivity, 85, 86
past (the), 18, 181
pendulum, 106
penetration, 123, 152; penetrability, 38, 92
penumbra, 151
perfection (metallic), 198
permeation, 218
perpendicularity (of elevation), 131
personality, 184
pervasion (of medium by base), 152
petrification, 52
phenomenology, 173; appearance, 44
philosophy, 17, 30, 32, 34, 47, 100, 103, 107, 108, 109, 141, 142, 154, 181, 195, 196; of nature, 62, 71, 88, 99, 101–102, 113
phonic substance, 73
phosphorescence, 16, 206
phosphorus, 122, 190, 206, 214

phrenology, 212
physics, 9, 11, 55, 94; physical inertia, 167
physiology, 137, 153
pianoforte, 77, 145
Pictet. M. A., 85
pigeon, 156
pigment, 120, 146, 156, 158
piston, 38, 75
pitch (musical), 19, 73, 79
plane, 74, 97, 100, 112, 114, 115
planet, 15, 16, 28, 29, 30, 31, 33, 181
plant, 15, 35, 83, 152, 158, 173
platinum, 64, 198, 199
Plato, 148, 177
plumage, 83
Pohl, G. F., 173, 193
point, 9, 11, 18, 30, 53, 55, 65, 67, 88, 92, 97, 98, 100, 101, 102, 115, 121, 125, 169, 176, 186
poison, 162
polarity, 23, 99, 101, 109, 175
polarization, 23, 141, 167
poles: acid and alkali, 194; hydrogen and oxygen, 182–194, 200; magnetic, 58, 99–110, 111, 114, 166, 174
poor metal, 207
porcelain jasper, 218
pore, 43, 57, 58, 61, 67, 73
positive, 209; electricity, 169, 171
potash, 197, 204, 207, 218
powder, 124, 218–219
power, 12
precious metal, 162, 198, 199
precipitate, 221
pressure, 13, 40, 62, 88, 137, 156, 172, 199
presupposition, 56, 188, 215, 220, 222
primary colour, 152
prism, 115, 138, 140, 143, 144, 145, 146, 147, 150, 151, 152
probability (theory of), 27
process: chemical, 16, 31, 88, 95, 121, 162, 163, 164, 173, 174, 177, 178, 188, 189, 205, 216, 219, 222; electrical, 109, 168, 186, 189; galvanic, 177, 181, 182, 190, 192, 200, 204, 206, 213; totality of, 210
professionals, 154
progression: arithmetical, 78; logical, 178
propagation: light, 20; sound, 70
property, 117, 222
protoxide (of tin), 213
pull, 64
pulverization, 82, 155

puncticity, 27, 218; punctiformity, 89, 113, 115, 135, 137, 155, 157; punctuality, 63
pupil (of eye), 154
purpose, 97, 114; purposiveness (of nature), 114
pyramid, 134
pyrites (magnetic), 104
Pythagoras, 32, 75, 76

quadrature, 28
quicksilver, 31, 46, 49, 60, 89, 184, 197, 198, 199, 201, 204
quiescence, 96, 114

radical, 191, 197, 217
rain, 45, 49, 50, 52, 170
rainbow, 158
ray (of light), 17, 23, 144
reagent, 205
reason, 37, 117, 148
receptivity, 169
recursion, 74
refining (of metal), 184
reflection (of light), 22–25, 135, 155, 167
refraction (of light), 13, 20, 125–133, 155; angle of 131; double, 133–135
refrangibility, 145
regulus (metallic), 104, 162, 187, 190, 198, 204, 216, 218, 221
relativity, 209
religion, 19; religiosity, 15
repulsion, 61, 82, 108, 111, 113, 168, 175
reservoir, 52
residuum, 200
resin, 44, 171, 172, 198, 201; resinous electricity, 167, 171
resistance, 62, 65
resonance, 71
retort, 44
revolving disc (Newton's), 144
Richter, J. B., 103, 210, 212
rigidity, 26, 27, 28, 32, 48, 53, 63, 71, 81, 82, 83
ring (colour), 155
ring (sound), 69, 71, 220
Ritter, J. W., 46, 182, 199, 204
rock-crystal, 115, 124
rotation, 16, 44, 106, 110; Erman's circuit, 110
rough sea (colour), 154
rubber, 44
Rumford, Count, 85, 86

Russian horn music, 145
rust, 186

sage (plant), 153
sailor, 44
St. Gotthard pass, 115
sal ammoniac, 201
salinity, 163, 206
salt: acid and base, 211–212, 216; and chemical process, 186, 191, electricity, 171, magnetism, 104, water, 118, 163; as product, 211, 212; classification, 217–218; colour, 221; combination, 196; crystallinity, 116; dissolution, 40, 204; element, 32; formation, 208–210; heat, 216; neutrality, 186, 191, 207, 216
Santa Cruz, 83
satellite, 20, 26
saturation, 179, 184, 195, 210, 211
Saturn, 31
Saussure, H. B. de, 45
scale (musical), 76, 77
scales, 145
scar, 29
Schelling, F. W. J. von, 31, 62, 64, 158, 175, 199
Schiller F. von (quoted), 160
scholastics, 170
Schulz, C. F. L., 122, 152, 154
Schuster, J. C., 209
Schweigger, J. S. C., 200, 213
scientific form, 214
scoria, 219
sealing wax, 44, 154, 171, 172
sea-level, 60
season, 48, 182
sea water, 218
seed, 173
semi-metal, 104
semi-tone, 77
sensation, 119, 203
sense, 118, 119, 161, 165, 200
sentience, 96, 119, 160
separation, 213–218
serpentine rock, 104
shade, 20, 140, 152
shadow, 139, 143, 152, 153; line, 151
shape, 96–98
sheen, 83, 158
shock (electric), 167, 168
shooting (of fish), 127
shooting star, 26, 52

Siberia, 53
sidereal power, 29
sight, 119, 149, 160
silica, 32, 124, 204, 209, 218
silk, 172, 173
silver, 31, 65, 73, 158, 183, 184, 190, 197, 198, 199, 202, 203, 204, 215
sine, 132
sky, 44, 170; black of, 149; blue of, 143, 152, 153; brightness of, 155
sleep, 29
smell, 117, 119, 160, 162, 168, 169, 221
smelting, 71
smoke, 149
Snellius. W., 131
snow, 52, 91
soapy water, 200
softness, 68
soft solder, 68
solar: eclipse, 182; system, 9, 17, 28, 33
solubility, 118, 163
sonority, 74, 81
soul: and body, 114, crystal, 96, 115, 123, fire, 222, form, 83, fusion, 83, hearing, 119, life, 96, light, 123, 177, materiature, 169, pervasion, 55, sound, 92; inner, 71; mouse, 131
sound, 19, 57, 69–82, 87, 164, 165, 166
south pole, 99, 102, 104, 110, 174, 211, 212
space, 12, 13, 58, 67, 100, 107, 130; content of, 57; generation of, 14
spatial: attraction, 168; forms, 63; repulsion, 168
spatiality, 92, 100, 107
specific: coherence, 199; cohesion, 70; density, 183; dimension, 63; *gravity*, 57–61, 92, 220; and coherence, 64, cohesion, 92, crystal shape, 116, elasticity, 66, heat, 84, 87, 88, 89, illumination, 137, matter, 92, opacity, 124, oxidation, 187, 197, shape, 157, sight, 129, 131, synsomation, 183, 184, transparency, 124; alteration of, 87, 88; as form, 89; change of, 74; continuity in, 84, 104; in organics, 90; negation of, 69, 85; of air, 51, chemical body, 221, mass, 106, metal, 32, 90, 124, 187, 192, 197, 199, physical medium, 125, water, 131; *heat*, 88; motion, 108; quantity, 210; weight, 45, 59, 61, 93, 132, 183
spectre, 21, 146
spectrum, 122, 146, 152

sphere (metaphysical), 11, 12, 18, 20, 43, 44, 51, 70, 71, 72, 75, 81, 92, 95, 111, 116, 118, 119, 136, 142, 159, 160, 168, 175, 178, 179, 217, 221, 222
sphere (shape), 97, 103, 113, 132, 176; sphericity, 113
spinal nerve, 201
spirit, 31, 39, 44, 114, 158; spiritualization, 128
Spix, J. B., 83
sponge, 169, 170
spring (water), 51, 52
stage (metaphysical), 43, 165, 181, 189, 190, 192, 214, 216; cf. level; 32.7
star, 15, 16, 21, 28
steam, 38, 40, 89
steel, 65, 68, 104, 158
Steffens, H., 31, 64, 186, 199, 209
stimulation, 33, 104, 178, 201, 204
stoichiometry, 212
stone, 53, 84, 97, 171, 217; slab, 72
storm, 49, 52, 170, 180
stratus cloud, 52
stream, 47
stretching, 65
strontian, 207, 209
subjective colour, 122; image, 153; unity, 181
substratum, 107, 174
suffocation, 187
sulphur: and acid, 190, 207, 216, air, 207, base, 216, fire, 190, scoria, 219, water, 207; brittleness, 198; classification, 136, 214, 215; combustibility, 205, 206, 217; electricity, 171, 172, 213; element, 32, 218; matter, 162; molten, 172, 213
sulphuret of potash, 209; sulphuric acid, 200, 207, 208, 209, 217, 218,
sultriness, 51
summer, 46, 47, 48, 52, 91, 155
Sun, 9, 15, 27, 28, 29, 31, 48, 60, 91, 102, 122, 167, 169, 170, 181; sunbeam, 23, 141; sunlight, 15, 24, 143, 149, 167, 169, 206
surface, 21, 22, 24, 85, 92, 98, 113, 115, 172; force, 64; pressure, 166; superficity, (63), 89
Swabia, 161
Swinden, J. H. van, 105
Swiss: Alps, 152; mountains, 46
syllogism, 29, 62, 99, 101, 175, 186, 192, 200, 207, 216

symbolism (of colours), 153
symmetry, 75, 176
synsomation, 183, 184, 191, 221
syzygy, 28

talc, 124, 218
tar, 90
Tartini, G., 74, 80
taste, 39, 40, 118, 119, 160, *163–164*, 168, 169, 174, 179, 200, 203, 221
teleology, 219
telescope, 28, 140
telluric cause, 60
temperature, 48, 49, 87, 88, 89, 91, 152, 184, 195, 211, 216
tenacity, 63
tension, 48, 49, 50, 75, 174, 176, 178, 180, 213; electrical, 165, 166, 167, 168, 170, 175
tensioned: bodies, 177; conflict, 192; extremities, 175; light, 165, 169,
textbook, 125, 132, 140, 190
texture: crystal, 115; metal, 219
thermal: capacity, 87, 89, 90; increase and decrease, 48
thermometer, 59
thirst, 28, 182, 189
thought, 14, 19, 67, 93, 108, 117, 119, 131
thunder, 50; storm, 49, 50, 51
tide, 28
timbre, 70
time, 20, 30, 38, 39, 67, 71, 217, 222
tin, 31, 73, 116, 184, 200, 202; -foil, 203; oxides, 213
tinder, 38
tongue, 203
tone (musical), 69, 70, 72, 73, 77
Töpel, Töplitz, 59
touch, 72, 119, 120, 160
tourmaline, 176
trade-wind, 52
transition, 11, 22, 40, 43, 72, 86, 92, 134, 161, 164, 189, 191, 218, 220, 221, 222
translucency, 28, 124
transmission of: electricity, 168, 169, 175, 192, 202; heat, 83, 84, 85, 86, 87, 88, 89, 190; an image, 134; light, 20, 22; sound, 70, 71, 73
transparency, 13, 24, 36, *121–124*, 136, 137,

143, 149, 150, 155, 157, *167*, 170, 220, 221
tree, 149
tremor, 72
tremulation, 74
triad, 117, 216
Trommsdorff, J. B., 186, 198
tropical bird, 83
tropics, 83
truth, 17, 222
turpentine (oil of), 132
twilight, 144, 153

undulation, 98, 156
unison, 75

vapour, 45, 198
vascular system, 196
vegetable, 186; acid, 217; consistituent, 34; material, 199–200; oil 217; substance, 172, 214
velocity, 12, 71
Venus, 27, 31
verticality, 65
vibration of: body, 68; cohesion, 105; heat, 90; matter, 74; sound, 20, 69, 70, 72, 73, 166; strings, 74, 75, 76, 79, 80
Vienna, 59, 60
vinegar, 90
violin, 72
virgin earth, 32
virtue, 47
visibility, 22, 24, 126, 133; vision, 177
vitreous electricity, 167, 171; vitrified metal, 129; vitriol, 124, 132,
Vogler, G. J., 80
voice, 72
volatilization, 161, 164, 177
volcano, 27, 50, 51
Volta, A., 201, 202; voltaic pile, 108, 193, 194, 197, 202; Volta's pistol, 177
volume, 57, 58, 59, 68, 125
vulcanism, 51

water: adhesion, 63; and acid, 186, 207, 208, air, 208; alcohol, 183, chemical process, 39, 189, 202, crystal of Earth, 52, earth, 217, electricity, 177, 202, galvanism, 201, metal, 186, 214, oxidation, 201, salt, 217, stone, 217, transmission of sound, 72, Volta's pistol, 177; as bond, 207, insulator, 202, 203, medium, 192, 210; base, 206; cohesion, 70, 218; conductor, 203; decomposition, 177; density, 132; diremption, 187; element, *39–41*, 44, 118, 123, 215; formation, 177; germ, 97; neutrality, 52, 185, 189; opacity, 124; process, *208–210*; production, 216; realization, *217*; refractive power, 132; salt content, 192; synsomation, 183; tone, 70, 72; transparency, 128; volume, 59; weight, 59, 61

watering (of metal), 116

water-system, 73

wave-theory (of light), 20

wax, 172

weather, 29, 104; -vane, 105

weight, 57, 58, 60, 63, 68, 85, 86, 114, 183; -ratio, 213; weighted matter, 55, 87, 92, 117, 199; weightedness, 70

Weimar, 59

welding, 202

Werner, A. G., 115

whalebone, 73, 110

white, 124, 144, 173, 221

wind, 49, 52

wine, 30, 90

wing, 98

winter, 46, 48

Winterl, J. J., 183, 206

wire (iron), 65

wolfram, 204

Wollaston, W. H., 200, 202, 212

wood, 16, 64, 86, 88, 90, 91, 149, 159, 177

wool, 84, 172, 173

world (creation of), 46

Zeno, 67

zero, 89

zinc, 197, 198, 199, 204

Abernethy, J., 431
accident, 440
achromaticism, 358, 359
Achterberg, E., 225
acid: and base, 429; oxygen, 428
acidum sanguinis, 438
Ackermann, J. F., 262, 431
Adams, G., 231
Adamson, R., 362
Adsiger, P., 312
Aepinus, F. M. U. T., 395
aerolite, 278
affinity (chemical), 385
aggregation (crystalline), 330
agriculture, 228
Aikin, A. and C. R., 352, 383, 398, 403, 441,
    420, 424, 425, 439
air: composition, 272; definition, 258
Alberti, C. E., 308
Aldini, G., 414, 416, 417, 418
Aldis, W. S., 229
Alfano, G. B., 388
Alfieri, V., 228
Algol, 227
Allard, M., 335
Allemann, G. A., 257
Allix, J. A. F., 227
Altenstein, K. F. S., 338
alum crystal, 334, 439
alumina, 427
amalgam, 403
amber, 266
American song-birds, 300
ammonia, 421
Ampère, A. M., 311, 393
Anaxagoras, 257, 258
andronia, 400, 401
animal: electricity, 412, 416, 417, 418, 420;
    magnetism, 321; prophecy, 274
Anquetil Duperron, A. H., 224
aqua regia, 404, 411
Aquinas, St Thomas, 308
Arago, D. F. J., 234, 238, 240, 242, 243, 260,
    323, 325, 349, 374, 381

Archer-Hind, R. D., 287, 396
archetypal phenomenon, 370, 372
Archimedes, 402, 403
Aristotle, 256, 257, 258, 260, 265, 266, 288,
    289, 306, 366, 440
Arnhold, E., 364, 372
Arnold, T. J., 356
arsenic oxide, 424
artist (and Goethe's theory of colour), 369
Ash, J., 414
astronomy, 409
atheism, 254
atmosphere: lunar, 244; planetary, 247
atomic theory, 406, 434
attraction and repulsion, 279, 280
aurora borealis, 275
Austin, W., 421
Avogadro, A., 231, 438
axial rotation, 243

Baader F. X., 304
Babbitt F. C., 289
Babitz, 293
Bach, J. C., 296
Bach, J. S., 289
Bächtold-Stäubli H., 226
Bacon, F., 269
Badcock, J., 335
Baeumker, C., 260
Bähr, J. K., 369
Bain. W., 322
Bakewell, F. C., 386
Balfour, F., 250, 275
ballooning, 226
Bancroft, E. N., 352
Banks, J., 300, 324, 415
barometer, 275
Bartholin, R., 235, 239, 350
Bartoldy, G. W., 430
Bartsch, K., 225
basalt (magnetism of), 316
battery (electric), 271
Baumgartner, A. von, 317

Bayreuth, 315
Bechstein, J. M., 298, 378
Beckmann, J., 395
Beddoes, T., 303
Bengol, 275
Benner, A., 412
Bennet, A., 389
Berard, J. E., 261
Bergmann, T. O., 255, 314
Berkeley, G., 230
Berlin: Academy, 284; University, 363; weather, 372
Berlin, J. D., 290
Bermudo, F. J., 291
Bernhardi, J. J., 329, 333
Bernoulli, D., 287, 347
Bernoulli, J., 347
Berthollet, C. L., 284, 318, 385, 398, 401, 404, 405, 421, 425, 427, 428, 430, 433
Berzelius, J. J., 315, 329, 376, 384, 388, 389, 407, 409, 410, 427, 429, *432*, 433, 434, 435, 438, 441
Bessel, F. W., 323
Bessemer, H., 318
Bestuscheff, Count, 367
Beyer, H., 255
Biedermann, W., 373
Billiard, F. J. M. A., 331
Biot, J. B., 226, 231, 239, 240, 243, 260, 276, 277, *285*, 293, 295, 313, 323, 340, 347, 348, 349, 351, 361, 362, 378, 381, 389, 391, 392, 409, 410, 416, 419
Birch T., 265
Black, John, 433
Black, J., 272
Blackadder, H. H., 352
Blankenburg, W., 365
Blair, R., 360, 370
Blein, A. F. A., 295
Blöde, K. A., 410
blood acid, 438
Blum, R., 388
Blumhof, (J. G. L.), 332
Bobertag, F., 233
Bode, J. E., 227, 224, 250, 251; law, 250
Boehme, F. M., 365
Boehme, J., 257, 336
Boerhaave, H., 416
Boetzmann, F., 308
Bollak, J., 258
Bonnet, C., 268
Boorde, A., 233

Borda, J.C., 312
Borneo, 309
Boscowich, R. J., 231
Bose, E. G., 235
Bouguer, 340, 376
Boumann, L., 369, 377
Bower, A., 289
Boyd, J., 277
Boyer, C. B., 235
Boyle, R., 231, 260, 261, 370
Bradley, J., 237, 238
Brahe T., 225, 235
Brandt, G., 314, 315
Bratranek, F. T., 364, 371
Brazil, 299, 316
Breuning, H. J., 337
Brewster, D., 240, 279, 321, 349, 351, 360, 369, 381, 382, 388, 390, 395
Briggs, H., 362
Brooke, H. J., 328, 333
Browne, T., 282, 306
Brücken, E., 369
Brugmans, A., *319*, 320
Brugnatelli, L. V., 386
Brunnmark, G., 433
Brydone, P., 352
Buchan, A. P., 352
Bucholz, C. F., 314, 401, 438
Buée, A. Q., 332
Burnet, J., 258, 441
Burney, C., 287, 293
Burthogge, R., 306
Busby, T., 289
Buttmann, P., 266
Büttner, C. W., 358, 411
Bywater, I., 267, 441

calcination (of metal), 302
calculus (differential), 362
Callisen, A. C. P., 285
calx, 383
camera obscura, 231
Camerarius, R. J., 371
Campe, J. H., 233
Camper, P., 235
Canton, J., 312, 394, 395
Capadose, H., 431
carbonic acid, 425
Carlisle, A., 271, 409
Carlyle, T., 356
Carminati, 471, 418

Catnot, N. L. S., 261, 263
Carpi, Dr., 317
Carradori, G., 417
Carrière, J., 433
Carthenser, J. F., 371
Casper, M., 251, 252, 256
Cassini, J., 230
Cassini, J. D., 235, 243
Cassini, J. J. D., 312
Catherine (the Great), 304
catoptric colour, 394
Cavallo, T., 312, 386, 393, 412, 417
Cavendish, H., 270, 397, 428
Cesare, G., 319
Chance, B., 380
Changeux, P. N. de, 328
Chaptal, J. A. C., 422, 433
charcoal (as conductor), 413
Charles VI, 292
chemical: affinity, 385, change; 416; colour,
    339; combination, 430
chemism, 323
Chenevix, R., 314, 401, 441
Chevreul, M. E., 433
Children, J. G., 419, 433
Chinese compass, 311
Chladni, E. F., 278, 281, 282, *283*, 284, 285,
    286, 287, 387
Chladni's figures, 286
Christie, S. H., 317
circuit (Erman's rotation), 325
Clairault, A. C., 248
Clarke, S., 357, 370
clavicylinder, 283
cleavage nucleus (crystalline), 328, 330
Cless, H. D. von, 272
Cliff, B., 352
climate (influence of), 250
cloud, (types), 276
Clouston, W. A., 233
cobalt (purification), 314
Cohen, I. B., 229, 235, 253
cohesion (transition to sound), 281
cohesive property, 280
cold (Pictet's experiment), 301
Coleridge, S. T., 255
Collet-Descotils, H. V., 412
collision (of clouds), 389
Cologne pipes, 285
Colombia, 309
colophony, 387
colour: and metal, 352; Goethe's and

Newton's theories, 348, 353, 380;
    primary, 366; -square, 355; subjective,
    356; wave theory, 366
coloured light, 366
Combe G., 431
combination (chemical), 430
combination tone, 292
combustion, 262; spontaneous, 304–305
comet, 246; Halley's, 248; nucleus, 248;
    orbit, 248, 251
cometary collision, 246, 249
comma (musical), 290
Compagnoni, G., 228
compass: Chinese, 311; variation, 322
conductor (electric), 324
constant proportions (law of), 385
Constantine, V., 289
Conti, Abbé., 388
Conybeare, F. C., 255
Cooper, M., 268
copper (oxides of), 441
Cornford, F. M., 288, 396
corpuscle (light), 232
Costa, P., 319
Coulomb, C. A. de, 313, 395
Cousineau, P. J., 291
Cranz, H. J. N., 400
Crawford, A., 302, 387
Crell, L. F. F. von, 318, 385
Creve, J. C. I. A., 413
Croll, O., 256
Cronstedt, A. F., 314
crystal: aggregation, 330; cleavage nucleus,
    330; molecule decrement, 333; outer
    form, 330; rational indices, 332; structure,
    307, 328, 330, 334
crystallinity (of Earth), 339
crystallization, 327; electricity, 328; mag-
    netism, 328; water, 384
cube, 348
Cullen, C., 421
culmination (point), 320
current (electric), 311, 323
Cushing, H., 418
Cuthbertson, J., 397
Cuvier, G., 333
Czernischev, I., 304, 305

Dahl, B. T., 254
Dalberg, J. F. H., 277, 287, 289
Daniell, J. F., 335

Dalton, J., 259, 261, 264, 270, 276, 384, 406, 407, 430, 433, 434
Dalyell, J. G., 368
D'Arcet, J., 403, 404
Darracq, 405, 427
Daubenton, L. J. M., 332
Davy, H., 271, 303, 317, 324, 327, 406, 410, 413, 415, 419, 421, 423, 429, 433, 435, 438
Davy, J., 415, 423
Dechales, C. F. M., 347
declination (of magnetic needle), 312
decomposition (of water), 409
Deiman, J. R., 270, 323
Delambre, J. B. J., 321
Delaroche, F., 261
Delaval, E. H., 352
Delisle, J. N., 374
Deluc, J. A., 266, 268, 269, 270, 278, 387, 419
demagnetization, 317
Deneker, O., 371
'De Orbitis Planetarum', 251
dephlogisticated air, 263
Descartes, R., 313, 345, 347
Deschamps, B., 367
Desormes, C. B., 405
dialectic, 225, 309
diamond cutting, 331
Dibner, B., 393
Diels, H., 258, 267, 289
diffraction: grating, 353; of light, 374
dimming, 355, 376
dioptric colour, 349
Dirksen, H. W., 250
Diruf, C. J., 278
dispersion (of light), 360
divergency (of light), 360
Dizé, M. J. J., 404
Dizi, F. J., 291
Dlabacz, G. J., 368
Döbereiner, J. W., 240
Dodson, J., 313
Dollond, J., 359
Dominis, A. de, 376
Don Pedro, 299
Doren, C. van, 387
double refraction, 229, 239, 348, 349, 350
Dove, H. W., 367
Drieberg, F. von, 289
dry electric pile, 419
Du Chesne, J., 256, 336
Dufay, C. F., 385
Duhamel, J. P. F., 379

Dulong, P. L., 261, 287, 304, 330
Dumotiez, M., 262
Dunn, S., 244
Düntzer, H., 338, 339
Dupin, C., 351
Düring, I., 256
dye, 352

Earth: crystallinity, 339; magnetism, 313, 322
earth sciences, 307
Eastlake, C. L., 369
Echtermeyer, T., 366
eclipse, (solar), 399
Egyptian music, 290
Einstein, A., 229
electricity: and crystallization, 328, magnetism, 325; animal, 406–418, 420; atmospheric, 266; colour, smell, taste of, 386; conduction, 324; laboratory, 388–389; of molten sulphur, 390–391, tourmaline, 310; physiological, 271; trans-mission, 409; vitreous and resinous, 385
electrochemistry, 324, 434
electrodynamics, 311
electro-magnetism, 392
electrometer, 389
element, 257, 258, 263, 265; Aristotelian, 256; definition, 435, 436; fire, 266
elevation (perpendicularity of), 342–346, 367
Elhuyar, F., and J. J., de, 421
Ellis, A. J., 295
Empedocles, 257, 258
Empress Elizabeth, 367
enharmonic music, 290
entomology, 367
entoptic colour, 349, 350, 378
epoptic colour, 349
equivalent (chemical), 430
Erard, S., 291
Erigena, John Scotus, 308
Erk, L., 365
Erman, P., 262, 315, 325, 326
Ersch, J. S., 246
Erxleben, J. C. P., 263, 269, 275
Eschenbach, C. G., 319, 320
Esslinger, Me., 434
ether, 230, 242
eudiometer, 272
Euler, L., 234, 242, 244, 287, 313, 340, 359, 377,

euphon, 283
Everett, C. C., 362
Ewing, J. A., 318

Fabricius, D., 227
Fabricius, J. C., 254
Falconer, W., 250
family, 398
Faraday, M., 264, 271, 287, 311, 327
Farquhar, J., 275
fata morgana, 351
feather (colour), 378
Fechner, G. T., 364
feeling (and colour), 377
Ferguson, J., 388
Fermat, P., 347
Fichte, J. G., 254
figures, (Lichtenberg), 386
Fikentscher, F. C., and W. K., 372, 373
Fischer, E. G., 267, 430
Fischer, H., 337, 367, 383
fire: and time, 437; -ball, 278; element, 263
fits (Newtonian), 229, 361
fixed polarization, 239
Flaugergues, H., 374
folia (passage of), 349
Fontana, F., 417
Forkel, J. N., 289, 290
Forster, E. S., 266
Forster, J. R., 387
Forster, L., 380
fossil, 333
Fothergill, A., 305
Fourcroy, A. F., 383, 401, 405, 412, 424, 425, 437
Fourier, J. B. J., 287
Fournier, d'Albe, E. F., 311
Fowler, R., 417, 420
Franklin, B., 234, 266, 276, 302, 365, 387, 390, 396, 397
Fraunhofer, J., 234, 353, 374, 381
Frederick, I. (Württemberg), 337
freezing water (pressure), 264
French, J., 388
frequency ratio (musical), 290
Fresnel, A. J., 229, 234, 235, 240, 242, 243, 351, 364, 374, 381
Freygang, W. von, 278
friction, 277
friendship (Newtonian), 370
Fries, J. F., 280

Froriep, R., 307
Fulton, W., 418

Gadolin, J., 304
Gage, W. L., 255
Galen, P. van, 323
Galilei, V., 252, 291
Galileo, 235, 238
Gall, F. J., 285, 430, *431*
Galvani, L., 412, 413, 416, 417, 418, 420
galvanism, 271, 285, 407
Gänsbacher, J. B., 296
gas, 231, 260
Gay-Lussac, L. J., 226, 260, 261, 271, 334, 409, 433
Geer, C. de, 367
Gehlen, A. F., 314, 400, 401, 409, 414
Gehler, J. S. T., 226, 244, 245, 259, 264, 265, 269, 273, 280, 284, 304, 305, 317, 332, 346, 347, 358, 375, 378, 386, 389, 392, 396, 399
Gellibrand, H., 312
Gelpke, A. H. C., 238, 251
geodesy, 323
geognosy, 246
geometry, 329
George, III., 300
Georgi, J. G., 305
Gerhard, C. A., 301
Germain, G., 300
German philosophy, 309
Gersdorff, A. T. von, 387
Gibbs, G., 317
Giesecke, C., 316
Gilbert, L. W., 226, 234, 241, 242, 250, 261, 262, 265, 271, 272, 276, 277, 278, 295, 304, 311, 313, 315, 317, 323, 325, 328', 329, 335, 352, 360, 365, 384, 386, 393, 398, 407, 408, 415, 419, 420, 429, 430
Gilbert, W., 312, 319
Girtanner, C., 302, 437
Glockner, H., 230, 244, 246, 263, 378, 382, 398, 407, 408
G. L. T., 252, 292
Gluck, C. W., 368
God, 336
Goethe, J. W. von, 240, 241, 243, 249, 254, 273, 274, 275, 276, 277, 279, 280, 293, 338, 339, 344, 348, 349, 350, 351, 353, 354, 355, 356, 357, 358, 359, 360, 361, 362, 363, 364, 366, 367, 368, 369, 370,

371, 372, 373, 375, 376, 377, 378, 379,
  380, 381
Goldsmith, O., 300
goniometer, 330
Goodricke, J., 227
Gordon, J., 431
Göttingen, 361
Göttling, J. F. A., 437
Götze, A., 421
Gouffès, J. A. M., 250
Gough, J., 295
Graham, G., 312
Grattan, W. H., 291
Graumann, J. P., 432
Gray, J., 265
Green, J., 307, 327
Green, R. M., 413, 416, 418
Greenland, 316
Gregory, D., 358
Greig, S., 304
Gren, F. A. K., 267, 268, 269, 270, 280, 288,
  301, 302, 314, 323, 340, 347, 360, 364,
  376, 383, 413, 414, 419, 428, 438
Gretschel, H. F., 361
Grimaldi, F. M., 374
Grimsel pass, 331
Grodzinski, P., 331
Gronau, C. L., 372
Grotthuss, T. von, 264, 409, 410
Gruber, J. G., 246
Gruber, Pastor, 438
Grundtvig, N. F. S., 253, 254
Guericke, O. von., 265
gunnery, 228
gunpowder, 264
Gunther, R. W. T., 412
Guyton de Morveau, L. B., 401, 405, 422,
  429

Haber, L. F., 424
Hagen, K. G., 259
Haldane, E. S., 257, 258, 260, 263, 288, 437
Hall, C. M., 359, 360
Haller, A. von, 260
Halley, E., 229, 246, 248, 249, 275, 313
Halvorsen, J. B., 308
Hampel, A. J., 367
Hann, J. von, 312
Hansteen, C., 276, 312, 322, 399
Hare, R., 389
harmonic interval, 287

harmony, 287
harp (history), 291
Harris, W., 424
Hassenfratz, J. H., 364
Hauy, R.-J., 286, 310, 328, 329, 330, 331,
  332, 333, 334, 390, 395
Hawkins, J., 292
heat: latent, 223, 272, 304; materiality of,
  302; Rumford's experiments, 302–303;
  specific, 304
Heath, T. L., 403
Hedenius, P., 433
Heeren, F., 336
Hegel: diary, 272
Hegelianism, 408
Heiberg, J. L., 403
Heidel, W. A., 289
Heim, J. L., 245, 246
Heintz, E., 354
Heisenberg, W., 368, 369, 380, 382
Hellmann, G., 312
Helmholtz, H. von, 295, 368, 380
Henning, L. von, 338, 350, 363, 364, 392
Henry IV (France), 336
Henry, W., 421
Heraclitus, 266, 267, 437, 441
Herder, J. G. von, 270
Hermbstädt, S. F., 427, 429, 437
hero, 344
Herschel, J. F. W., 240, 304
Herschel, W., 225, 226, 227, 238, 239, 243,
  244, 247, 248
Hessel, J. F. C., 332
Hevelius, J., 227
Heyse, G., 398
Higgins, W., 430
Hildebrand, B., 359
Hildebrandt, G. F., 259
Hillary, W., 302
Himly, J. F. W., 431
Hinrichs, J. C., 368
Hire, P. de la, 376
Hisinger, W., 314, 409, 432,
historicism, (Goethe's), 370
Hjelmslev, J. T., 403
Hoang-ti, 311
Hochbrucker, G., 291
Hoefer, J. C. F., 434
Hoffmann–Krayer, E., 226
Hoffmeister, J., 224, 228, 230, 247, 256, 272,
  312, 313, 323, 333, 362, 372, 375, 382, 407
Hogarth, W., 268

Holland, V., 255
Hollandus, J., 404
Holmberg, A., 434
Holtzendorff-Vietmannsdorf, F. von, 284
Holmes, T. W., 331
Homberg W., 232
Hooke, R., 233, 237, 241, 374
Hooykaas, R., 256
Hope, T. C., 301
Hoppe, J., 369
Hopson, C. R., 305
Hopkinson, F., 370
Horn, A., 339
horn music (Russian), 367
Hornstedt, C. F., 432
Hotham, D., 257
Howard, E. F., 277
Howard, L., 273, 274, 276, 277, 280
Huddart, J., 366
Huesmann, E., 255
Humboldt, A. von, 271, 311, 313, 315, 414, 418
Hutton, C., 266, 238, 244, 259, 263, 279, 342, 346, 347
Hutton, J., 268, 269, 270, 301
Huyghens, C., 229, 233, 234, 239, 242, 340, 345, 350, 374
Hwasser, I., 433
Hyde, T., 224
hydrochloric acid, 437
hydrogenation, 420
hydrometer, 320
hydrophane, 340
hygrometer, 268
hypothesis, 360

iatrochemistry, 256
ice, 384; formation, 263; island, 305; -spicula, 327
Iceland spar (double refraction), 350
impression method, 377
Indian music, 290
indifference (point of), 319
induction (of electricity), 394
infinity, 230, 253
inflection, 370, 374
influence machine, 227
Ingenhousz, J., 397
insulation, 390
integrality (of light), 223
interference, 378

iridium, 411
iron and steel industry, 318
Irvine, W., 304
Isle, J. B. L., de Romé de l', 307, 334
isomorphism, 333
Izarn, J., 261

Jacobi, E. R., 293
Jameson, R., 331
Jan, C., von, 256
jasper, 439
Jefferson, T., 363
Jeffrey, F., 431
Jeffries, D., 331
Jeffries, J., 226
Jöcher, C. G., 292
John VI (Portugal), 299
John, J. F., 439
Johnston, W. H., 223, 259, 260
Jorgensen, D., 293
Jupiter: atmosphere, 247; satellites, 235, 243

Kämtz, L. F., 279
Kanitz. A., 426
Kant, I., 279, 428
Karmarsch, K., 336
Karsten, C. J. B., 405
Karsten, D. L. G., 310, 332, 390
Karsten, W. J. G., 267, 387
Kästner, A. G., 347
Kastner, K. W. G., 267, 280, 295, 330
Kelly, J., 359
Kennedy, R., 424
Kepler, J., 231, 235, 251, 253, 256; laws, 251; son, 235
Kerr, R., 423, 427
Kiesewetter, K., 388
Kinsky, Count, 292
Kirby, W., 367
Kircher, A., 290, 294, 302, 376
Kirk, G. S., 267
Kirnberger, J. P., 252, 253, 292
Kirwan, R., 276, 385, 421, 427, 429
Kitaibel, P., 426
Kjelstrup, K., 308
Klaproth, J., 311
Klaproth, M. H., 285, 331, 334, 398, 405, 420, 421, 424, 430, 434, 436, 438
Klingenstjerna, S., 359
Klotz, M., 369

Knight, G., 279
Knoerzer, G., 387
Knox, T. M., 259
Koch, R., 255
Kohlschütter, V., 284
Kopp, H., 437
Körner, F., 240
Korteweg, D. J., 345
Kossel, W., 387
Köstlin, C. H., 397
Kotzebue A. von, 431
Koyré, A., 388
Kramer, P., 345
Kranz, W., 267
Kremer, H., 233
Kries, F. C., 248, 268, 377
Kuhn, D., 240, 273, 274, 276, 279, 338, 348, 350, 355, 358, 359, 361, 370, 375, 376, 377, 378, 379, 396

laboratory electricity, 388, 389
Lagrange, J. L., 294
Lalande, J. J., 246
Lambert, J. H., 250, 340
Lampadius, W. A., 270, 314, 388, 439
Lancaster, J., 322
Land, E. H., 354
Lane, T., 318
Laplace, P. S., 247, 251, 261, 265, 284
Lasson, G., 224, 228, 230, 238, 251, 232, 381
latency (of heat), 272, 304
Lavoisier, A. J., 263, 270, 384, 403, 405, 406, 423, 427, 428, 436, 437
Law, W., 336
Leade, J., 257
Leblanc, N., 334
Lebouvier-Desmontier, V. R. T., 262
Lee, F., 257
Leeuwenhoek, A., 319
Legendre, A. M., 321
Lémery, L., 395
Lémery, N., 424
Lenz, J. J., 240
lepidoptera, 367
Lessing, G. E., 308
Lévy, A., 333
Lewalter, J., 365
Lewes, G. H., 358, 370, 380
Lhomond, C. F., 332
Lichtenberg, G. C., 244, 246, 263, 264, 268, 269, 270, 275, 386, 387

Lichtenberg, L. C., 268
Liebe, F., 260
Liebig, J. von, 405, 433
life, 228
light: and magnetism, 317; corpuscle, 232; electric, 226; Hegel's views on, 242; inflection (diffraction), 374; integrality of, 223; polarization, 234, 239, 241, 349; obliquated, 241; oscillation of, 361; ray, 229, 230, 231; refrangibility of, 362; solar, 227, 228; stellar, 227; velocity of, 235–238; weight of, 232; wave theory, 229, 233, 242
lightning conductor, 396
Lindsay, R., 327
line (crystalline and organic), 308
Link, H. F., 265
Linnaeus, C. von, 395
liquidity, 264
Livy, T., 277
Lloyd, H. E., 299
Locke, J., 246
logic, 223, 259, 260, 232, 384, 440
longitudinal vibration, 284
Lüdicke, A. G., 329
Luther, M., 258
Luthmer, D. J. J., 227
Luyart, F. de, 421
Luyart, J. J. de, 421
Lys, C. N. H. du, 327

Macartney, Earl of, 311
McPike, E. F., 249
Macquer, P. J., 232, 354, 383
McTaggart, J. M. E., 223
Madagascar, 331
Madeira, 316
Magellan, J., 304
magnetic: field, 311; line, 334; needle, 312, 321; property, 319
magnetism: and crystallization, 328, electricity, 325, light, 317; animal, 321; molecular current, 311; of basalt, 316, Earth, 312–313, 322, nickel and cobalt, 314, serpentine, 315
magnetite, 315
Magyar, G., 354
Maillac, J. A. M. de Moyria de, 311
Mairan, J. J. D. de, 232, 276, 327, 347, 399
Malcolm, A., 289

sodium, 423
Söderbaum, H. G., 433
solar: furnace, 242; light, 227, 228
solder, soft, 404
solution, 384
Soldani, A., 278
Somerville, M., 317
Sommer, G. M., 238
song-bird, 300
Sorby, H. C., 334
Sorge, G. A., 294
soul, 282, 287, 441
space (infinitum of), 230
specific heat, 304
spectroscopy, 353
spectrum, 356, 370
Speirs, E. B., 224, 232
Speiser, A., 369
Spence, W., 367
spider, 274
Spies, H., 297
Spix, J. B., *298*, 299, 316
Spohr, L., 368
Sponsel, J. U., 289
spontaneous combustion, 304
Sprengel, K., 336
Sprengel, M. C., 311
Spurzheim, J. C., 431
Stäblein, B., 365
Stahl, G. E., 262, 263, 302, 406
star, 227, 228, 230, 238
Stauffer, R. C., 392, 400
Staunton, G. L., 311
steam, 263, 264
Steffens, H., *253*, 254, 255, 281, 307, 308,
    331, 371, 406, 408, 412, 425
Steinbuch, J. G., 260, 383
stellar light, 227
Stewart, D., 301
Stillingfleet, B., 293
Stillingfleet, E., 388
Stirling, J. H., 306
stoichiometry, 428, 431
stone (from sky), 277
storm, 275
Storr, G. K. C., 331
Strehlke, F., 373
Struck, W., 257
Strunk, O., 252
Struthers, L. G., 223, 259, 260
Sturz, F. G., 257
Sudhoff, K., 336

sulphur, 390, 391, 425
sulphuric: acid, 424; ether, 437
Sulzer, J. G., 386
Sun (rotation of), 227
sunbeam, 360
sunlight, 367
surface force, 280, 348
Swabia, 337, 382
Swammerdam, J., 416
Swinden, J. H. van, 319, *320*
Sydney, R., 337
Symmer, R., 387, 391
symmetry (crystalline), 332
synsomation, 401
syzygy, 247

tachopyrion (pneumatic tinder-box), 261
Tartini, G., *292*, 293, 294, 296
taste, 384
Tata, D., 278
Taylor, A. E., 396
temperament (musical), 252, 291
temperature: and electricity, 414; seasonal,
    273
Tennant, S., 411, 433, 436
Tessan, L. U. de, 389
tetrad (Pythagorean), 288
Teyler, P., 269, 270
Thales, 263
Thénard, L. J., 314, 330, 409, 433
theory of colour, 240
thermodynamics, 261
Thompson, B., *300*, 301, 302, 303, 340, 364
Thompson, J. A., 301
Thompson, S. P., 233
Thomson, J., 264
Thomson, T., 242, 286, 304, 314, 325,
    333, 384, 398, 403, 406, 420, 421, 422,
    425, 427, 430, 436, 437, 439, 441
thunder, 389
Thurston, R. H., 261
Tieck, L., 308
Tiemann, W. A., 315, 318
Tilloch, A., 271, 275, 304, 313, 314, 315,
    318, 335, 366, 405, 419, 425
time, and fire, 437
tinder, 261, 262
Titius, J. D., 250
tonal sequence, 253
tone, 292, 293–296
Töpfer, G., 297

tourmaline, 310, 395
tradewind, 275
Tralles, J. G., 321
transition: chemism-physics, 339; cohesion-sound, 281; colour-odour, 383; magnet-ism-crystal, 327; sound-heat, 297
transparency, 340
Trapp, J., 331
tremulation (of sound), 282
Treschow, N., 253, 254
triangulation, 345
Trommsdorff, C. W. H., 405
Trommsdorff, J. B., 314, 397, 404, 411, 415, 424
Trommsdorff, W. B., 267
Troostwyk, A. P. van, 270, 323
tropical birds, 298
Tuscany, Duke of, 416
Tyndall, J., 382

universe (theory of), 228
university (idea of), 255
Urals, 309
Uranus, 244
Ure, A., 335

valley (formation), 245
Vallot, J. U., 367
Vandermonde, C. A., 318
Vargas-Bedemar, E. R. von. 371
Vauquelin, L. N., 318, 401, 412, 424, 433, 437
vegetable (potash content), 423
velocity (of light), 235–238
vibration: node, 288; of air, 287
Vieth, G. U. A., 290, 295, 365
Vieussens, R. de, 438
Vinci, L. da, 376
Virchow, R. L. C., 284
Vischer, F. T., 369
vision, 231, 338, 396,
vitreous (and resinous) electricity, 385
Vitruvius, M., Pollio, 305, 403
Vogler, G. J., 296, 297
Voigt, J. G., 288
Voigt, J. H., 240, 271
volatilization (of gold), 397
Vollgraf, J. A., 345
Volta, A., 271, 323, 324, 325, 397, 409, 412, 413, 414, 416, 417, 418, 419

voltaic: apparatus, 419; battery, 399; pile, 324; pistol, 397

Wachsmuth, G., 354
Waerden, L. van der, 256
Wagemann, K., 305
Wasielewski, W., 275
Waite, A. E., 388
Walker, C. V., 277, 389
Wall, Dr., 266
Wallace, W., 223, 230, 260, 323, 373, 384, 415, 440
Wallerius, J. G., 315
Wallis, J., 292
Ward, J., 424
Waschnitus, V., 255
water, 264; decomposition, 270, 409; formation, 270; of crystallization, 327, 384
Watts, I., 253
wave-theory (of light), 299, 233, 242, 351, 366
weather prophecy, 274
Weaver, T., 308, 329, 330
Weber, C. M. von, 296
Weber, J., 274, 397
weight (of light), 232
Weinhold, K. A., 328
Weiss, C. S., 330
Weisse, M., 365
Wenzel, C. F., 429
Werner, A. G., 254, 307, 308, 328, 329, 330; Society, 327
Whateley, R., 431
Wheelwright, P., 267, 441
Whewell, W., 360
Whiston, W., 246
white (composition of), 364
Whitehead, W. F., 388
Whitehurst, J., 245
Whittaker, E., 230
Wickner, J., 365
Wicksteed, P., 257, 266
Widmannstätten, A. B. von, 334
Wiegleb, J. C., 255, 305
Wilcke, J. K., 390
Wilde, E., 317, 345, 353, 358
Wilkins, W., 247
Wilson, A., 250
Wilson, B., 395
Wilson, G., 415
Winkler, J. H., 266

Winterl, J. J., 399, *400*, 401, 422, 426, 427, 438
Witelo, 231
Wittich, J., 371
Wittich, W., 398
Woeste, J. F. L., 225
Wöhler, F., 315, 329, 389
Wolf, F. A., 266
Wolff, C., 250, 302
Wolff, F. B., 285, 331, 334, 398, 407, 420, 421, 424, 427, 430, 434, 436, 438
wolfram, 420
Wollaston, W. H., 309, 330, 332, 412, *415*, 419, 424, 430, 433
Wood, A., 292
Woodman, T. B., 305
Wright, G., 275
Wundt, W., 369, 377
Wurm, J. F., 227

Young, M., 292, 294
Young, T., 229, 234, 242, 279, 283, 294, 295, 296, 351, 364, 366, 374, 381, 387, 433

Zach, F. X. von, 235, 242, 245, 246, 248, 250, 251, 278
Zamboni, G., 419
Zannichelli, G. G., 334
Zaunick, R., 386
Zedinek, H., 373
Zeller, E., 287
Zelter, C. F., 338, 363, 372
Zend-Avesta, 224
Zingel, H. J., 291
Zschokke, J. H. D., 364
Zyka, J., 367
Zylius, J. D. O., 268, 269